COMPREHENSIVE SERIES IN PHOTOCHEMISTRY AND PHOTOBIOLOGY

Series Editors

Donat P. Häder
Professor of Botany

and

Giulio Jori
Professor of Chemistry

European Society for Photobiology

COMPREHENSIVE SERIES IN PHOTOCHEMISTRY AND PHOTOBIOLOGY

Series Editors: Donat P. Häder and Giulio Jori

*Titles in this Series:*

Volume 1   UV Effects in Aquatic Organisms and Ecosystems
            Edited by E.W. Helbling and H. Zagarese

Volume 2   Photodynamic Therapy
            Edited by T. Patrice

Volume 3   Photoreceptors and Light Signalling
            Edited by A. Batschauer

Volume 4   Lasers and Current Optical Techniques in Biology
            Edited by G. Palumbo and R. Pratesi

Volume 5   From DNA Photolesions to Mutations, Skin Cancer and Cell Death
            Edited by É. Sage, R. Drouin and M. Rouabhia

Volume 6   Flavins: Photochemistry and Photobiology
            Edited by E. Silva and A.M. Edwards

Volume 7   Photodynamic Therapy with ALA: A Clinical Handbook
            Edited by R. Pottier, B. Krammer, R. Baumgartner, H. Stepp

Volume 8   Primary Processes of Photosynthesis, Part 1: Principles and Apparatus
            Edited by G. Renger

Volume 9   Primary Processes of Photosynthesis, Part 2: Principles and Apparatus
            Edited by G. Renger

Visit our website at http://www.rsc.org/Publishing/Books/PPS

COMPREHENSIVE SERIES IN PHOTOCHEMISTRY AND PHOTOBIOLOGY–VOLUME 8

# Primary Processes of Photosynthesis, Part 1
## Principles and Apparatus

Editor

Gernot Renger
Technische Universität Berlin
Max-Volmer-Laboratorium für Biophysikalische Chemie
Sekr. PC 14
Strasse des 17. Juni 135
D–10623 Berlin, Germany

RSCPublishing

ISBN: 978-0-85404-369-9

ISBN of set: 978-0-85404-364-4

A catalogue record for this book is available from the British Library

© European Society of Photobiology 2008

*All rights reserved*

*Apart from fair dealing for the purposes of research for non-commercial purposes or for private study, criticism or review, as permitted under the Copyright, Designs and Patents Act 1988 and the Copyright and Related Rights Regulations 2003, this publication may not be reproduced, stored or transmitted, in any form or by any means, without the prior permission in writing of The Royal Society of Chemistry, or in the case of reproduction in accordance with the terms of licences issued by the Copyright Licensing Agency in the UK, or in accordance with the terms of the licences issued by the appropriate Reproduction Rights Organization outside the UK. Enquiries concerning reproduction outside the terms stated here should be sent to The Royal Society of Chemistry at the address printed on this page.*

Published by The Royal Society of Chemistry,
Thomas Graham House, Science Park, Milton Road,
Cambridge CB4 0WF, UK

Registered Charity Number 207890

For further information see our web site at www.rsc.org

# Preface for the ESP Series in Photochemical and Photobiological Sciences

"Its not the substance, it's the dose which makes something poisonous!" When Paracelsius, a German physician of the $14^{th}$ century made this statement he probably did not think about light as one of the most obvious environmental factors. But his statement applies as well to light. While we need light, for example for vitamin D production, too much light might cause skin cancer. The dose makes the difference. These diverse findings of light effects have attracted the attention of scientists for centuries. The photosciences represent a dynamic multidisciplinary field that includes such diverse subjects as behavioral responses of single cells, cures for certain types of cancer and the protective potential of tanning lotions. It also includes photobiology and photochemistry, photomedicine as well as the technology for light production, filtering and measurement. Light is a common theme in all these areas. In recent decades a more molecular centered approach has changed both the depth and the quality of the theoretical as well as the experimental foundation of photosciences.

An example of the relationship between global environment and the biosphere is the recent discovery of ozone depletion and the resulting increase in high-energy ultraviolet radiation. The hazardous effects of high-energy ultraviolet radiation on all living systems is now well established. This discovery of the result of ozone depletion put photosciences at the center of public interest with the result that, in an unparalleled effort, scientists and politicians worked closely together to come to international agreements to stop the pollution of the atmosphere.

The changed recreational behavior and the correlation with several diseases in which sunlight or artificial light sources play a major role in the causation of clinical conditions (e.g., porphyrias, polymorphic photodermatoses, *Xeroderma pigmentosum* and skin cancers) have been well documented. As a result, in some countries (e.g., Australia) public services inform people about the potential risk of extended periods of sun exposure every day. The problems are often aggravated by the phototoxic or photoallergic reactions produced by various environmental pollutants, food additives or therapeutic and cosmetic drugs. However, if properly used, light-stimulated processes can induce important beneficial effects in biological systems, such as the elucidation of several aspects of cell structure and function. Novel developments are centered around photodiagnostic and phototherapeutic modalities for the treatment of cancer, arthrosclerosis, several autoimmune diseases, neonatal jaundice and others. In addition, classic research areas such as vision and photosynthesis are still very active. Some of these developments are unique to photobiology, since the peculiar physicochemical properties of electronically excited biomolecules often lead to the promotion of reactions that are characterized by high levels of selectivity in space and time. Besides the biologically centered areas, technical developments have paved the way for the harnessing of solar energy to produce warm water and electricity or the development of environmentally friendly techniques for addressing problems of large social impact (e.g., the decontamination of polluted waters). While also in use in Western countries, these techniques are of great interest for developing countries.

The European Society for Photobiology (ESP) is an organization that aims to develop and coordinate the very different fields of photosciences in terms of public knowledge and scientific interests. Owing to the ever increasing demand for a comprehensive overview of the photosciences the ESP decided to initiate an encyclopedic series, the "Comprehensive Series in Photochemical and Photobiological Sciences". This series is intended to give an in-depth coverage over all the very different fields related to light effects. It will allow investigators, physicians, students, industry and laypersons to obtain an updated record of the state-of-the-art in specific fields, including ready access to the recent literature. Most importantly, such reviews give a critical evaluation of the directions that the field is taking, outline hotly debated or innovative topics and even suggest a redirection if appropriate. It is our intention to produce the monographs at a sufficiently high rate to generate a timely coverage of both well established and emerging topics. As a rule, the individual volumes are commissioned; however, comments, suggestions or proposals for new subjects are welcome.

Donat-P. Häder and Giulio Jori<br>Spring 2002

# Volume Preface

The interaction of living matter with electromagnetic radiation in the near-ultraviolet (NUV), visible (Vis) and near-infrared (NIR) regions is a most important topic in life sciences. The radiation from a huge extraterrestrial fusion reactor, the sun, not only provides the unique Gibbs energy for the development and sustenance of almost all forms of life on our planet but also plays a key role in several regulatory functions such as synchronizing biological clocks and information transfer processes (e.g., vision, photomorphogenesis, phototaxis, communication via bioluminescence signals).

It is, therefore, not surprising that the sun played a central role in mankind's cultural development and religious admiration throughout the world, ranging from the great Aton hymn of the old Egyptians, to the worshippers of the sun in India and to the highly advanced ancient Indian societies (Mayas and Incas) in the Western hemisphere.

Among the different light-induced processes, photosynthesis is fundamental and unique because it enables the biological transformation of solar radiation into (electro)chemical Gibbs energy. Furthermore, it is the most abundant chemical reaction on the earth's surface (land and oceans), with an estimated turnover of 300–500 billion tons of $CO_2$ per year, converted into carbohydrates and subsequent products. The crucial role of photosynthesis can be best summarized in only four words: "Life is bottled sunshine" [Wynword Read, *Martyrdom of Man*, 1924].

Studies on photosynthesis date back to the early days of the development of natural sciences. The fundamental principles of energy transformation in general and photosynthesis in particular, described by the first and second law of thermodynamics, were outlined in the nineteenth century by R.J. Mayer and L. Boltzmann, respectively (Chapter 1). Nowadays, the unraveling of the underlying structural and functional organization of photosynthesis focuses on intensive research activities. The high scientific relevance of topics related to the subject is best illustrated by the impressive list of about 20 Nobel laureates that were awarded the Prize for their work performed in this field, starting with Richard Willstätter in 1915 and Hans Fischer in 1930 and their pioneering studies on the chemistry of chlorophylls as the key pigments of the photosynthetic apparatus [for an excursion into the history of photosynthesis research, I recommend the excellent book *Discoveries in Photosynthesis* (Govindjee, J. T. Beatty, H. Gest, J. F. Allen, eds.), Springer, 2005].

The overall process of photosynthesis consists of several reactions, which take place in quite different time domains, covering a range from femtoseconds (light absorption) up to hours (long-term acclimation) and even days or months (plant growth). Within this wide time region the light-driven reactions leading to the primary metabolites ("energy rich" bound hydrogen and ATP) are the fastest reactions, which are accomplished within milliseconds and referred to as "Primary Processes of Photosynthesis". Research on this topic is not only a fascinating part of pure science but it can also offer nature's masterpiece for solar energy exploitation as a blueprint for the technical development of devices aiming at contributing to solutions of mankind's Gibbs energy demands.

This edition of two volumes is restricted to topics on the "Primary Processes of Photosynthesis". As several books in this field already exist (see, for example, *Advances in Photosynthesis and Respiration*, Series editor Govindjee, Springer), one might ask: Why publish another two? The major reason for doing so is the enormous progress achieved in molecular biology and X-ray diffraction crystallography of membrane proteins during the last two decades, which has enabled, in combination with developments of sophisticated spectroscopic methods of very high time resolution, much deeper insight into the mechanisms and structure of the apparatus down to the level of atomic dimensions. Furthermore, significant advances in the methodology of theory (quantum chemistry, molecular mechanics) offer a new basis for a better understanding of structure–function relationships, including the role of dynamic processes.

This publication is an ambitious attempt to provide a synoptic state-of-the-art picture of the primary processes of photosynthesis by casting together the mosaics of detailed knowledge described by leading experts in the field. Twenty two chapters have been written by 42 authors from Europe, USA, Japan and Australia. The wealth of information appears to be best presented in two different volumes (Parts 1 and 2). Part 1 describes the photophysical principles, photosynthetic pigments and light harvesting/adaptation/stress. It is divided into five sections: Section I is an introduction to the field, giving an overview on the primary processes of photosynthesis in a single chapter presented by G. Renger. Section II also contains a single chapter, by T. Renger, which provides the basic theoretical background of the underlying photophysical principles (excitation energy and electron transfer) for light harvesting and the electron transport chain. Section III describes the properties of the main pigments in two chapters, *i.e.* the chlorophylls in Chapter 3 by H. Scheer and the carotenoids in Chapter 4 by Koyama et al. In Section IV, five chapters deal with light harvesting, and regulatory control of excitation energy fluxes. Chapter 5, presented by Law and Cogdell, provides an insight into the structure and function of the antenna system of anoxygenic photosynthetic bacteria, and in Chapter 6, presented by Mimuro et al., the properties of the antenna system of oxygenic cyanobacteria are described. Morosinotto and Bassi, in Chapter 7, and van Amerongen and Croce, in Chapter 8, summarize our knowledge on the antenna systems of Photosystem I and Photosystem II, respectively, of higher plants. Chapter 9, by Gilmore and Li, presents information on the regulatory control of the antenna function in plants. Section V describes, in a single Chapter 10 by Vass and Aro, the effects induced by light stress.

Part 2 is divided into three sections: Section VI (the numbering is continued from Part 1) is devoted to the structure and function of reaction centers in anoxygenic photosynthetic bacteria and the two photosystems of oxygen evolving organisms. Lancaster in Chapter 11 and Parson in the complementary Chapter 12 summarize the current state of knowledge on the structure and the functional pattern, respectively, of reaction centers in anoxygenic bacteria. Analogously, structure and functional pattern of Photosystem I (PS I) and Photosystem II (PS II) in oxygen-evolving organisms are described in the following five chapters presented by Fromme et al. (Chapter 13: structure of PS I), Setif and Leibl (Chapter 14: functional pattern of PSI), Zouni (Chapter 15: structure of PS II), G. Renger (Chapter 16: functional pattern of PS II) and J. Messinger and G. Renger (Chapter 17: oxygen evolution). Section VII on electron transport chains and photophosphorylation contains four chapters: anoxygenic bacteria are described by Verméglio (Chapter 18), oxygen-evolving cyanobacteria by Peschek (Chapter 19), the cytochrome $b_6f$ complex by Cramer et al. (Chapter 20), and in Chapter 21 Junge summarizes our knowledge on photophosphorylation. In Section VIII, Larkum describes, in Chapter 22, the evolution of photosynthetic organisms.

All the chapters in these two parts provide a modern and updated view of the corresponding topics. Accordingly, this edition is not only a most valuable text for graduate students but it is also addressed to all scientists who are interested in the field of the primary processes of photosynthesis. It is my sincere hope that these two books will entice young people into this exciting research area with the aim of addressing successfully the challenging problems of high relevance that are still awaiting a satisfactory answer.

I have many people to thank. First of all, the authors for their efforts to offer the reader excellent chapters and for their positive responses to my suggestions. Without their invaluable cooperation there would be no books. My thanks also go to Susanne Renger and Solweig Nothing for their continuous help in the preparation of electronic versions of figures and typing of manuscripts, respectively.

I am most grateful to my wife Eva for all her enthusiasm in supporting this work and her invaluable help during periods of frustration and disappointment by sharing her optimism in finally reaching the desired goal.

I wish all readers a pleasant and stimulating journey through the fascinating "world" of the primary processes of photosynthesis.

Gernot Renger

# Contents

**Part 1: Photophysical Principles, Pigments and Light Harvesting/Adaptation/Stress**

### I. Introduction

Chapter 1    Overview of Primary Processes of Photosynthesis    5
*Gernot Renger*

### II. Basic Photophysical Principles

Chapter 2    Absorption of Light, Excitation Energy Transfer and Electron Transfer Reactions    39
*Thomas Renger*

### III. Pigments

Chapter 3    Chlorophylls    101
*Hugo Scheer*

Chapter 4    Photophysical Properties and Light-Harvesting and Photoprotective Functions of Carotenoids in Bacterial Photosynthesis: Structural Selections    151
*Yasushi Koyama, Yoshinori Kakitani and Yasutaka Watanabe*

### IV. Structure and Function of Antenna Systems

Chapter 5    The Light-Harvesting System of Purple Anoxygenic Photosynthetic Bacteria    205
*Christopher J. Law and Richard J. Cogdell*

Chapter 6    Oxygen-Evolving Cyanobacteria    261
*Mamoru Mimuro, Masami Kobayashi, Akio Murakami, Tohru Tsuchiya and Hideaki Miyashita*

| | | |
|---|---|---|
| Chapter 7 | Antenna System of Higher Plants' Photosystem I and Its Interaction with the Core Complex<br>*Tomas Morosinotto and Roberto Bassi* | 301 |
| Chapter 8 | Structure and Function of Photosystem II Light-Harvesting Proteins (Lhcb) of Higher Plants<br>*Herbert van Amerongen and Roberta Croce* | 329 |
| Chapter 9 | Regulatory Control of Antenna Function in Plants<br>*Adam M. Gilmore and Xiao-Ping Li* | 369 |

### V. Light Stress

| | | |
|---|---|---|
| Chapter 10 | Photoinhibition of Photosynthetic Electron Transport<br>*Imre Vass and Eva-Mari Aro* | 393 |

Subject Index     427

## Part 2: Reaction Centers/Photosystems, Electron Transport Chains, Photophosphorylation and Evolution

### VI. Structure and Function of Reaction Centers and Photosystems

| | | |
|---|---|---|
| Chapter 11 | Structures of Reaction Centers in Anoxygenic Bacteria<br>*C. Roy D. Lancaster* | 5 |
| Chapter 12 | Functional Pattern of Reaction Centers in Anoxygenic Photosynthetic Bacteria<br>*William W. Parson* | 57 |
| Chapter 13 | Structure and Function of Photosystem I<br>*Raimund Fromme, Ingo Grotjohann and Petra Fromme* | 111 |
| Chapter 14 | Functional Pattern of Photosystem I in Oxygen Evolving Organisms<br>*Pierre Sétif and Winfried Leibl* | 147 |
| Chapter 15 | From Cell Growth to the 3.0 Å Resolution Crystal Structure of Cyanobacterial Photosystem II<br>*Athina Zouni* | 193 |
| Chapter 16 | Functional Pattern of Photosystem II<br>*Gernot Renger* | 237 |

# CONTENTS

| Chapter 17 | Photosynthetic Water Splitting<br>*Johannes Messinger and Gernot Renger* | 291 |

## VII. Electron Transport Chains and Phosphorylation

| Chapter 18 | Anoxygenic Bacteria<br>*André Verméglio* | 353 |
| Chapter 19 | Electron Transport Chains in Oxygenic Cyanobacteria<br>*Günter A. Peschek* | 383 |
| Chapter 20 | Structure–Function of the Cytochrome $b_6f$ Complex: A Design that has Worked for Three Billion Years<br>*William A. Cramer, Huamin Zhang, Jivsheny Yan, Genji Kurisu, Eiki Yamashita, Naranbaatar Dashdorj, Hanyovp Kim and Sergei Savikhin* | 417 |
| Chapter 21 | Photophosphorylation<br>*Wolfgang Junge* | 447 |

## VIII. Evolution

| Chapter 22 | The Evolution of Photosynthesis<br>*Anthony W.D. Larkum* | 491 |

Subject Index     523

# Contributors

**Eva-Mari Aro**, *Department of Biology, University of Turku, Turku, Finland*
**Roberto Bassi**, *Dipartimento Scientifico e Tecnologico, Università di Verona. Strada Le Grazie, 15-37134 Verona, Italy*
**Richard J. Cogdell**, *Microbial Photosynthesis Laboratory, Division of Biochemistry & Molecular Biology, Institute of Biomedical and Life Sciences, University of Glasgow, Glasgow G12 8QQ, UK*
**W. A. Cramer**, *Department of Biological Sciences, Purdue University, West Lafayette, IN 47907, USA*
**Roberta Croce**, *Institute of Biophysics CNR, C/o ITC. 38100 Povo, Trento, Italy Present address: Biophysical Chemistry, University of Groningen, Nijenborg 4, 9747 AG Groningen, The Netherlands*
**N. Dashdorj**, *Department of Physics, Purdue University, West Lafayette, IN 47907, USA*
**Petra Fromme**, *Department of Chemistry and Biochemistry, Arizona State University, Box 871604, 85287-1607 Tempe, Arizona, USA*
**Raimund Fromme**, *Department of Chemistry and Biochemistry, Arizona State University, Box 871604, 85287-1607 Tempe, Arizona, USA*
**Adam M. Gilmore**, *Fluorescence Division, Horiba Jobin Yvon Inc., 3880 Park Avenue, Edison, NJ 08820, USA*
**Ingo Grotjohann**, *Department of Chemistry and Biochemistry, Arizona State University, Box 871604, 85287-1607 Tempe, Arizona, USA*
**Wolfgang Junge**, *Department of Biophysics, University of Osnabrück, 49069 Osnabrück, Germany*
**Yoshinori Kakitani**, *Faculty of Science and Technology, Kwansei Gakuin University, 2-1 Gakuen, Sanda 669-1137, Japan*
**H. Kim**, *Department of Physics, Purdue University, West Lafayette, IN 47907, USA*
**Masami Kobayashi**, *Institute of Materials Science, University of Tsukuba, Tsukuba, Ibaraki 305–8573, Japan*
**Yasushi Koyama**, *Faculty of Science and Technology, Kwansei Gakuin University, 2-1 Gakuen, Sanda 669-1337, Japan*
**G. Kurisu**, *Department of Biological Sciences, Purdue University, West Lafayette, IN 47907, USA*

Present address: Department of Life Sciences, Graduate School of Arts and Sciences, University of Tokyo, Komaba 3-8-1, Meguro-ku, Tokyo 153-8902, Japan

**C. Roy D. Lancaster**, Max Planck Institute of Biophysics, Department of Molecular Membrane Biology, P.O. Box 55 03 53, D-60402, Frankfurt am Main, Germany

**Anthony W.D. Larkum**, School of Biological Sciences, University of Sydney and Sydney University Biological Information and Technology Centre (SUBIT), Medical Foundation Building, University of Sydney, NSW 2006, Australia

**Christopher J. Law**, Microbial Photosynthesis Laboratory, Division of Biochemistry & Molecular Biology, Institute of Biomedical and Life Sciences, University of Glasgow, Glasgow G12 8QQ, UK

**Winfried Leibl**, Service de Bioénergétique and URA CNRS 2096, Département de Biologie Joliot-Curie, CEA Saclay, 91191 Gif sur Yvette, France

**Xiao-Ping Li**, Biotechnology Center for Agriculture and the Environment, Foran Hall, Cook Campus, Rutgers, The State University of New Jersey, 59 Dudley Road, New Brunswick, NJ 08901–8520, USA

**Johannes Messinger**, Max-Planck-Institut für Bioanorganische Chemie, Stiftstrasse 34–36, D-45470 Mülheim an der Ruhr, Germany

**Mamoru Mimuro**, Department of Technology and Ecology, Hall of Global Environmental Research and Graduate School of Human and Environmental Studies, Kyoto University, Yoshida-Honmachi, Sakyo-ku, Kyoto 606–8501, Japan

**Hideaki Miyashita**, Department of Technology and Ecology, Hall of Global Environmental Research and Graduate School of Human and Environmental Studies, Kyoto University, Yoshida-Honmachi, Sakyo-ku, Kyoto 606–8501, Japan

**Tomas Morosinotto**, Dipartimento Scientifico e Tecnologico, Università di Verona. Strada Le Grazie, 15-37134 Verona, Italy.
Present address: Dipartmento di Biologia, Università di Padova, Via Ugo Bassi 58 B, 35131 Padova, Italy

**Akio Murakami**, Kobe University Research Center for Inland Seas, Iwaya, Awaji, Hyogo 656–2401, Japan

**William W. Parson**, Department of Biochemistry, Box 35–7350, University of Washington, Seattle, WA 98195–7350, USA

**Günter A. Peschek**, Molecular Bioenergetics Group, Institute of Physical Chemistry, University of Vienna, Althanstrasse 14, A-1090 Wien, Austria

**Gernot Renger**, Technische Universität Berlin, Institut für Chemie, Max-Volmer-Laboratorium für Biophysikalische Chemie, Straße des 17. Juni 135, D-10623 Berlin, Germany

**Thomas Renger**, Institut für Chemie (Kristallographie), Freie Universität Berlin, Takustrasse 6, D-14195 Berlin, Germany

**S. Savikhin**, Department of Physics, Purdue University, West Lafayette, IN 47907, USA

**H. Scheer**, Dept. Biologie I – Bereich Botanik, Universität München, Menzinger Str. 67, D-80638 München, Germany

CONTRIBUTORS

**Pierre Sétif**, *Service de Bioénergétique and URA CNRS 2096, Département de Biologie Joliot-Curie, CEA Saclay, 91191 Gif sur Yvette, France*

**Tohru Tsuchiya**, *Department of Technology and Ecology, Hall of Global Environmental Research and Graduate School of Human and Environmental Studies, Kyoto University, Yoshida-Honmachi, Sakyo-ku, Kyoto 606–8501, Japan*

**Herbert van Amerongen**, *Laboratory of Biophysics, Wageningen University, P.O. Box 8128, 6700 ET Wageningen, The Netherlands*

**Imre Vass**, *Institute of Plant Biology, Biological Research Center, Hungarian Academy of Sciences, 6726 Szeged, Temesvári krt. 62, Hungary*

**André Verméglio**, *Laboratoire de Bioénergétique Cellulaire, UMR 6191 CNRS-CEA-Aix-Marseille II DEVM CEA, Cadarache 13108, Saint Paul lez Durance, France*

**Yasutaka Watanabe**, *Faculty of Science and Technology, Kwansei Gakuin University, 2-1 Gakuen, Sanda 669–1137, Japan*

**E. Yamashita**, *Department of Biological Sciences, Purdue University, West Lafayette, IN 47907, USA*

**J. Yan**, *Department of Biological Sciences, Purdue University, West Lafayette, IN 47907, USA*
*Present address: Department of Pharmacology, University of California-Davis, Davis, CA 95616, USA*

**H. Zhang**, *Department of Biological Sciences, Purdue University, West Lafayette, IN 47907, USA*

**Athina Zouni**, *Institute for Chemistry/Max Volmer Laboratory for Biophysical Chemistry, Technical University Berlin, Strasse des 17. Juni 135, D-10623 Berlin, Germany*

# Abbreviations and Symbols

A or $A_0$, special chlorophyll $a$ molecules acting as electron acceptors in type I RCs
A, antheraxanthin
$A_1$, special phylloquinone molecule(s) acting as electron acceptor in PS I (see also $PhQ_A$ and $PhQ_B$)
aa or AA, amino acid
Acc, electron acceptor
ALA, 5-aminolevulinic acid
APC, allophycocyanin
ATP, adenosine triphosphate
$B_A$, $B_B$, "accessory" BChls in proteobacterial RCs
BC, before Christ
(B)Chl, (bacterio)chlorophyll
(B)Pheo or (B)Phe, (bacterio)pheophytin
BIC, butyl isocyanide
$B_X$, $B_y$, higher energy optical absorption bands (Soret bands) of (bacterio)chlorins and porphyrins
CAB, chlorophyll $a/b$ binding protein
CAC, chlorophyll $a/c$ binding protein
CAM crassulacean acid metabolism
Car, carotenoid
CcO, cytochrome $c$ oxidase
CD, circular dichroism
CM, cytoplasmic or plasma membrane(s)
CP$X$, chlorophyll binding protein of molecular mass $X$
cyt, cytochrome
d.w., dry weight
D1, D2, central polypeptides of PS II RCs
DBMIB, 2,5-dibromo-3-methyl-6- isopropyl-$p$-benzoquinone
DCCD, dicyclohexylcarbodiimide
DCMU, 3-(3,4-dichlorophenyl)-1,1-dimethylurea
DGDG, digalactosyldiacylglycerol
DOPC, dioleoyl-phosphatidylcholine
EET, excited state energy transfer (excitation energy transfer)

ELIP, early light induced protein
EM, electron microscopy
$E_m$, midpoint oxidation–reduction potential
ENDOR, electron nuclear double resonance
EPR, electron paramagnetic resonance
ER, endoplasmatic reticulum
ESEEM, electron spin echo envelope modulation
ESR, electron spin resonance
ET, electron transfer
*ETC*, Electron transport chain
ETP, electron transport phosphorylation
EXAFS, extended X-ray absorption fine structure
$F_A$, $F_B$, $F_x$, Iron-sulfur centers in PS I and chlorobial RCs
$F_{AB}$ protein, subunit PsaC of photosystem I which binds the two iron-sulfur clusters $F_A$ and $F_B$
FCWD, Franck–Condon weighted density of states
Fd or fd, ferredoxin
FDP, flavo-diiron proteins
FIOP, flash-induced oxygen evolution pattern
Fld, flavodoxin
FNR, ferredoxin-NADP$^+$-oxidoreductase
FTIR, Fourier-transform infrared
FWHM, full-width at half-maximum
Ga, giga years ago
GAP, glyceraldehyde 3-phosphate
GAP-DH, glyceraldehyde 3-phosphate dehydrogenase
$H_A$, $H_B$, bacteriopheophytins in proteobacterial RCs
HiPIP, high-potential iron-sulfur protein
HLIP, high light-induced protein
IC, internal conversion
ICM, intracytoplasmic membrane
IChM, inner chloroplast membrane
IEF, isoelectric focusing
IEP, (pH of) isoelectric point
IR, infrared
ISC, intersystem crossing
isiA, iron stress-induced protein A
ISP, iron-sulfur protein
ISP-s, 139 residue *p*-side soluble domain of the ISP
$K_z$, equilibrium binding (association) constant between Z (or A) and one PS II unit;
L, lutein
L, M, H, subunits of proteobacterial RCs
LD, linear dichroism
LH, light harvesting

# ABBREVIATIONS AND SYMBOLS

LHC I, II (or Lhc I, II), light-harvesting chlorophyll complexes of Photosystem I, II
LH(C)P, light harvesting (chlorophyll) protein
MDGD, monogalactosyldiacylglyccrol
MgDVP, Mg-2, 4-divinyl phaeoporphyrin methyl ester
MIMS, membrane inlet mass spectrometry
MK, $MKH_2$, menaquinone, menaquinol
MSH, membrane spanning helix (see also TMH)
N, neoxanthin
$NAD^+$, NADH, nicotinamide adenine dinucleotide (oxidized and reduced, respectively)
NHFe, nonheme iron
NIR, near-infrared spectral range (700–1200 nm)
NMR, nuclear magnetic resonance
NPQ, nonphotochemical quenching (of PS II chlorophyll fluorescence)
NQNO, 2-$n$-nonyl-4-hydroxyquinoline N-oxide
OChM, outer chloroplast membrane
OEC oxygen evolving complex
$p$- and $n$-, electrochemically positive and negative sides of the membrane
P, special pair, photochemically active pigment of bacterial RCs
P870, special pair in proteobacterial RCs
p.m.f., proton motive force
P680 (or $P_{680}$), photochemically active pigment of PS II
P700, photochemically active pigment (or electron donor) in PS I
P798, photochemically active pigment in heliobacterial RCs
P840, photochemically active pigment in chlorobial RCs
PAR, photosynthetically active radiation
PBRC (or PbRC), purple bacteria reaction center
PC, phycocyanin
PC, also used as abbreviation for plastocyanin
pcb, prochlorophyte chlorophyll binding protein
PCET, proton coupled electron transfer
PE, phycoerythrin
PEC, phycoerythrocyanin
PET, photosynthetic electron transport
PG, Phosphatidylglycerol
$PhQ_A$ and $PhQ_B$, the two phylloquinones A- of PS I associated to the A- and B-branches of electron transfer
PQ, plastoquinone
(P)Chlide, (Proto)Chlorophyllide
Proto, protoporphyrin IX
PS I (or PS1), Photosystem I (1)
PS II (or PS2), Photosystem II (2)
PS II CC, PS II core complex
PsaA, PsaB, subunits of PS I RCs
PsbS (also called CP22), 22 kDa PS II protein

PscA, PscB, polypeptides of chlorobial RCs
$Q_A$, primary quinone electron acceptor of type II RCs
$Q_B$, secondary plastoquinone acceptor of type II RCs
$Q_x$, $Q_y$, low energy optical absorption bands of (bacterio)chlorins and porphyrins
RC, reaction centre
RET, respiratory electron transport
RIXS, resonant inelastic x-ray scattering
ROS reactive oxygen species
rRNA ribosomal ribose nucleic acid
S (or $S_i$) states, formal oxidation states of the water-oxidizing complex
SDS-PAGE, sodium dodecyl sulfate polyacrylamide gel electrophoresis
SQDG, sulfoquinovosyldiacylglycerol
TA, transient absorption
TDS, tridecyl-stigmatellin
TMH, trans-membrane helix (see also MSH)
TRO, terminal respiratory oxidase
T-S, triplet minus singlet
UQ, ubiquinone (coenzyme Q)
UV, ultraviolet spectral range (200–400 nm)
V, violaxanthin
VDE, violaxanthin de-epoxidase
Vis, Visible spectral range (400–700 nm)
$W_f$, $W_s$, fast and slowly exchanging substrate (water) molecules bound to the WOC
WOC, water-oxidizing complex (= OEC, oxygen-evolving complex)
WT, wild type
XANES, X-ray absorption near edge structure
Xanth, xanthophyll
XRD(C), X-ray diffraction (crystallography)
$Y_Z$, $Y_D$, redox active tyrosine of polypeptides D1 and D2, respectively, in PS II
Z, zeaxanthin
$\Delta pH$, trans-membrane difference of pH
$\Delta \tilde{\mu}_H^+$, trans-membrane proton electrochemical potential difference
$\varepsilon$, molar extinction coefficient ($M^{-1}$ $cm^{-1}$)
$\lambda$, wavelength (nm)
$\mu E$, micro Einstein (Einstein is the unit for one mole photons)

# Part 1: Photophysical Principles, Pigments and Light Harvesting/Adaption/Stress

# I. Introduction

*Chapter 1*

# Overview of Primary Processes of Photosynthesis

## Gernot Renger

**Table of Contents**

1.1  Introduction.................................................... 7
1.2  Basic Principles of Photosynthetic Solar Energy Transformation.... 12
     1.2.1  Light Harvesting...................................... 14
     1.2.2  Light-Induced Charge Separation ...................... 15
1.3  Electron Transport Chains ..................................... 18
1.4  Architecture of the Photosynthetic Apparatus .................. 22
     1.4.1  Anoxygenic Bacteria................................... 22
     1.4.2  Oxygen Evolving Organisms ............................ 23
1.5  Biomimetic Systems ............................................ 26
     1.5.1  Biomimetic Antennas .................................. 27
     1.5.2  Biomimetic Reaction Center ........................... 27
     1.5.3  Biomimetic Antenna–Reaction Center Systems............ 28
     1.5.4  Biomimetic Proton Pump ............................... 28
     1.5.5  Biomimetic ATP Synthesis ............................. 29
     1.5.6  Catalysts for Oxidative Water Cleavage and Reductive $CO_2$ Fixation............................................... 29
1.6  Concluding Remarks and Future Perspectives .................... 30
Acknowledgments .................................................... 30
References.......................................................... 30

# OVERVIEW OF PRIMARY PROCESSES OF PHOTOSYNTHESIS

## Abstract

This introductory chapter describes the general principles of photosynthetic solar energy exploitation as the unique Gibbs energy source of living matter. The overall process can be subdivided into two sequences: (a) light-driven reactions, referred to as "Primary Processes of Photosynthesis", which lead to the formation of "energy rich" bound hydrogen ($TH_2$) and ATP, and (b) fixation of primordial carbon, nitrogen and sulfur compounds (where $CO_2$ transformation into carbohydrates is by far the most abundant process) with $TH_2$ as reductant and ATP as driving force for the endergonic reactions.

This chapter focuses on the functional and structural organization of the "Primary Processes of Photosynthesis". After a brief discussion of the underlying principles of harvesting of light and its transformation into electrochemical Gibbs energy by radical pair formation in pigment–protein complexes, the two types of reaction centers (type I and type II) and the two different modes of photosynthesis in anoxygenic (non-oxygen evolving) and oxygenic (oxygen evolving) organisms are outlined. It is emphasized that anoxygenic (bacterial) photosynthesis is energetically driven by only one type of reaction center (RC) (either RC I or RC II) while in oxygenic photosynthesis both types of RCs act in series, leading to electron transport from water to $NADP^+$.

Anisotropic incorporation of the functional complexes into membranes leads to vectorial electron transfer and spatial separation of oxidant- and reductant-induced reactions concomitant with the formation of a transmembrane electrochemical potential difference for protons, providing the driving force for ATP synthesis.

The general architecture of the photosynthetic apparatus and its structural organization within different membrane systems of anoxygenic and oxygenic organisms are described. Finally principles and strategies for construction of biometric systems are briefly discussed.

## 1.1 Introduction

> *Hence the general struggle of life is not for resources of material and not for energy, which in form of heat, unfortunately nontransducible, plentifully exists in every organism, but it is the fight for entropy which becomes disposible through the transition from the hot sun to the cold earth. In order to make use of this transition, plants unfold unmeasurable areas of their leaves and forces the energy of the sun, in still unresolved ways, before it sinks to the temperature of the earth's surface, to carry out chemical synthesis which no one in our laboratories can even imagine. [1]*
> *(L. Boltzmann, 1886, see Ref. [1])*

Biological organisms are open systems that are far from thermodynamic equilibrium (about 20–25 kJ $mol^{-1}$) [2]. Therefore, Gibbs (free) energy[†] fluxes are indispensable for their development and sustenance [2,3]. Electromagnetic radiation in the near-UV, visible and near-infrared red region emitted from a huge extraterrestrial nuclear power station, the sun, is the unique source that

---

[†]The term "Gibbs energy" will be used throughout this chapter instead of "free energy".

satisfies the Gibbs energy demand of life on earth. The relevance of solar radiation as the energetic prerequisite of the biosphere was already recognized in 1845 by R. J. Maier, and the underlying thermodynamic principle correctly formulated by L. Boltzmann in 1886 (vide supra, [1]). The annual energy input from the sun on our planet is estimated to be about $5 \cdot \times 10^{21}$ kJ mol$^{-1}$ [4]. Nearly half of this amount is either reflected by the atmosphere or absorbed by it (giving rise to storms and water movement in the oceans), the other half irradiates the earth surfaces, *i.e.*, oceans and land (at a ratio of 2–2.5). Only a very small fraction, <0.1% of this $2.5 \cdot \times 10^{21}$ kJ mol$^{-1}$ year$^{-1}$, is eventually transformed via photosynthesis into chemical Gibbs energy. In the overall balance, the earth releases energy as black body radiation in the far-infrared region (the maximum of the wavelength distribution is at about 10 μm), thus keeping the average temperature virtually constant.

Among living matter two types of organisms exist that differ entirely with respect to their mode of exploitation of solar radiation as Gibbs energy source: (i) photoautotrophs, which can use the light energy directly as driving force, and (ii) heterotrophs, which can not perform direct solar energy exploitation and therefore need the uptake of "energy rich" substances (food) eventually synthesized by photoautotrophs, to extract Gibbs energy through metabolic digestions.

In a general way these basic fundamental processes of bioenergetics can be described by a very simple scheme depicted in Figure 1. In photoautotrophic organisms the solar radiation increases the Gibbs energy content of a suitable storage system in state A by its light-induced transition into a state B. This process is referred to as photosynthesis and the specific amount of stored Gibbs energy will be symbolized by $\Delta G_{store}(h\nu)$. In the reverse direction, food molecules with a Gibbs energy content B' are catabolized by the heterotrophic organisms into a state A' under the release of Gibbs energy that is made available in form of the "energy currency" ATP of biological systems. This

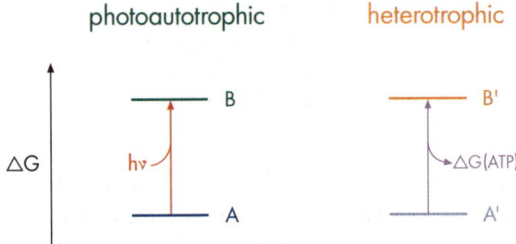

**Figure 1.** General scheme of the fundamental bioenergetic transformations of solar radiation as unique Gibbs energy: direct use in photoautotrophic organisms (left-hand side) and indirect exploitation via the uptake of food originating from photoautotrophic systems (right-hand side).

process is denoted respiration (for the sake of simplicity no distinction is made between aerobic respiration and anaerobic fermentation; see biochemistry textbooks for details) and the specific amount of available Gibbs energy will be symbolized by $\Delta G(\text{ATP})$.‡

The description of the fundamental principles of solar energy exploitation summarized in Figure 1 raises questions about the nature of molecules that substantiate states A/B and B'/A'. Biological organisms use very few substances. Based on considerations of van Niel [5] the photosynthetic transition A → B can be described by the overall reaction:

$$H_2X + T \xrightarrow{h\nu} TH_2 + X \qquad (1)$$

where $H_2X$ is a suitable hydrogen donor and T a hydrogen acceptor with $G°(TH_2) > G°(XH_2)$. In fact, this reaction is coupled with ATP formation. In subsequent reaction sequences both species $TH_2$ and ATP give rise to assimilation of the primordial elements carbon, nitrogen and sulfur. The most important among these reactions is the well-known $CO_2$ fixation into carbohydrates via a sequence of dark reactions referred to as the Calvin–Benson cycle [6–8] which by far is quantitatively the largest chemical process on the earth surface. The estimated annual turnover is of the order of 200–300 billion tons of fixed $CO_2$ [4].

Correspondingly, state B' of the Gibbs energy converter in photoheterotrophic organisms is symbolized by hydrogen donor $T'H_2$ that becomes oxidized under the release of $\Delta G(\text{ATP})$, as the analogous reversal of reaction [1].

If one takes into account the evolutionary principle of the "survival of the fittest", understandably, any improvement in the efficiency of these fundamental bioenergetic processes was of advantage in the competition of living systems for Gibbs energy sources. Basically, two parameters are of physiological relevance: (i) the specific storage capacity $\Delta G_{\text{store}}(h\nu)$ that describes the molar Gibbs energy increase of the transition A → B and $\Delta G(\text{ATP})$ the corresponding decrease of the reaction B' → A' (Figure 1), and (ii) the nature of the chemicals that enable these large-scale state transitions through sufficient availability and control of the reactivity of the molecular species participating in these processes.

The development towards more efficient systems of both photosynthesis and respiration was inevitably restricted by a theoretical thermodynamic limit that emerges from the dependence of life on water. As a consequence, $\Delta G_{\text{Store}}(h\nu)$ can reach its possible maximum level at the stage of water cleavage into the elements $H_2$ and $O_2$. This value $\Delta G_{\text{store}}^{\max}(h\nu)$ is 237.17 kJ mol$^{-1}$ [9]. In reality, however, the hydrogen is bound to $T = NADP^+$ so that $\Delta G_{\text{store}}(h\nu)$ is about 20 kJ mol$^{-1}$ lower. The bioenergetic limit of photosynthetic water cleavage into molecular oxygen and metabolically bound hydrogen was reached 2–3 billion years ago at the evolutionary level of prokaryotic cyanobacteria ([10–12]; for further reading, see Chapters 19 and 22]. This process is the thermodynamically

---

‡The symbol $\Delta G(\text{ATP})$ is a simplification because it suggests that ATP is the only "Gibbs energy currency" in biological systems.

highest possible form of solar energy transformation into chemical Gibbs energy that could be achieved in the biosphere.

The "invention" of a biomolecular device that enables this reaction had two consequences of paramount importance: (a) it allowed the water pool on the earth surface to become available as hydrogen source for the biosphere and (b) the resulting formation of dioxygen as a photosynthetic "waste" product led to the present day aerobic atmosphere [13,14], thus opening the road for a much more efficient (about one order of magnitude) exploitation of the Gibbs energy content of food through the aerobic respiration of heterotrophic organisms (for thermodynamic considerations, see [15,16]). Accordingly, the "discovery" of oxygenic photosynthesis and the concomitant formation of an aerobic atmosphere was the bioenergetic prerequisite for the development of all higher forms of life on earth. Furthermore, the release of molecular oxygen led to the generation of the stratospheric ozone layer as the indispensable protective "umbrella" against deleterious UV-B irradiation.

As the result of the interplay between oxygenic photosynthesis and respiration a global steady state emerges that can be summarized by the overall equation:

$$CO_2 + H_2O \underset{\text{respiration}}{\overset{\text{oxygenic photosynthesis}}{\rightleftharpoons}} -CH_2O- + O_2 \qquad (2)$$

where $-CH_2O-$ represents a unit of carbohydrate.

However, the great bioenergetic advantages of life under aerobic conditions are only one side of the "oxygen coin" – the other is the toxicity of molecular oxygen [17]. Because of the latter, the global accumulation of molecular oxygen in the atmosphere and, in particular, the dissolved gas in the oceans was disastrous for almost all existing organisms. The vast majority were eventually killed, a small fraction survived in anoxygenic ecological niches (for broader discussions of the dual role of molecular oxygen and the implications for the life on earth, see [17]).

In addition to its paramount role as the indispensable Gibbs energy source for the biosphere, solar radiation is also most important for information transfer. Signaling by light is well known for the process of vision but it also gives rise to a multitude of other processes such as the ticking of "biological clocks", morphogenesis via light-regulated gene expression, triggering of enzyme activities and phototactic movements of microorganisms. These processes comprising different types of photoreceptors (see [18–21] and references therein). Figure 2 gives a simplified schematic summary of the essential light-induced processes in biological organisms.

This book focuses on a description of the bioenergetic function of light through its photosynthetic transformation into chemical Gibbs energy. The overall process of photosynthesis consists of, essentially, two types of reaction sequences: (a) an electron transport chain with light energy as driving force, leading to the formation of suitable metabolically bound hydrogen (mostly NADPH) and ATP. This sequence is often summarized by the term "primary processes of photosynthesis", and (b) a chain of enzyme-catalyzed steps that

# OVERVIEW OF PRIMARY PROCESSES OF PHOTOSYNTHESIS

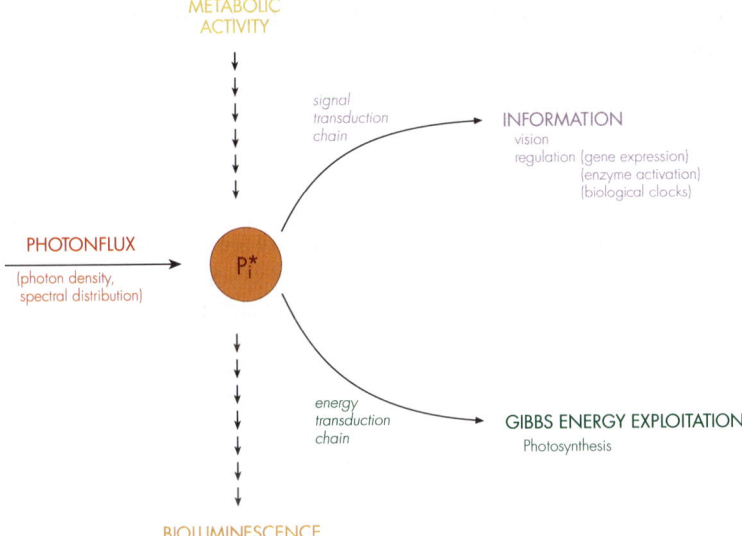

**Figure 2.** Overall scheme of generation and transformation of electronically excited states (symbolized by $P_i^*$) in biological systems.

give rise to $CO_2$ fixation with the products of the "primary processes", with NADPH and ATP acting as powerful hydrogen donor and Gibbs energy source, respectively. The overall reaction sequence of the Calvin–Benson cycle leading to $CO_2$ fixation can be summarized by the equation:

$$2\text{NADPH} + 3\text{ATP}^{4-} + CO_2 + 2H_2O \rightarrow \\ -CH_2O- + 2\text{NADP}^+ + 3\text{ADP}^{3-} + 3P_i^{2-} + H^+ \quad (3)$$

where $-CH_2O-$ symbolizes a carbohydrate unit and $P_i^{2-}$ is $HPO_4^{2-}$; the protonation states of the species are those attained at physiological pH values.

The Calvin–Benson cycle reactions [6–8] are sometimes referred to as "secondary processes of photosynthesis". They do not contribute to solar energy transformation into Gibbs energy but rather provide a transduction of the products of the "primary processes" into substances that are more appropriate for long-term storage. An extreme example of most important relevance for mankind's technological way of life are the fossil Gibbs-energy resources oil and coal. The total fossil fuel reserve is estimated to be about $4 \times 10^{19}$ kJ (see [4]), corresponding to about 100 times the current annual photosynthetic carbon dioxide fixation.

This chapter provides not only a brief summary on the general features of the "primary processes of photosynthesis" but its more ambitious goal is to stimulate the readers' interest on detailed information about apparatus and mechanisms of this key part of photosynthesis Subsequent chapters, written by leading experts, provide excellent descriptions of different facets of this fascinating field.

## 1.2 Basic Principles of Photosynthetic Solar Energy Transformation

Solar radiation is absorbed by suitable pigment molecules that are indispensable constituents of the photosynthetic apparatus. Essentially three classes of chromophores are used for this purpose: (i) (bacterio-)chlorophylls with a cyclic π-electron system of tetrapyrrole rings, (ii) phycobilins with an open chain tetrapyrrole and (iii) carotenoids with a mainly linear chain of conjugated double bonds. Figure 3 shows representative molecules of these pigment classes (for reviews, see [22,23]; Chapters 3 and 4 give details of the structure and properties of these pigments).

A landmark in our understanding of the functional pigment organization was the classical experiment of Emerson and Arnold [24]. The results of this study revealed that only one oxygen molecule is evolved per about 2500 chlorophylls when *Chlorella* cells are illuminated with repetitive short flashes (about 10 μs) of saturating intensity ("single turnover flashes").

As a consequence, only a small fraction of all chlorophylls in the organisms can be directly involved in the process of transformation of an electronically excited state into the primary (electro-)chemical product. This experimental observation led Gaffron and Wohl [25] to the conclusion that the pigments are organized in "photosynthetic units" and functionally distinguished in performing two basically different types of reactions: the vast majority of the pigments (>99% of the total content) are involved in light absorption and efficient transfer of the electronically excited states to a special pigment where the photochemical reaction takes place. The former type of pigments (symbolized by $P_A$) forms a light harvesting device (antenna) that enhances the optical cross section of the photochemically active pigment (designated as $P_{RC}$) by about two orders of magnitude. Numerous investigations have shown that the functional subdivision into a large number of antenna pigments $P_A$ and a small number of photochemically active pigments $P_{RC}$ is a general feature of all photosynthesizing organisms.

The basic principles underlying the function of $P_A$ and $P_{RC}$ are illustrated in Figure 4 by a simple HOMO (highest occupied molecular orbital)/LUMO (lowest unoccupied molecular orbital) scheme of two interacting pigments $P_1$ and $P_2$, with one molecule in the first excited electronic singlet state ($^1P_1^*$); and the other one staying in the ground state ($P_2$). Two possible modes of electronic interactions between pigment molecules $^1P_1^*$ and $P_2$ lead to quite different results: (i) radiationless excitation energy transfer (EET) or (ii) electron transfer (ET). In the former case the electronically excited state (exciton)[§] is transferred from one pigment molecule to another one, thus representing the function of $P_A$. EET is the underlying principle of the antennae function that is established by formation of ordered arrays of pigment molecules. Depending

---

[§]In photosynthesis research "exciton" is used as an operational term to describe an excited electronic state that resides during its lifetime on more than one pigment in a group of molecules [28].

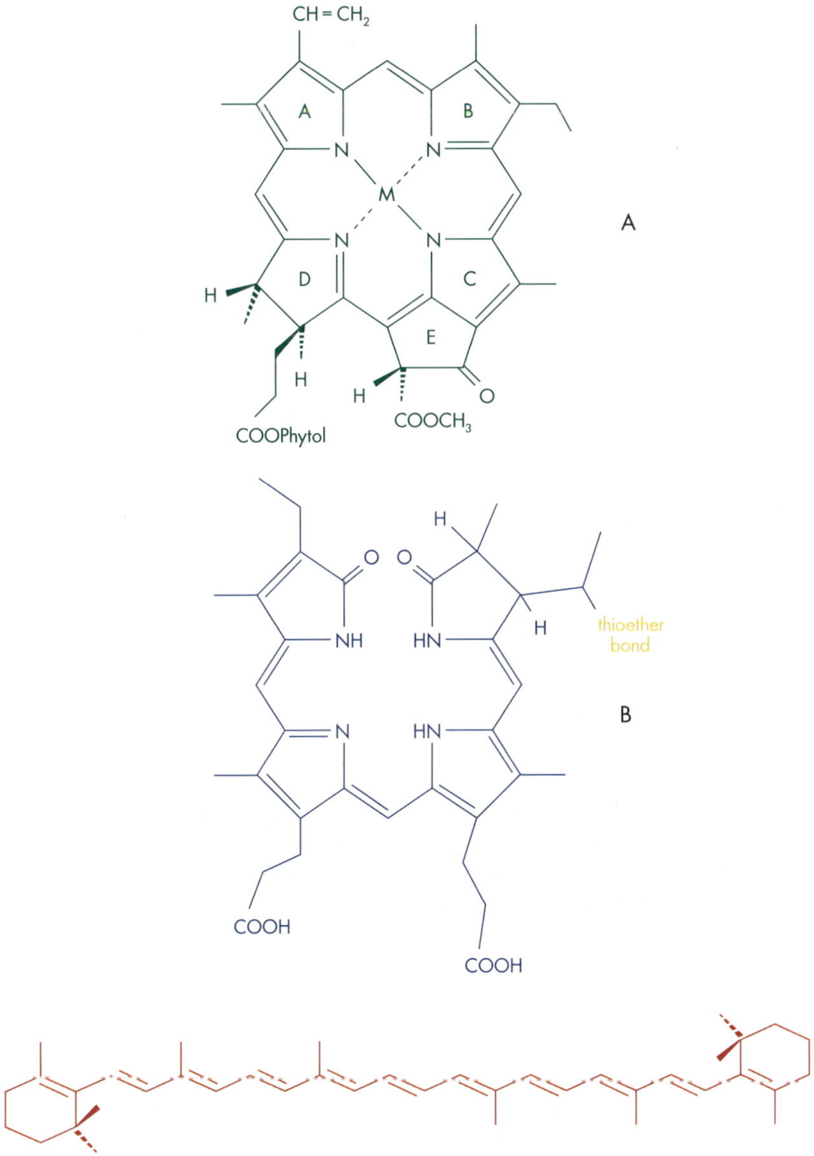

# OVERVIEW OF PRIMARY PROCESSES OF PHOTOSYNTHESIS

**Figure 3.** Chemical structure of chlorophyll *a* (A), phycocyanobilin (B) and all-trans-β-carotene (C) as representative species of chlorophylls, phycobilins and carotenoids.

on the mode of electronic coupling between the pigments, *i.e.*, Coulomb or exchange interaction, two different EET mechanisms emerge (Förster and Dexter type, respectively, see [26,27]), as is outlined in more detail in Chapter 2. These EET reactions are not coupled with a net charge transfer between pigments. In marked contrast, the ET reaction leads to formation of the ion radical pair $P_1^{+\bullet}P_2^{-\bullet}$ and therefore an electronically excited pigment $^1P_1^*$, which

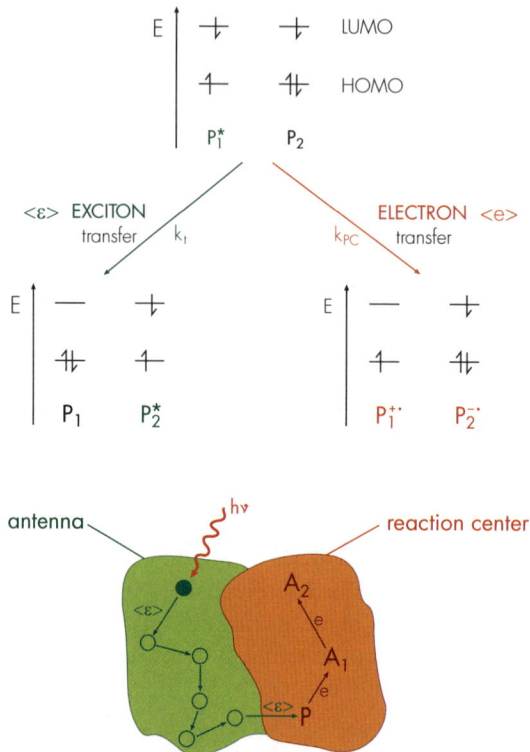

**Figure 4.** Electronic coupling between two pigment molecules ($P_1$ and $P_2$) with the same orbital structure; one in the first excited electronic singlet state ($^1P_1^*$) and the other one in the electronic ground state ($P_2$). The top part illustrates the processes of excitation energy transfer (EET) (green symbols) and electron transfer (ET) (red symbols) while the lower part shows a schematic representation of an antenna (in green) and reaction center (orange) complex.

transfers an electron to $P_2$ as its coupled electron acceptor, reflects $P_{RC}$. This type of ET is the key step in the overall transformation process of solar radiation into (electro-)chemical Gibbs energy through the process of photosynthesis. The mechanism of ET reactions can be described within the framework of the Marcus theory [29] (for details, see Chapter 2).

The general scheme of Figure 4 immediately raises questions about the nature of the biological devices that were evolved to perform these reactions with high efficiency in the photosynthetic apparatus.

### 1.2.1 Light Harvesting

Photosynthetic organisms are exposed to quite different illumination conditions that drastically change due to diurnal variations. Likewise, seasonal changes are also often important. Furthermore, the radiation strongly varies (by orders of magnitude) in biotopes like tropical rainforests or marine systems at different levels of the oceans. Therefore, suitable adaptation mechanisms are required to cope with these conditions. Essentially, two functional demands have to be satisfied: (i) at weak irradiations the few quanta have to be collected and efficiently transferred to the photoactive pigment $P_{RC}$ and (ii) at exposure to strong light the organism must be protected from destruction due to deleterious side reactions, in particular by the formation of very reactive singlet oxygen. Most of the regulatory processes take place at the level of electronically excited states that are formed by light absorption of the antenna pigments. The number and spectral properties of the $P_A$ molecules permit an optimal adaptation of the photosynthetic apparatus to the irradiation conditions in the environment. Therefore, unsurprisingly, during evolution, several types of pigment–protein complexes have been developed that markedly differ in structure and pigment composition among the various photosynthetic organisms (for evolution of antennas, see [30] and references therein). The pigments of the antenna systems are incorporated into well-defined pigment–protein complexes – the only exceptions so far known are self-aggregated bacteriochlorophylls in the chlorosomes in green sulfur bacteria (see [31] and references therein). Enormous progress has been made during the last decade in unraveling the structure and the mechanisms of antenna systems. Details on our current state of knowledge are described in Chapters 6–9.

### 1.2.2 Light-Induced Charge Separation

In marked contrast to the great variations among the antenna systems, the reaction centers (RCs), where the primary light-induced charge separation and its subsequent stabilization take place, follow in principle the same masterpiece of structural and functional organization. The mechanism of all photosynthetic reaction centers can be described by eqn. (4):

$$\begin{aligned}[\text{ANT}]P_{RC}\,\text{Acc}_1\,\text{Acc}_2 &\xrightarrow{h\nu} {}^1[\text{ANT}-P_{RC}]^*\text{Acc}_1\,\text{Acc}_2 \\ &\xrightarrow{k_{pc}} [\text{ANT}]P_{RC}^{+\bullet}\,\text{Acc}_1^{-\bullet}\,\text{Acc}_2 \qquad (4)\\ &\xrightarrow{k_{stab}} [\text{ANT}]P_{RC}^{+\bullet}\,\text{Acc}_1\,\text{Acc}_2^{-\bullet}\end{aligned}$$

where the first step summarizes $^1P_{RC}^*$ formation by light absorption and EET from pigments of the antenna [ANT] leading to excited state equilibration (without specifying the details of the process), $k_{pc}$ is the rate constant of the primary charge separation step giving rise to the radical ion pair, with $\text{Acc}_1$ acting as primary acceptor, and $k_{stab}$ is the rate constant for stabilization of the charge separation by rapid ET from $\text{Acc}_1^{-\bullet}$ to component $\text{Acc}_2$. This generalized description does not explicitly account for the participation of additional cofactors in the ET pathway from $\text{Acc}_1^{-\bullet}$ to $\text{Acc}_2$. Likewise, for simplicity, the back reactions are omitted in eqn. (4).

In all photosynthetic organisms the cofactors for reaction sequence (4) are embedded into a protein matrix that consists of two polypeptides. These operational units are referred to as the reaction center (RC). In general, two types of RCs can be distinguished that differ in the chemical nature of the $Acc_2$ cofactor: type I RCs use an iron-sulfur cluster whereas in type II RCs a special noncovalently bound *para*-quinone molecule ($Q_A$) takes the function of $Acc_2$. According to our current state of knowledge, the photoactive pigment $P_{RC}$ is a special dimer of two bacteriochlorophyll molecules in all non-oxygen evolving (anoxygenic) photosynthetic bacteria (Chapter 12) and a Chl *a* complex in both PSI and PSII of all oxygen-evolving organisms, with only one exception unraveled so far, *i.e.*, the cyanobacterium *Acaryochloris marina*, which contains Chl *d* at least in $P_{RC}$ of PSI (see [32] and Chapters 6, 16). The symbols for $P_{RC}$ are deduced from the peak position of the bleaching band in the red (PSI and PSII) and near-infrared (NIR) (anoxygenic bacteria) of the oxidized minus reduced difference spectrum, e.g., P870 is the photoactive special pair of the RC of *Rhodobacter (Rb.) spheroides*; P700 and P680 are the corresponding species in PSI and PSII, respectively.

Anoxygenic photosynthetic bacteria contain only one type of RC, *i.e.*, green sulfur bacteria (Chlorobiaceae) and heliobacteria (Heliobacteriaceae) contain type I RCs, whereas the RCs of purple bacteria (Protobacteriaceae) and green filamentous nonsulfur bacteria (Chloroflexaceae) are type II. In most cases the protein matrix is a heterodimer consisting of two different polypeptides, but at least in one phylum (Heliobacteriaceae) it is a homodimer. Different BChl derivates are used for the special pair of the photoactive pigment $P_{RC}$: BChl *a* and BChl *b* in type II RCs and in addition BChl *g* in the type I RCs of Heliobacteriaceae (for details see Chapters 3 and 12).

In marked contrast to anoxygenic bacteria, both types of RCs are present in all oxygen evolving photosynthetic organisms (cyanobacteria, algae, plants) and are part of complexes referred to as Photosystems: (a) Photosystem II (PSII) with a type II RC enables light-induced water splitting into molecular oxygen and hydrogen bound in the form of plastoquinol with a moderate reduction potential (about +80 mV) and (b) Photosystem I (PSI) with a type I RC, which increases the reduction power of the bound hydrogen up to the level of NADPH with a reduction potential of –320 mV at pH 7. This is only about 100 mV less negative than that of molecular hydrogen at pH = 7.0 [15]. PSII and PSI operate in series. This functional array of the two photosystems, with $PQH_2$ generated at PSII and acting as reductant for the formation of the electron donor for PSI at the cytochrome $b_6/f$ complex (Cyt $b_6/f$), is required to achieve a sufficiently low reduction potential of the bound hydrogen. Theoretically, a specially tailored PSII with $Pheo^-$ as reductant rather than $Q_A^{-\bullet}$ should satisfy the thermodynamic requirement for light-induced formation of NADH (for a discussion, see [33] and references therein). However, reports of the existence of PS II complexes that can form directly the reductant for $CO_2$ fixation in *Chlamydomonas* mutants [34] turned out to be wrong due to the contamination of samples by PS I [35].

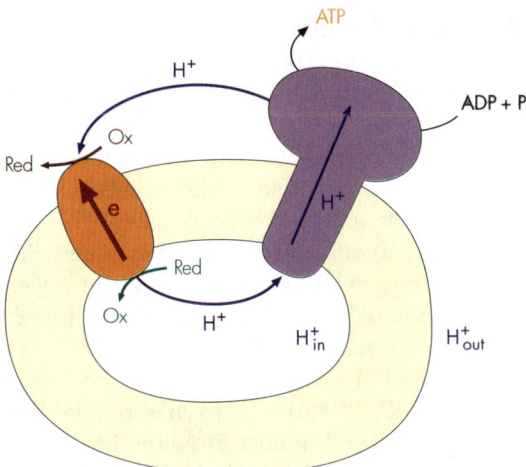

**Figure 5.** Schematic representation of the anisotropic incorporation of reaction centers (photosystems) (in red) and ATP synthase (purple) into photosynthetic membranes. The redox sequences of the reducing (Ox → Red) and oxidizing (Red → Ox) side of the reaction centers (RCs) are marked in brown and green, respectively, and the coupled proton fluxes including the vectorial transfer through the ATP synthase are marked in blue.

The reaction centers are the "solar energy power stations" of the photosynthetic apparatus, with the species of $P_{RC}^{+\cdot}$ and $Acc_2^{-\cdot}$ acting as the oxidant and reductant, respectively, that energetically drive "downhill" electron transfer reaction sequences. Subsequent biochemical reactions of the Calvin–Benson cycle lead to $CO_2$ assimilation [Eq.(3)].

The reaction centers/photosystems are anisotropically incorporated into membranes, as illustrated schematically in Figure 5. This has the important consequence that the oxidative and reductive sequences take place in different reaction compartments. Furthermore, regardless of the detailed membrane structure, the light-induced charge separation within the RCs is a vectorial process with respect to the membrane normal so that an electrical potential difference across the vesicle membrane is concomitantly generated by $P_{RC}^{+\cdot}Acc_2^{-\cdot}$ formation. Likewise, coupled protonation (acceptor side) and deprotonation (donor side) reactions give rise to formation of a transmembrane $\Delta pH$ [36,37]. In this way Gibbs energy is transiently stored as an electrochemical potential difference of protons¶ (protonmotive force = pmf) and according to Mitchell [38] used for ATP synthesis (Chapter 21 gives a detailed description).

---

¶The term "proton gradient" is often used in an incorrect manner. It should not be confused with "$\Delta pH$" because the gradient, by definition, is $\nabla[H^+(\vec{r})]$ where $\nabla$ is an operator (derivative to space coordinates) and $[H^+(\vec{r})]$ the scalar field of the local proton concentration at position $\vec{r}$. Accordingly the gradient is a space dependent quantity and its actual value difficult to determine in biological membrane systems.

## 1.3 Electron Transport Chains

Figure 6 summarizes the energetics of the charge separation and subsequent ET reactions in both anoxygenic bacteria and oxygen evolving organisms. An inspection of these schemes reveals two striking features for the light-induced $P_{RC}^{+\bullet}Acc_2^{-\bullet}$ formation: (i) the exceptionally high reduction potential of P680 in PSII (compared with P700 and the special pair P of BRCs) that is the indispensable energetic prerequisite for oxidative water cleavage under the formation of molecular oxygen and (ii) the markedly stronger reducing power of $Acc_2$ in type I RCs compared with that of type II RCs (note the higher Gibbs energy levels of $F_X$, $F_A F_B$ versus $Q_A Q_B$).

The Gibbs energy content of the radical pair $P_{RC}^{+\bullet}Acc_2^{-\bullet}$ related to that of the lowest exited singlet state $^1P_{RC}^*$ varies between about 35% for typical type II RCs of purple bacteria [39] and almost 70% for PS II of oxygenic photosynthesis [40]. This large difference is entirely due to the much more positive reduction potential of P680 compared with that of the special pair P of type II RCs in anoxygenic bacteria (Figure 6).

The reactions driven by $P_{RC}^{+\bullet}$ and $Acc_2^{-\bullet}$ are all exergonic, i.e., each step leads to a decrease of the Gibbs energy. In most anoxygenic bacteria with type II RCs the electron transport is a cyclic pathway that has a cytochrome $bc_1$ (Cyt $bc_1$) complex as an essential constituent. The quinol formed at the $Q_B$ site

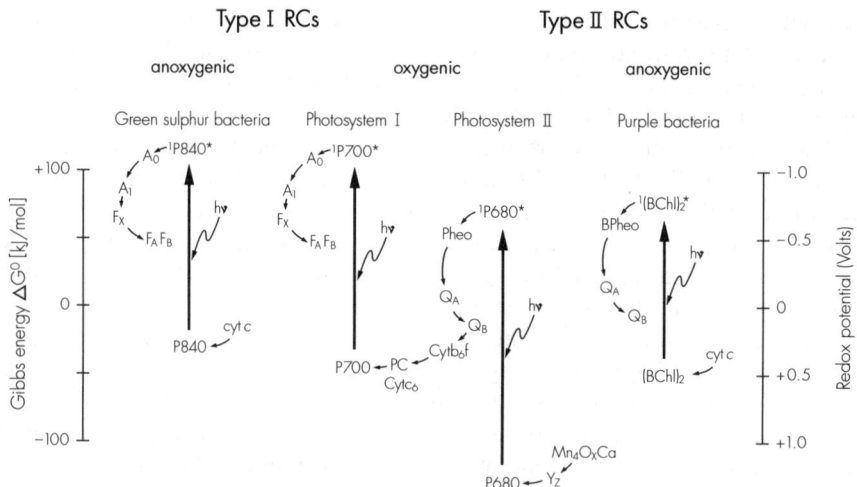

**Figure 6.** Energetics of light-induced electron transfer chains in anoxygenic bacteria with type I and type II reaction centers and of oxygen evolving organisms (left-hand scale: $\Delta G°$ values; right-hand scale: redox potentials). P840, (BChl)$_2$, P700 and P680 are the photoactive pigments $P_{RC}$ of green sulfur bacteria, purple bacteria, Photosystem I and Photosystem II, respectively, (B)Pheo = (bacterio)pheophytin, $Q_A$, $Q_B$ = quinone acceptors, $F_X$ and $F_{A,B}$ = iron sulfur clusters, Cyt = cytochrome and $Mn_4O_xCa$ = catalytic site of the water oxidizing complex.

# OVERVIEW OF PRIMARY PROCESSES OF PHOTOSYNTHESIS

of type II RCs becomes reoxidized at the Cyt $bc_1$ complex that in turn reduces different cytochrome c (Cyt c) forms (for details see Chapters 12 and 18). The reduced Cyt c eventually reduces the photooxidized $P_{RC}^{+*}$. This cyclic electron pathway generates a transmembrane $\Delta pH$ as the driving force for ATP synthesis.

For linear electron transport, anoxygenic photosynthetic bacteria use substances that need much less driving force for electron abstraction than for the oxidation of water. Compounds like $H_2$, $H_2S$ or small organic molecules (formate, acetate or methanol) serve as electron donors (for further discussion, see Chapters 12 and 18).

Heliobacteriaceae and Chloroflexaceae are obligate anaerobic organisms with type I RCs and the compound $NAD^+$ used as the characteristic terminal electron acceptor of the ET chain. In marked contrast, type II RCs cannot directly reduce $NAD^+$ for energetic reasons (the midpoint potential of quinol is not low enough). These anoxygenic bacteria perform cyclic electron flow and in this way solar energy is stored in form of ATP, which can be used as driving force to support endergonic $NAD^+$ reduction with suitable electron donors (Chapter 18).

In marked contrast to anoxygenic photosynthetic bacteria, in all oxygen evolving organisms a linear electron transport from $H_2O$ to $NADP^+$ takes place that is energetically driven by the light reactions of PSI containing a type I RC (Chapters 13 and 14) and PSII with a type II RC (Chapters 15 and 16). Both photosystems are functionally connected via the integral $Cytb_6f$ complex (Chapter 20) and the mobile lipophilic electron carrier system $PQH_2/PQ$ within the thylakoid membrane and the soluble redox proteins plastocyanin (PC) in plants or cytochrome $c_6$ (Cyt $c_6$) in many cyanobacteria.

Linear ET from $H_2O$ to $NADP^+$ consists of three reaction sequences, which are summarized by the following equations:

$$4H^+_{stroma} + 2H_2O + 2PQ \xrightarrow{h\nu} 2PQH_2 + O_2 + 4H^+_{lumen} \quad (5)$$

$$4H^+_{stroma} + 2PQH_2 + 4PC_{ox}(Cytc_{6,ox})$$
$$\xrightarrow{dark} 2PQ + 4PC_{red}(Cytc_{6,red}) + 8H^+_{lumen} \quad (6)$$

$$2H^+_{stroma} + 4PC_{red}(Cytc_{6,red}) + 2NADP^+$$
$$\xrightarrow{h\nu} 4PC_{ox}(Cytc_{6,ox}) + 2NADPH \quad (7)$$

where $H^+_{stroma}$ and $H^+_{lumen}$ represent proton uptake from the cytoplasma (stroma) and proton release into the lumen, respectively.

Figure 7 shows a structural model of the array of the integral ET complexes within the thylakoid membrane and the participation of soluble ET carriers in the stroma and lumen.

In addition to the linear electron transport from $H_2O$ to $NADP^+$ cyclic pathways exist that are driven solely by PSI. In green plants, the cycle from the

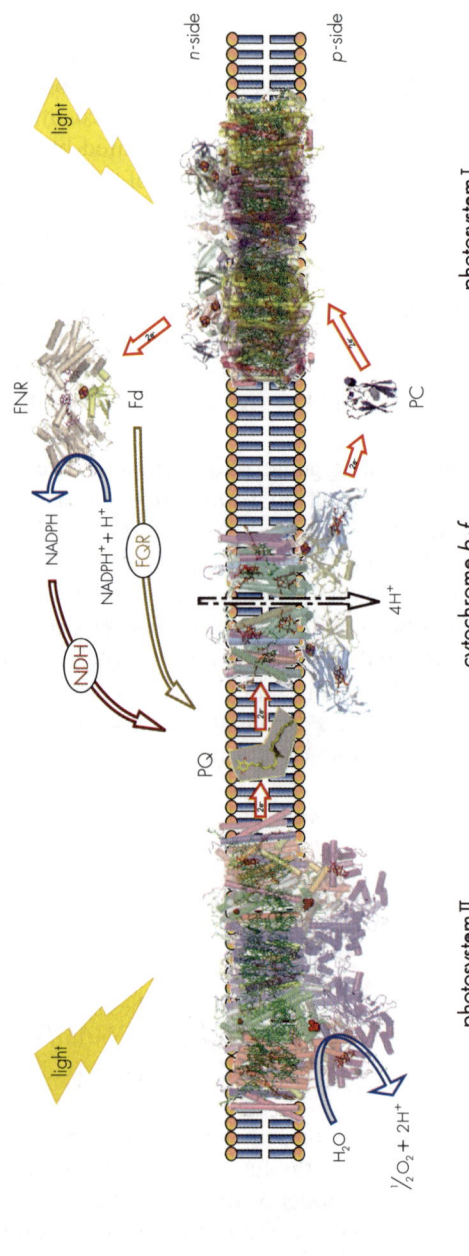

**Figure 7.** Structural model of the electron transport chain in oxygen evolving organisms (original figure kindly provided by Professor W.W. Cramer and modified by S. Renger). The structures of putative FQR and NDH are not shown (the enzymes are symbolized by ellipses). For details, see text.

stroma side of PSII to the PQ pool can occur via two different routes, either starting directly from the soluble ferredoxin (Fd) or including NADPH, as is illustrated in Figure 7 [41,42]. The former route involves the putative ferredoxin-plastoquinone-oxidoreductase (FQR), the latter the NAD(P)H dehydrogenase complex NDH [43,44]. The physiological function of the cyclic electron flow is probably an additional ATP production [41] to maintain the correct stoichiometry of 3ATP/2NADPH [eqn. (3)] that is required to satisfy the conditions for $CO_2$ fixation. This idea is supported by the finding that the ratio of cyclic to linear electron transport is regulated by the ATP concentration [45]. Without this control an over-reduction of the stroma by accumulation of excess NADPH could occur. Marked differences probably exist among the various green plants (algae, mosses, higher plants) with respect to the extent of regulation via cyclic electron transport.

The overall rate of the linear electron transport is limited by the turnover of the $PQ/PQH_2$ redox system [46]. Oxidation of $PQH_2$ and concomitant reduction of $PC_{ox}$ ($Cytc_{6,ox}$) occur via exergonic dark reactions at the $Cytb_6f$ complex. This process is coupled with a transmembrane $\Delta pH$ formation, leading to acidification of the lumen at a net stoichiometric ratio of $2H^+/e$ (Eq. (6)). The underlying mechanism of the $Cytb_6f$ turnover is a special reaction sequence (Q-cycle) that involves electrogenic ET steps and two different sites of $PQH_2/PQ$ reactions (for details, see Chapter 20).

The extent of PQ pool reduction also provides a trigger signal (redox signaling) that is generated at the $Cytb_6f$ complex and induces the activation of a kinase for phosphorylation of the light harvesting complex LHCII [47]. This mechanism is important for regulation of excitation energy distribution between PSII and PSI in plants ([48]; for further details, see Chapter 9).

The $P680^{+\bullet}$ formed by the light-induced charge separation of PSII is the strongest oxidant with an estimated midpoint potential $E_m(P680/P680^+)$ of about $+1.25$ V ([49]; for details, see Chapter 16) and provides the driving force for oxidative water splitting ($2H_2O$) into molecular oxygen and four protons. This process takes place via a sequence of oxidation steps at a $Mn_4O_xCa$ cluster with the tyrosine $Y_Z$ of polypeptide D1 acting as redox active link between $P680^{+\bullet}$ and $Mn_4O_xCa$. Despite significant progress in unraveling the structure and properties of the $Mn_4O_xCa$ unit, key mechanistic questions of this process (e.g., O–O bond formation) are still not clarified [50] and are a "hot" topic of current research (for details of this key reaction of oxygenic photosynthesis, see Chapter 17).

The $PQH_2$ formed at the $Q_B$ site of PSII diffuses within the membrane to the $Cytb_6f$ complex where it becomes reoxidized to PQ (vide supra) and moves back to PSII. The concomitantly reduced soluble proteins PC and/or $Cytc_6$ are mobile in the lumen and act as electron donors for $P700^{+\bullet}$. The light-induced charge separation of PSI gives rise to reduction of bound ferredoxin ($F_A, F_B$) acting as electron donor for soluble ferredoxin (Fd) that in turn reduces $NADP^+$ to NADPH at the $Fd_{red}$-$NADP^+$ oxidoreductase (FNR) (for details, see Chapter 14). Under iron deficiency growth conditions, cyanobacteria and several algae synthesize flavodoxin instead of Fd [51]. The flavodoxin replaces Fd in mediating the ET between PSI and FNR [52].

Notably, the stoichiometry of the complexes PSI:PSII:Cytb$_6$f markedly deviates from a 1:1:1 ratio. In particular, the PSI:PSII ratio greatly varies among different organisms and depends on the illumination conditions during growth. This ratio is comparatively high (in extreme cases up to about 10) in cyanobacteria [53,54] and attains values below 1.0 in many higher plants, in particular in land plants (in some cases ratios lower than 0.5 are found) [55].

## 1.4 Architecture of the Photosynthetic Apparatus

All RCs of photosynthetic organisms are anisotropically incorporated into membranes that form vesicles (Section 1.2.2). The structure of these vesicles has changed markedly during evolution (Figure 8).

*1.4.1 Anoxygenic Bacteria*

The RCs of Chloroflexaceae and Chlorobiaceae are incorporated into the cytoplasmic membrane where large pigment protein complexes (chlorosomes) are attached to the RCs at the inside of these membranes and act as antenna

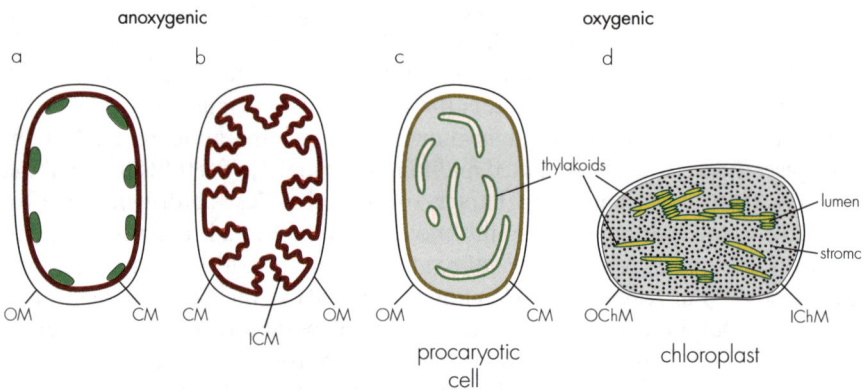

**Figure 8.** Schematic representation of membrane systems containing the photosynthetic apparatus in prokaryotic cells and chloroplasts of plants. (a) Anoxygenic bacteria with type I RCs; the cytoplasmic membrane (CM) is marked in purple and the attached chlorosomes marked in green, OM: outer cell membrane. (b) Anoxygenic bacteria with type II RC; OM: outer cell membrane, the localization of the photosynthetic membrane within the cresped ICM sections are symbolized by red dots. (c) Cyanobacterial cell; OM: outer cell membrane, CM: cytoplasmic membrane, thylakoid membranes (intracytoplasmic membranes) are marked in green, the luminal phase in pink and the cytoplasm in grey. For the sake of simplicity other constituents of the cytoplasm (DNA, enzymes) are omitted. (d) Chloroplast from higher plants; OChM: outer chloroplast membrane; IChM: inner chloroplast membrane; the thylakoid membranes are marked in green; the luminal space in yellow.

OVERVIEW OF PRIMARY PROCESSES OF PHOTOSYNTHESIS   23

systems. No special segmentation of the cytoplasmic membrane occurs, i.e., the photosynthetic apparatus is not laterally segregated from other membrane-bound enzymes such as hydrogenases. As a striking difference in structural organization, the cytoplasmic membrane of phototrophic Protobacteriaceae exhibit marked invaginations (intracytoplasmic membranes, ICMs). The formation of ICM sections leads to an increase of the photosynthetic capacity of the cells. The invaginations exhibit vesicle-like substructures of different shapes (tubular, vesicular and lamellar forms are known). Furthermore, the antenna system is completely integrated into the ICM with two types of ring- or ellipse-shaped pigment–protein complexes: ($\alpha$) light-harvesting complex 1 containing the RC in the middle (LH1-RC), and ($\beta$) light-harvesting complex 2 (LH2) (for details, see Chapter 5). The ICM sections can be isolated as sealed vesicles referred to as chromatophores [56], thus providing most suitable sample material for functional studies of the photosynthetic apparatus (Chapters 5, 12 and 18 ).

*1.4.2 Oxygen Evolving Organisms*

In marked contrast to anoxygenic purple bacteria, the apparatus of "the primary processes of photosynthesis" in all oxygen evolving organisms is incorporated into separate membrane systems (the currently only known exception is the cyanobacterium *Gloeobacter violaceus*, see [57] and Chapter 19). These "photosynthetic membranes" form closed vesicular structures, the thylakoids (the term "thylakoids" coined by Menke [58] is derived from the Greek and means "sack-like"). Accordingly, these membranes are designated as thylakoid membranes. A particular situation emerges for cyanobacteria, the first organisms in evolution that were able to evolve oxygen ([59] and Chapter 19). Cyanobacteria are characterized by the presence of both the components of photosynthetic electron transport from $H_2O$ to $NADP^+$ in the thylakoid membrane and the complexes of the respiratory electron transport (RET) chain in the cytoplasmic membrane without obvious anastomoses between them [59]. The thylakoid membrane of cyanobacteria houses not only the complexes of the photosynthetic ET chain but also typical enzymes of the RET like $aa_3$-type cytochrome c oxidase. In contrast, the cytoplasmic membrane contains only components of the RET without any photosynthetic RCs [59]. Accordingly, with respect to photosynthetic activity the cytoplasmic membranes of cyanobacteria markedly differ from those of anoxygenic photosynthetic bacteria. Details on the peculiarities of photosynthetic electron transport in cyanobacteria are described in Chapter 19.

In eukaryotic cells the membrane organization reaches a much higher complexity through the differentiation into organelles. "Ancestor" eukaryotic cells incorporated cyanobacteria via phagocytosis and used them as phototrophic "Gibbs energy slaves" by their transformation into cell organelles, the plastids (endosymbiosis [60,61]; for details, see Chapter 22).

There exist marked differences between algae and higher plants with respect to size and shape of the chloroplasts and their number per cell. Among the different phyla of eukaryotic algae (*Rhodophyta*, *Chromophyta*, *Chlorophyta etc.*) the cells contain only few chloroplasts (in special cases, e.g., *Spirogyra*, only a single chloroplast is present) with large variations in size and shape [62]. In marked contrast to the variability of eukaryotic algae, the chloroplasts of mosses, ferns and higher plants are basically very similar. Typical leaf cells with high photosynthetic activity (mesophyll cells) contain 100–200 chloroplasts with diameters of 3–10 μm and a thickness of 1–4 μm. The essential structural characteristics are summarized in Figure 8(d) (for simplicity, only the thylakoid membrane system is shown and particles in the stroma, like plastoglobuli and DNA, are omitted). A characteristic feature of higher plant chloroplasts is the marked diversification of the thylakoid membranes into grana stacks and intergrana lamellae. This phenomenon is connected with a pronounced lateral heterogeneity of the functional complexes (PSII, PSII, $Cytb_6f$ and ATP-synthase) within the thylakoid membranes [63,64] (Figure 9).

The lateral segregation of PS I and ATP-synthase (localized in stroma lamellae) versus PS II (localized in grana stacks) within the thylakoid membrane system originates from the quite different overall structural feature of these complexes. Subunits of the PS I complex that are involved in reduction of soluble ferredoxin (Fd) and the functional connection to the $Fd_{red}$-$NAD^+$-oxidoreductase (FNR) are exposed to the stroma and form a bulky extension into this phase, whereas the lumen-exposed part of PS I is rather flat (Chapter 13).

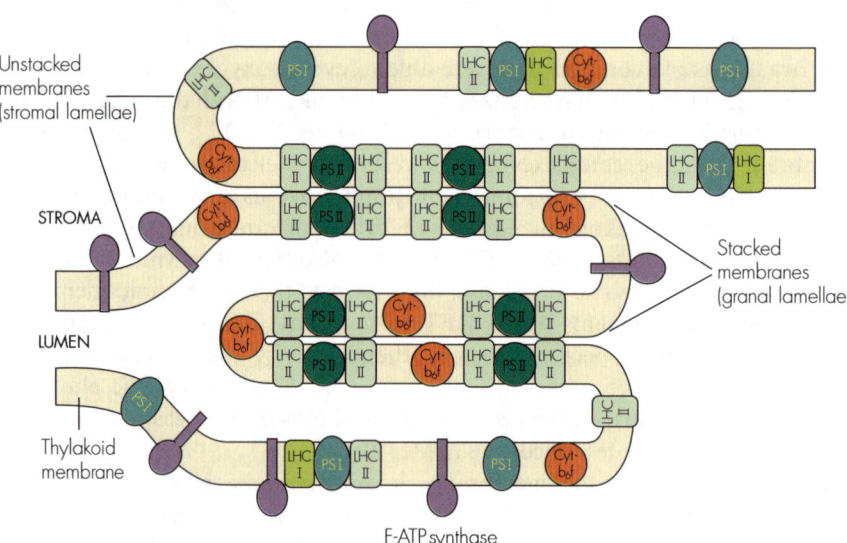

**Figure 9.** Lateral distribution of the main functional complexes of the photosynthetic apparatus in the thylakoid membrane of chloroplasts in higher plants (for details, see text). (Figure provided by D. Difiore and redrawn by S. Renger.)

Likewise, the large catalytic CF1 part of the ATP-synthase is also located on the stroma side of the membrane (Chapter 21). Therefore, these two complexes cannot be located in the appressed membrane regions of the grana stacks. On the contrary, the PSII complexes exhibit a characteristic feature of strikingly opposite structural arrangement: the surface exposed to the stroma side exhibits virtually no significant extensions while the exceptionally large loops of the core complex proteins CP43 and CP47, which consist of about 190 amino acids, are exposed to the lumenal side. Likewise, the regulatory extrinsic proteins of the water-oxidizing complex (WOC) are bound at the lumenal side (for structural details see Chapter 15). It is interesting to note that the quite different structural extensions of PS I and PS II into the lumenal space are related to the nature of the electron donor to $P700^{+\cdot}$ and $P680^{+\cdot}$, respectively. The cation radical $P700^{+\cdot}$ is directly reduced by the large diffusible extrinsic protein molecules PC (plants) or Cyt $c_6$ (cyanobacteria), whereas the reductant of $P680^{+\cdot}$ is the intrinsic redox component $Y_Z$ which in turn accepts electrons delivered from the WOC by oxidation of the small substrate water molecules. Furthermore, the overall structure of the pigment–protein complexes, which form the peripheral antenna, drastically differs within the oxygen evolving organisms. In cyanobacteria and red algae, phycobilisomes with discoidal or hemi-discoidal shape are attached from the cytoplasma to the thylakoid membrane (Chapter 6) whereas in plants the pigment–protein complexes of this antenna system are integrated into the thylakoid membrane (Chapters 7 and 8). As a consequence, PSII complexes from plants structurally favor grana stack formation, in marked contrast to cyanobacteria and red algae. In contrast, structure and functional pattern of the PSII core complex are highly conserved during evolution; in particular the distances between the cofactors remained virtually invariant despite differences in the protein scaffold between cyanobacteria and higher plants [65].

For all considerations on structure–function relationships at different levels of complexity (isolated antennas and reaction centers or photosystem core complexes, thylakoid membranes, chloroplasts) it is most important to take into account the dynamics of these systems. At the level of chloroplasts, the three-dimensional thylakoid membrane organization, schematically shown in Figures 8 and 9, is not a static structure but represents a dynamic system. The method of high-pressure freezing (HPF) in combination with freeze substitution (FS) offer a suitable tool for reliable ultrastructural analyses of chloroplasts by electron microscopy [66]. Studies on barley leaves revealed significant changes in the thylakoid organization during the diurnal light–dark rhythm [67]. The implications of these phenomena for the function of the whole photosynthetic apparatus are of high relevance for plant biologists but are outside the scope of this volume.

The lateral heterogeneity is also of functional relevance for the regulation of the ratio between cyclic and non-cyclic electron transport in thylakoids (for a discussion, see [45] and references therein).

## 1.5 Biomimetic Systems

The antennas and reaction centers of photosynthetic organisms are masterpieces of equipments of nanometer-scale dimensions for exploitation of solar radiation as a Gibbs energy source. It is therefore most attractive to use nature's "inventions" as blueprints for the construction of biomimetic systems that can fulfill (with sufficiently high efficiency) specific functions like light harvesting, "stable" charge separation, reductive and oxidative water splitting to produce powerful hydrogen donor compounds and molecular oxygen, respectively, and ATP synthesis. This goal is an important challenge because its successful performance at a highly advanced technological level can pave a new road for the exploitation of solar radiation as source for mankind's increasing Gibbs energy demands. It must be emphasized that alternative devices have been developed for solar energy exploitation, e.g., solid state solar cells, interfacial titan oxide photovoltaic cells, organic thin film arrays etc. (for a review, see [68]). This section considers by a concise description only systems of artificial photosynthesis.

In general, two problems have to be solved: (a) the assembly of pigments and other reactive species into operational units with specific functions, and (b) functional connection of these units to build up entities of integrated activities (e.g., antenna–reaction centers, electron transport chains) and/or vectorial incorporation into bilayer membranes for their energization and further use of the transmembrane electrochemical potential difference (e.g., driving ATP formation or enabling information/signal transfer).

General considerations on the synthesis of biomimetic systems have to be kept in mind, such as that nature uses the unique biopolymer material of polypeptides to tune both the energetic properties of individual cofactors and their spatial arrangement (mutual distance and orientation) that are required for optimized functionality. Accordingly, two strategies have been developed to address this fundamental problem: (a) linkage of reactive constituents with engineered properties via covalent and/or noncovalent bonds (hydrogen bonds, salt bridges) and (b) de novo synthesis of artificial proteins that provide the scaffold for the catalytically active cofactors. Alternatively, structured materials such as specifically tailored non-proteinaceous polymers, electropolymerized thin films or sol–gels can be successfully applied.

Both approaches have been used during the last decade, with great success in the "chemical way" (strategy a) and promising results for significant progress in the near future in the field of "protein-like" based assays (strategy b). Since this volume does not include a separate chapter on artificial photosynthesis, readers are recommended to consult excellent review articles (e.g., [69–73]). Key parameters for design and engineering of photosynthetic light harvesting and electron transfer have been summarized in [74]. To give an impression of the wealth of efforts and great success in the field of biomimetic photosynthesis, a few illustrative examples are briefly described below.

## 1.5.1 Biomimetic Antennas

Various multichromophore systems have been reported that mimic the antennas of photosynthetic organisms. Most of these arrays are built by covalently linked porphyrins and related chromophores [75]. Complexes with different geometries of various chromophores have been synthesized: a star-shaped multiporphyrin-phthalocyanine array where the chromophores are covalently linked via ethyne bridges [76] or a hexaporphyrin with either Zn-porphyrins or free base porphyrins connected with a central benzene core also via ethyne bridges [77]. Both systems form flat two-dimensional pigment arrays. Alternatively, well-defined wheel shaped antennas have been generated that contain four, six or eight directly meso-meso linked porphyrin rings. In the latter case the pigment–pigment interaction is rather strong and, therefore, very fast electronically excited excitation energy transfer (EET) between the chromophores is achieved, with transfer times of 120–350 fs [78], which are comparable with those of the fast EET components of photosynthetic antennas (Chapters 5–8). Recently, a different approach for the assembly of biomimetic antennas was described that represents an illustrative example of the second strategy, i.e., the formation of biomimetic units via de novo protein synthesis. A protein was synthesized that binds and assembles BChls in octylglucoside micelles to complexes that closely resemble the natural light harvesting pigment proteins of anoxygenic purple bacteria [79].

## 1.5.2 Biomimetic Reaction Center

Devices of nanometer-scale dimension that can mimic stable light-induced charge separation of photosynthetic reaction centers (RCs) are of paramount importance. Efficient systems with this function can not only be used as building blocks for the construction of biosolar energy converters (molecular power stations) but are also of great interest as light-triggered molecular electrical switches in microelectronics (optoelectronic devices at molecular level). Unsurprisingly, therefore, many efforts have been made to synthesize biomimetic systems of RCs.

A prototype of artificial reaction centers must contain pigments (P) that are capable of absorbing visible light, thus forming an electronically excited state that either reduces an electron acceptor (A) or oxidizes an electron donor (D). Accordingly, the simplest devices are dyads of the type P-A or P-D. The key problem that needs to be solved for biomimetic reaction centers is the ratio of the rates of forward light-induced charge separation and dissipative back reaction(s). A high ratio is crucial for the efficiency and a sufficiently long lifetime of the charge separated state is essential for the use of the systems as operational units. This goal is difficult to achieve by dyads. In this respect, it is important to emphasize that "stable" charge separation in all natural photosynthetic RCs is a multi-step process [see Section 1.2.2 and eqn. (4)]. Accordingly, analogous systems were constructed by chemical means.

Efficient devices could be obtained by the synthesis of triads and pentads where three or five components are covalently linked and the primary charge separation is stabilized by rapid secondary electron transfer. The general mechanisms of a triad (and analogously of pentads) can be summarized by eqn. (8):

$$C - P - Q \xrightarrow{h\nu} C - P^* - Q \rightarrow C - P^{+\cdot} - Q^{-\cdot} \rightarrow C^{+\cdot} - P - Q^{-\cdot} \quad (8)$$

The components of these biomimetic reaction centers are to be selected on the basis of their kinetic and energetic properties and the length and nature of the connecting covalent bridges to optimize the system within the frame work of the Marcus theory of non-adiabatic electron transfer (for reviews, see [69,80,81] and references therein).

A prominent example of a pentad is $C-P_{Zn}-P-Q_A-Q_B$, where C = carotenoid, $P_{Zn}$ = Zn-porphyrin, P = free base porphyrin, $Q_A$ is a naphthoquinone moiety and $Q_B$ a $p$-benzoquinone linked to $Q_A$ via a fixed bridge. This system permits the formation of the radical pair $C^{+\cdot} - P_{Zn} - P - Q_A - Q_B^{-\cdot}$ with an overall efficiency of 83% and a life time of about 500 ms [69].

Among different chemical species used as acceptor component A, fullerenes were shown to provide a suitable material because the reorganization energy of the electron transfer reaction is rather small (for further reading, see [82,83] and references therein).

*1.5.3 Biomimetic Antenna–Reaction Center Systems*

The next step in the construction of artificial systems that mimic the functions of photosynthesis is the functional connection of antennas and reaction centers. Arrays of synthetic antenna–reaction center hybrids have been reported [84]. An illustrative example is a wheel-shaped complex that contains five bis(phenylethynyl) anthracene moieties acting as antenna pigments that transfer electronic excitation energy to a porphyrin–fullerene dyad charge-transfer unit. These antenna pigments and the dyad are covalently linked with a central hexylphenylbenzene core. The quantum yield of the charge separation leading to $P_{Zn}^{+\cdot} - C_{60}^{-\cdot}$ was found to be about 96% for photons absorbed by the antenna pigments and the lifetime of the radical ion pair is of the order of several nanoseconds (the quantum efficiency decreases to 80% when $P_{Zn}$ is replaced by the free base porphyrin P). The rate constants are about 2.5 ps$^{-1}$ for interchromophore EET between neighbor chromophores of the antenna and in the range of 0.14–0.83 ps$^{-1}$ for the EET from the antenna to $P_{Zn}$, where the charge separation takes place with $k_{CS}$ = 12 ns$^{-1}$ [84].

*1.5.4 Biomimetic Proton Pump*

The formation of an artificial proton pump requires the anisotropic incorporation of biomimetic reaction centers into lipid bilayer membranes and the coupling of the vectorial electron transfer to proton translocation. A C–P–NQ triad (P = porphyrin, C = carotenoid and NQ = naphthoquinone derivatives) can be successfully inserted into a liposomal bilayer membrane and coupled with a lipophilic shuttle [85]. In this system the light-induced charge separation in each triad leads to the radial pair $C^{+\cdot}-P-NQ^{-\cdot}$. The anion radical $NQ^{-\cdot}$ near the outer surface reduces the quinone molecule to the neutral semiquinone under proton uptake from the solution. This species it lipophilic and diffuses across the membrane to the inner surface of the membrane where it becomes reoxidized under $H^+$ release into the intraliposomal volume. The result of these processes is the light-induced formation of a transmembrane electrochemical potential difference of protons across the liposome membrane. Values of about two pH units and about 70 mV were obtained for $\Delta pH$ and $\Delta \psi$, respectively, after several minutes of illumination.

*1.5.5 Biomimetic ATP Synthesis*

The artificial proton pump described in the former section provides the driving force for ATP syntheses according to the coupling scheme illustrated in Figure 5 and outlined in detail in Chapter 21. Therefore, this system needs to be extended by the incorporation of ATP-synthase complexes into the liposome vesicles. At present, biomimetic ATP-synthases are not available and therefore $CF_0 \ F_1$-ATP complexes isolated from spinach chloroplasts were used. This approach was shown to be successful [85].

*1.5.6 Catalysts for Oxidative Water Cleavage and Reductive $CO_2$ Fixation*

The construction of a catalyst that can perform the multiple four electron transformation of oxidizing equivalents to produce molecular oxygen with water as substrate is a great challenge for chemists in the field of molecular approaches for artificial photosynthesis. In this respect, the water oxidizing complex (WOC), containing a $Mn_4O_xCa$ unit in the catalytic center, is the single unique catalyst of all oxygen-evolving photosynthetic organisms. At present, only limited information is available on the structure and the mechanism of this WOC, in particular the mode of O–O bond formation and the type of coupling between electron and proton transfer in individual redox steps remain to be clarified (for details see Chapter 17). Numerous attempts have been reported on the construction of multinuclear manganese complexes that can mimic the function of the WOC ([86] and references therein). However, so far, no corresponding stable manganese cluster could be synthesized that acts as catalyst for oxidative water cleavage with energetics and turnover numbers (stability) comparable with those of the WOC [86–89]. One key parameter in establishing active units is a proper array of the metal centers as is nicely illustrated for synthetic binuclear manganese complexes that catalyze water oxidation to molecular oxygen with $Ce^{4+}$ as oxident only after their adsorption on mica or kaolin as suitable scaffolding matrix [90].

Alternative artificial WOCs are based on the use of multinuclear complexes containing either Mn-porphyrins [91] or other transition metals, e.g., ruthenium.

A suitable ensemble of the latter type of compounds is the binuclear cis,cis-[(bipyridyl)$_2$(H$_2$O)Ru$^{III}$–O–Ru$^{III}$(H$_2$O)(bipyridyl)$_2$]$^{4+}$ complex, which gives rise to formation of molecular oxygen from water after chemical (Ce$^{4+}$) or electrochemical oxidation of both Ru(III) centers to Ru(V) [92,93]. A comparison of the energetics of the oxidation steps of this complex [92] with those of the WOC (Chapter 17) reveals that the synthetic systems require a much higher driving force. A general and more serious problem with these catalysts, however, is dissipative (e.g., dismutation) reactions leading to inactive species.

The next step in the hierarchy is the connection of synthetic reaction centers with a water oxidizing catalyst to create an artificial photosystem II. Attempts in this direction have been reported (for a review, see [73]). These systems are able to perform light-induced charge separation and to oxidize a covalently bound binuclear manganese cluster, but water cleavage activity could not be achieved so far.

With respect to CO$_2$ fixation, the reduction of CO$_2$ to simple molecules like formate by catalysts has been reported (for further reading, see [94]).

## 1.6 Concluding Remarks and Future Perspectives

This chapter briefly describes general principles of the exploitation of solar radiation as Gibbs energy source for living matter through the primary processes of photosynthesis. It also offers a short overview on attempts to synthesize biomimetic systems for artificial photosystems. A fundamental topic of high scientific interest is the functionalizing of cofactors (molecules/metal ions) by the unique material of proteins that is available for fine tuning in biological systems. Unraveling the underlying mechanisms is a challenging task for future research, in particular investigations on the role of protein dynamics for specific functions are expected to be a major topic. Different facets of these problems in the primary processes of photosynthesis are outlined in subsequent chapters.

### Acknowledgments

I am very grateful to Susanne Renger for drawing and/or modifying the figures in the electronic version. I also thank Annegret Wilde for careful reading of the manuscript. The financial support by Deutsche Forschungsgemeinschaft (SFB 429) is gratefully acknowledged.

### References

1. L. Boltzmann, Der zweite Hauptsatz der mechanischen Wärmetheorie. In: *Populäre Schriften* (1905) J. A. Barth, Leipzig (in German).
2. H.J. Morowitz, *Foundations of Bioenergetics* (1978) Academic Press, New York.

3. G. Nicolis, I. Prigogine, *Self Organization in Nonequilibrium Systems* (1977) Wiley, New York.
4. K.I. Zamaraev, V.N. Parmon, Potential methods and perspectives of solar energy conversion via photocatalytic processes. *Rev. Sci. Eng.* **22** (1980) 261–324.
5. C.B. van Niel, The bacterial photosynthesis and their importance of the general problem of photosynthesis. *Act. Enzymology* **1** (1941) 263–328.
6. A.A. Benson, M. Calvin, Carbon dioxide fixation by green plants. *Annu. Rev. Plant Physiol.* **1** (1950) 25–42.
7. M. Calvin, Forty years of photosynthesis and related activities. *Photosynth. Res.* **21** (1989) 3–16.
8. A.A. Benson, Following the path of carbon in photosynthesis: A personal story. *Photosynth. Res.* **73** (2002) 29–49.
9. P.W. Atkins, *Physical Chemistry* (2000) 6th Edn, Oxford University Press, Oxford.
10. R. Buick, The antiquity of oxygenic photosynthesis; evidence from stromatolites in sulphate-deficient Archaen lakes. *Science* **255** (1992) 74–77.
11. D.J. de Marais, Evolution. When did photosynthesis emerge on Earth? *Science* **289** (2000) 1703–1705.
12. Xiong, C.E. Bauer, Complex evolution of photosynthesis. *Annu. Rev. Plant Biol.* **53** (2002) 503–521.
13. J.F. Kasting, J.F. Seifert, Life and the evolution of earth's atmosphere. *Science* **296** (2002) 1066–1067.
14. N. Lane, *Oxygen-The Molecule that made the World* (2002), Oxford University Press, Oxford.
15. G. Renger, Biological energy conservation. in: *Biophysics* (1983), (W. Hoppe, W. Lohmann, H. Markl, H. Ziegler, eds.) Springer, Berlin, pp. 347–371.
16. D.G. Nicholls and S. J. Fergusion, *Bioenergetics* (1982) Academic Press, London, vol. 2.
17. D.L. Gilbert, *Oxygen and Living Processes: An Interdisciplinary Approach* (1981) Springer, New York.
18. C.L. Partch, A. Sancar, Cryptochrome and circadian photoreception in animals. *Methods Enzymol.* **393** (2005) 726–745.
19. V.A. Sineshchekov, Phytochromes: molecular structure, photoreceptor process and physiological function, in: *Concepts in Photobiology: Photosynthesis and Photomorphogenesis* (1999) (G.S. Singhal, G. Renger, Govindjee, K.-D. Irrgang, S.K Sopory, eds.), Kluwer Academic Publishers, Narosa Publishing Co., Delhi. pp. 755–795.
20. S.K. Sopory, N. Sanan, R. Oelmüller, Light signal transduction and gene expression, in: *Concepts in Photobiology: Photosynthesis and Photomorphogenesis* (1999) (G.S. Singhal, G. Renger, Govindjee, K.-D. Irrgang, S.K. Sopory, eds.), Kluwer Academic Publishers, Narosa Publishing Co., Delhi. pp. 897–929.
21. A.R. Grossman, M. Lohr, C.S. Im, *Chlamydomonas reinhardtii* in the landscape of pigments. *Annu. Rev. Gen.* **38** (2004) 119–173.
22. H. Scheer (ed.), *Chlorophylls* (1991) CRC Press, Boca Raton, FL.
23. T. Polivka, V. Sundstrom, Ultrafast dynamics of carotenoid excited states-from solution to natural and artificial systems. *Chem. Rev.* **104** (2004) 2021–2072.
24. R. Emerson, W. Arnold, The photochemical reaction in photosynthesis. *J. Gen. Physiol.* **16** (1932) 191–205.
25. H. Gaffron, K. Wohl, On the theory of assimilation. *Naturwissenschaften* **24** (1936) 81–90.

26. T. Förster, Delocalised excitation and excitation transfer. In: *Modern Quantum Chemistry, Vol. 3, Action of Light and Organic Crystals* (1965) (O. Sinanoglu, ed.), Academic Press, New York, pp. 93–137.
27. D.I. Dexter, A theory of sensitized luminescence in solids. *J. Chem. Phys.* **21** (1953) 836–850.
28. R.M. Pearlstein, Chlorophyll singlet exciton. In: *Photosynthesis 1, Energy Conversion by Plants and Bacteria* (Govindjee, ed.) (1982), Academic Press, New York, pp. 293–330.
29. R.A. Marcus, N. Sutin, Electron transport in chemistry and biology. *Biochem. Biophys. Acta* **811** (1985) 265–322.
30. B.R. Green, The evolution of light harvesting antennas, in: *Light Harvesting Antennas in Photosynthesis* (2003) (B.R. Green, W.W. Parson, eds.), Kluwer Academic Press, Dordrecht, pp. 129–168.
31. T.S. Balaban, A.R. Holzwarth, K. Schaffner, G.-J. Boender, H.J.M. de Groot, CP-MAS $^{13}$C-NMR dipolar correlation spectroscopy of $^{13}$C-enriched chlorosomes and isolated bacteriochlorophyll *c* aggregates of *Chlorobium tepidum*: The self-organization of pigments is the main structural feature of chlorosomes. *Biochemistry* **34** (1995) 15259–15266.
32. M. Akiyama, H. Miyashita, H. Kise, T. Watanabe, M. Mimuro, S. Miyachi, M. Kobayashi, Quest for minor but key chlorophyll molecules in photosynthetic reaction centers-Unusual pigment compositions in the reaction centers of the chlorophyll *d*-dominated cyanobacterium *Acaryochloris marina*. *Photosynth. Res.* **74** (2002) 97–107.
33. S.I. Allakhverdiev, M.S. Karacan, G. Somer, N. Karacan, E.M. Khan, S.Y. Rane, S. Padhye, V.V. Klimov, G. Renger, Binuclear manganese(III) complexes as electron donors in D1/D2/Cyt *b*559 preparations isolated from spinach PS II membrane fragments. *Z. Naturforsch.* **49** (1994) 587–592.
34. E. Greenbaum, J.W. Lee, C.V. Tebault, S.L. Blankinship, L.J. Mets, $CO_2$ fixation and photoevolution of $H_2$ and $O_2$ in a mutant of *Chlamydomonas* lacking Photosystem I. *Nature* **376** (1995) 438–441.
35. V.A. Boichenko, Can Photosystem II be a photogenerator of low potential reductant for $CO_2$ fixation and $H_2$ photoevolution? *Photosynth. Res.* **47** (1996) 291–292.
36. H.T. Witt, Coupling of quanta, electrons, fields, ions and phorphorylation in the functional membrane of photosynthesis. *Q. Res. Biophys.* **4** (1971) 365–477.
37. W. Junge, J.B. Jackson, The development of electrochemical potential gradients across photosynthetic membranes, in: *Energy conservation by plants and bacteria* (1982) (Govindjee, ed.), Academic Press, New York, pp. 589–646.
38. P. Mitchell, Coupling of photophosphorylation to electron and hydrogen transfer by a chemiosmotic type of mechanism. *Nature* **191** (1961) 144–148.
39. K. Warncke, P.S. Dutton, Influence of $Q_A$ site redox cofactor structure on equilibrium binding, in situ electrochemistry and electron-transfer performance in the photosynthetic reaction center protein. *Biochemistry* **32** (1993) 4769–4779.
40. G. Renger and A.-R. Holzwarth, Primary electron transfer. In: *Photosystem II: The Water/Plastoquinone Oxido-Reductase in Photosynthesis* (2005) (T. Wydrzynski, K. Satoh, eds.), Kluwer Academic Publishers, Dordrecht, pp. 139–175.
41. Y. Munekage, M. Hashimoto, C. Miyake, K.-I. Tomizawa, T. Endo, M. Tasaka, T. Shikanai, Cyclic electron flow around photosystem I is essential for photosynthesis. *Nature* **429** (2004) 579–582.

42. M. Havaux, D. Rumeau, J.-M. Ducruet, Probing the FQR and NDH activities involved in cyclic electron transport around Photosystem I by the 'afterglow' luminescence. *Biochim. Biophys. Acta* **1709** (2005) 203–213.
43. T. Joët, L. Cournac, G. Peltier, M. Havaux, Cyclic electron flow around Photosystem I in $C_3$ plants. In vivo control by the redox state of chloroplasts and involvement of the NADH-dehydrogenase complex. *Plant Physiol.* **128** (2002) 760–769.
44. D.S. Bendall, R.S. Manasse, Cyclic photophosphorylation and electron transport. *Biochim. Biophys. Acta* **1229** (1995) 23–38.
45. P. Joliot, A. Joliot, Quantification of cyclic and linear flows in plants. *Proc. Natl. Acad. Sci. U.S.A.* **102** (2005) 4913–4918.
46. H.H. Stiehl, H.T. Witt, Quantitative treatment of the function of plastoquinone in photosynthesis. *Z. Naturforsch.* **24b** (1969) 1588–1598.
47. W.A. Cramer, J. Yan, H. Zhang, G. Kurisu, J.L. Smith, Structure of the cytochrome $b_6f$ complex: new prosthetic groups, Q-space, and the 'hors d'oeuvres hypothesis' for assembly of the complex. *Photosynth. Res.* **85** (2005) 133–143.
48. J.F. Allen, A. Nilsson, Redox signalling and the structural basis of regulation of photosynthesis by protein phosphorylation. *Physiol. Plant.* **100** (1997) 863–868.
49. F. Rappaport, M. Guergova-Kuras, P.J. Nixon, B.A. Diner, J. Lavergne, Kinetics and pathways of charge recombination in Photosystem II. *Biochemistry* **41** (2002) 8518–8527.
50. G. Renger, Coupling of electron and proton transfer in oxidative water cleavage in photosynthesis. *Biochim. Biophys. Acta* **1655** (2004) 195–204.
51. L.J. Rogers, Ferredoxins, flavodoxins and related proteins: Structure, function and evolution, in: *The Cyanobacteria* (1987) (P. Fay, C. van Baalen, eds.) Elsevier, Amsterdam, pp. 35–67.
52. I. Nogués, M. Hervás, J.R. Peregrina, J.A. Navarro, M.A. de la Rosa, C. Gómez-Moreno, M. Medina, *Anabaena* Flavodoxin as an electron carrier from Photosystem I to ferredoxin-$NADP^+$ reductase. Role of flavodoxin residues in protein-protein interaction and electron transfer. *Biochemistry* **44** (2005) 97–104.
53. Y. Fujita, K. Ohki, A. Murakami, Acclimation of photosynthetic light energy conversion to the light environments, in: *Algal Adaptation to Environmental Stresses* (2001) (L.C. Rai, J.P. Gaur eds.), Springer, Berlin, pp. 135–171.
54. A. Murakami, Y. Fujita, Regulation of stoichiometry between PS I and PS II in response to light regime for photosynthesis observed with *Synechocystis* PCC6714. Relationship between redox state of Cyt $b_6$-$f$ complex and regulation of PS I. *Plant Cell Physiol.* **34** (1993) 1175–1180.
55. A. Melis, Dynamics of photosynthetic membrane composition and function. *Biochim. Biophys. Acta* **1058** (1991) 87–106.
56. J. Oelze, G. Drews, Membranes of photosynthetic bacteria. *Biochim. Biophys. Acta* **265** (1972) 209–239.
57. G. Guglielmi, G. Cohen-Bazire, D.A. Bryant, The structure of *Gloeobacter violaceus* and its phycobilisomes. *Arch. Microbiol.* **129** (1981) 181–189.
58. W. Menke, Retrospective of a botanist. *Photosynth. Res.* **25** (1990) 77–82.
59. M. Paumann, G. Regelsberger, C.H. Obinger, G.A. Peschek, The bioenergetic role of dioxygen and the terminal oxidase(s) in cyanobacteria. *Biochim. Biophys. Acta* **1707** (2005) 231–253.
60. M.W. Gray, The endosymbiont hypothesis revisited. *Int. Rev. Cytol.* **141** (1992) 233–257.
61. G.I. Mc Fadden, Endosymbiosis and evolution of the plant cell. *Curr. Opin. Plant Biol.* **2** (1999) 513–519.

62. E. Haag, G. Renger, Chloroplasts. in: *Treatise on Bioelectrochemistry, Vol. 2: Bioenergetics* (1997) (P. Gräber, G. Milazzo, eds.), Birkhäuser, Basel, pp. 212–273.
63. B. Andersson, J.M. Anderson, Lateral heterogeneity in the distribution of chlorophyll-protein complexes of the thylakoid membranes of spinach chloroplasts. *Biochim. Biophys Acta* **593** (1980) 173–474.
64. P.-Å. Albertsson, E. Andreasson, P. Svensson, The domain organization of the plant thylakoid membrane. *FEBS Lett.* **273** (1990) 36–40.
65. C. Büchel, W. Kühlbrandt, Structural differences in the inner part of Photosystem II between higher plants and cyanobacteria. *Photosynth. Res.* **85** (2005) 3–13.
66. T. M. Bourett, K. J. Czymmek, R. J. Howardt, Ultrastructure of chloroplast protuberance in rice: Leaves preserved by high-pressure freezing. *Planta* **208** (1999) 472–479.
67. S. Pfeiffer, K. Krupinska, New insights in thylakoid membrane organization. *Plant Cell Physiol.* **46** (2005) 1443–1451.
68. A.J. Nozik, Spectroscopy and hot electron relaxation dynamics in semiconductor quantum wells and quantum dots. *Annu. Rev. Phys. Chem.* **52** (2001) 193–231.
69. M.R. Wasielewski, Photoinduced electron transfer in supramolecular systems for artificial photosynthesis. *Chem. Rev.* **92** (1992) 435–461.
70. D. Gust, T.A. Moore, A.L. Moore, Mimicking photosynthetic solar energy transduction. *Acc. Chem. Res.* **34** (2001) 40–48.
71. J.H. Alstrum-Acevedo, M.K. Brennaman, T.J. Meyer, Chemical approaches to artificial photosynthesis. *Inorg. Chem.* **44** (2005) 6802–6827.
72. B.R. Gibney, C. Tommos, De novo protein design in respiration and photosynthesis, in: *Photosystem II: The Water/Plastoquinone Oxido-Reductase in Photosynthesis* (2005) (T. Wydrzynski, K. Satoh, eds.), Kluwer Academic Publishers, Dordrecht, pp. 729–751.
73. A. Magnuson, S. Styring, L. Hammarström, Understanding Photosystem II function by artificial photosynthesis, in: *Photosystem II: The Water/ Plastoquinone Oxido-Reductase in Photosynthesis* (2005) (T. Wydrzynski, K. Satoh, eds.), Kluwer Academic Publishers, Dordrecht, pp. 753–775.
74. D. Noy, C.C. Moser, P.L. Dutton, Design and engineering of photosynthetic light-harvesting and electron transfer using length, time, and energy scales. *Biochim. Biophys. Acta* **1757** (2006) 90–105.
75. A. Harriman, Energy transfer in synthetic porphyrin arrays, in: *Supramolecular Photochemistry* (1987) (V. Balzani, ed.), D. Reidel Publishing Company, Boston, pp. 207–223.
76. J. Li, J.R. Diers, J. Seth, S.I. Yang, D.F. Bocian, D. Holten, J.S. Lindsey, Synthesis and properties of star-shaped multiporphyrin-phthalocyanine light-harvesting arrays. *J. Org. Chem.* **64** (1999) 9090–9100.
77. A. Morandeira, E. Vauthey, A. Schuwey, A. Gossauer, Ultrafast excited state dynamics of tri- and hexaporphyrin arrays. *J. Phys. Chem. A* **108** (2004) 5741–5751.
78. Y. Nakamura, I.-W. Hwang, N. Aratani, T.K. Ahn, D.M. Ko, A. Takagi, T. Kawai, T. Matsumoto, D. Kim, A. Osuka, Directly *meso-meso* linked porphyrin rings: synthesis, characterization, and efficient excitation energy hopping. *J. Am Chem. Soc.* **127** (2005) 236–246.
79. D. Noy, P.L. Dutton, Design of a minimal polypeptide unit for bacteriochlorophyll binding and self-assembly based on photosynthetic bacterial light-harvesting proteins. *Biochemistry* **45** (2006) 2103–2113.

80. D. Gust, T.A. Moore, A.L. Moore, Molecular mimicry of photosynthetic energy and electron transfer. *Acc. Chem. Res.* **26** (1993) 198–205.
81. A. Osuka, S. Marumo, N. Mataga, S. Taniguchi, T. Okada, I. Yamazaki, Y. Nishimura, T. Ohno, K. Nozaki, A stepwise electron-transfer relay mimicking the primary charge separation in bacterial photosynthetic reaction center. *J. Am. Chem. Soc.* **118** (1996) 155–168.
82. D.M. Guldi, Fullerene–porphyrin architectures; photosynthetic antenna and reaction center models. *Chem. Soc. Rev.* **31** (2002) 22–36.
83. S.N. Smirnov, P.A. Liddell, I.V. Vlassiouk, A. Teslja, D. Kuciauskas, C.L. Braun, A.L. Moore, T.A. Moore, D. Gust, Characterization of the giant transient dipole generated by photoinduced electron transfer in a carotene-porphyrin-fullerene molecular triad. *J. Phys. Chem. A* **107** (2003) 7567–7573.
84. G. Kodis, Y. Terazono, P.A. Liddell, J. Andreasson, V. Garg, M. Hambourger, T.A. Moore, A.L. Moore, D. Gust, Energy and photoinduced electron transfer in a wheel-shaped artificial photosynthetic antenna-reaction center complex. *J. Am. Chem. Soc.* **128** (2006) 1818–1827.
85. G. Steinberg-Yfrach, P.A. Liddell, S.-C. Hung, L. Moore, D. Gust, T.A. Moore, Conversion of light energy to proton potential in liposomes by artificial photosynthetic reaction centers. *Nature* **385** (1997) 239–241.
86. S. Mukhopadhyay, S.K. Mandal, S. Bhaduri, W.H. Armstrong, Manganese clusters with relevance to Photosystem II. *Chem. Rev.* **104** (2004) 3981–4026.
87. C. Baffert, S. Romain, A. Richardot, J.-C. Leprêtre, B. Lefebvre, A. Deronzier, M.-N. Collomb, Electrochemical and chemical formation of $[Mn_4^{IV}O_5(terpy)_4(H_2O)_2]^{6+}$, in relation with the Photosystem II oxygen-evolving center model $[Mn_2^{III,IV}O_2(terpy)_2(H_2O)_2]^{3+}$. *J. Am. Chem. Soc.* **127** (2005) 13694–13704.
88. M. Yagi, K.V. Wolf, P.J. Baesjou, S.L. Bernasek, G.C. Dismukes, Selective photoproduction of $O_2$ from the $Mn_4O_4$ cubane: core a structural and functional model for the photosynthetic water-oxidizing complex. *Angew. Chem. Int. Ed.* **40** (2001) 2925–2928.
89. J. Limburg, J.S. Vrettos, H. Chen, J.C. de Paula, R.H. Crabtree, G.W. Brudvig, Characterization of the O2-evolving reaction catalyzed by [(terpy)$(H_2O)Mn^{III}(O)_2Mn^{IV}(OH_2)$(terpy)]$(NO_3)_3$ (terpy = 2,2′:6,2″-Terpyridine). *J. Am. Chem. Soc.* **123** (2001) 423–430.
90. K. Narita, T. Kuwabara, K. Sonc, K. Shimizu, M. Yagi, Characterization and activity analysis of catalytic water oxidation induced by hybridization of [(OH$_2$)(terpy)Mn($\mu$-O)$_2$Mn(terpy)(OH$_2$)]$^{3+}$ and clay compounds. *J Phys. Chem. B* **110** (2006) 23107–23114.
91. R.A. Binstead, C.W. Chronister, J. Ni, C.M. Hartshorn, T.J. Meyer, Mechanism of water oxidation by the μ-oxo dimer $[(bpy)_2(H_2O)Ru^{III}ORu^{III}(OH_2)(bpy)_2]^{4+}$. *J. Am. Chem. Soc.* **122** (2000) 8464–8473.
92. Y. Naruta, M. Sasayama, T. Sasaki, Oxygen evolution by oxidation of water with manganese porphyrin dimers. *Angew. Chem. Int. Ed.* **33** (1994) 1839–1841.
93. H. Yamada, W.F. Siems, T. Koike, J.K. Hurst, Mechanisms of water oxidation catalyzed by the *cis,cis*-[(bpy)$_2$Ru(OH$_2$)]$_2$O$^{4+}$ ion. *J. Am. Chem.* **126** (2004) 9786–9795.
94. J.R. Pugh, M.R.M. Bruce, B.P. Sullivan, T.J. Meyer, Formation of a metal-hydride bond and the insertion of carbon dioxide. Key steps in the electrocatalytic reduction of carbon dioxide to formate anion. *Inorg. Chem.* **30** (1991) 86–91.

# II. Basic Photophysical Principles

*Chapter 2*

# Absorption of Light, Excitation Energy Transfer and Electron Transfer Reactions

## Thomas Renger

**Table of Contents**

- 2.1 Introduction. . . . . . . . . . . . . . . . . . . . . . . . . . . . . . . . . . . . . . . 41
- 2.2 Weak Coupling Limit. . . . . . . . . . . . . . . . . . . . . . . . . . . . . . 48
  - 2.2.1 Semiclassical Harmonic Oscillator Approach . . . . . . . . . . . . 49
  - 2.2.2 Quantum Description . . . . . . . . . . . . . . . . . . . . . . . . . . . 53
  - 2.2.3 Optical Spectra – Theory of Lax and Kubo . . . . . . . . . . . . . 57
  - 2.2.4 Excitation Energy Transfer – Förster Theory . . . . . . . . . . . . 59
  - 2.2.5 Electron Transfer – Marcus Theory. . . . . . . . . . . . . . . . . . 60
- 2.3 Strong Excitonic Coupling . . . . . . . . . . . . . . . . . . . . . . . . . . 62
  - 2.3.1 Density Matrix Theory. . . . . . . . . . . . . . . . . . . . . . . . . . . 67
    - 2.3.1.1 Markov Approximation – Redfield Theory . . . . . . . . 72
  - 2.3.2 Modified Redfield Theory. . . . . . . . . . . . . . . . . . . . . . . . 73
  - 2.3.3 Generalized Förster Theory. . . . . . . . . . . . . . . . . . . . . . . 75
- 2.4 Extraction of Parameters . . . . . . . . . . . . . . . . . . . . . . . . . . . . 77
  - 2.4.1 Spectral Density of Excitation Energy Transfer and Optical Spectra. . . . . . . . . . . . . . . . . . . . . . . . . . . . . . . . . . . . . 77
  - 2.4.2 Spectral Density for Electron Transfer: The Dispersed Polaron Model . . . . . . . . . . . . . . . . . . . . . . . . . . . . . . . . . . . . . 81
  - 2.4.3 Reorganization Energy of Electron Transfer from Microscopic Simulations . . . . . . . . . . . . . . . . . . . . . . . . . . . . . . . . . 83
  - 2.4.4 Excitonic Coupling. . . . . . . . . . . . . . . . . . . . . . . . . . . . . 83
    - 2.4.4.1 Point-Dipole Approximation . . . . . . . . . . . . . . . . . 84
    - 2.4.4.2 Extended-Dipole Approximation. . . . . . . . . . . . . . . 84
    - 2.4.4.3 Transition Density Quantum Chemical Methods . . . . 85

        2.4.5   Electron Transfer Coupling................. 85
        2.4.6   Local Excitation Energies of Pigments............ 86
        2.4.7   Redox Potentials ...................... 88
Acknowledgements ............................ 89
References.................................. 89

# Abstract

The present chapter gives an overview of photophysical principles underlying the primary photosynthetic reactions in pigment–protein complexes, i.e., the absorption of light, excitation energy transfer and electron transfer reactions. From a common viewpoint the description of the above reactions requires theories that can include both the pigment–pigment (electronic) as well as the pigment–protein (electron–vibrational) coupling in an appropriate manner. Different theories are classified according to the relative strength of the two types of couplings. In the weak electronic coupling limit, a semiclassical and a quantum Fermi's Golden Rule type rate constant and their relation are discussed and applied to absorption and fluorescence, excitation energy transfer, and electron transfer, yielding the standard results by Lax/Kubo, Förster, and Marcus, respectively. Whereas for electron transfer reactions the weak electronic coupling limit is appropriate, in the case of excitation energy transfer and optical spectra, usually, the pigment–pigment coupling is of the same strength or even stronger than the pigment–protein coupling, a situation that is treated by theories that take into account delocalized excited states of the pigments. Multilevel Redfield theory describes excitation energy relaxation between different delocalized states and relates the relaxation times to optical line widths. In non-Markovian density matrix theories, besides a life time broadening due to exciton relaxation, vibrational sidebands of the optical lines are included. Another extension of Redfield theory, the modified Redfield theory, takes into account the reorganization of nuclei during exciton relaxation between different delocalized states. The generalized Förster theory allows a description of transfer between aggregates with strong intra- and weak inter-aggregate couplings. How the parameters (couplings, energies and spectral densities) of the dynamical theories can be extracted from experimental data and independent calculations is outlined also.

## 2.1 Introduction

In photosystems light energy absorbed by antenna pigments (chlorophylls, bacteriochlorophylls and carotenoids) is transferred to the reaction center where it drives transmembrane charge transfer reactions. In oxygenic photosynthesis water is used as an electron source and a proton gradient is built up across the photosynthetic membrane to drive the formation of ATP by the ATPase. In this way, light energy is transformed into chemical energy. As a by-product, oxygen is released that forms a basis of our life. Although the overall scheme of the primary photosynthetic reactions is well understood, the molecular identity of the involved electronic states is open to discussion in many cases.

For example, it is not known which pigment is the primary electron donor in the reaction centers of photosystems I and II. In electron transfer reactions, a delicate dielectric environment is provided by the protein to tune the redox potentials of cofactors and in this way trigger electron transfer reactions. It is still an open question as to why electrons in the bacterial reaction center and in photosystem II reaction centers are transferred only along one of the two symmetrical branches, and how the directionality of this transfer is in the reaction center of photosystem I. In excitation energy transfer reactions the optical transition energies of the pigments are shifted by the proteins, which trigger in this way the pathway of the excitation energy.

A combined approach by high-resolution structural models, spectroscopy and theory is necessary to understand the building principles of photosynthetic systems and how the function of such nanoscale machines is related to their structure. The present chapter reviews the theoretical part of this venture. Clearly, the biggest challenge for the theory is to find the right description for the proteins and their coupling to the pigments. The pigment–protein complex has to be characterized by parameters that describe the dynamic and static modulation of pigment energies by the proteins, and the inter–pigment excitation energy and charge transfer couplings.

The large number of vibrational degrees of freedom of the protein make dynamical calculations difficult. A simple quantity that captures the essence of the pigment–protein (electron–vibrational) coupling is the spectral density $J(\omega)$. The spectral density describes how the different vibrational modes with frequency $\omega$ couple to an optical transition or a charge transfer reaction. Although usually obtained within a harmonic oscillator model for the vibrations, the spectral density has a more general meaning [1]. It is related to the Fourier transform of the correlation function of the energy gap between the initial and final state of the reaction. Even for strongly anharmonic systems it turns out that, when the energy gap is used as a generalized reaction coordinate, the related free energy functions are harmonic and thus a description in terms of effective harmonic oscillators is still valid [1–4]. With excitation energy transfer, the spectral density can be extracted from optical spectra [5–8]. For the spectral density of electron transfer reactions there are no independent experiments –molecular dynamics simulations are used instead [2,9].

Figure 1 gives an illustration of the spectral density of excitation energy transfer. The free-energy surfaces of the ground and excited state of a pigment in its protein environment are depicted in the right-hand part of the figure. The left-hand part shows the structure of a one pigment system, the so-called B777 complex, for which the spectral density was extracted [8] from fluorescence line narrowing spectra measured at 1.6 K [10]. The B777 complex consists only of an α-helix and a bound bacteriochlorophyll *a* molecule. It appears to be the only example at present of a successful step by step separation of a photosynthetic antenna complex into single pigment–protein units, namely the preparation of the B777 complex starting from the bacterial LH1 core antenna. The structure of the B777 complex in Figure 1 was adapted from the known structure of the bacterial LH2 antenna system [11] by removing the B800 bacteriochlorophyll that is missing in the LH1 antenna complex. A low-resolution structural study exists for the LH1 complex [12]. It appears that the basic pigment–protein subunits of the bacterial antennae LH1 and LH2 are related to each other and also to the bacterial reaction center. The latter is the ancestor of the plant reaction centers of photosystem II [13]. There is also a close similarity between photosystem I and II [14]. (For evolutionary aspects see Chapter 22.) The electron–vibrational coupling of the optical transition of

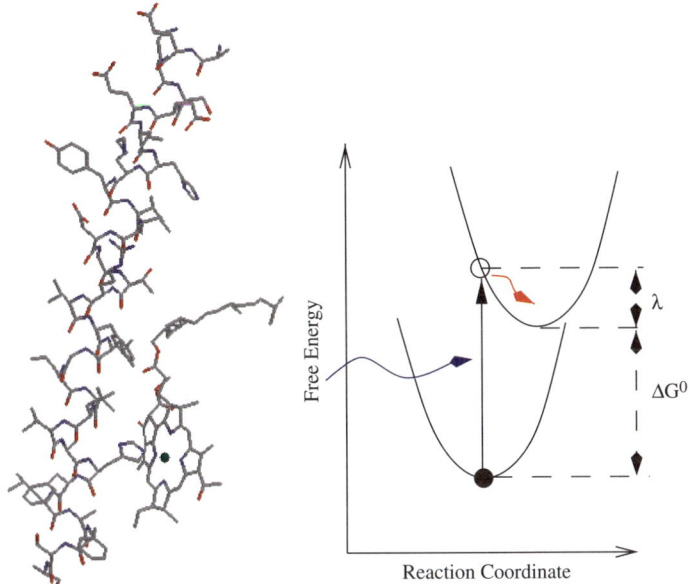

**Figure 1.** Left-hand side: Structure of the B777 complex. Right-hand side: Free-energy surfaces of the ground and excited states of the B777 complex.

the B777 complex in Figure 1 appears as a mutual shift in the minimum position of the free-energy surfaces of the two electronic states along the axis of the reaction coordinate. The spectral density $J(\omega)$ describes how the different vibrational modes of the protein contribute to this shift. After optical excitation the vibrational degrees of freedom of the protein and the pigment relax to a new equilibrium position in response to the change in the electronic structure of the pigment. The energy difference between the minima is termed standard free energy ($\Delta G^\circ$) and the energy that is released during the relaxation in the upper free-energy surface is called the reorganization energy ($\lambda$), which is related to the spectral density $J(\omega)$ by $\lambda = \hbar \int_0^\infty d\omega J(\omega) \omega$. Section 2.4.1 shows how $J(\omega)$ can be extracted from fluorescence line narrowing spectra.

Two important types of pigment–pigment coupling are the excitonic and the charge transfer coupling. The latter requires wavefunction overlap and, therefore, depends exponentially on the donor–acceptor separation. The excitonic coupling does not rely on such overlap and for distances larger than the extension of the wavefunctions depends on the third inverse power of the distance between the donor and acceptor pigment. These different distance dependencies of the two types of couplings allowed nature to optimize antenna systems for light harvesting and reaction center complexes for charge transfer. In general, in photosynthetic systems the charge transfer couplings are smaller than the reorganization energies of nuclei related to the charge transfer. Therefore, the charge separated states are localized on single pigments (a notable exception being the special pair of the bacterial reaction center [15,16]).

For charge transfer, the electronic coupling is weak enough to justify a second-order perturbation theory and to apply the standard non-adiabatic electron transfer theory [17–19]. The rate constant is related to the absolute square of the charge transfer coupling and an expression that contains the spectral density and the standard free energy of the charge transfer reaction. Two free-energy surfaces that describe the primary electron transfer in photosystem II reaction centers are depicted in the upper part of Figure 2. The middle part of this figure contains the structure of the PS-II reaction center according to recent X-ray data at 3.0 Å resolution [20]. A detailed description of the structure, including references to earlier studies with lower resolutions is given by A. Zouni in Chapter 15. Although, at present, a final conclusion cannot be drawn as to which one of the six central pigments in the PS-II reaction center is the primary electron donor $D^*$ and which one the primary electron acceptor $A^-$, there is accumulating evidence that electron transfer starts from the accessory chlorophyll of the D1-branch and that the primary acceptor is the neighboring pheophytin molecule [21–28] (For further details, see Chapter 16). The relative shift of the minimum position of the two free-energy surfaces of the initial state $|D^*A>$ and the charge separated state $|D^+A^->$ in Figure 2 is larger than between the states involved in optical transitions and excitation energy transfer because of the polar nature of the charge separated state. In the semiclassical Marcus theory [17–19] the expression for the rate constant contains just three parameters, the charge transfer coupling, the standard free energy ($\Delta G^o$), and the reorganization energy ($\lambda$).

Whereas the charge transfer couplings in PS-II reaction centers are weak, the excitonic couplings between the six central pigments are large. In addition, there are weak excitonic couplings between the two peripheral chlorophylls (Chlz) and the six central pigments in Figure 2. Another example of a system with strong excitonic couplings is given in Figure 3, where the structure of the monomeric subunit of the trimeric so-called FMO complex [29,30] of green sulfur bacteria is shown. One monomeric subunit binds seven bacteriochlorophyll *a* molecules. The FMO-complex of *Prosthecochloris aestuarii* was the first pigment protein complex for which the structure was determined by X-ray crystallography [29,30]. In the meantime, the resolution of the electron density map could be refined to 1.9 Å [31] and the structure of the FMO-complex of a strongly related bacterium *Chlorobium tepidum* was also determined [32]. The two structures are very similar but, interestingly, the spectra look different. The molecular origin of this difference is unknown and most likely is related to the difference in local transition energies of the pigments. A complex with only weak excitonic interactions between chlorophyll molecules is the peridinin-chlorophyll *a* complex [33]. The monomer unit of this trimeric complex contains two weakly coupled chlorophyll *a* molecules (Figure 4).

For strong excitonic couplings, not a single pigment is excited optically but an exciton state is formed that contains contributions from excited states of different pigments. The extent of delocalization is determined by the relative strength of pigment–protein and pigment–pigment coupling. Static and dynamic disorder, caused by slow and fast protein dynamics, tend to localize the

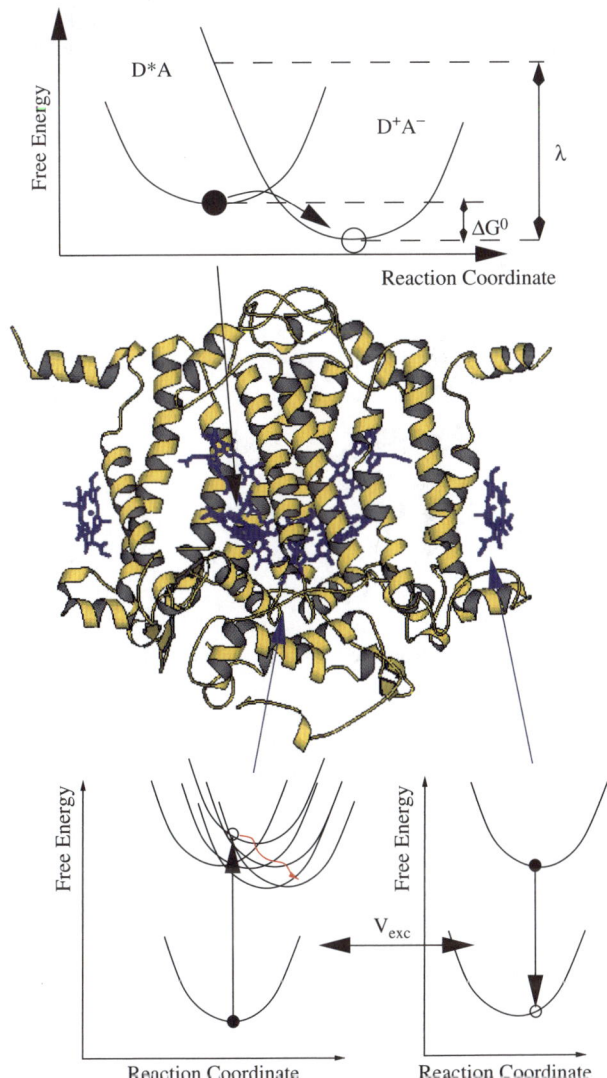

**Figure 2.** Upper part: Free-energy surfaces of the primary electron transfer reaction in photosystem II reaction centers. Middle part: Structure of the PS-II reaction center [20]. Lower part: Free-energy surfaces of the ground state and the exciton states of the six strongly coupled pigments (left-hand side) and of the ground and excited state of a peripheral Chlz (right-hand side), as used in modified Förster theory. $V_{exc}$ denotes the excitation energy transfer coupling between Chlz and the exciton states of the six core pigments.

electronic states of the complex. In addition, the local protein environments lead to different mean transition energies, the so-called site energies. This difference is an additional source of localization. There exist standard theories to describe excitation energy transfer in the limiting cases where either the

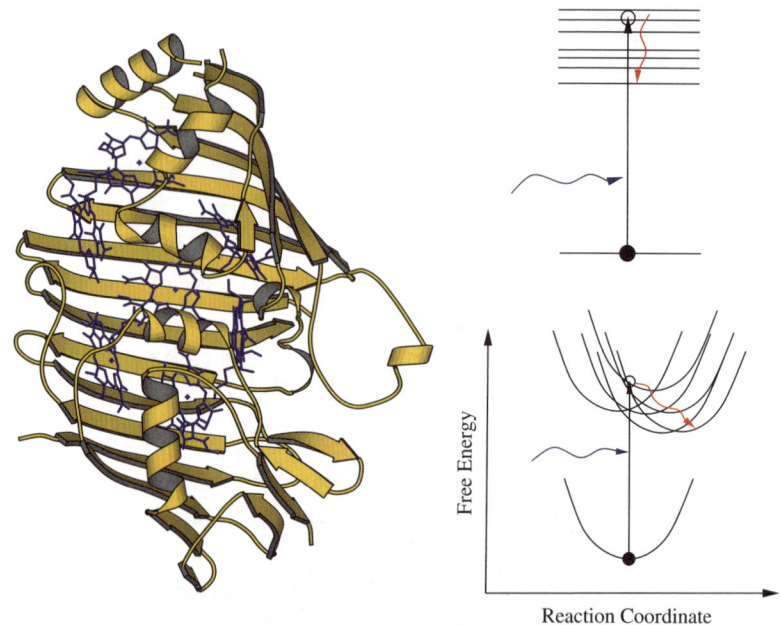

**Figure 3.** Left-hand side: Structure of the monomeric subunit of the trimeric FMO-complex of *Prosthecochloris aestuarii* [31] containing seven bacteriochlorophyll *a* molecules. Right-hand side, upper part: ground state and seven delocalized excited states (exciton states) of the FMO-complex. Right-hand side, lower part: Free-energy surfaces of the seven exciton states. The mutual horizontal shift of the free-energy surfaces is neglected in Redfield theory and taken into account in modified Redfield theory and non-Markovian density matrix theories.

pigment–protein or the pigment–pigment coupling dominates. In the first case, depicted in Figure 4, the excited states are localized and the Förster theory of excitation energy transfer applies [34–37], in which the rate constant is expressed in terms of an overlap integral of donor emission and acceptor absorption spectra.

If the excitonic coupling dominates, the multi-level Redfield theory [37–46] describes optical spectra and exciton relaxation between delocalized excited states (upper right-hand part of Figure 3). In this theory the exciton–vibrational coupling leads to a life-time broadening of exciton states and Lorentzian lineshapes are obtained for the optical transitions between the ground state and the different exciton states. As will be shown in detail later, the spectral density $J(\omega)$ of the local optical transitions is an important factor that determines the lifetime broadening by describing how the protein can dissipate the excess energy of excitons during relaxation.

For a more accurate description of optical spectra and excitation energy transfer the intermediate regime of equal pigment–pigment and pigment–protein coupling needs to be studied. A theoretical description in this case is difficult because neither of the two couplings is small enough to justify a

# ABSORPTION OF LIGHT

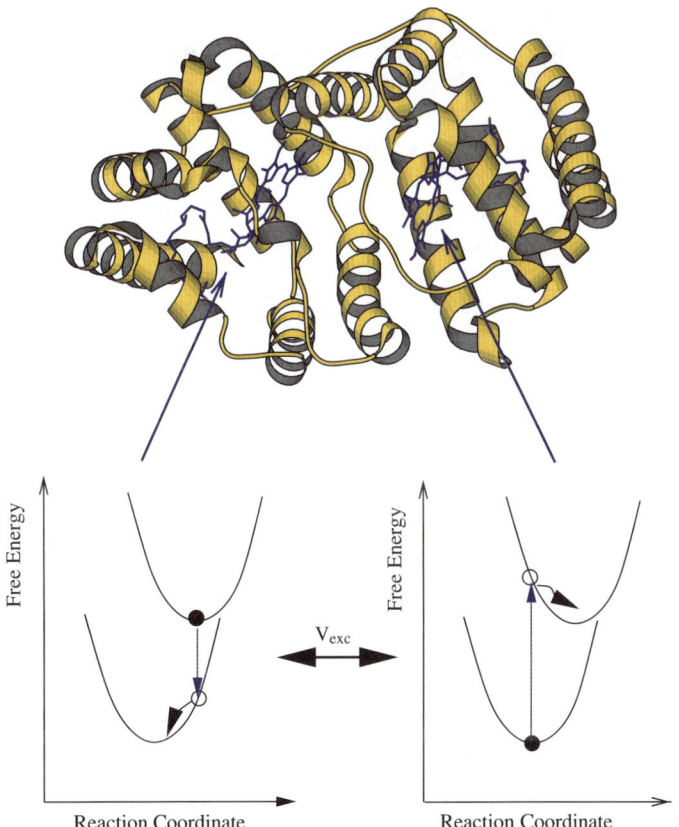

**Figure 4.** Upper part: Structure of the monomeric subunit of the peridinin-chlorophyll *a* complex [33] (carotenoids not shown for clarity). Lower part: Free-energy surfaces of ground and excited states of the two chlorophyll *a* molecules of the complex, as used in Förster theory. The coupling $V_{\text{exc}}$ is responsible for excitation energy transfer between the two chlorophylls.

treatment in perturbation theory. Attempts at a non-perturbative description are made in non-Markovian density matrix theories [47–51,8] and in the modified Redfield theory [52–56]. The free-energy surfaces used in those theories are illustrated in the lower right-hand part of Figure 3 and in the lower part of Figure 2. The mutual shifts of the free-energy surfaces of the different exciton states and their shift with respect to the minimum of the ground state surface in Figure 3 reflect reorganization effects of nuclei that occur in exciton relaxation reactions and optical transitions. Within non-Markovian density matrix theory and modified Redfield theory those reorganization effects can be described by a non-perturbative description of the diagonal part of the exciton–vibrational coupling. In optical spectra the nuclear reorganization effects appear as vibrational sidebands. Notably, at present, there is no unified theory that covers the whole range between weak and strong pigment–pigment coupling. In non-Markovian density matrix theory and in the modified Redfield theory a dynamic localization of excited states is neglected.

If an aggregate of strongly coupled pigments interacts weakly with a single pigment, the standard Förster theory for transfer between two weakly coupled pigments can be extended to take into account the strong coupling inside the aggregate. In this generalized Förster theory [25,57–61], optically dark states of the aggregate also contribute to the transfer, if the extension of the aggregate is comparable or smaller than the edge to edge distance between the aggregate and the pigment. An example is given in the lower part of Figure 2, where the free-energy surfaces are shown of the strongly coupled states of the reaction center of photosystem II and of two weakly coupled peripheral chlorophylls (Chlz) of the reaction center.

An interesting effect is observed if exciton states mix with charge transfer states. Owing to the strong electron–vibrational coupling of the latter, the former also couple stronger to vibrational degrees of freedom, and so exhibit strong vibrational sidebands in the optical spectra [62–65]. The strong coupling may lead to a dynamic localization of the coupled exciton-charge transfer states. Recently, a theory of such a localization was used [65] to explain a 35 nm blue-shift of the low-energy absorption band of the bacterial reaction center observed [66] between 4 K and room temperature.

This chapter contains three further parts. The first part discusses the weak electronic coupling limit. Starting with a simple *semi-empirical* harmonic oscillator model, the energy gap between the initial and the final state of the reaction is introduced as a generalized reaction coordinate and an expression is derived for the rate constant. Next, a generalization of the semi-empirical approach is given that takes into account the full quantum dynamics of the vibrational degrees of freedom. The rate constants are then related to standard expressions for the description of optical spectra, excitation energy transfer, and non-adiabatic electron transfer.

The second part deals with theories of excitation energy transfer reactions and optical spectra that take into account a strong and intermediate excitonic coupling, namely, the multi-level Redfield theory, non-Markovian density matrix theories, the modified Redfield theory, and the generalized Förster theory.

The third part discusses how the parameters of the dynamical theories, i.e., the spectral densities, electronic couplings and free energy differences, can be extracted from independent experiments and calculations.

## 2.2 Weak Coupling Limit

This section reviews a semiclassical description (see, for example, [67,68]) that gives an intuitive and simple way to obtain an expression for a (non-adiabatic) transfer rate between two weakly coupled electronic states. The rate constant obtained by using this approach will be discussed within a harmonic oscillator model for the vibrations. Next, using a full quantum treatment [1,69,70], a more general theory will be described that also includes anharmonic vibrational dynamics [1]. The expressions obtained for the rate constant are then related to standard results by Lax [69] and Kubo [70] for optical spectra, Förster-excitation energy transfer [34,35], and Marcus–Levich–Jortner electron transfer [17–18,71].

### 2.2.1 Semiclassical Harmonic Oscillator Approach

In some semiclassical theories the motion of nuclei is treated classically, whereas the electrons are described by wavefunctions $|\phi(\mathbf{r},\mathbf{R})\rangle$ that depend on the electronic coordinates $\mathbf{r}$ and contain the coordinates of nuclei $\mathbf{R}(t)$ as parameters (Born–Oppenheimer approximation). In the weak coupling limit treated here, the Hamiltonian:

$$H = H_0 + V \tag{1}$$

is split into a diagonal part $H_0$ and a small perturbation $V$. The so-called diabatic states $|\phi_j(\mathbf{r},\mathbf{R})\rangle$ are defined as the eigenstates of the stationary Schrödinger equation for $H_0$:

$$H_0|\phi_j(\mathbf{r},\mathbf{R})\rangle = U_j(\mathbf{R})|\phi_j(\mathbf{r},\mathbf{R})\rangle \tag{2}$$

that contains the potential energy surfaces $U_j(\mathbf{R})$ as eigenenergies, which describe the electronic energies of the diabatic states as a function of the nuclear coordinates $\mathbf{R}$.

The small non-diagonal part:

$$V = \sum_{k \neq j} V_{kj} |\phi_k(\mathbf{r},\mathbf{R})\rangle \langle \phi_j(\mathbf{r},\mathbf{R})| \tag{3}$$

contains the weak coupling between different electronic states $|\phi_k(r,R)\rangle$ and $|\phi_j(r,R)\rangle$. For simplicity it is assumed that $V_{kj}$ can be approximated by its value at the equilibrium position of nuclei in the initial state, i.e. $V_{kj}(R) = V_{kj}(R_0)$. The time-dependent wavefunction $|\varphi(\mathbf{r},\mathbf{R},t)\rangle$ of the system is expanded with respect to the diabatic states:

$$|\varphi(\mathbf{r},\mathbf{R},t)\rangle = \sum_j a_j(t)|\phi_j(\mathbf{r},\mathbf{R})\rangle e^{-i/\hbar \int_0^t d\tau U_j(\mathbf{R}(\tau))} \tag{4}$$

where the time-dependent coefficients $a_j(t)$ allow for a mixing of different states. Applying the above ansatz to the time-dependent Schrödinger equation $(H_{el} + \hat{V})|\varphi(\mathbf{r},\mathbf{R},t)\rangle = i\hbar \frac{\partial}{\partial t}|\varphi(\mathbf{r},\mathbf{R},t)\rangle$, the following expression for the expansion coefficients results:

$$i\hbar \frac{da_j}{dt} = \sum_k V_{kj} a_k e^{-i/\hbar \int_0^t d\tau (U_j(\mathbf{R}) - U_k(\mathbf{R}))} \tag{5}$$

Here, terms of the form $\langle \phi_k(\mathbf{r},\mathbf{R})|\frac{\partial}{\partial t}|\phi_j(\mathbf{r},\mathbf{R})\rangle$ have been neglected [68]. In the case of strong coupling, adiabatic states $\psi$, i.e., eigenstates of the full Hamiltonian $H$ have to be used and the coupling between different adiabatic states is then determined by expressions like $<\psi_k(\mathbf{r},\mathbf{R})|\frac{\partial}{\partial t}|\psi_j(\mathbf{r},\mathbf{R})>$ as in Tully's surface hopping approach [67].

In the weak coupling limit, the transition rate constant between states $k=i$ and $j$ is obtained in first-order perturbation theory, as described in the following. The expansion coefficients $a_j(t)$ in eqn. (4) are expanded in powers of the coupling $V_{kj}$ in eqn. (5):

$$a_j(t) \approx a_j^{(0)}(t) + a_j^{(1)}(t) \tag{6}$$

Inserting this expansion into eqn. (5) then yields separate equations for the different orders in the coupling. The zeroth order expansion coefficient $a_j^{(0)}(t)$ obeys:

$$i\hbar \frac{da_j^{(0)}}{dt} = 0 \tag{7}$$

and in first order in the coupling we have:

$$i\hbar \frac{da_j^{(1)}}{dt} = \sum_k V_{kj} a_k^{(0)} e^{-i/\hbar \int_0^t d\tau [U_j(\mathbf{R}) - U_k(\mathbf{R})]} \tag{8}$$

If it is assumed that the coupling is switched on at $t=0$ and that the system is initially in state $k=i$, the zeroth order coefficient at $t=0$ is $a_k^{(0)}(t=0) = \delta_{i,k}$ and from eqn. (7) it follows that:

$$a_k^{(0)}(t) = \delta_{i,k} \tag{9}$$

The first-order coefficient $a_j^{(1)}(t)$ is then obtained, using eqn. (8), from:

$$\frac{da_j^{(1)}}{dt} = -\frac{i}{\hbar} V_{ij} e^{-i/\hbar \int_0^t d\tau [U_j(\mathbf{R}) - U_i(\mathbf{R})]} \tag{10}$$

and the rate constant $k_{i \to j}$ follows as [68]:

$$k_{i \to j} = \lim_{t \to \infty} \frac{1}{t} <|a_j^{(1)}(t)|^2> \tag{11}$$

The bracket $<\ldots>$ denotes an average with respect to the initial distribution of the nuclear position $\mathbf{R}(t=0)$ on the potential energy surface $U_i(\mathbf{R})$. It is instructive to introduce the energy gap:

$$X(\mathbf{R}) = U_j(\mathbf{R}) - U_i(\mathbf{R}) \tag{12}$$

as a reaction coordinate and to rewrite $|a_j^{(1)}(t)|^2$ as $\int_0^t dt_1 \frac{da_j^{(1)}}{dt_1} \left( \int_0^t dt_2 \frac{da_j^{(1)}}{dt_2} \right)^*$. With this expression, the rate constant in eqn. (11) is obtained, using eqn. (10), as:

$$k_{i \to j} = \lim_{t \to \infty} \frac{1}{t} \frac{|V_{ij}|^2}{\hbar^2} \left< \int_0^t dt_1 \int_0^t dt_2 e^{iF(t_1 - t_2)} \right> \tag{13}$$

# ABSORPTION OF LIGHT

with:

$$F(t_1 - t_2) = \int_0^{t_1-t_2} d\tau X[\mathbf{R}(\tau)] \tag{14}$$

Next, the integration variables are changed to $t_1' = t_1 - t_2$ and $t_2$ for $t_1 > t_2$ and to $t_1' = t_2 - t_1$ and $t_2$ for $t_1 < t_2$. Taking into account the Jacobian $\partial(t_1',t_2)/\partial(t_1,t_2) = 1$ then yields:

$$\begin{aligned} k_{i \to j} &= \lim_{t \to \infty} \frac{1}{t} \frac{|V_{ij}|^2}{\hbar^2} \left\langle \int_0^t dt_1'(t-t_1')\left(e^{iF(t_1')} + e^{-iF(t_1')}\right) \right\rangle \\ &= \frac{|V_{ij}|^2}{\hbar^2} \int_{-\infty}^{\infty} d\tau \left\langle e^{iF(\tau)} \right\rangle \end{aligned} \tag{15}$$

where $\tau = t_1'$ was used in the first part and $\tau = -t_1'$ in the second. To shift the average $\langle \ldots \rangle$ into the exponent, a cumulant expansion is used [72]. For this purpose a function:

$$\Phi(\eta) = \left\langle e^{iF(\tau)\eta} \right\rangle \tag{16}$$

is introduced, and another function:

$$\Psi(\eta) = \ln \Phi(\eta) \tag{17}$$

is expanded into a Taylor series:

$$\Psi(\eta) = \sum_{n=1}^{\infty} \frac{1}{n!} \frac{\partial^n \ln \Phi}{\partial \eta^n}\bigg|_{\eta=0} \eta^n \tag{18}$$

and approximated by the first two terms of this expansion:

$$\Psi(\eta) \approx i\langle F \rangle \eta + \tfrac{1}{2}(\langle F \rangle^2 - \langle F^2 \rangle)\eta^2 \tag{19}$$

Noting that $\langle e^{iF(\tau)} \rangle = \Phi(\eta=1) = \exp\{\Psi(\eta=1)\}$, the rate constant is obtained, renaming the integration variable $\tau \to t$, as [68]:

$$k_{i \to j} = \frac{|V_{ij}|^2}{\hbar^2} \int_{-\infty}^{\infty} dt\, e^{\frac{i}{\hbar}\langle X \rangle t | \gamma_{\rm cl}(t)} \tag{20}$$

where $\gamma_{\rm cl}(t)$ is related to the auto-correlation function of the reaction coordinate (i.e., the energy gap) via:

$$\gamma_{\rm cl}(t) = -\frac{1}{\hbar^2} \int_0^t d\tau(t-\tau)\langle \delta X(\tau)\delta X(0) \rangle \tag{21}$$

with $\delta X(\tau) = X(\tau) - X(0)$.

The Hamiltonian $H_{\rm vib}^{(k)}$ for the vibrational motion in the diabatic states $|\phi_k(\mathbf{r},\mathbf{R})\rangle$ contains the kinetic energy of nuclei $T_{\rm nucl}$ and the PES $U_k(\mathbf{R})$ [eqn. (2)]:

$$H_{\rm vib}^{(k)} = T_{\rm nucl} + U_k(\mathbf{R}) \tag{22}$$

For small displacements $\mathbf{R}(t)$ of nuclei from their equilibrium positions, the PES $U_k(\mathbf{R})$ is expanded into a Taylor series up to second order in the displacements. Normal coordinates $q_\xi$ are introduced and the vibrational Hamiltonian can be written as a sum over $\xi$ independent harmonic oscillators:

$$H_{\text{vib}}^{(k)} = \sum_\xi \frac{p_\xi^2}{2\mu_\xi} + U_0(k) + \frac{\mu_\xi \omega_\xi^2}{2}\left(q_\xi - q_\xi^{(k)}\right)^2 \tag{23}$$

where $p_\xi$, $\mu_\xi$ and $\omega_\xi$ are the momentum, the reduced mass and frequency of the $\xi$th oscillator, respectively, and $q_\xi^{(k)}$ denotes the minimum position of the potential energy surface for the electronic state $|k>$.

The $X(t) - X(0)$ then reads $\sum_\xi \mu_\xi \omega_\xi^2 \Delta q_\xi q_\xi(t)$, where $\Delta q_\xi = q_\xi^{(f)} - q_\xi^{(i)}$ is the difference in equilibrium positions of nuclei between the final and initial electronic state.

We introduce for later use the dimensionless coupling constant:

$$g_\xi = \sqrt{\frac{\mu_\xi \omega_\xi}{2\hbar}} \Delta q_\xi \tag{24}$$

The potential energy surfaces are illustrated in Figure 5.

Solving Hamilton's classical equations of motion in the PES of the initial electronic state $\dot{q}_\xi = -\frac{\partial H_{\text{vib}}^{(i)}}{\partial p_\xi}$ and $\dot{p}_\xi = \frac{\partial H_{\text{vib}}^{(i)}}{\partial q_\xi}$ for the harmonic oscillator yields the following time-dependence of the vibrational coordinate $q_\xi(t) = q_\xi(0) \cos(\omega_\xi t) + p_\xi(0)/(\mu_\xi \omega_\xi) \sin(\omega_\xi t)$. The classical correlation function $C_{\text{cl}} = <\delta X(t) \delta X(0)>$ then reads:

$$\begin{aligned} C_{\text{cl}} &= <\delta X(t) \delta X(0)> \\ &= \sum_\xi 2 g_\xi^2 \mu_\xi \hbar \omega_\xi^3 [<q_\xi(0)^2> \cos(\omega_\xi t) \\ &\quad + <q_\xi(0) p_\xi(0)>/(\omega_\xi \mu_\xi) \sin(\omega_\xi t)] \end{aligned} \tag{25}$$

According to the equality of the average kinetic and average potential energy we have $<q_\xi(0)^2> \mu \omega^2/2 = \frac{1}{2}\hbar\omega_\xi(n(\omega_\xi) + \frac{1}{2})$ with $n(\omega_\xi) = [\exp(\hbar\omega_\xi/kT) - 1]^{-1}$. The

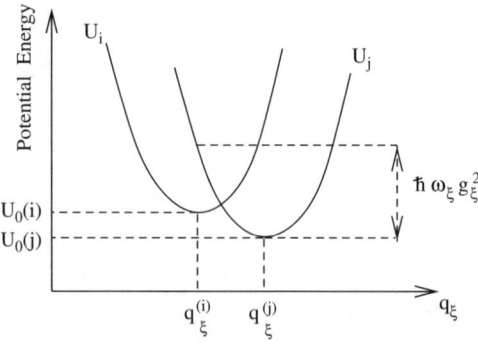

**Figure 5.** Potential energy surfaces of initial and final electronic states.

# ABSORPTION OF LIGHT

initial classical values for coordinate and momentum are uncorrelated, i.e., $<q_\xi(0)p_\xi(0)> = 0$ and the correlation function $C_{cl}(t)$ is obtained as:

$$C_{cl}(t) = \sum_\xi [2n(\omega_\xi) + 1]g_\xi^2 \omega_\xi^2 \cos(\omega_\xi t)$$

$$\approx 2\frac{kT}{\hbar} \sum_\xi g_\xi^2 \omega_\xi \cos(\omega_\xi t) \qquad (26)$$

The $\gamma_{cl}(t)$ in eqn. (21), using the above result, then reads [73]:

$$\gamma_{cl}(t) = \sum_\xi [2n(\omega_\xi) + 1]g_\xi^2 [\cos(\omega_\xi t) - 1)] \qquad (27)$$

It is valid at high temperatures $\left[2n(\omega_\xi) + 1 \approx 2\frac{kT}{\hbar\omega_\xi}\right]$. The mean value $<X>$ entering eqn. (20) can be written as $\hbar\omega_{ji} + \lambda$, where $\hbar\omega_{ji} = U_j^{(0)} - U_i^{(0)}$ is the energy difference between the minima of the two PES, and $\lambda$ is the so called reorganization energy:

$$\lambda = \hbar \sum_\xi g_\xi^2 \omega_\xi \qquad (28)$$

It is the difference $U_f(\{q_\xi^{(i)}\}) - U_f(\{q_\xi^{(f)}\})$, i.e., the energy difference between the minimum of the PES of the final state and the value of this PES at the equilibrium position of the initial state. If a spectral density $J(\omega)$ of the coupling of nuclei to the electronic transition is introduced as:

$$J(\omega) = \sum_\xi g_\xi^2 \delta(\omega - \omega_\xi) \qquad (29)$$

the reorganization energy $\lambda$ is given as:

$$\lambda = \int_0^\infty d\omega\, \hbar\omega J(\omega) \qquad (30)$$

and the classical correlation function $C_{cl}(t)$ in eqn. (26) reads:

$$C_{cl}(t) \approx 2\frac{kT}{\hbar} \int d\omega J(\omega)\omega \cos(\omega t) \qquad (31)$$

The above relation between $C_{cl}(t)$ and $J(\omega)$ is used to extract $J(\omega)$ from classical molecular dynamics simulations [68] as discussed in detail later.

### 2.2.2 Quantum Description

If the nuclear motion is treated quantum mechanically, Fermi's Golden Rule gives for the rate constant:

$$k_{i\to f} = \frac{2\pi}{\hbar}|V_{if}|^2 \sum_{\alpha,\beta} b(i\alpha)|<i\alpha|f\beta>|^2 \delta(E_{i\alpha} - E_{f\beta}) \qquad (32)$$

The high-dimensional states $|i\alpha\rangle = \Pi_\xi |i\alpha_\xi\rangle$ and $|f\beta\rangle = \Pi_\xi |f\beta_\xi\rangle$ contain a product of vibrational eigenstates of the initial and final electronic states, respectively. The factor $b(i\alpha)$ describes a Boltzmann distribution for the vibrational states of the initial electronic state.

The Hamiltonian of the initial electronic state $|i\rangle$ is defined via $H_i|i\alpha\rangle = E_{i\alpha}|i\alpha\rangle$, with the energy $E_{i\alpha} = \sum_\xi E_{i\alpha_\xi}$. Similarly, for the final electronic state we have $H_f|f\beta\rangle = E_{f\beta}|f\beta\rangle$.

By writing the $\delta$-function in eqn. (32) as $\delta(E_{i\alpha} - E_{f\beta}) = \frac{1}{2\pi\hbar}\int_{-\infty}^{\infty} dt \exp\{(E_{i\alpha} - E_{f\beta})t/\hbar\}$ and using the completeness relation, i.e., $\sum_\beta |f\beta\rangle\langle f\beta| = 1$, Fermi's Golden rule becomes:

$$k_{i\to f} = \frac{|V_{if}|^2}{\hbar^2} \int_{-\infty}^{\infty} dt \langle e^{iH_i t/\hbar} e^{-iH_f t/\hbar} \rangle \tag{33}$$

where $\langle ... \rangle$ denotes an average with respect to the equilibrium statistical operator of the vibrational degrees of freedom of the initial state $|i\rangle$. In complete analogy with the semiclassical case the reaction coordinate:

$$\hat{X} = H_f - H_i \tag{34}$$

is introduced [1]. In the following, use is made of the identity [69]:

$$e^{iH_i t/\hbar} e^{-iH_f t/\hbar} = \hat{T} e^{-i\int_0^t d\tau \hat{X}(\tau)/\hbar} \tag{35}$$

which contains the time ordering operator $\hat{T}$ that acts on a product of operators at different times $\hat{O}(t_1)\hat{O}(t_2)$ by time ordering of all the possible permutations:

$$\hat{T}\hat{O}(t_1)\hat{O}(t_2) = \theta_{t_1-t_2}\hat{O}(t_1)\hat{O}(t_2) + \theta_{t_2-t_1}\hat{O}(t_2)\hat{O}(t_1) \tag{36}$$

where $\theta_t$ is the heavy side function that is zero for $t < 0$ and one for $t > 0$. The time evolution of the reaction coordinate $\hat{X}(\tau) = e^{i/\hbar H_i \tau}\hat{X}(0)e^{-i/\hbar H_i \tau}$ is defined by the Hamiltonian $H_i$ of the initial potential energy surface.

Using a second-order cumulant expansion [72] the quantum analog to eqn. (20) is obtained [1]:

$$k_{i\to f} = \frac{|V_{if}|^2}{\hbar^2} \int_{-\infty}^{\infty} dt e^{-i\langle \hat{X}\rangle t/\hbar + \gamma(t)} \tag{37}$$

with:

$$\gamma(t) = -\frac{1}{\hbar^2} \int_0^t d\tau (t-\tau) C(\tau) \tag{38}$$

where $C(t=\tau)$ is the correlation function:

$$C(t) = \langle \delta\hat{X}(t)\delta\hat{X}(0)\rangle = \langle \hat{X}(t)\hat{X}(0)\rangle - \langle X\rangle^2 \tag{39}$$

For harmonic oscillators, the Hamiltonian $H_{i/f}$ is given by the $H_{\text{vib}}^{(k=i/f)}$ in eqn. (23). For notational convenience a dimensionless coordinate

## ABSORPTION OF LIGHT

$Q_\xi = q_\xi \sqrt{2\omega_\xi \mu_\xi / \hbar}$ is used (e.g., [37]), where the $q_\xi$ are the normal coordinates in eqn. (23). The $Q_\xi$ can be written as $C_\xi^+ + C_\xi$, i.e., in terms of the usual creation and annihilation operators of vibrational quanta of protein mode $\xi$. These operators act on a vibrational state $|M_\xi\rangle$ with $M_\xi$ vibrational quanta as $C_\xi^+|M_\xi\rangle = \sqrt{M_\xi}|M_\xi + 1\rangle$ and $C_\xi|M_\xi\rangle = \sqrt{M_\xi - 1}|M_\xi - 1\rangle$ by creating or annihilating, respectively, a vibrational quantum. Choosing the origin of the $Q_\xi$ axis at the minimum position of the PES of the initial state results in the following Hamiltonians:

$$H_i = T_{\text{nucl}} + U_i^{(0)} + \sum_\xi \frac{\hbar\omega_\xi}{4} Q_\xi^2 \qquad (40)$$

and:

$$H_f = T_{\text{nucl}} + U_f^{(0)} + \sum_\xi \frac{\hbar\omega_\xi}{4} (Q_\xi + 2g_\xi)^2 \qquad (41)$$

The $\delta \hat{X}(t) = X(t) - \langle X \rangle$ in eqn. (39) is given as:

$$\delta \hat{X}(t) = \sum_\xi \hbar\omega_\xi Q_\xi(t) \qquad (42)$$

By writing the $H_i$ in eqn. (40) in terms of the $C_\xi^\dagger$ and $C_\xi$, $H_i = \sum_\xi \hbar\omega_\xi(C_\xi^+ C_\xi + \frac{1}{2})$, the time dependence $Q_\xi(t) = e^{iH_i t/\hbar} Q_\xi(0) e^{-iH_i t/\hbar}$ is obtained as [74]:

$$Q_\xi(t) = e^{i\omega_\xi t C_\xi^\dagger C_\xi}(C_\xi + C_\xi^\dagger) e^{-i\omega_\xi t C_\xi^\dagger C_\xi} = C_\xi e^{i\omega_\xi t} + C_\xi^\dagger e^{-i\omega_\xi t} \qquad (43)$$

and the average over the equilibrium statistical operator $W_{\text{eq}} = e^{-H_i/kT} / \text{Tr}_{\text{vib}}\{e^{-H_i/kT}\}$ of the vibrations in the initial state in eqn. (39) is carried out and yields the correlation function:

$$C(t) = \sum_\xi \hbar^2 \omega_\xi^2 \text{Tr}_{\text{vib}}\{W_{\text{eq}} Q_\xi(t) Q_\xi(0)\}$$
$$= \sum_\xi \hbar^2 \omega_\xi^2 g_\xi^2 \{[1 + n(\omega_\xi)] e^{-i\omega_\xi t} + n(\omega_\xi) e^{i\omega_\xi t}\} \qquad (44)$$

The Bose–Einstein distribution function $n(\omega_\xi)$ describes the mean number of vibrational quanta with energy $\hbar\omega_\xi$ that are excited at a given temperature $T$:

$$n(\omega_\xi) = \text{Tr}_{\text{vib}}\{W_{\text{eq}} C_\xi^\dagger C_\xi\} = \frac{1}{e^{\hbar\omega_\xi/kT} - 1}. \qquad (45)$$

With the above correlation function $C(t)$ the function $\gamma(t)$ in eqn. (38) reads [69]:

$$\gamma(t) = \gamma_{\text{cl}}(t) - i \sum_\xi g_\xi^2 [\sin(\omega_\xi t) - \omega_\xi t] \qquad (46)$$

It contains the classical $\gamma_{cl}(t)$ in eqn. (27) as a real part and an additional imaginary part that is not obtained in a classical description and reflects the correlation between initial momentum and coordinate, i.e., the uncertainty principle.

However, without the harmonic oscillator picture, a more general result can be obtained as outlined in [1]. One first introduces the Fourier transform $C(\omega)$ of the correlation function $C(t)$ in eqn. (39):

$$C(\omega) = \frac{1}{2\pi} \int_{-\infty}^{\infty} dt\, e^{i\omega t} C(t) \tag{47}$$

To explore an important property of $C(\omega)$, the time integration is manipulated ($\tau \to i/kT - \tau$) and the trace rearranged to show that:

$$\int_{-\infty}^{\infty} dt <\hat{X}(t)\hat{X}(0)> e^{i\omega t}$$

$$= \frac{1}{Z} \int_{-\infty}^{\infty} dt\, \text{Tr}\{e^{-H_i/kT} e^{iH_i t/\hbar} X e^{-iH_i t/\hbar} X\} e^{i\omega t}$$

$$= \frac{1}{Z} \int_{-\infty}^{\infty} dt\, \text{Tr}\{e^{-iH_i t/\hbar} X e^{-H_i/kT} e^{iH_i t/\hbar} X\} e^{-i\omega t} e^{\hbar\omega/kT}$$

$$= e^{\hbar\omega/kT} \int_{-\infty}^{\infty} dt <\hat{X}(t)\hat{X}(0)> e^{-i\omega t}$$

Thereby, one obtains [75]:

$$C(\omega) = e^{\hbar\omega/kT} C(-\omega) \tag{48}$$

By applying this property the correlation function $C(t)$ can be rewritten as:

$$C(t) = \int_0^{\infty} d\omega [C(\omega) - C(-\omega)]\{[1 + 2n(\omega)] \cos(\omega t) - i \sin(\omega t)\} \tag{49}$$

This relation results in the following general expression for the function $\gamma(t)$:

$$\gamma(t) = \frac{1}{\hbar^2} \int_0^{\infty} d\omega J(\omega)\{[1 + 2n(\omega)] \cos(\omega t) - i[\sin(\omega t) - \omega t]\} \tag{50}$$

where the spectral density $J(\omega)$ was defined as:

$$J(\omega) = \frac{C(\omega) - C(-\omega)}{\omega^2} \tag{51}$$

A comparison of the general result eqns. (50) and (51) with the harmonic oscillator result eqns. (46) and (27) implies that each system with temperature independent spectral density may be mapped onto an harmonic system with the same spectral density [1], which in the case of harmonic oscillators is given in eqn. (29). Of course, the use of a second order cumulant expansion (which for harmonic oscillators is exact) is an approximation. In cases where the high-dimensional potential energy surfaces (PES) are anharmonic, the free-energy

## ABSORPTION OF LIGHT

surfaces may well be harmonic and the second order cumulant approximation would be valid in this case.

### 2.2.3 Optical Spectra – Theory of Lax and Kubo

The absorption cross section $\delta(\omega)$ is given as the ratio of the rate of energy loss $-\frac{d}{dt}E_{\text{rad}}$ of the external field and its energy flux $S$ [76]:

$$\delta(\omega) = -\left(\frac{d}{dt}E_{\text{rad}}\right)/S \tag{52}$$

The energy flux (Poynting vector) $S$ equals $\frac{c}{8\pi}nE_0^2$, where $c$ is the velocity of light in vacuum, $n$ is the refractive index of the medium and $E_0$ is the amplitude of the external field $\vec{E}(t)$:

$$\vec{E}(t) = \frac{E_0}{2}\vec{\varepsilon}(e^{i\omega t} + e^{-i\omega t}) \tag{53}$$

with frequency $\omega$. The vector $\vec{\varepsilon}$ is a unit vector along the polarization direction of the field. The energy loss $-\frac{d}{dt}E_{\text{rad}}$ of the external field is related to the rate constant $k_{g\to e}$ of the optical induced transition between the ground and excited state of the pigment by [76]:

$$-\frac{d}{dt}E_{\text{rad}} = \hbar\omega k_{g\to e} \tag{54}$$

The matrix element $V_{ge}(t)$ that describes the coupling between the ground state and the excited state induced by the external field, in rotating wave and dipole approximation, is given as:

$$V_{ge}(t) = -\frac{E_0}{2}e^{-i\omega t}\vec{\varepsilon}\,\vec{\mu}_{eg} \tag{55}$$

where $\vec{\mu}_{eg}$ is the transition dipole moment of the pigment. Applying Fermi's Golden Rule, and neglecting the coupling of the optical transition to vibrational degrees of freedom the rate constant $k = \frac{2\pi}{\hbar}|V_{ge}|^2\delta(\omega_{eg} - \omega)$ is obtained as:

$$k_{g\to e} = \frac{E_0^2\pi}{2\hbar^2}\left\langle|\vec{\mu}_{eg}\vec{\varepsilon}|^2\right\rangle_{\text{orient}}\delta(\omega_{eg} - \omega) = \frac{E_0^2\pi}{6\hbar^2}|\vec{\mu}_{eg}|^2\delta(\omega_{eg} - \omega) \tag{56}$$

where $\langle|\vec{\mu}_{eg}\vec{\varepsilon}|^2\rangle_{\text{orient}} = \frac{1}{3}|\vec{\mu}_{eg}|^2$ describes an average over a random orientation of complexes (transition dipole moments) in the sample.

If the electron–vibrational coupling is taken into account within the Condon approximation, i.e., neglecting any dependence of the transition dipole moment $\vec{\mu}_{eg}$ on the nuclear coordinates, the rate constant $k_{g\to e}$ is obtained from eqn. (37) by taking into account eqn. (55) for the coupling and the energy $\hbar\omega$ of the absorbed photon $\langle X \rangle = \hbar\omega_{eg} + \lambda - \hbar\omega$, where $\hbar\omega_{eg} = U_e^{(0)} - U_g^{(0)}$ is the $0 \to 0$ transition energy between the two potential energy surfaces (PES) and $\lambda$ is the reorganization energy in eqn. (30).

Noting that $\gamma(t) - i\lambda t = G(t) - G(0)$ where the function $G(t)$ is introduced as:

$$G(t) = \int_0^\infty d\omega \{[1 + n(\omega)]J(\omega)e^{-i\omega t} + n(\omega)J(\omega)e^{i\omega t}\} \tag{57}$$

the rate constant for the radiative transition reads:

$$k_{g \to e} = \frac{E_0^2 \pi}{6\hbar^2} |\vec{\mu}_{eg}|^2 D_\alpha(\omega) \tag{58}$$

where the δ-function in eqn. (56) is replaced now by the lineshape function [37,69]:

$$D_\alpha(\omega) = \frac{1}{2\pi} \int_{-\infty}^\infty dt e^{i(\omega - \omega_{eg})t} e^{G(t) - G(0)} \tag{59}$$

The absorption cross section is then obtained from eqns. (52), (54), and (58) as:

$$\delta(\omega) = \frac{4\pi^2}{3\hbar c n} \omega |\vec{\mu}_{eg}|^2 D_\alpha(\omega) \tag{60}$$

The absorption cross section $\delta(\omega)$ is related to the absorption coefficient $\alpha(\omega)$ by $\delta(\omega) = n_{\text{mol}} \alpha(\omega)$ where $n_{\text{mol}}$ is the density of absorbing molecules. In an absorption experiment $\alpha(\omega)$ is measured using Lambert-Beer's law $I(\omega)/I_0(\omega) = \exp(-\alpha(\omega)d)$, with the intensity $I_0(\omega)$ of the incoming light and the intensity $I(\omega)$ of the light after passing through the sample with path length $d$. In the case of fluorescence the initial state is the excited electronic state, and hence the energy difference $<X>$ in eqn. (37) equals $\hbar\omega + \lambda - \hbar\omega_{eg}$ and the fluorescence signal $I(\omega)$ is obtained as [69]:

$$I(\omega) \propto \omega^3 |\mu_{eg}|^2 D_I(\omega) \tag{61}$$

with the lineshape function:

$$D_I(\omega) = \frac{1}{2\pi} \int_{-\infty}^\infty dt e^{-i(\omega - \omega_{eg})t} e^{G(t) - G(0)} \tag{62}$$

We note that the two lineshape functions $D_\alpha(\omega)$ and $D_I(\omega)$ are mirror symmetric with respect to the $0 \to 0$ transition energy $\hbar\omega_{eg}$, i.e., $D_\alpha(\omega_{eg} - \omega) = D_I(\omega_{eg} + \omega)$. This relation holds because equal vibrational frequencies have been assumed for the two electronic states.

The lineshape functions eqns. (59) and (62) can be written as a sum of two terms, a zero-vibrational quantum $(0 \to 0)$ transition and vibrational sidebands [77]:

$$D_{\alpha/I}(\omega) = \frac{e^{-G(0)}}{2\pi} \int_{-\infty}^\infty dt e^{i(\omega - \omega_{eg})t} \\ + \frac{e^{-G(0)}}{2\pi} \int_{-\infty}^\infty dt e^{\pm i(\omega - \omega_{eg})t} (e^{G(t)} - 1) \tag{63}$$

which can also be expressed as:

$$D_{\alpha/I}(\omega) = e^{-G(0)} \delta(\omega - \omega_{eg}) + \phi[\pm(\omega - \omega_{eg})] \tag{64}$$

Here, $\delta(\omega - \omega_{eg})$ refers to the $0 \to 0$ transition and the $\phi[\pm(\omega - \omega_{eg})]$ to the absorption (+) or fluorescence (−) vibrational sidebands. The integrated intensity of the vibrational sideband $\int_{-\infty}^{\infty} d\omega \phi(\omega - \omega_{eg})$, relative to that of the zero-vibrational quantum transition $e^{-G(0)}$, equals $e^{G(0)} - 1$, and is a measure of the exciton–vibrational coupling strength. The significance of $G(0)$ is that at temperature $T = 0$, it is seen from eqn. (57) to equal $S$, the well-known Huang Rhys factor:

$$S = \int_0^\infty d\omega J(\omega) = \sum_\xi g_\xi^2 \qquad (65)$$

where $g_\xi^2$ also equals the average change [69] in number of vibrational quanta with energy $\hbar\omega_\xi$ in an optical transition from any specific initial vibrational state. Since the displacement of the minima of the potential energy surfaces of the two electronic states with respect to each other equals $-2g_\xi$, the more this displacement the larger is $S$.

The exciton–vibrational coupling is weak when $S \ll 1$, and strong when $S \gg 1$. The typical coupling in photosynthetic antenna complexes lies in an intermediate range $S \approx 1$ [5–7,78], a notable exception being the red-absorbing antenna states of photosystem I ($S > 2$) [79–81]. In the latter case, as in bacterial reaction centers [62,63], the mixing of exciton states with intermolecular charge transfer states leads to the stronger electron–vibrational coupling.

The excitation energy transfer between two localized excited states is discussed next.

### 2.2.4 Excitation Energy Transfer – Förster Theory

In excitation transfer reactions, an excited electronic state is transferred between two pigments, which will be denoted as $m$ and $n$ in the following. In the initial state $|m>= |m(e)n(g)>$ pigment $m$ is assumed to be excited and pigment $n$ is in its ground state, and in the final state $|n>$ the excitation was transferred from $m$ to $n$, i.e., $|n>= |m(g)n(e)>$. The coupling matrix element $V_{mn}$ for this reaction, in the present weak coupling limit, is given as the dipole–dipole interaction between optical transition dipole moments of the two pigments, as will be discussed in detail later (Section 2.4.4.1 on the point-dipole approximation).

It is assumed that the two pigments couple to different vibrational degrees of freedom, i.e., that their electronic energies fluctuate independently. The average energy difference $<X>$ between the final and initial state then is given as $<X_m> + <X_n>$ and is obtained as $\omega_{eg}^{(n)} + \lambda^{(n)} - \omega_{eg}^{(m)} + \lambda^{(m)}$. Similarly, the function $G(t)$ is given as $G_m(t) + G_n(t)$ and the rate constant is obtained as:

$$k_{m \to n} = \frac{|V_{mn}|^2}{\hbar^2} \int_{-\infty}^\infty dt\, e^{i\omega_{eg}^{(m)} t} e^{G_m(t) - G_m(0)} e^{-i\omega_{eg}^{(n)} t} e^{G_n(t) - G_n(0)} \qquad (66)$$

From eqn. (59) we note that $e^{i\omega_{eg}^{(m)} t} e^{G_m(t) - G_m(0)} = \int_{-\infty}^\infty d\omega e^{i\omega t} D_\alpha^{(n)}(\omega)$ and from eqn. (62) it follows that $e^{-i\omega_{eg}^{(n)} t} e^{G_n(t) - G_n(0)} = \int_{-\infty}^\infty d\omega e^{-i\omega t} D_I^{(m)}(\omega)$. With those relations the rate constant in eqn. (66) becomes:

$$k_{m \to n} = \frac{2\pi}{\hbar^2} |V_{mn}|^2 \int_{-\infty}^{\infty} d\omega D_\alpha^{(n)}(\omega) D_I^{(m)}(\omega) \tag{67}$$

and with eqns. (60) and (61) it can be expressed in terms of donor emission and acceptor absorption spectra $I_m(\omega)$ and $\alpha_n(\omega)$, respectively:

$$k_{m \to n} = \frac{2\pi}{\hbar^2} |V_{mn}|^2 \frac{\int_{-\infty}^{\infty} d\omega \alpha_n(\omega) I_m(\omega) \omega^{-4}}{\int_{-\infty}^{\infty} d\omega I_m(\omega) \omega^{-3} \int_{-\infty}^{\infty} d\omega \alpha_n(\omega) \omega^{-1}} \tag{68}$$

In the original expression derived by Förster [35] the explicit calculation of $|V_{mn}|^2$ was avoided by including the transition dipole strengths of the donor and the acceptor occurring in $|V_{mn}|^2$ in the radiative life time of the donor and the molar extinction coefficient of the acceptor.

The above Förster theory has had a enormous impact on biology, chemistry and physics. However, in photosynthetic antennae usually the interpigment distances are too small to apply this theory (a notable exception being the peridin–chlorophyll a complex shown in Figure 4). Therefore, extensions of the Förster theory are necessary, and are discussed in Section 2.3.

### 2.2.5 Electron Transfer – Marcus Theory

In electron transfer (ET) theory, the following two approximations are commonly used: (i) the vibrations are treated classically in the high-temperature limit and (ii) in addition to the classical treatment one effective high frequency mode is described quantum mechanically. Approximation (i) has the advantage of providing physical insights into three different regimes of the transfer: the normal, the activation-less and the inverted region. Such insight is possible because the number of parameters is reduced to three essential quantities of the reaction, the charge transfer coupling $V_{if}$, the standard free energy $\Delta G^{(0)}$, which corresponds in the harmonic oscillator model to the energy difference between the two minima of the potential energy surfaces of the initial and final state and the reorganization energy $\lambda$. The related free-energy surfaces are illustrated in Figure 6. In the normal region there is a barrier between the two minima of free-energy surfaces and the crossing point has to be reached by thermal fluctuations of nuclei, before the electron transfer can occur. In the activation-less region no thermal activation is necessary and the rate has its maximum value. In the inverted region a lowering of the free energy of the final state leads to a decrease of the rate constant, because of a barrier created between the two free-energy surfaces. If, as in approximation (ii), parts of the vibrations are treated quantum mechanically, the nuclei can tunnel through that barrier and in this way the inverted effect becomes weaker.

In the following, the classical result is derived from eqn. (37). At high temperatures the correlation function of the energy gap and hence the function $\gamma(t)$ in eqn. (46) can be assumed to decay rapidly. A short time approximation for the imaginary part, $\sin(\omega_\xi t) \approx \omega_\xi t$, in eqn. (46) removes the imaginary part

# ABSORPTION OF LIGHT

and $\gamma(t)$ becomes the classical $\gamma_{cl}(t)$ in eqn. (27). A short time approximation for the real part, $\cos(\omega_\xi t) \approx 1 - (\omega_\xi t)^2/2$, then yields, using eqn. (28):

$$\gamma(t) \approx -\frac{kT}{\hbar}\sum_\xi g_\xi^2 \omega_\xi t^2 = -\frac{kT}{\hbar^2}\lambda t^2 \qquad (69)$$

where also the high-temperature assumption $kT >> \hbar\omega_\xi$ was used to approximate $n(\omega_\xi)$ by $kT/\hbar\omega_\xi$ in eqn. (27). The integral in eqn. (37) then yields the rate

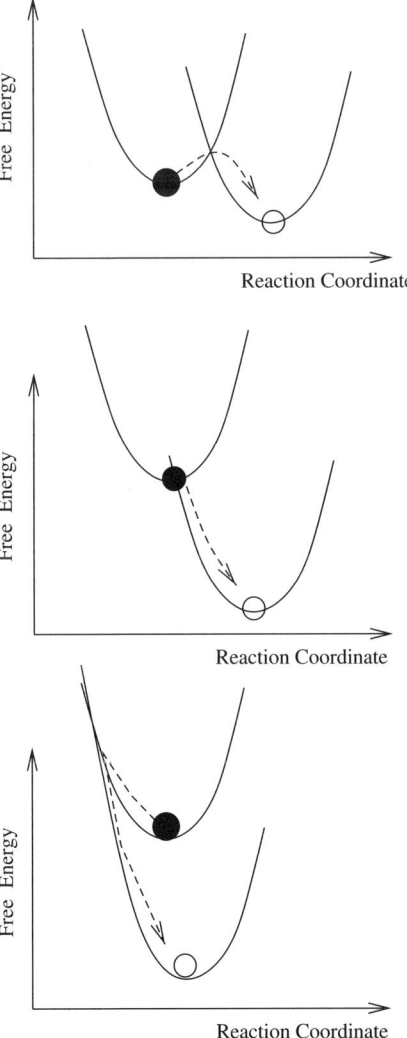

**Figure 6.** Different regimes of electron transfer reactions; upper part: normal region ($-\Delta G^{(0)} < \lambda$), middle part: activation-less region ($\Delta G^{(0)} = \lambda$), lower part: inverted region ($\Delta G^{(0)} > \lambda$).

constant [19]:

$$k = \frac{2\pi}{\hbar}|V_{if}|^2 \frac{1}{(4\pi\lambda kT)^{\frac{1}{2}}} e^{-\left(\frac{\Delta G^0 + \lambda}{4\lambda kT}\right)^2} \quad (70)$$

If one vibrational mode $\xi = v$ is treated quantum mechanically, and its energy is sufficiently high, i.e., $\hbar\omega_v \gg kT$, whereas the remaining modes are treated classically as above, the function $\gamma(t)$ in eqn. (46) becomes:

$$\gamma(t) \approx -\frac{kT}{\hbar^2}\lambda t^2 + g_v^2[\cos(\omega_v t) - i\sin(\omega_v t)] + ig_v^2\omega_v t \quad (71)$$

and the mean energy difference $<X>$ reads:

$$<X> = \Delta G^{(0)} + \lambda + S_v\hbar\omega_v \quad (72)$$

where $S_v = g_v^2$ is the Huang Rhys factor of the quantum mode $v$. Using the above two equations, the rate constant is obtained as:

$$k = \frac{|V_{if}|^2}{\hbar^2} e^{-S_v} \int_{-\infty}^{\infty} dt\, e^{-\frac{i}{\hbar}(\Delta G^{(0)} + \lambda)t} e^{-\frac{kT}{\hbar^2}\lambda t^2} e^{S_v e^{-i\omega_v t}} \quad (73)$$

After expanding the last term in the above equation into an exponential series, the integral for the terms of that series can be performed and the final expression for the rate constant reads [37,71]:

$$k = 2\pi \frac{|V_{if}|^2}{\hbar} \frac{1}{(4\pi\lambda kT)^{1/2}} e^{-S_v} \sum_{N=0}^{\infty} \frac{(S_v)^N}{N!} e^{-\left(\frac{\Delta G^0 + \lambda + N\hbar\omega_v}{4\lambda kT}\right)^2} \quad (74)$$

Figure 7 gives an illustration of the nuclear tunneling in the inverted region of electron transfer. As is seen there, by excitation of high-frequency vibrational quanta in the final electronic state, the regime of electron transfer changes from inverted for $N=0$ to activation-less for $N=3$ excited quanta. The relative weight of the different transitions is given by the Franck–Condon factor $\frac{(S_v)^N}{N!}$ in eqn. (74), which describes the overlap of the vibrational ground state wavefunction of the initial state with the different vibrational wavefunctions of the final electronic state.

## 2.3 Strong Excitonic Coupling

For strong excitonic coupling, delocalized excited states $|M>$ are formed in the aggregate that are given as a linear combination of localized excited states $|m>$, for which the $m$th pigment is in the excited state with wavefunction $|\varphi_m^*>$ and all others ($n \neq m$) are in the ground state $|\varphi_n>$:

$$|M> = \sum_m c_m^{(M)}|\varphi_m^*> \prod_{n\neq m}|\varphi_n> \equiv \sum_m c_m^{(M)}|m> \quad (75)$$

# ABSORPTION OF LIGHT

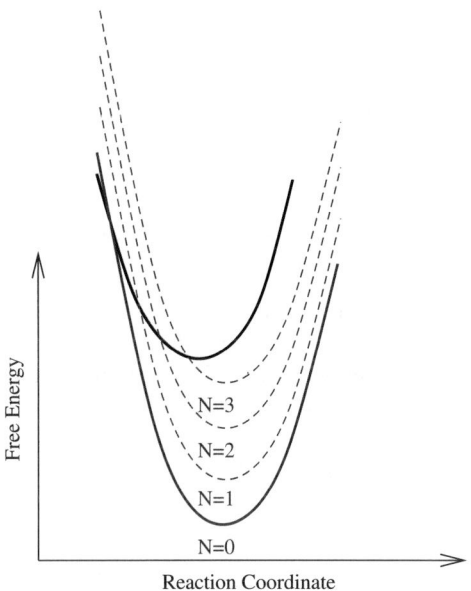

**Figure 7.** Free-energy surfaces of the initial state and different final states with $N = 0$–$3$ excited high-frequency vibrational quanta. The case $N = 0$ (solid line) is the same as in the lower part of Figure 6.

To treat strong couplings the aggregate Hamiltonian is first represented in terms of localized states $|m\rangle$ and afterwards transformed to the basis of delocalized states $|M\rangle$.

The Hamiltonian is divided into four parts:

$$H = H_{\text{ex}} + H_{\text{ex-rad}} + H_{\text{vib}} + H_{\text{ex-vib}} \tag{76}$$

The excitonic Hamiltonian $H_{\text{ex}}$:

$$H_{\text{ex}} = \sum_m E_m |m\rangle\langle m| + \sum_{m \neq n} V_{mn} |m\rangle\langle n| \tag{77}$$

contains the local excitation energies (so-called site energies) of the pigments $E_m$ and the excitation energy transfer (excitonic) couplings $V_{mn}$. The site energies $E_m$ are defined as the vertical transition energies at the equilibrium position of nuclei in the electronic ground state $|0\rangle$.

Within rotating wave approximation the coupling to an external field $\vec{E}e^{-i\Omega t} + c.c.$ is described by the Hamiltonian:

$$H_{\text{ex-rad}} = \sum_m e^{-i\Omega t} \vec{E} \cdot \vec{\mu}_m |m\rangle\langle 0| + h.c \tag{78}$$

where $\vec{\mu}_m$ is the optical transition dipole moment of the $m$th pigment and $h.c$ denotes the hermitian conjugated of the first term. The vibrations are described by harmonic oscillators with frequencies $\omega_\xi$ and kinetic energy $T_{\text{nucl}}$, as before:

$$H_{\text{vib}} = T_{\text{nucl}} + \sum_\xi \frac{\hbar\omega_\xi}{4} Q_\xi^2 \equiv \sum_\xi \hbar\omega_\xi (C_\xi^+ C_\xi + \tfrac{1}{2}) \tag{79}$$

A linear exciton–vibrational coupling is assumed in the Hamiltonian:

$$H_{\text{ex-vib}} = \sum_m \sum_\xi \hbar\omega_\xi g_\xi^{(m)} Q_\xi |m\rangle\langle m| \tag{80}$$

that contains the dimensionless coupling constant $g_\xi^{(m)}$ and depends linearly on the dimensionless coordinate $Q_\xi$ introduced above.

It is instructive to rewrite $H_{\text{ex}} + H_{\text{vib}}$ in terms of potential energy surfaces (PES) of localized exciton states:

$$H_{\text{ex}} + H_{\text{vib}} = T_{\text{nucl}} + U_0|0\rangle\langle 0| + \sum_m U_m |m\rangle\langle m| \\ + \sum_{m\neq n} V_{mn} |m\rangle\langle n| \tag{81}$$

with the PES $U_0$ of the electronic ground state:

$$U_0 = \sum_\xi \frac{\hbar\omega_\xi}{4} Q_\xi^2 \tag{82}$$

the PES $U_m$ of the $m$th localized excitonic state:

$$U_m = U_0^{(m)} + \sum_\xi \frac{\hbar\omega_\xi}{4} \left[Q_\xi + 2g_\xi^{(m)}\right]^2 \tag{83}$$

with:

$$U_0^{(m)} = E_m - \sum_\xi (g_\xi^{(m)})^2 \hbar\omega_\xi \equiv E_m - \lambda^{(m)} \tag{84}$$

where $\lambda^{(m)}$ is the reorganization energy of the optical transition of the $m$th pigment. The completeness relation $1 = |0\rangle\langle 0| + \sum_m |m\rangle\langle m|$ was used to write $H_{\text{vib}}$ as $T_{\text{nucl}} + \sum_\xi \frac{\hbar\omega_\xi}{4} Q_\xi^2 (|0\rangle\langle 0| + \sum_m |m\rangle\langle m|)$.

In the weak coupling theories of optical spectra and Förster excitation energy transfer, the transitions occur between the PES of the electronic ground state $|0\rangle$ and the PES of the $m$th localized excited state $|m\rangle$.

In the case of strong excitonic coupling the optical transitions occur between the PES of ground state $|0\rangle$ and the PES of the $M$th exciton state $|M\rangle$ and the vibrations do not relax in potential energy surfaces of localized electronic states $|m\rangle$ but in the PES of delocalized states $|M\rangle$. To introduce the latter PES, we transform the above Hamiltonian into the basis of the $|M\rangle$ states, which are defined as the eigenstates of the Hamiltonian $H_{\text{ex}}$ in eqn. (77), i.e.,

$$H_{\text{ex}}|M\rangle = E_M |M\rangle \tag{85}$$

# ABSORPTION OF LIGHT

From the solution of this eigenvalue problem, the eigencoefficients $c_m^{(M)}$ in eqn. (75) and the exciton energies $E_M$ in eqn. (85) are obtained. Expressing the local excited states by $|m> = \sum_M c_m^{(M)} |M>$, the coupling to the external field in eqn. (78) becomes:

$$H_{\text{ex-rad}}(t) = \sum_M e^{-i\Omega t} \vec{E} \cdot \vec{\mu}_M |M><0| + h.c \tag{86}$$

where the exciton transition dipole moment:

$$\vec{\mu}_M = \sum_m c_m^{(M)} \vec{\mu}_m \tag{87}$$

is given by the exciton coefficients $c_m^{(M)}$ and the local transition dipole moments $\vec{\mu}_m$. Using the same transformation, the exciton vibrational coupling Hamiltonian $H_{\text{ex-vib}}$ in eqn. (80) becomes:

$$H_{\text{ex-vib}} = \sum_{MN} \hat{V}_{MN} |M><N| \tag{88}$$

with the coupling operator $\hat{V}_{MN}$ that depends linearly on the vibrational coordinates and contains besides the diagonal elements also non-diagonal elements that couple different exciton states $|M>$ and $|N>$:

$$\hat{V}_{MN} = \sum_m c_m^{(M)} c_m^{(N)} \sum_\xi \hbar\omega_\xi g_\xi^{(m)} Q_\xi \equiv \sum_\xi \hbar\omega_\xi g_\xi(M,N) Q_\xi \tag{89}$$

The vibrational Hamiltonian $H_{\text{vib}}$ in eqn. (79) is written as:

$$H_{\text{vib}} = T_{\text{nucl}} + \sum_\xi \frac{\hbar\omega_\xi}{4} Q_\xi^2 \left( \sum_M |M><M| + |0><0| \right) \tag{90}$$

where the unity operator $1 = (\sum_M |M><M| + |0><0|)$ was added on the right-hand side. The diagonal elements $g_\xi(M,M)$ can be used to introduce potential energy surfaces $U_M$ of exciton states by rewriting $H_{\text{vib}} + H_{\text{ex-vib}}$ as:

$$H_{\text{vib}} + H_{\text{ex-vib}} = T_{\text{nucl}} + U_0|0><0| + \sum_M U_M |M><M| \\ + \sum_{M \neq N} \hat{V}_{MN} |M><N| \tag{91}$$

with the PES of the ground state in eqn. (82) and the PES $U_M$:

$$U_M = U_M^{(0)} + \sum_\xi \frac{\hbar\omega_\xi}{4} [Q_\xi + 2g_\xi(M,M)]^2 \tag{92}$$

where:

$$U_M^{(0)} = E_M - \lambda^{(M)} \tag{93}$$

Here, the reorganization energy of the $M$th exciton state is introduced as:

$$\lambda^{(M)} = \sum_\xi \hbar\omega_\xi [g_\xi(M,M)]^2 \qquad (94)$$

In contrast to the weak coupling limit discussed above no exact analytic solution exists for relaxation rates of a multi-level system coupled to a large manifold of harmonic or effective harmonic oscillators. Accordingly, approximate theories have been used, as in [8,37–44,50,53,55,65,75,82–89]. The multi-level Redfield theory [37–40], an example of a Markovian theory, has been applied to photosynthetic antenna systems [41–43]. In a Markovian theory for a statistical density operator $\hat{\rho}(t)$ the equation of motion $d\hat{\rho}(t)/dt$ depends only on the properties of the system at $t$ and not on properties at earlier times, i.e., there are no memory effects of the earlier behavior. As noted below, $\hat{\rho}(t)$ is a reduced statistical operator describing the electronic motion, reduced in the sense that it is thermally averaged over an equilibrium distribution of the vibrational motion. In general, it is the reduction in degrees of freedom from the description of the dynamics of a large system to that of a small subsystem that gives rise to non-Markovian, or memory, effects.

If, for example, the coupling of the exciton to some selected vibrational modes is treated non-perturbatively, as was done in some effective mode models [90–92], all "memory" is automatically included for the coupling to these modes. There is no reduced description involved. However, such an approach is computationally intensive and so has been limited to a small number of electronic pigment states and effective vibrational modes. The largest system treated so far is a chlorophyll dimer consisting of nine electronic states coupled to two effective vibrational modes [91]. An alternative approach of comparable numerical intensity is given by a path integral formulation [93,94].

An alternative and numerically less intensive approach that uses perturbation theory for part of the exciton–vibrational coupling is the non-Markovian density matrix theory. When non-Markovian effects are studied the choice of an operator (the projection operator) used for the derivation of the equations of motion for the reduced statistical operator is critical. Different projection operators can be best compared by a generalized cumulant expansion method developed by Kubo [95] and by van Kampen [96]. As pointed out by Hashitsume et al. [97] and Mukamel et al. [47] the time-convolution less projection operator technique developed by Shibata et al. [97,98] and by Tokuyama and Mori [99] corresponds to a so-called partial ordering prescription (POP) in the time-ordering of the cumulant expansion [47,97,98], whereas a more widely used projection operator technique developed by Zwanzig [100] corresponds to a chronological ordering prescription (COP) [47,97,98]. The POP theory leads to an ordinary differential equation of motion with time-dependent coefficients for the reduced statistical operator $\hat{\rho}(t)$, whereas COP results in an integro-differential equation for $\hat{\rho}(t)$ containing a convolution. In POP the memory effects appear in the time-dependent coefficients while in COP they appear in the history of $\hat{\rho}(t)$. Besides mathematical convenience the guidelines for the choice of the time-ordering prescription may not be clear. At infinite order both prescriptions become equivalent. In the Markovian limit they also become equivalent.

One way, chosen by Palenberg et al. [101], to evaluate the convergence of the two time-ordering prescriptions is to compare with an exact result. However, such results exists only for relatively simple systems. In their study of a dimer with a dichotomously fluctuating site energies, POP yielded the better results for the time-dependent population of dimer states. The electronic coupling between the two states was included exactly. On the other hand, for a two-level system where the levels are coupled weakly by an external field and the correlation function of the energy gap decays exponentially Mukamel showed [48] how the ordering prescription is related to the stochastic properties of the energy gap: The COP equation for such a system yields the optical absorption lineshape known [72] for a two-level system with dichotomously fluctuating energy gap. The POP equation for the same system gives [48] the lineshape function obtained [72] for a system where the energy gap is modulated by a Gaussian random process. The spin-boson system has been used as a simple model system as well [149–151]. Using path integral functionals Xu et al. [150] obtained a hierarchical set of equations of motion for the reduced statistical operator. Different truncation schemes for this hierarchy were tested and the one that corresponds to a POP treatment yielded the most accurate results [150]. A similar hierarchical set was used by Schröder et al. [151] to investigate the population decay of a damped harmonic oscillator. In a certain parameter range POP was found to be converged already in second order, whereas COP showed artificial oscillations that vanished only in higher order. Renger and Marcus [8] have extracted the spectral density of the optical transition of the B777-monomer complex in Figure 1 using the exact theory by Lax and Kubo described above, and then applied this quantity in approximate calculations of fluorescence line narrowing spectra of the related B820-dimer complex. Only the POP theory gave agreement with the experimental data [10] over the whole spectrum, whereas, in COP, deviations where obtained for the low-frequency part of the vibrational sideband. By varying the temperature the convergence of POP and COP was investigated in calculations of inhomogenously broadened absorption spectra of the so-called WSCP-complex that contains two strongly coupled chlorophyll b pigments in "open-sandwich" geometry. Whereas POP describes the experimental spectrum between 2 K and room temperature, strong deviations were obtained for COP at higher temperatures [152].

*2.3.1 Density Matrix Theory*

A reduced statistical operator $\hat{\rho}(t)$ of the excitonic degrees of freedom is introduced as a trace over the vibrational degrees of freedom of the statistical operator $\hat{W}(t)$ of the entire system (excitons and vibrations):

$$\hat{\rho}(t) = \text{Tr}_{\text{vib}}\{\hat{W}(t)\} \qquad (95)$$

When there is no coupling to external light fields the system is in its ground state and the statistical operator $\hat{W}(t)$ factorizes into a vibrational and an excitonic part $\tilde{W}(t) = W_{eq}|0><0|$. This factorization occurs prior to a time $t_0$, the time of the first interaction with an external field. The $W_{eq}$ is the equilibrium statistical operator of the vibrations in the electronic ground state of the system:

$$W_{eq} = \frac{e^{-H_{vib}/kT}}{Tr_{vib}\{e^{-H_{vib}/kT}\}} \tag{96}$$

with $H_{vib}$ given by eqn. (79).

The coupling with the external field then causes the excitonic and vibrational part to depart from equilibrium. Because the excited states are coupled to the vibrations the statistical operator of the optically excited states does not factorize as for the ground state. The density matrix theory provides a way to treat the correlations between excitonic and vibrational degrees of freedom that appear in the dissipative part $\frac{\partial}{\partial t}\hat{\rho}(t)|_{dissi}$ of the equation of motion for $\hat{\rho}(t)$:

$$\frac{\partial}{\partial t}\hat{\rho}(t) = -\frac{i}{\hbar}[H_{ex}, \hat{\rho}(t)] - \frac{i}{\hbar}[H_{ex-rad}(t), \hat{\rho}(t)] + \frac{\partial}{\partial t}\hat{\rho}(t)|_{dissi} \tag{97}$$

where the square brackets denote commutators, as usual. The first term of eqn. (97) describes the dissipation-free dynamics of the excitonic system, and the second the exciton–radiational coupling. The last term in eqn. (97) contains the dissipative part due to the exciton–vibrational coupling. Different prescription schemes for the cumulant expansion have been used to obtain this dissipative part [47,95], as discussed above. In the following, the partial ordering prescription (POP) [47,102] is used, since it was shown [8,152] to be the more appropriate of the two for the description of optical spectra. Results obtained from the alternative chronological ordering prescription (COP) can be found in [8,47,50,85,100].

The dissipative part of the equation of motion obtained from second-order POP is [47]:

$$\frac{\partial}{\partial t}\hat{\rho}(t)|_{dissi} = -\frac{1}{\hbar^2} \int_0^{t-t_0} d\tau <L_{ex-vib}(t)e^{-iL_{ex}\tau}L_{ex-vib}(t-\tau)e^{iL_{ex}\tau}>\hat{\rho}(t) \tag{98}$$

where the $< >$ in eqn. (98) denotes an equilibrium average over the vibrational degrees of freedom $<\hat{O}> = Tr_{vib}\{\hat{O}W_{eq}\}$ with the $W_{eq}$ in eqn. (96). The time $t_0$ in eqn. (98) is a time for onset of an external field. For finite pulse widths the choice of $t_0$ is somewhat arbitrary. One has to cut off the pulse for earlier times, which is an approximation that is not necessary in the COP treatment [8,47,50,85,100]. Any dependence of dissipation on the intensity of the external field has been neglected in eqn. (98). The Liouville operator $L_{ex-vib}(t)$ in eqn. (98) acts on an arbitrary operator $\hat{O}$ according to $L_{ex-vib}(t)\hat{O} = [H_{ex-vib}(t), \hat{O}]$, with $H_{ex-vib}(t)$ being the exciton–vibrational Hamiltonian in the interaction representation:

$$H_{ex-vib}(t) = e^{iH_{vib}t/\hbar} H_{ex-vib} e^{-iH_{vib}t/\hbar} \tag{99}$$

## ABSORPTION OF LIGHT

To treat linear absorption, the dipole–dipole correlation function $D(t) = \langle \hat{\mu}(t)\hat{\mu}(0) \rangle$ needs to be calculated and a subsequent Fourier–Laplace transform yields the absorption spectrum:

$$\alpha(\omega) \propto \omega \Re \int_0^\infty dt\, e^{i\omega t} d(t) \qquad (100)$$

where $\Re$ denotes the real part. The dipole–dipole correlation function $d(t)$ is calculated from the off-diagonal elements of the density matrix $\rho_{M0} = \langle M|\hat{\rho}|0 \rangle$ as:

$$d(t) = \sum_M \sum_{i=x,y,z} (\mu_M)_i \rho_{M0}^{(i)}(t) \qquad (101)$$

where $(\mu_M)_i$ is the $i$th component of the transition dipole vector $\vec{\mu}_M$ in eqn. (87) and $\rho_{M0}^{(i)}(t)$ is the density matrix $\rho_{M0}(t)$ that is propagated with initial condition $\rho_{M0}(t_0 = 0) = (\mu_M)_i$. This treatment is equivalent to assuming a delta-pulse excitation at $t_0 = 0$, i.e., at earlier times the system is in its electronic ground state and the equation of motion for $\rho_{M0}(t)$ is obtained from eqn. (98) as [8]:

$$\frac{\partial}{\partial t}\rho_{M0}(t) = -i\omega_{M0}\rho_{M0}(t) - \sum_{K,L} \int_0^t d\tau\, C_{MKKL}(\tau) e^{i\omega_{LK}\tau} \rho_{L0}(t) \qquad (102)$$

where $\hbar\omega_{LK} = E_L - E_K$ and $\hbar\omega_{M0} = E_M$ with the exciton energies $E_N$ in eqn. (85). The correlation function $C_{MKKL}(\tau)$ in eqn. (102) is:

$$C_{MKKL}(t) = \sum_{mn} c_m^{(M)} c_m^{(K)} c_n^{(K)} c_n^{(L)} \langle \delta X_m(t) \delta X_n(0) \rangle \qquad (103)$$

The latter contains the eigencoefficients of exciton states $c_m^{(M)}$ and a two-site correlation function:

$$\langle \delta X_m(t) \delta X_n(0) \rangle = \langle e^{iH_{vib}t/\hbar} \delta X_m e^{-iH_{vib}t/\hbar} \delta X_n \rangle \qquad (104)$$

The time-dependence in eqn. (104) is the same as that in eqn. (99). The $\delta X_m$ is the deviation of the transition energy of the $m$th pigment from its mean value:

$$\delta X_m = X_m - \langle X_m \rangle = \sum_\xi \hbar\omega_\xi g_\xi^{(m)} Q_\xi \qquad (105)$$

as used before in eqn. (42). For $m \neq n$ eqn. (104) describes the correlation of the modulation of electronic energies at site (i.e., pigment) $m$ with that at site $n$.

To take into account such a correlation, a radius $R_c$ is introduced [8,43,44] for the protein vibrations, assuming an exponential decay for the dependence on the distance $R_{mn}$ between the pigments $m$ and $n$:

$$\langle \delta X_m(t) \delta X_n(0) \rangle = e^{-R_{mn}/R_c} \langle \delta X(t) \delta X(0) \rangle \qquad (106)$$

The $\langle \delta X_m(t) \delta X_m(0) \rangle$ has $R_{mn} = 0$ and will be assumed to be site-independent and is given by the $C(t)$ in eqn. (49). Often, the limit $R_c \to 0$ is considered, i.e., the site energies are assumed to fluctuate independently. In this case, eqn. (106) yields $\langle \delta X_m(t)\delta X_n(0)\rangle = \delta_{mn}C(t)$.

Using eqn. (106) the correlation function $C_{MKKL}(t)$ in eqn. (103) is given as:

$$C_{MKKL}(t) = \gamma_{MKKL} C(t) \tag{107}$$

with:

$$\gamma_{MKKL} = \sum_{m,n} e^{-R_{mn}/R_c} c_m^{(M)} c_m^{(K)} c_n^{(K)} c_n^{(L)} \tag{108}$$

The secular approximation [8,37,39,49], which neglects certain oscillating parts in the equation of motion by setting $L = M$ in eqn. (102), is next used. This approximation simplifies eqn. (102) to yield a homogeneous equation that can be solved analytically:

$$\frac{\partial}{\partial t} \rho_{M0}(t) = \left[ -i\omega_{M0} - \sum_K \gamma_{MK} \int_0^t d\tau C(\tau) e^{i\omega_{MK}\tau} \right] \rho_{M0}(t) \tag{109}$$

where:

$$\gamma_{MK} \equiv \gamma_{MKKM} \tag{110}$$

The solution of eqn. (109) is [8]:

$$\rho_{M0}(t) = \rho_{M0}(0) \exp\left\{ -i\omega_{M0}t - \sum_K \gamma_{MK} \int_0^t d\tau (t-\tau) C(\tau) e^{i\omega_{MK}\tau} \right\} \tag{111}$$

For simplicity, a Markov approximation will next be applied to the off-diagonal part of the exciton–vibrational coupling, namely to the terms in eqn. (111) with $K \neq M$. This approximation is valid either when the $K = M$ terms dominate the exciton–vibrational coupling ($\gamma_{MM} \gg |\gamma_{MK}|$), as is the case in the presence of static disorder [8], or when on a coarse grained time axis $t \gg 1/|\omega_{MK}|$. The latter condition follows from the oscillating factor $e^{i\omega_{MK}\tau}$ in eqn. (111), which tends to cancel the contributions to the integral for times $\tau \gg 1/|\omega_{MK}|$. The diagonal terms with $M = K$ do not contain such an oscillating factor.

The integral in eqn. (111) for the off-diagonal terms $K \neq M$ then becomes:

$$\gamma_{MK} \int_0^t d\tau (t-\tau) C(\tau) e^{i\omega_{MK}\tau} \approx \gamma_{MK} t \int_0^\infty d\tau C(\tau) e^{i\omega_{MK}\tau} = \gamma_{MK} t \tilde{C}(\omega_{MK}) \tag{112}$$

The Fourier–Laplace transform $\tilde{C}(\omega_{MK})$ of the correlation function $C(\tau)$:

$$\tilde{C}(\omega_{MK}) = \tilde{C}^{(\text{Re})}(\omega_{MK}) + i\tilde{C}^{(\text{Im})}(\omega_{MK}) \tag{113}$$

contains a real and an imaginary part. The real part $\tilde{C}(\text{Re})$ is related to the local spectral density $J(\omega)$ by [8]:

$$\tilde{C}^{(\text{Re})}(\omega) = \pi\omega^2 \{[1+n(\omega)]J(\omega) + n(-\omega)J(-\omega)\}, \tag{114}$$

with $\omega = \omega_{MK}$ and $J(\omega) = 0$ for $\omega < 0$ as seen from eqn. (51). The $n(\omega)$ is given in eqn. (45). The imaginary part $\tilde{C}^{(\text{Im})}(\omega_{MK})$ satisfies a Kramers–Kronig relation [50]:

$$\tilde{C}^{(\text{Im})}(\omega_{MK}) = \frac{1}{\pi} \wp \int_{-\infty}^{\infty} d\omega \frac{\tilde{C}^{(\text{Re})}(\omega)}{\omega_{MK} - \omega} \tag{115}$$

where $\wp$ denotes the principal part of the integral. The diagonal part of the exciton–vibrational coupling is taken into account exactly in the integral:

$$\gamma_{MM} \int_0^t d\tau (t - \tau) C(\tau) = \gamma_{MM} \left[ -i\frac{\lambda}{\hbar} t - G(t) + G(0) \right] \tag{116}$$

where the function $G(t)$ was introduced in eqn. (57) and where $\lambda$ is the reorganization energy of the local optical transitions [eqn. (30)]. The solution for $\rho_{M0}(t)$ then is:

$$\rho_{M0}(t) = \rho_{M0}(0) e^{i(\omega - \tilde{\omega}_{M0})t} \, e^{G_M(t) - G_M(0)} e^{-t/\tau_M} \tag{117}$$

where $\tilde{\omega}_{M0}$ is the $0 \to 0$ transition frequency:

$$\tilde{\omega}_{M0} = \omega_{M0} - \gamma_{MM} \lambda/\hbar + \sum_{K \neq M} \gamma_{MK} \tilde{C}^{(\text{Im})}(\omega_{MK}) \tag{118}$$

that is shifted due to the exciton–vibrational coupling with respect to the vertical transition frequency $\omega_{M0}$. The time-dependent function $G_M(t)$ in eqn. (117) is given as a product of the function $\gamma_{MM}$ in eqns. (108) and (110) and the function $G(t)$ of the local optical transitions of the pigments in eqn. (57):

$$G_M(t) = \gamma_{MM} G(t) \tag{119}$$

The inverse dephasing time $\tau_M^{-1}$ in eqn. (117) contains the function $\gamma_{MK}$ and the real part of the Fourier–Laplace transform of the correlation function of the local optical energy gap in eqn. (114):

$$\tau_M^{-1} = \sum_K \gamma_{MK} \tilde{C}^{(\text{Re})}(\omega_{MK}) \tag{120}$$

It will be shown below that this inverse dephasing time is determined by the exciton relaxation rate constants $k_{M \to K}$ and it holds $\tau_M^{-1} = \frac{1}{2} \sum_{K \neq M} k_{M \to K}$.

The absorption spectrum is next obtained from the Fourier–Laplace transform [eqn. (100)] of the dipole–dipole correlation function $d(t)$ in eqn. (101) using the $\rho_{M0}$ in eqn. (117):

$$\alpha(\omega) \propto \omega \sum_M |\mu_M|^2 D_M(\omega) \tag{121}$$

with the normalized lineshape function $D_M(\omega)$:

$$D_M(\omega) = \frac{1}{\pi} \Re \int_0^\infty dt \, e^{i(\omega - \tilde{\omega}_{M0})t} \, e^{G_M(t) - G_M(0)} e^{-t/\tau_M} \tag{122}$$

It is instructive to compare eqn. (122) with the lineshape function for absorption of a single pigment in eqn. (59). The structure of the two lineshape functions is similar. Two differences are (i) the time-dependent function $G(t)$ in eqn. (59) is replaced by the function $G_M(t) = \gamma_{MM} G(t)$ in eqn. (122), which depends on the exciton coefficients, i.e., on the delocalization of excited states, and (ii) eqn. (122) contains the dephasing time $\tau_M$ due to exciton relaxation between different states that leads to a broadening of the zero $\to$ zero line, which is absent in eqn. (59). We note that the present $D_M(\omega)$ in eqn. (122) reduces to the exact one-pigment limit $D(\omega)$ [eqn. (59)], a result that is not obtained in the alternative time-non-local COP theory.

Similar to the localized transition it is possible to extract a Huang Rhys factor $S_M$ from the function $G_M(t)$ to characterize the strength of the exciton–vibrational coupling of the optical transition [50]:

$$S_M = G_M(t=0)|_{T=0} = \gamma_{MM} S = \sum_{m,n} e^{-R_{mn}/R_c} \left[c_m^{(M)}\right]^2 \left[c_n^{(M)}\right]^2 S \qquad (123)$$

with the local Huang Rhys factor $S$ in eqn. (65). For completely delocalized vibrations ($R_c \to \infty$) the Huang Rhys factor of the exciton transition is seen to equal the local Huang Rhys factor, whereas for localized vibrations ($R_c \to 0$) it becomes $S_M = L_M^{-1} S$ where $L_M^{-1} = \sum_m (c_m^{(M)})^4$ is the inverse participation ratio that varies between 1 for localized states and $1/N_{\text{del}}$ for excites states that are delocalized over $N_{\text{del}}$ pigments. It is seen thereby that a delocalization of excited states decreases the exciton–vibrational coupling of the optical transition.

### 2.3.1.1 Markov Approximation – Redfield Theory

The Markovian limit of the above density matrix theory gives expressions of the well-known Redfield theory [37,38]. To apply this limit the upper integration limit in eqn. (109) is set to $\infty$, implying that the correlation function $C(\tau)$ in the integral decays sufficiently fast. The resulting equation for $\rho_{M0}$ then does not contain memory in the form of time-dependent coefficients as in eqn. (109):

$$\frac{\partial}{\partial t}\rho_{M0}(t) = \left[-i\tilde{\omega}_{M0} - \tau_M^{-1}\right]\rho_{M0}(t) \qquad (124)$$

where the $\tilde{\omega}_{M0}$ is given in eqn. (118) and the $\tau_M^{-1}$ in eqn. (120). The resulting integral for the lineshape function $D_M(\omega)$ equals eqn. (122), but setting $G_M(t) = G_M(0) = 0$, i.e., neglecting the function that is responsible for the vibrational sideband. The integral can be performed analytically in this case and the Markovian lineshape function is obtained as:

$$D_M(\omega) = \frac{\tau_M^{-1}}{(\omega - \tilde{\omega}_{M0})^2 + \tau_M^{-2}} \qquad (125)$$

The Lorentzian lineshape $D_M(\omega)$ contains a life time broadening that is due to exciton relaxation between the $M$th and the other exciton states.

# ABSORPTION OF LIGHT

Next, exciton relaxation is discussed in the Markov approximation. Within Markov and secular approximation, from eqn. (98) the following master equation is obtained for the population $\rho_{MM}(t)$ of the $M$th exciton state:

$$\frac{\partial}{\partial t}\rho_{MM}(t)\Big|_{diss} = -\sum_{K\neq M}[k_{M\to K}\rho_{MM}(t) - k_{K\to M}\rho_{KK}(t)] \quad (126)$$

In eqn. (126) the rate constant of exciton relaxation between states $|M\rangle$ and $|K\rangle$ was introduced as:

$$\begin{aligned}k_{M\to K} &= \gamma_{MK}\tilde{C}^{(Re)}(\omega_{MK}) \\ &= \gamma_{MK}2\pi\omega_{MK}^2\{[1+n(\omega_{MK})]J(\omega_{MK}) + n(\omega_{KM})J(\omega_{KM})\}\end{aligned} \quad (127)$$

where $J(\omega) = 0$ for $\omega < 0$, as noted before. It is seen also that the ratio of rates $k_{M\to K}$ and $k_{K\to M}$ fulfills detailed balance, i.e.:

$$\frac{k_{M\to K}}{k_{K\to M}} = \frac{1+n(\omega_{MK})}{n(\omega_{MK})} = e^{\hbar\omega_{MK}/kT} \quad (128)$$

using the $n(\omega)$ in eqn. (45). Interestingly, the spectral density $J(\omega)$ enters the rate constant $k_{M\to K}$ in eqn. (127) at the transition frequencies $\omega = \omega_{MK}$ between the states $M$ and $K$. It is seen, thereby, that the spectral density contains information about how well the protein can dissipate the electronic excess energy of excitons during relaxation. A shortcoming of the Redfield relaxation rate constant is that the vibrations are assumed to be relaxed with respect to the electronic ground state at all times and hence any reorganization of nuclei that is connected with exciton relaxation is neglected. Such effects can be described by the modified Redfield theory described below.

## 2.3.2 Modified Redfield Theory

In the modified Redfield theory the diagonal part of the exciton vibrational coupling, i.e., the $g_\xi(M,M)$ terms in eqn. (89) are taken into account non-perturbatively. Those terms define the shift of the excitonic PES $U_M$ along the coordinate axis, as seen in eqn. (92). An exact treatment of those terms therefore allows to describe the reorganization of nuclei upon exciton relaxation between different excitonic PES. The first exact treatment was given by Mukamel and co-workers [52,53] using a Brownian oscillator model [82]. Subsequently, a simpler expression for the rate constant was derived by Renger and Marcus using a harmonic oscillator model [55]. In the Brownian oscillator approach [52,53] dissipation is described by the damping of the vibrational motion of a few primary harmonic oscillators that couple to the electronic transition. The damping results from the coupling of the primary oscillators with a large number of bath oscillators. In the alternative harmonic oscillator approach [55], all oscillators couple directly to the electronic transition and dissipation occurs because of destructive interference of the many harmonic modulations of electronic energies. If the number of primary oscillators in the

Brownian oscillator approach becomes very large and the damping by the bath oscillators becomes zero the two models become equivalent, and the two expressions for the rate constants are identical (as shown in [55]). In the following, the harmonic oscillator approach [55] is summarized.

The statistical operator $\hat{W}(t)$ of the aggregate is expanded with respect to the basis $|M\rangle$ of exciton states defined above. The occupation probability $P_M$ of the state $|M\rangle$ is given as:

$$P_M(t) = tr_{\text{vib}}\{\hat{W}(t)|M\rangle\langle M|\} = tr_{\text{vib}}\{\hat{W}_{MM}(t)\} \qquad (129)$$

A perturbation theory second-order in the coupling $\hat{V}_{MN}$ between different extended states $M$ and $N$ in eqn. (89) is used to obtain a master equation for the populations $P_M(t)$:

$$\frac{d}{dt}P_M(t) = -k_{M\to N}P_M(t) + k_{N\to M}P_N(t) \qquad (130)$$

where the rate constant $k_{M\to N}$ is:

$$k_{M\to N} = \frac{1}{\hbar^2}\int_{-\infty}^{\infty} dt\, e^{i\omega_{MN}t} tr_{\text{vib}}\{U_M^\dagger(t)\,\hat{V}_{MN}\,U_N(t)\,\hat{V}_{NM}\,W_{eq}(M)\} \qquad (131)$$

The term $\omega_{MN}$ in eqn. (131) denotes the transition frequency between two vibrationally relaxed delocalized excited states [eqn. (93)]:

$$\omega_{MN} = (U_M^{(0)} - U_N^{(0)})/\hbar \qquad (132)$$

$W_{eq}(M)$ is the equilibrium statistical operator of the vibrations in the $M$th PES, and $U_M(t)$ is the respective time-evolution operator of this PES:

$$W_{eq}(M) = e^{-H_{\text{vib}}(M)/kT} \qquad (133)$$

$$U_M(t) = e^{-iH_{\text{vib}}(M)t/\hbar} \qquad (134)$$

with:

$$H_{\text{vib}}(M) = T_{\text{nucl}} + U_M \qquad (135)$$

where $U_M$ is the PES of the $M$th state defined in eqn. (92). The rate constant $k_{M\to N}$ in eqn. (131) obeys detailed balance:

$$\frac{k_{M\to N}}{k_{N\to M}} = e^{\hbar\omega_{MN}/kT} \qquad (136)$$

(This relation can be obtained by substituting $t$ by $-t - \frac{i\hbar}{kT}$ in eqn. (131), a substitution that corresponds to an interchange of the symbols $M$ and $N$.)

Since harmonic PES are assumed the rate constant $k_{M\to N}$ in eqn. (131) can be calculated without further approximation. The result is [55]:

$$k_{M\to N} = \int_{-\infty}^{\infty} d\tau\, e^{i\omega_{MN}\tau} e^{\phi_{MN}(\tau)-\phi_{MN}(0)} \left\{\left[\frac{\lambda_{MN}}{\hbar} + G_{MN}(\tau)\right]^2 + F_{MN}(\tau)\right\} \qquad (137)$$

# ABSORPTION OF LIGHT

where the time-dependent functions:

$$\phi_{MN}(t) = \sum_i (|c_i^{(M)}|^2 - |c_i^{(N)}|^2)^2 \, \phi_0(t) \tag{138}$$

$$G_{MN}(t) = \sum_i \left\{ \left[c_i^{(M)}\right]^3 c_i^{(N)} - \left[c_i^{(N)}\right]^3 c_i^{(M)} \right\} \phi_1(t) \tag{139}$$

$$F_{MN}(t) = \sum_i |c_i^{(M)}|^2 |c_i^{(N)}|^2 \, \phi_2(t). \tag{140}$$

were introduced that contain a function $\varphi_n(t)$, with $n = 0,1,2,$:

$$\phi_n(t) = \int_{-\infty}^{\infty} d\omega \, e^{-i\omega t} [1 + n(\omega)] \omega^n [J(\omega) - J(-\omega)]) \tag{141}$$

The same spectral density $J(\omega)$ for the local optical transitions of the pigments is assumed for all sites and the correlation between fluctuations at different sites is neglected, i.e., a correlation radius $R_c \to 0$ is used. The time-independent part in the integrand in eqn. (137) ($\lambda_{MN}$) is:

$$\lambda_{MN} = \sum_i \left\{ \left[c_i^{(M)}\right]^3 c_i^{(N)} + \left[c_i^{(N)}\right]^3 c_i^{(M)} \right\} \lambda \tag{142}$$

with the reorganization energy $\lambda$ of the local optical transitions given in eqn. (30). A generalization of the present result for $R_c \neq 0$ is reported in [25], where the theory was applied to study exciton relaxation among the six strongly coupled pigments of PS-II reaction centers, shown in Figure 2.

Finally, it is demonstrated that the modified Redfield rate constant in eqn. (137) reduces to the Redfield rate constant in eqn. (127) if the diagonal part of the exciton–vibrational coupling is neglected. As discussed in detail elsewhere [55] the only function in eqn. (137) that does not contain a diagonal part of the coupling (which is now assumed to vanish) is the $F_{MN}(t)$ in eqn. (140). After setting all other functions zero, eqn. (137) becomes $k_{M \to N} = \int_{-\infty}^{\infty} d\tau \, e^{i\omega_{MN}\tau} F_{MN}(\tau)$. If the $F_{MN}(t)$ in eqn. (140) is introduced and integration over $\tau$ is carried out, the rate constant reads $k_{M \to N} = 2\pi \gamma_{MN} \omega_{MN}^2 [1 + n(\omega_{MN})][J(\omega_{MN}) - J(\omega_{NM})]$, where $\gamma_{MN}$ is given in eqns. (108) and (110), and is used here in the limit $R_c \to 0$. By noting that $-[1 + n(\omega_{MK})] = n(\omega_{KM})$, the equality of the above rate constant with the Redfield result in eqn. (127) is seen.

### 2.3.3 Generalized Förster Theory

If weakly coupled donor and acceptor states are themselves formed by strongly coupled pigments, the Förster theory has to be modified, in the case where the extension of the donor and (or) acceptor aggregates is in the range of the center to center distance of the donor and acceptor. The excitonic coupling $V_{M_D N_A}$ between aggregate state $|M_D\rangle$ of the donor and aggregate state $|N_A\rangle$ of the acceptor is given in terms of a linear combination of local couplings $V_{m_D n_A}$ between monomer transition dipole moments $\mu_{m_D}$ and $\mu_{n_A}$ of the molecules that form the aggregates, [57]:

$$V_{M_D N_A} = \sum_{m_D, n_A} c_{m_D}^{(M_D)} c_{n_A}^{(N_A)} V_{m_D n_A} \qquad (143)$$

where $c_{m_D}^{(M_D)}$ and $c_{n_A}^{(N_A)}$ are the exciton coefficients of the two aggregate states $|M_D\rangle$ and $|N_A\rangle$. If the center to center distance between the donor and acceptor aggregates is large compared with their individual extensions, the distance vector between monomer $m_D$ and monomer $n_A$ approximately equals the center to center distance vector between the two aggregates, $\vec{R}_{m_D n_A} \approx \vec{R}$, and in this case the coupling $V_{M_D N_A} \approx \frac{\vec{\mu}_{M_D} \vec{\mu}_{N_A}}{R^3} - \frac{(\vec{\mu}_{M_D} \vec{R})(\vec{\mu}_{N_A} \vec{R})}{R^5}$ is given as the dipole–dipole coupling of the exciton transition dipoles $\vec{\mu}_{M_D}$ and $\vec{\mu}_{N_A}$ of the two aggregates, i.e., the conventional Förster theory discussed in Section 2.2.4 is recovered, in the sense that the two aggregates behave like two molecules in Förster-type excitation energy transfer. However, if the donor–acceptor distance gets smaller, the above approximation becomes invalid and also optically dark exciton states, i.e., those with vanishing dipole moment, can contribute significantly to the transfer.

This idea has been applied to study excitation energy transfer in chlorosomes of green bacteria [57], to explain the ultrafast exciton transfer between the B800 and B850 states in the LH2 antenna of purple bacteria [59–61], and to study excitation energy transfer between the two peripheral chlorophylls Chlz and the six central pigments in the PS-II reaction center [25] (Figure 2). A still somewhat open question is how to describe the part of the rate constant that describes in essence the thermally averaged overlap of vibrational wavefunctions of the initial and final states. General formally exact expressions have been derived by Sumi [58] and by Jang, Newton, and Silbey [61]. However, for practical applications additional approximations have to be made, even in the simple case of a localized donor state $|m_D\rangle$ and an aggregate acceptor state $|N_A\rangle$. In this case the rate constant is given as:

$$k_{m_D \to N_A} = 2\pi \frac{|V_{m_D N_A}|^2}{\hbar^2} \int_{-\infty}^{\infty} d\omega D_I^{(m_D)}(\omega) D_\alpha^{(N_A)}(\omega) \qquad (144)$$

where $D_\alpha^{(N_A)}(\omega)$ is the lineshape function of absorption of the aggregate state, $D_I^{(m_D)}(\omega)$ is the fluorescence lineshape function of the localized state, and $V_{m_D N_A} = \sum_{n_A} V_{m_D n_A} c_{n_A}^{(N_A)}$ is the excitonic coupling between the two states. Mukai, Abe and Sumi [59] used a Green's function technique to obtain the lineshape function of the aggregate, whereas Jang and Silbey [61] solve a second order non-Markovian quantum master equation. The two results are identical in secular approximation. Jang and Silbey's theory also contains non-secular terms, which, however, for the system studied were found to be small [61]. The lineshape functions used in the two theories correspond to time-non-local COP

# ABSORPTION OF LIGHT

expressions. Scholes and Fleming have chosen a different approach [60], using three pulse photon echo experiments to estimate the lineshape functions. Their expression is similar to the POP theory discussed above.

## 2.4 Extraction of Parameters

To calculate charge and excitation energy transfer reactions, the couplings, spectral densities and local energies (optical transition energies and redox potentials) are needed. The following discusses how the different parameters can be obtained either from independent experiments [$J(\omega)$ for excitation energy transfer], molecular dynamics simulations [$J(\omega)$ for electron transfer], fit of optical spectra (excitation energies), structural data (excitation energy transfer couplings), by empirical formulae and quantum chemical calculations (electron transfer couplings) and by quantum chemical/electrostatic calculations (redox potentials).

### 2.4.1 Spectral Density of Excitation Energy Transfer and Optical Spectra

The spectral density $J(\omega)$ entering eqns. (114) and (141 → 137) for the different rate constants in excitation energy transfer theories can be extracted from homogeneous optical lineshapes [8], as will be shown in the following. Because of disorder effects, the homogeneous lineshapes of pigments in ordinary absorption experiments are hidden under the inhomogeneous broadening. In hole burning and fluorescence line narrowing spectroscopy the homogenous lineshape becomes accessible by site-selective excitation. In the following, we consider fluorescence line-narrowing spectra of the B777 complex in Figure 1, measured by Creemers et al. [10] at 1.6 K. A simplifying feature of the experiments [10] on the B777 complex is that the specific interaction occurs between a single pigment and the protein, rather than involving in addition larger aggregate pigment–pigment and pigment–protein interactions. As discussed at the end of this section the spectral density of larger complexes appears to be very similar to that of the B777 complex.

In fluorescence line narrowing spectroscopy the fluorescence signal $I(\omega,\omega_{exc})$ of selectively excited pigments depends on the excitation energy $\hbar\omega_{exc}$ [77]:

$$I(\omega, \omega_{exc}) = \int_{-\infty}^{\infty} d\omega_{eg} \, \alpha_h(\omega_{exc}, \omega_{eg}) \, I_h(\omega, \omega_{eg}) \, P_{inh}(\omega_{eg} - \bar{\omega}_{eg}) \qquad (145)$$

where $\alpha_h$ and $I_h$ are the homogeneous absorption and fluorescence spectra, respectively, of the complex, where $\omega_{eg}$ is the (0 → 0) transition frequency of the pigment. A Gaussian distribution function $P_{inh}(\omega_{eg} - \bar{\omega}_{eg})$ is assumed, for the inhomogeneity in 0 → 0 transition frequencies $\omega_{eg}$ of the complexes in the sample, with a maximum at $\bar{\omega}_{eg}$.

Introducing the results for the homogeneous absorption and fluorescence lineshape functions eqns. (63) and (64) into eqn. (145), yields the fluorescence line narrowing spectrum detected at a frequency $\omega$, after the sample was excited at a frequency $\omega_{exc}$ [8]:

$$I(\omega, \omega_{exc}) \sim e^{-2G(0)} \delta(\omega - \omega_{exc}) P_{inh}(\omega_{exc} - \bar{\omega}_{eg})$$
$$+ e^{-G(0)} \phi(\omega_{exc} - \omega) (P_{inh}(\omega_{exc} - \bar{\omega}_{eg}) + P_{inh}(\omega - \bar{\omega}_{eg})) \qquad (146)$$
$$+ \int d\omega_{eg} \, \phi(\omega_{exc} - \omega_{eg}) \phi(\omega_{eg} - \omega) P_{inh}(\omega_{eg} - \bar{\omega}_{eg})$$

The first term on the right-hand side in eqn. (146) is the resonant fluorescence at the excitation wavelength and originates from the $0 \to 0$ transitions $\delta(\omega_{exc} - \omega_{eg})$ in absorption followed by the $0 \to 0$ transition $\delta(\omega - \omega_{eg})$ in fluorescence.

The second term on the right-hand side of eqn. (146) contains two types of sidebands: The first arises from excitation of the $0 \to 0$ transition $\delta(\omega_{exc} - \omega_{eg})$ followed by fluorescence, yielding the sideband $\varphi(\omega_{eg} - \omega)$, and the second from excitation of the sideband $\varphi(\omega_{exc} - \omega_{eg})$ and followed by fluorescence at the $0 \to 0$ transition $\delta(\omega - \omega_{eg})$. The last term on the right-hand hand side of eqn. (146) contains excitation of a sideband and fluorescence to a sideband.

The above expression simplifies when the pigment–protein coupling is weak. This case was used as a first step in an iterative procedure to extract $J(\omega)$ from the data: For weak coupling the shape of the vibrational sideband $\varphi(\omega)$ at low temperatures is the same as that of the spectral density $J(\omega)$, as can be seen by approximating $e^{G(t)} - 1$ by $G(t)$ in eqn. (63) and setting $n(\omega) = 0$ in eqn. (57). Further, since the vibrational sideband in absorption at low temperatures must be only on the high-energy side of the $0 \to 0$ transition, a $0 \to 0$ transition is the major contributor to the low-energy wing of the absorption spectrum. In this case the shape of the vibrational sideband in fluorescence line narrowing spectra is given by the $\varphi(\omega_{exc} - \omega)$ appearing in eqn. (146). The following strategy was therefore chosen to extract $J(\omega)$ from the spectrum.

The shape of the sideband in the fluorescence line narrowing spectrum excited in the low-energy wing of the absorption spectrum was used as a first guess for the spectral density $J(\omega)$. An empirical functional form that is an extension of earlier [7,42,43,50,84,86] functional forms was used for $J(\omega)$:

$$J(\omega) = \sum_{i=1,2} s_i k_i \omega^q e^{-(\omega/\omega_i)^p} \qquad (147)$$

It contains the parameters $s_i$, $\omega_i$, $p$ and $q$. The $k_i = p/\{\omega_i^{(q+1)} \Gamma[(q+1)/p]\}$ are normalization factors, and the sum $s_1 + s_2$ equals $S$ of $J(\omega)$ in eqn. (65). An initial value $S = 1$ was used, typical for pigment–protein complexes as discussed before. The fit was iterated by next calculating $\phi(\omega)$ in eqns. (57–64) numerically and then calculating the spectrum from eqn. (146). This fit was performed for the lowest excitation energy $\hbar\omega_{exc}$ used in the experiment. Using this first estimate for the shape of $J(\omega)$, the $S = s_1 + s_2$ was varied next to fit the dependence of $I(\omega, \omega_{exc})$ on the excitation frequency $\omega_{exc}$ in eqn. (146). At higher excitation energies the last contribution in eqn. (146) involving sidebands

# ABSORPTION OF LIGHT

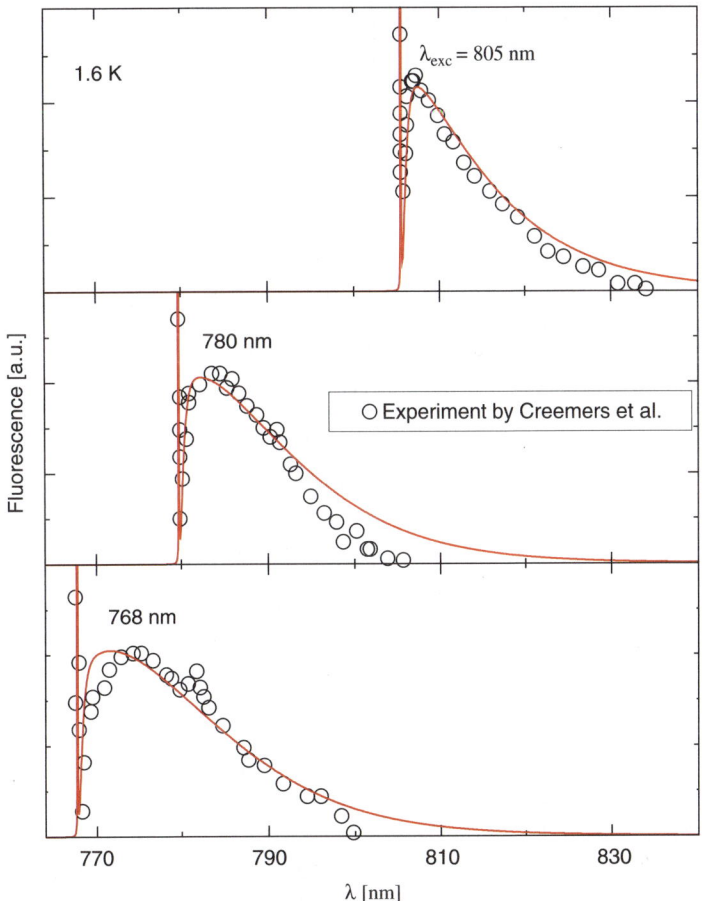

**Figure 8.** 1.6-K Fluorescence line narrowing spectra of the B777 complex (structure shown in Figure 1). Experimental data by Creemers et al. [10] are shown as circles, and calculations [8], using the spectral density in Figure 9, as solid lines.

in absorption and in emission becomes important and leads to a broadening of the sideband seen in the spectrum in Figure 8. Since the weight of the sidebands is determined by $S$ this broadening effect can be used to estimate $S$.

The $J(\omega)$ so-determined is shown in the upper part of Figure 9. The optimized parameters are $s_1 = 0.8$, $s_2 = 0.5$, $\hbar\omega_1 = 0.069$ meV, $\hbar\omega_2 = 0.24$ meV, $p = 0.5$, $q = 3$. For $p = 0.5$ and $q = 3$ the spectral density eqn. (147) is:

$$J(\omega) = \sum_{i=1,2} \frac{s_i}{7!2\omega_i^4} \omega^3 e^{-(\omega/\omega_i)^{1/2}} \qquad (148)$$

The maxima of the two contributions in the above sum occur at frequencies $36\omega_i$, i.e., at 20 and 70 cm$^{-1}$. Because $s_1 > s_2$ the first maximum determines the maximum of $J(\omega)$ in Figure 9.

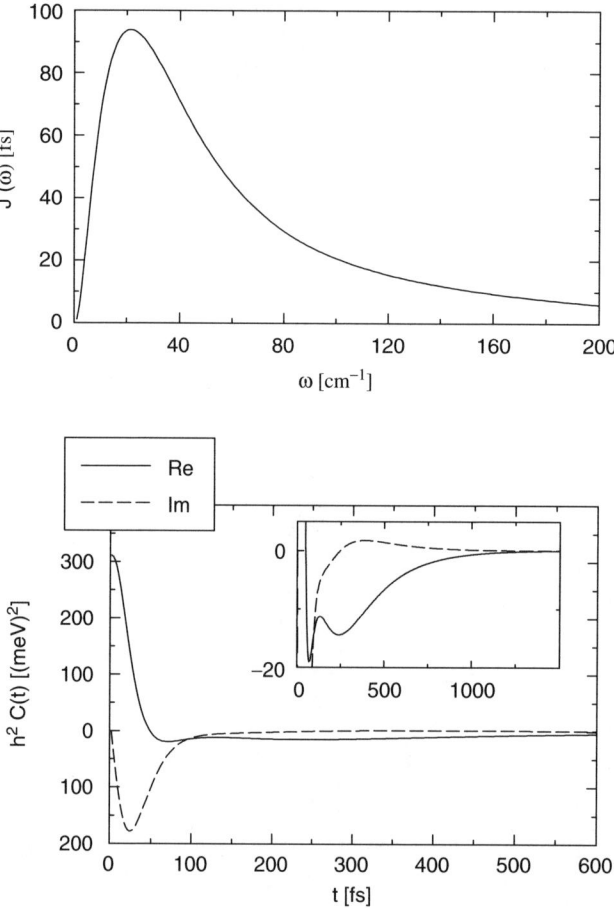

**Figure 9.** Upper part: Spectral density $J(\omega)$ for optical transition of the B777 complex extracted from the fit of fluorescence line narrowing spectra shown in Figure 8. Lower part: Real and imaginary part of the correlation function $C(t)$ [eqns. (49) and (51)], of the transition energy. Inset: an enlarged view on the slowly decaying part of $C(t)$.

From the spectral density the correlation function of the optical energy gap of the B777 complex is obtained from eqn. (49), using eqn. (51). As seen in the lower part of Figure 9 the real part of $C(t)$ exhibits a strongly damped oscillation. It and the imaginary part of $C(t)$ are essentially zero after about 100 fs. Approximately 5% of the initial correlation is seen in the inset of Figure 9 to decay on a 500 fs time scale.

The density of vibrational states $\sum_\xi \delta(\omega - \omega_\xi)$ of protein vibrations was recently extracted by Pieper et al. [103a] from their neutron diffraction experiments on the light harvesting complex LHC-II of photosystem II. An interesting finding is that the functional form of the density of states resembles closely the form of the spectral density of the low energy optical transition

# ABSORPTION OF LIGHT

inferred earlier from hole burning spectra [7]. Hence, a rather uniform coupling strength can be assumed for the different vibrational modes. The spectral density of the LHC-II complex [7] is similar to that of the B777 complex in Figure 9. There is a dominant contribution from low-frequency protein vibrations.

By noting the similarity of the one pigment lineshape function $D(\omega)$ in eqn. (59) and the larger aggregate exciton lineshape function $D_M(\omega)$ in eqn. (122), it is clear that also for larger aggregates, for weak exciton vibrational coupling, the shape of the vibrational sideband should resemble the spectral density. A comparison of the fluorescence line narrowing spectrum measured [103b] on FMO-complexes and the spectral density $J(\omega)$ extracted above for the B777 complex is shown in the upper part of Figure 10. The similarity of the two curves indicates that the exciton–vibrational coupling is very similar also in the FMO complex.

A functional reason for the similarity of the spectral density in different antenna complexes might be that is optimized to dissipate the excess energy of excitons during relaxation, and this excess energy is similar in different complexes. In the lower part of Figure 10 the function $\tilde{C}^{(\text{Re})}(\omega) \propto \omega^2 J(\omega)$ which enters the rate constant of exciton relaxation in eqn. (127) at the transition frequencies $\omega = \omega_{MN}$ between different exciton states is shown together with the energy differences between exciton states in the FMO complex. As seen there, the function $\tilde{C}^{(\text{Re})}(\omega)$ covers the whole range of transition energies, i.e., the $J(\omega)$ is optimized for exciton relaxation.

It is clearly one of the challenges to calculate the spectral density directly from structural data. Schulten's group has provided a first attempt using a combination of molecular dynamics and quantum chemical calculations [104]. Despite the enormous numerical effort (the MD simulations included also a lipid layer and water layers; altogether 87055 atoms), the spectral density calculated has a maximum at about $1600\,\text{cm}^{-1}$, i.e., at about two orders of magnitude larger energies than the spectral density that was extracted above from optical spectra. One reason for the discrepancy might be a too simplified treatment of the protein by background charges.

## 2.4.2 Spectral Density for Electron Transfer: The Dispersed Polaron Model

In the case of electron transfer there are no experiments that can be used for an extraction of the spectral density. Warshel et al. have suggested a method that uses classical MD simulations to extract the spectral density of proteins in electron transfer reactions [9,68]. Their approach, which is known as the dispersed polaron model, will be briefly described in the following. The $J(\omega)$ can be extracted by solving the classical equations of motion for sufficiently high temperature, i.e., average kinetic energy on the initial potential energy surface, and by monitoring the time-dependent energy gap $X(t)$ between the initial and final state of the reaction. If this energy gap has been calculated for a large set of thermally distributed initial coordinates the correlation function $C_{\text{cl}}(t)$ of this energy gap is calculated. From eqn. (31) it is seen that the spectral

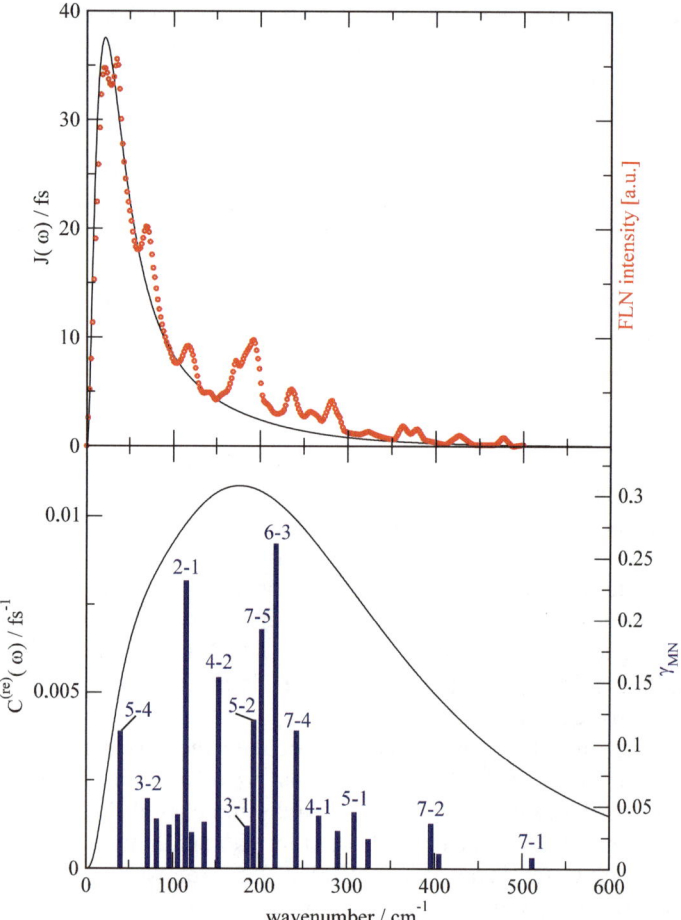

**Figure 10.** Upper part: Spectral density $J(\omega)$ for optical transition of the B777 complex, extracted from the fit of fluorescence line narrowing spectra in Figure 8, in comparison with fluorescence line narrowing spectra measured on FMO complexes of *Chlorobium tepidum*. Lower part: Resulting function $\tilde{C}^{(\text{Re})}(\omega)$ (Eq. 127). Bars of height $\gamma_{MN}$ are positioned at the disorder averaged transition energies between exciton states $M$ and $N$ of the FMO complex.

density $J(\omega)$ can be obtained from $C_{\text{cl}}(t)$ by a Fourier transform $J(\omega) = \hbar/(2\pi kT\omega)\int dt e^{i\omega t}C_{\text{cl}}(t)$. An important property of $J(\omega)$ is its relation to the reorganization energy $\lambda$ in eqn. (30). The numerically obtained $J(\omega)$ is correct up to a constant factor. To determine the factor and hence the complete $J(\omega)$ one has to estimate the reorganization energy of the reaction in an independent way, as described below, and use eqn. (30).

The strength of the dispersed polaron model lies in the fact that once the spectral density is known the low-temperature quantum behavior can also be calculated [eqns. (37, 50)] [9].

# ABSORPTION OF LIGHT

## 2.4.3 Reorganization Energy of Electron Transfer from Microscopic Simulations

To determine the reorganization energy $\lambda$ of electron transfer reactions the free-energy surfaces of the reactant and product states are calculated first. Using the energy gap $X$ as a generalized reaction coordinate the free-energy surface of the initial (reactant) state $\Delta g_i(X)$ is obtained from [73]:

$$\Delta g_i(X) = -kT \ln(P(X)_i) \tag{149}$$

where $P(X)_i$ is the probability that a certain value $X$ of the energy gap occurs during a propagation of trajectories on the potential energy surface of the initial state. A similar expression is obtained for the free-energy surface $\Delta g_f(X)$ of the final (product) state from trajectories propagated in the potential energy surface of the latter. Both are related by [105]:

$$\Delta g_f(X) = \Delta g_i(X) + X \tag{150}$$

i.e., the energy gap $X$ equals the free-energy difference between the two states. Once the free-energy surfaces have been calculated the reorganization energy is extracted from those curves as the free energy of the final state at the equilibrium position $X$ of the initial state. For fast electron transfer reactions, for which the reaction barrier is small, the probability $P(X)_i$ can be obtained directly from a molecular dynamics simulation. For large barriers the simulation time required to bring the system often enough to the transition state of equal free energies would be too long. A combination of free energy perturbation and an umbrella sampling method can be used in this case. The idea is to force the system to the transition state by adding an artificial potential (see [73] and references cited therein).

However, for fast electron transfer reactions the first more direct method has the advantage [105] that it takes into account the fact that electron transfer might be faster than some slow conformational relaxation and that, therefore, not the whole conformational subspace of the initial state is sampled prior to electron transfer. The free energy perturbation method, in contrast, assumes fast equilibration of all conformations of the initial state.

## 2.4.4 Excitonic Coupling

Excitonic coupling involves Coulomb coupling between a pigment in an excited electronic state and another pigment in the ground state. This coupling between the pigments is responsible for the non-radiative transition of excitation energy between the pigments, a mechanism that was first proposed by Förster [34]. The respective excitation energy transfer matrix element $V_{mn}$ reads:

$$V_{mn} = <\phi_m^{(e)} \phi_n^{(g)} | V_{\text{Coulomb}} | \phi_m^{(g)} \phi_n^{(e)}> \tag{151}$$

where $\phi_k^{(e)}$ and $\phi_k^{(g)}$ denote the excited and ground state wavefunctions of pigment $k = m, n$, and $V_{\text{Coulomb}}$ is the Coulomb coupling between the electrons and nuclei of the two pigments.

### 2.4.4.1 Point-Dipole Approximation

If the extension of the electronic wavefunctions of the pigments is small when compared with the center to center distance between the pigments, $V_{\text{Coulomb}}$ can be expanded in a Taylor series and the first non-vanishing element of that series is the well-known point-dipole approximation (e.g., [106]):

$$V_{mn} = \frac{\vec{\mu}_m \vec{\mu}_n}{R_{ab}^3} - 3\frac{(\vec{\mu}_m \vec{R}_{mn})(\vec{\mu}_n \vec{R}_{mn})}{R_{mn}^5} \quad (152)$$

where $\vec{\mu}_m$ and $\vec{\mu}_n$ are the optical transition dipoles of the two pigments and $\vec{R}_{mn}$ is the center to center spatial vector between the two pigments. Equation (152) expresses the excitonic coupling as the dipole–dipole coupling between optical transition dipoles. The orientations of transition dipoles of photosynthetic pigments and distance vectors can be obtained from structural data. The $Q_y$ transition dipole moment of chlorophylls and bacteriochlorophylls is known to be approximately oriented along the $N_B \rightarrow N_D$ axis (a quantum chemical verification is given, for example, in [107]). The dipole strengths are estimated [108] from optical spectra measured on (bacterio)chlorophylls in different solvents. Therefore, the above equation provides a very practical tool to estimate excitonic couplings. In eqn. (152), screening effects of the Coulomb coupling and local field corrections (for a discussion of the latter see, for example, [106]) can be included in an effective way by rescaling the dipole strengths.

### 2.4.4.2 Extended-Dipole Approximation

Within the above point-dipole approximation the optical transition dipoles of the pigments are treated as ideal point-dipoles. A first correction of this approximation, which can take into account a certain extension of the electronic wavefunctions of the pigments, is the extended dipole approximation where the optical transition dipoles of the pigments are described by two partial charges of opposite sign $\delta q_m^\pm$ that are placed along the direction of the optical transition dipoles of the pigments in a distance $l$ that effectively describes the extension of the electronic wavefunctions. The charges $\delta q_m^\pm$ are chosen such as to result in the (effective) dipole strength $|\mu_m|^2 = (l\delta q_m^\pm)^2$ of the optical transition. The excitonic coupling is then obtained from the Coulomb interaction between the point charges of the two pigments $m$ and $n$:

$$V_{mn} = \sum_{i,j=\pm} \frac{\delta q_m^i \delta q_n^j}{|\mathbf{r}_m^i - \mathbf{r}_n^j|} \quad (153)$$

where $|\mathbf{r}_m^i - \mathbf{r}_n^j|$ is the distance between the partial charges $\delta q_m^i$ and $\delta q_n^j$. The extent $l$ of the dipole is not exactly known. Madjet et al. [107] suggest, based on a comparison of extended dipole couplings with couplings obtained by a quantum chemical method, the use of $l = 8.5\,\text{Å}$. This value was obtained for the special pairs of three reaction centers that have similar geometry.

## ABSORPTION OF LIGHT

*2.4.4.3 Transition Density Quantum Chemical Methods*
If the closest distance between pigments becomes comparable or smaller than the extension of their electronic wavefunctions the above approximations become invalid and the excitonic coupling has to be calculated by a quantum chemical method. For this purpose the coupling $V_{mn}$ is written in terms of a Coulomb coupling between transition densities:

$$V_{mn} = \int d\mathbf{r}_1 d\mathbf{r}_2 \rho_m(\mathbf{r}_1) \frac{1}{|\mathbf{r}_1 - \mathbf{r}_2|} \rho_n(\mathbf{r}_2) \tag{154}$$

where the transition density of pigment $m$ is defined as an integral of the product of the ground- and excited-state wavefunctions $\phi_g^m$ and $\phi_e^m$, respectively:

$$\rho_m(\mathbf{r}_1) = \int_s ds \int d\mathbf{r}_2 \ldots d\mathbf{r}_N \phi_g^m(\mathbf{r}_1, \mathbf{r}_2 \ldots \mathbf{r}_N)(\phi_e^m)^*(\mathbf{r}_1, \mathbf{r}_2 \ldots \mathbf{r}_N) \tag{155}$$

The integration in eqn. (155) is over the $N$ spin and $N-1$ spacial degrees of freedom.

Once, those transition densities are calculated by a quantum chemical method, different ways exist to evaluate the excitonic coupling. One way is to approximate this coupling by the Coulomb interaction between transition charges of the two pigments. The latter are obtained from the transition densities by integration over certain volume elements. In the transition monopole method [109,110] the transition charges are obtained for every atom of a pigment from the atomic expansion coefficients of the molecular $\pi$-orbitals, using a semi-empirical Pariser–Parr–Pople method.

In the transition density cube (TDC) method [111] the space around each pigment is divided into cubes by a three-dimensional (3D) grid and the integral in eqn. (154) is performed numerically. The numerical integration converges for small cube sizes, i.e., volume elements. For chlorophylls and bacteriochlorophylls about 500000 cubes per pigment are necessary. In the alternative TrEsp approach [107] atomic transition charges are determined from a fit of the electrostatic potential of the quantum chemical transition density. This method contains the full 3D information of the molecular transition density, because the alternative TDC couplings were found to converge against the TrEsp results for small volume elements. The TrEsp method is numerically more efficient than the TDC method. The transition density in those methods is obtained from ab initio calculations.

*2.4.5 Electron Transfer Coupling*

Numerous theoretical methods can be applied to calculate electron transfer couplings [112–121]. However, it is not trivial to extract the coupling from experimental data to check the quality of a theoretical method. One way is the study of non-adiabatic electron transfer reactions at different driving forces $\Delta G^\circ$.

From eqn. (70) it is seen that for $\Delta G^\circ = -\lambda$ the classical rate constant takes its maximum value:

$$k = \frac{|V_{if}|^2}{\sqrt{4\pi\lambda kT}} \qquad (156)$$

and the coupling is obtained from the rate constant $k$ and the reorganization energy $\lambda$. Dutton and co-workers [118,119] have performed an extensive analysis of electron transfer reactions in different proteins and found that the coupling roughly varies as $\exp(-\beta R)$ with donor–acceptor distance $R$, and $\beta \approx 1.4\,\text{Å}^{-1}$ [118]. They found a simple empirical expression for the logarithm of the rate constant [118]:

$$\log_{10} k = 15 - 0.6R - 3.1(\Delta G^0 + \lambda)^2/\lambda \qquad (157)$$

that was later refined to [119]:

$$\log_{10} k = 13.0 - (1.2 - 0.8\rho)(R - 3.6) - 3.1(\Delta G^0 + \lambda)^2/\lambda \qquad (158)$$

The latter expression includes more microscopic information, in the form of a packing density $\rho$ that characterizes the medium between the redox active cofactors. For fully packed media $\rho = 1$ and in vacuum $\rho = 0$, giving rise to $\beta$ values of 0.9 and 2.8 Å$^{-1}$, respectively. The packing density was virtually the same for redox active ($\rho = 0.76 \pm 0.1$, $\beta = 1.39 \pm 0.15$) as for redox inactive ($\rho = 0.76 \pm 0.06$) parts of the protein.

The Dutton ruler is an excellent starting point for the estimation of electron transfer couplings, but the inclusion of more microscopic information is desirable. It seems reasonable to assume that not only the density but also the energetics of the intervening medium is important for the electronic coupling in long-range electron transfer reactions. The intervening medium provides electronic states that are important for the superexchange coupling between the cofactors.

Beratan, Betts and Onuchic have developed a so-called tunneling-pathway model and predicted [120] that tunneling through β-sheet proteins is faster than through α-helical proteins, a prediction verified later by Gray and co-workers [122,123]. They found [122,123] $\beta$ values of 0.9–1.15 Å$^{-1}$ for β-sheet proteins and 1.25–1.6 Å$^{-1}$ for α helical proteins. More theoretical references on the role of the intervening medium can be found in [123]. An elegant theoretical so-called tunneling currents method for the calculation of the electronic coupling in complex systems has been developed by Stuchebrukhov and co-workers [121]. It has been implemented on different levels of quantum theoretical description for the intervening medium (from extended Hückel to density functional theory).

### 2.4.6 Local Excitation Energies of Pigments

Besides static and dynamic disorder caused by slow and fast protein dynamics, there is a specific change of the transition energy of every pigment due to the different protein environments. The local excitation energies of the pigments, which are commonly called site energies, are important parameters in the calculations of optical spectra and excitation energy transfer reactions. Different pigment–protein interactions are assumed to influence the spectroscopic properties of the pigments, (i) electrostatic interactions with charged and aromatic amino acid side chains [124,125], (ii) differences in $Mg^{2+}$ ligation [126], (iii) differences in H-bonding [127–130], (iv) differences in the conformation of the pigment, e.g., the degree of planarity and the rotation angle of substituents [131,132]. A direct calculation of transition energies of pigments in the protein is difficult [125,132] because of the complexity of the above interactions. Often, therefore, the site energies are treated as parameters that are determined from the fit of optical spectra.

There is one pigment–protein complex, the so-called Fenna–Mathews–Olson (FMO) complex of green sulfur bacteria, that has been extensively used as a model system for larger antenna complexes, starting over 25 years ago with the pioneering work of Pearlstein [133] and co-workers. The FMO complex consists of a trimer formed by three identical monomers that each bind seven bacteriochlorophyll $a$ (BChl$a$) molecules (Figure 3).

Different sets of site energies of the seven BChl$a$ molecules have been extracted in the past from calculations of optical spectra [134–139,43], using different fit algorithms or simply "by hand". Until now, the best agreement between calculated and experimental spectra has been obtained by Vulto et al. [137,138] for the FMO-complex of *C. tepidum* and by Wendling et al. [139] for *P. aestuarii*. In both cases bacteriochlorophyll number 3 (BChl 3) was identified as the one with the lowest site energy. The crucial point of the above studies was the use of a smaller dipole strength of BChl$a$ [137] in the calculations of the excitonic couplings than assumed previously. An explanation was given for the low effective dipole strength of the optical transitions of the bacteriochlorophylls from electrostatic calculations of the excitonic couplings, taking into account a continuum dielectric of the protein with optical dielectric constant $n^2 = 2$ [140]. There is one study on the FMO-complex that tried to obtain the relative shift of site energies directly, from semi-empirical quantum chemical calculations [132]. Different factors as non-planarity of the bacteriochlorophyll, rotation of the acetyl group and charged amino acids (all charged amino acids within 5.5 Å of the pigments were included) were discussed, but the calculated site energies do not describe the experimental spectra.

A simple electrostatic method has been used in [140] to estimate electrochromic shifts of pigment transition energies of the FMO complex due to charged amino acids, assuming a standard protonation pattern of the titratable amino acid residues. The charged amino acids were represented by point charges and the site energy shifts were obtained from the Coulomb coupling of those charges with the dipole moment of the difference charge density between the excited and the ground state of the pigments. From the electrochromic shifts of five pigments with histidine ligands and a partial fit of the site energies of two pigments with different ligands the experimental absorption, linear dichroism and circular dichroism spectra at cryogenic temperature (5 K) could be explained, including the differences between the two species. Recently we used a combined quantum chemical/electrostatic approach to calculate the site energies without using a partial fit. It turned out that the most important factor is the charge density coupling between the protein and the ground and excited states of the pigments. It particular it was found that certain parts of the protein backbone determine the sink of the excitation energy in the FMO-complex [153].

In a quantum chemical study by the Fleming's group [125] the 96 site energies of photosystem I have been calculated using a semiempirical INDO/S method. In the calculations a pick criteria was used for the inclusion of protein-residues and water molecules: All atoms within 2.5 Å of any chlorophyll atom were included in the quantum chemical calculations. By comparing the site energies obtained with and without protein residues it was found that charged and aromatic residues have a large effect on the site energies – shifts of up to 18 nm were reported [125]. The titratable residues in the protein were chosen to be in their standard protonation state. To quantify the effect of charge resonance interactions of strongly coupled chlorophylls, dimer calculations were compared with monomer calculations and the energies obtained in the two calculations were related by an effective Hamiltonian that takes into account the excitonic coupling and a shift of the transition energies of the monomers that is caused by the inter monomer charge resonance interactions. Additional shifts of up to 12 nm were obtained [125] in this way. The absorption spectrum calculated using those 96 site energies looks qualitatively similar to the measured spectrum. A short coming of this approach is that only a small part of the protein environment can be considered in the quantum chemical calculations.

*2.4.7 Redox Potentials*

Knapp and co-workers have developed an electrostatic/quantum chemical method to calculate the redox potentials of cofactors in proteins [141–144]. The method contains a description in atomic detail of the whole pigment–protein complex, including the thermally fluctuating protonation pattern of the titratable amino acid residues. The wavefunctions of the reduced (oxidized) state and the neutral state of the cofactor are calculated quantum chemically and the resulting electrostatic potential is approximated by two sets of partial charges, one for the reduced (oxidized) state and one for the neutral state. Those partial charges are used together with atomic partial charges of the protein in electrostatic free energy calculations, solving a linear Poisson–Boltzmann equation with the program MEAD from Bashford and Karplus [145]. The partial charges of the protein are adopted from the all-atom parameter set of the molecular mechanics program CHARMM [146]. The titratable groups in the protein are represented by two sets of charges, one for the protonated and one for the deprotonated state. The conformational flexibility and the electronic polarizability of the protein are treated effectively by assuming a homogeneous dielectric, which is usually described by a dielectric constant $\varepsilon = 4$. The calculations provide the redox potential shift due to the transfer of the cofactor-molecule from the solvent into the protein environment. Hence, experimental redox potentials of the cofactor-molecules in the solvent are used to obtain the redox potentials in the protein. An important part of the calculations concerns a thermodynamic average over the possible protonation states of the protein, performed numerically by a Monte Carlo method using the program Karlsberg [147]. Recently, an answer was given to the long-standing question of why the three photosynthetic reaction centers, despite their very similar structure, have very different redox potentials [148]. Three important electrostatic interactions were identified [148], which enable the special chlorophyll pair P680 in photosystem II to develop a sufficiently high redox power for water splitting. These interactions involve the $Mn_4Ca$ cluster, the other cofactors, and the dipole moments of a transmembrane helix backbone [148].

## Acknowledgements

It is a pleasure to acknowledge support by the Deutsche Forschungsgemeinschaft through Emmy-Noether research grant RE 1610 and through the collaborative research centers Sfb 498 and Sfb 429. I thank G. Renger and Frank Müh for comments and discussions.

## References

1. Y. Georgievskii, C.-P. Hsu, R.A. Marcus, Linear response in electron transfer reactions as an alternative to the molecular harmonic oscillator model. *J. Chem. Phys.* **110** (1999) 5307–5317.
2. Z.T. Chu, A. Warshel, W.W. Parson, Microscopic simulation of quantum dynamics and nuclear tunneling in bacterial reaction centers. *Photosynth. Res* **22** (1989) 39–46.
3. R.F. Loring, Y.J. Yan, S. Mukamel, Time-resolved fluorescence and hole burning line shape of solvated molecules-longitudinal dielectric relaxation and vibrational dynamics. *J. Chem. Phys.* **87** (1987) 5840–5857.
4. D. Chandler, in: *Liquids, Freezing, and Glass Transition* (1991) (J.P. Hansen, D. Levesque, J. Zinn-Justin, eds.), Elsevier, Amsterdam, p. 193.
5. T. Pullerits, R. Monshouwer, F. van Mourik, R. van Grondelle, Temperature dependence of electron-vibronic spectra of photosynthetic systems. Computer simulations and comparison with experiment. *Chem. Phys.* **194** (1995) 395–407.
6. E.J.G. Peterman, T. Pullerits, R. van Grondelle, H. van Amerongen, Electron-phonon coupling and vibronic fine structure of light harvesting complex II of green plants: Temperature dependent absorption and high-resolution fluorescence spectroscopy. *J. Phys. Chem. B* **101** (1997) 4448–4457.
7. J. Pieper, J. Voigt, G. Renger, G.J. Small, Analysis of phonon structure in line-narrowed optical spectra. *Chem. Phys. Lett.* **310** (1999) 296–302.
8. T. Renger, R.A. Marcus, On the relation of protein dynamics and exciton relaxation in pigment–protein complexes: An estimation of the spectral density and a theory for the calculation of optical spectra. *J. Chem. Phys.* **116** (2002) 9997–10019.

9. A. Warshel, Z.T. Chu, W.W. Parson, Dispersed polaron simulations of electron transfer in photosynthetic reaction centers. *Science* **246** (1989) 112–116.
10. T.M.H. Creemers, C.A. De Caro, R.W. Visschers, R. van Grondelle, S. Völker, Spectral hole burning and fluorescence line narrowing in subunits of the light-harvesting complex LH1 of purple bacteria. *J. Phys. Chem. B* **103** (1999) 9770–9776.
11. G. McDermott, S.M. Prince, A.A. Freer, A.M. Hawthornthwaite-Lawless, M.Z. Papiz, R.J. Cogdell, N.W. Isaacs, Crystal-structure of an integral membrane light-harvesting complex from photosynthetic bacteria. *Nature* **374** (1995) 517–521.
12. S. Karrasch, P.A. Bullough, R. Ghosh, The 8.5 Å projection map of the light-harvesting complex-I from *Rhodospirillum-rubrum* reveals a ring composed of 16 subunits. *EMBO J.* **14** (1995) 631–638.
13. K.-H. Rhee, E.P. Morris, J. Barber, W. Kühlbrandt, Three-dimensional structure of plant photosystem II at 8 Å resolution. *Nature* **396** (1998) 283–286.
14. P. Fromme, H.T. Witt, W.-D. Schubert, O. Kluklas, W. Saenger, N. Krauß, Structure of photosystem I at 4.5 Å resolution: a short review including evolutionary aspects. *Biochim. Biophys. Acta* **1275** (1996) 76–83.
15. F. Müh, F. Lendzian, R. Mason, J.C. Williams, J.P. Allen, W. Lubitz, Pigment–protein interactions in bacterial reaction centers and their influence on oxidation potential and spin density distribution of the primary donor. *J. Phys. Chem. B* **106** (1985) 3226–3236.
16. J.R. Reimers, N.S. Hush, A unified description of the elctrochemical, charge distribution and spectroscopic properties of the special-pair radical cation in bacterial photosynthesis. *J. Am. Chem. Soc.* **126** (2004) 4132–4144.
17. R.A. Marcus, On the theory of oxidation–reduction reactions involving electron transfer. I. *J. Chem. Phys.* **24** (1956) 966–978.
18. V.G. Levich, R.R. Dogonadze, Theory of non-radiation electron transitions from ion to ion in solutions. *Dokl. Akad. Nauk. SSSR* **124** (1959) 123–126.
19. R.A. Marcus, N. Sutin, Electron transfer in chemistry and biology. *Biochim. Biophys. Acta* **11** (1985) 265–322.
20. B. Loll, J. Kern, W. Saenger, A. Zouni, J. Biesiadka, Towards complete cofactor arrangement in the 3.0 Å resolution structure of photosystem II. *Nature* **438** (2005) 1040–1044.
21. M.E. van Brederode, R. van Grondelle, New and unexpected routes for ultrafast electron transfer in photosynthetic reaction centers. *FEBS Lett.* **455** (1999) 1–7.
22. V. Prokhorenko, A.R. Holzwarth, Primary processes and structure of the photosystem II reaction center: a photon echo study. *J. Phys. Chem. B* **104** (2000) 11563–11578.
23. B.A. Diner, F. Rappaport, Structure, dynamics, and energetics of the primary photochemistry of photosystem II of oxygenic photosynthesis. *Annu. Rev. Plant Biol.* **53** (2002) 551–580.
24. R.N. Frese, M. Germano, F.L. de Weerd, I.H.M. van Stokkum, A.Y. Shuropatov, V.A. Shuvalov, H.J. van Gorkom, R. van Grondelle, J.P. Dekker, Electric field effects on the chlorophylls, pheophytins, and β-carotens in the reaction center of photosystem II. *Biochemistry* **42** (2003) 9205–9213.
25. G. Raszewski, W. Saenger, T. Renger, Theory of optical spectra of Photosystem II reaction centers: Location of the triplet state and the identity of the primary electron donor. *Biophys. J.* **88** (2005) 986–998.
26. M.L. Groot, N.P. Pawlowicz, L.J.G.W. van Wilderen, J. Breton, I.H.M. van Sokkum, R. van Grondelle, Initial electron donor and acceptor in isolated Photosystem II reaction centers identified with femtosecond mid-IR spectroscopy. *Proc. Natl. Acad. Sci U.S.A.* **102** (2005) 13087–13092.

27. G. Renger and A. Holzwarth, Primary electron transfer, in: *Photosystem II: The Light-Driven Water: Plastoquinone Oxidoreductase* (2005) (T. Wydrzynski, K. Satoh, eds.), Springer, Dordrecht, pp. 139–175.
28. A.R. Holzwarth, M.G. Müller, M. Reus, M. Nowaczyk, J. Sander, M. Rögner, Kinetics and mechanism of electron transfer in intact photosystem II and in isolated reaction center: Pheophytin is the primary electron acceptor. *Proc. Natl. Acad. Sci U.S.A.* **103** (2006) 6895–6900.
29. R.E. Fenna, B.W. Matthews, Chlorophyll arrangement in a bacteriochlorophyll protein from *Chlorobium–Limicola*. *Nature* **258** (1975) 573–577.
30. B.W. Matthews, R.E. Fenna, M.C. Bolognesi, M.F. Schmid, J.M. Olson, Structure of a bacteriochlorophyll $a$–protein from the green photosynthetic bacterium *Prosthecochloris-aestuarii*. *J. Mol. Biol.* **131** (1979) 259–285.
31. D.E. Tronrud, M.F. Schmid, B.W. Matthews, Structure and X-ray amino-acid-sequence of a bacteriochlorophyll-a protein from *Prosthecochloris-aestuarii* refined at 1.9 Å resolution. *J. Mol. Biol.* **188** (1986) 443–454.
32. Y.F. Li, W. Zhou, R.E. Blankenship, J.P. Allen, Crystal structure of the bacteriochlorophyll $a$–protein from *Chlorobium tepidum*. *J. Mol. Biol.* **271** (1997) 456–471.
33. E. Hofmann, P.M. Wrench, F.P. Sharples, R.G. Hiller, W. Welte, K. Diederichs, Structural basis of light harvesting by carotenoids: Peridin-chlorophyll-protein from *Amphidinium carterae*. *Science* **272** (1996) 1788–1791.
34. T. Förster, Zwischenmolekulare energiewanderung und fluoreszenz. *Ann. Phys. (Leipzig)* **2** (1948) 47–54.
35. T. Förster, Delocalized excitation and excitation transfer, in: *Modern Quantum Chemistry* (1965) (O. Sinnanoglu, ed.), Academic Press, New York, pp. 257–265.
36. F.J. Kleima, E. Hofmann, B. Gobets, I.H.M. van Stokkum, R. van Grondelle, K. Diederichs, H. van Amerongen, Förster excitation energy transfer in peridinin-chlorophyll-$a$-protein. *Biophys. J.* **78** (2000) 344–353.
37. V. May, O. Kühn, *Charge and Energy Transfer Dynamics in Molecular Systems: A Theoretical Introduction* (2000), Wiley-VCH, Berlin.
38. A.G. Redfield, On the theory of relaxation processes. *IBM J. Res. Develop.* **1** (1957) 19–31; *Adv. Magnetic Reson.* **1** (1965) 1–32.
39. K. Blum, *Density Matrix Theory and Application* (1981), Plenum, New York.
40. O. Kühn, V. May, M. Schreiber, Dissipative vibrational dynamics in a curve-crossing system. *J. Chem. Phys.* **101** (1994) 10404–10415.
41. J.A. Leegwater, J.R. Durrant, D.R. Klug, Exciton equilibration induced by phonons: Theory and application to PS II. *J. Phys. Chem. B* **101** (1997) 7205–7210.
42. O. Kühn, V. Sundström, Pump–probe spectroscopy of dissipative energy transfer dynamics in photosynthetic antenna complexes: A density matrix approach. *J. Chem. Phys.* **107** (1997) 4154–4164.
43. T. Renger, V. May, Ultrafast exciton motion in photosynthetic antenna complexes: The FMO–complex. *J. Phys. Chem. A* **102** (1998) 4381–4391.
44. T. Renger, V. May, O. Kühn, Ultrafast excitation energy transfer dynamics in photosynthetic pigment–protein complexes. *Phys. Rep.* **343** (2001) 138–254.
45. V. Novoderezhkin, M. Wendling, R. van Grondelle, Intra- and interband transfers in the B800-B850 antenna of *Rhodospirillum molischianum*: Redfield theory modeling of polarized pump–probe kinetics. *J. Phys. Chem. B* **107** (2003) 11534–11548.
46. V. Novoderezhkin, J.M. Salverda, H. van Amerongen, R. van Grondelle, Exciton modeling of energy-transfer dynamics in the LHCII complex of higher plants: A Redfield theory approach. *J. Phys. Chem. B* **107** (2003) 1839–1912.

47. S. Mukamel, I. Oppenheim, J. Ross, Statistical reduction for strongly driven simple quantum systems. *Phys. Rev. A* **17** (1978) 1988–1998.
48. S. Mukamel, Non-Markovian theory of molecular relaxation: I. Vibrational relaxation and dephasing in condensed phases. *Chem. Phys.* **37** (1979) 33–47.
49. J. Breton, A. Hardisson, F. Mauricio, S. Velasco, Relaxation of quantum systems weakly coupled to a bath. II. Formal analysis of the total-time-ordering-cumulant and partial-time-ordering cumulant spectral line shapes. *Phys. Rev. A* **30** (1984) 553–559.
50. T. Renger, V. May, Simulations of frequency domain spectra: Structure–function relationships in photosynthetic pigment–protein complexes. *Phys. Rev. Lett.* **84** (2000) 5228–5231.
51. S. Jang, R.J. Silbey, Theory of single molecule line shapes of multichromophoric macromolecules. *J. Chem. Phys.* **118** (2003) 9312–9323.
52. A. Okada, V. Chernyak, S. Mukamel, Solvent reorganization in long-range electron transfer: Density matrix approach. *J. Phys. Chem. A* **102** (1998) 1241–1251.
53. W.M. Zhang, T. Meier, V. Chernyak, S. Mukamel, Exciton-migration and three-pulse femtosecond optical spectroscopies of photosynthetic antenna complexes. *J. Chem. Phys.* **108** (1998) 7763–7774.
54. M. Yang, G.R. Fleming, Influence of phonons on exciton transfer dynamics: comparison of the Redfield, Förster, and modified Redfield equations. *Chem. Phys.* **275** (2002) 355–372.
55. T. Renger, R.A. Marcus, Variable-range hopping electron transfer through disordered bridge states: Application to DNA. *J. Chem. Phys.* **107** (2003) 8404–8419.
56. V.I. Novoderezhkin, M.A. Palacios, H. van Amerongen, R. van Grondelle, Energy-transfer dynamics in the LHCII complex of higher plants: Modified Redfield approach. *J. Phys. Chem. B* **108** (2004) 10363–10375.
57. Z. Fetisova, A. Freiberg, K. Mauring, V. Novoderezhkin, A. Taisova, K. Timpmann, Excitation energy transfer in chlorosomes of green bacteria: Theoretical and experimental studies. *Biophys. J.* **71** (1996) 995–1010.
58. H. Sumi, Theory on rates of excitation-energy transfer between molecular aggregates through distributed transition dipoles with application to antenna system in bacterial photosynthesis. *J. Phys. Chem. B* **103** (1999) 252–260.
59. K. Mukai, S. Abe, H. Sumi, Theory of rapid excitation-energy transfer from B800 to optically-forbidden exciton states of B850 in the antenna system LH2 of photosynthetic purple bacteria. *J. Phys. Chem. B* **103** (1999) 6069–6102.
60. G.D. Scholes, G.R. Fleming, On the mechanism of light harvesting in photosynthetic purple bacteria: B800 to B850 energy transfer. *J. Phys. Chem. B* **104** (2000) 1854–1868.
61. S. Jang, M.D. Newton, R.J. Silbey, Multichromophoric Förster resonance energy transfer. *Phys. Rev. Lett.* **92** (2004) art. no. 218301.
62. S.G. Boxer, T.R. Middendorf, D.J. Lockhart, Reversible photochemical hole-burning in *Rhodopseudomonas-viridis* reaction centers. *FEBS Lett.* **200** (1986) 237–241.
63. P.A. Lyle, S.V. Kolaczkowski, G.J. Small, Photochemical hole-burned spectra of protonated and deutorated reaction centers of *Rhodobacter sphaeroides*. *J. Phys. Chem.* **97** (1993) 6924–6933.
64. E.J.P. Lathrop, R.A. Friesner, Vibronic mixing in the strong electronic coupling limit. Spectroscopic effects of forbidden transitions. *J. Phys. Chem.* **98** (1994) 3050–3055.

65. Th. Renger, Theory of optical spectra involving charge transfer states: Dynamic localization predicts a temperature dependent optical band shift. *Phys. Rev. Lett.* **93** (2004) art. no. 188101.
66. H. Huber, M. Meyer, H. Scheer, W. Zinth, J. Wachtveitl, Temperature dependence of the primary electron transfer reaction in pigment-modified bacterial reaction centers. *Photosynth. Res.* **55** (1998) 153–162.
67. J.C. Tully, R.K. Preston, Trajectory surface hopping approach to nonadiabatic molecular collisions: The reaction of $H^+$ with $D_2$. *J. Chem. Phys.* **55** (1971) 562–572.
68. A. Warshel, J.-K. Hwang, Simulations of the dynamics of electron transfer reactions in polar solvents: Semiclassical trajectories and dispersed polaron approaches. *J. Chem. Phys.* **84** (1986) 4938–4957.
69. M. Lax, The Franck–Condon principle and its application to crystals. *J. Chem. Phys.* **20** (1952) 1752–1760.
70. R. Kubo, Y. Toyozawa, Application of the method of generating function to radiative and non-radiative transitions of a trapped electron in a crystal. *Prog. Theor. Phys.* **13** (1955) 160–182.
71. J. Jortner, Temperature-dependent activation energy for electron transfer between biological molecules. *J. Chem. Phys.* **64** (1976) 4860–4867.
72. R. Kubo, Generalized cumulant expansion method. *J. Phys. Soc. Jpn.* **17** (1962) 1100–1120.
73. A. Warshel, W.W. Parson, Computer simulations of electron-transfer reactions in solution and in photosynthetic reaction centers. *Annu. Rev. Phys. Chem.* **42** (1991) 279–309.
74. H. Haken, *Quantum Field Theory of Solids: An Introduction* (1976) North-Holland Pub. Co., Amsterdam, New York.
75. R. Kubo, M. Toda, N. Hashitsume, *Statistical Physics II* (1991), Springer, Berlin.
76. D.A. McQuarrie, *Statistical Mechanics* (2000), University Science Books, Sausalito.
77. R.I. Personov, in: *Spectroscopy and Excitation Dynamics of Condensed Molecular Systems* (1983) (V.M. Agranovich, R.M. Hochstrasser, eds.), Elsevier/North-Holland, Amsterdam, pp. 555–619.
78. E.J.G. Peterman, H. van Amerongen, R. van Grondelle, J.P. Dekker, The nature of the excited state of the reaction center of photosystem II of green plants: A high-resolution fluorescence spectroscopy study. *Proc. Natl. Acad. Sci. U.S.A.* **95** (1998) 6128–6133.
79. M. Rätsep, W.T. Johnson, P.R. Chitnis, G.J. Small, The red-absorbing chlorophyll a antenna states of photosystem I: A hole-burning study of Synechocystis sp PCC 6803 and its mutants. *J. Phys. Chem. B* **104** (2000) 836–847.
80. B. Gobets, R. van Grondelle, Energy transfer and trapping in photosystem I. *Biochim. Biophys. Acta* **1507** (2001) 80–99.
81. V. Zazubovich, S. Matsuzaki, T.W. Johnson, J.M. Hayes, P.R. Chitnis, G.J. Small, Red antenna states of photosystem I from cyanobacterium *Synechochocus elongatus:* A spectral hole burning study. *Chem. Phys.* **275** (2002) 47–59.
82. S. Mukamel, *Principles of Nonlinear Optical Spectroscopy* (1995), Oxford University Press, Oxford New York.
83. V. Chernyak, N.J. Wang, S. Mukamel, Four-wave mixing and luminescence of confined excitons in molecular aggregates and nanostructures. Many-body Green function approach. *Phys. Rep.* **263** (1995) 213–309.
84. C. Meier, D.J. Tannor, Non-Markovian evolution of the density operator in the presence of strong laser fields. *J. Chem. Phys.* **111** (1999) 3365–3376.

85. T. Mancal, V. May, Interplay of non-Markovian relaxation and ultrafast optical state preparation in molecular systems: The Laguerre polynomial method. *J. Chem. Phys.* **114** (2001) 1510–1523.
86. T. Mancal, V. May, Retardation effects in the dynamics of open molecular systems. *Chem. Phys.* **268** (2001) 201–219.
87. Q. Shi, E. Geva, A new approach to calculating the memory kernel of the generalized quantum master equation for an arbitrary system–bath coupling. *J. Chem. Phys.* **119** (2003) 12063–12076.
88. U. Kleinekathöfer, Non-Markovian theories based on a decomposition of the spectral density. *J. Chem. Phys.* **121** (2004) 2505–2514.
89. M. Yang, A reduced density-matrix theory of absorption line shape of molecular aggregate. *J. Chem. Phys.* **123** (2005) art. no. 124705.
90. A. Matro, J. Cina, Theoretical study of time-resolved fluorescence anisotropy from coupled chromophore pairs. *J. Phys. Chem.* **99** (1995) 2568–2582.
91. T. Renger, V. May, Multiple exciton effects in molecular aggregates: Application to a photosynthetic antenna complex. *Phys. Rev. Lett.* **78** (1997) 3406–3409.
92. V.I. Novoderezhkin, A.G. Yakovlev, R. van Grondelle, V.A. Shuvalov, Coherent nuclear and electronic dynamics in primary charge separation in photosynthetic reaction centers: A Redfield theory approach. *J. Phys. Chem. B* **108** (2004) 7445–7457.
93. N. Makri, E. Sim, D.E. Makarov, M. Topaler, Long-time quantum simulation of the primary charge separation in bacterial photosynthesis. *Proc. Natl. Acad. Sci. U.S.A.* **93** (1996) 3926–3931.
94. J. Ray, N. Makri, Short-range coherence in the energy transfer of photosynthetic light-harvesting systems. *J. Phys. Chem. A* **103** (1999) 9417–9422.
95. R. Kubo, Stochastic Liouville equations. *J. Math. Phys.* **4** (1963) 174–183.
96. N.G. van Kampen, A cumulant expansion for stochastic linear differential equations II. *Physica* **74** (1973) 239–247.
97. N. Hashitsume, F. Shibata, M. Shingu, Quantal master equation valid for any time scale. *J. Stat. Phys.* **17** (1977) 155–169.
98. S. Chaturvedi, F. Shibata, Time-convolutionless projection operator formalism for elimination of fast variables-application to Brownian motion. *Z. Phys. B* **35** (1979) 297–308.
99. M. Tokuyama, H. Mori, Statistical-mechanical theory of random frequency modulations and generalized Brownian motions. *Prog. Theor. Phys.* **55** (1976) 411–429.
100. R. Zwanzig, Ensemble method in the theory of irreversibility. *J. Chem. Phys.* **33** (1960) 1338–1341.
101. M.A. Palenberg, R. Silbey, C. Warns, P. Reineker, Local and nonlocal approximation for a simple quantum system. *J. Chem. Phys.* **114** (2001) 4386–4389.
102. J.H. Freed, Generalized cumulant expansion and spin relaxation theory. *J. Chem. Phys.* **49** (1968) 376–391.
103. (*a*) J. Pieper, K.-D. Irrgang, G. Renger, R.E. Lechner, Density of vibrational states of the light-harvesting complex II of green plants studied by inelastic neutron scattering. *J. Phys. Chem. B* **108** (2004) 10556–10565; (*b*) M. Wendling, T. Pullerits, M.A. Przyjalgowski, S.I.E. Vulto, T.J. Aartsma, R. van Grondelle, H. van Amerongen, Electron vibrational coupling in the Fenna-Matthews-Olson complex of Prosthecochloris aestuarii determined by temperature dependent absorption and fluorescence line narrowing measurements. *J. Phys. Chem. B* **104** (2000) 5825–5831.
104. A. Damjanovic, I. Kosztin, U. Kleinekathöfer, K. Schulten, Excitons in photosynthetic light-harvesting systems: A combined molecular dynamics, quantum chemistry, and polaron model study. *Phys. Rev. E* **65** (1999) art. no. 031919.

105. W.W. Parson, Z.T. Chu, A. Warshel, Reorganization energy of the initial electron-transfer step in photosynthetic bacterial reaction centers. *Biophys. J.* **74** (1998) 182–191.
106. H. van Amerongen, L. Valkunas, R. van Grondelle, *Photosynthetic Excitons* (2000), World Scientific, London.
107. M.E. Madjet, A. Abdurahman, Th. Renger, Intermolecular Coulomb couplings from *ab initio* electrostatic potentials: Application to optical transitions of strongly coupled pigments in photosynthetic antennae and reaction centers. *J. Phys. Chem. B* **110** (2006) 17268–17281.
108. R.S. Knox, B.Q. Spring, Dipole strengths in the chlorophylls. *Photochem. Photobiol.* **77** (2003) 497–501.
109. C. Weiss, The $\pi$ electron structure and absorption spectra of chlorophylls in solution. *J. Mol. Spectrosc.* **44** (1972) 37–80.
110. J.C. Chang, Monopole effects on electronic excitation interactions between large molecules. I. Application to energy transfer in chlorophylls. *J. Phys. Chem.* **67** (1977) 3901–3909.
111. B.P. Krüger, G.D. Scholes, G.R. Fleming, Calculation of couplings and energy transfer pathways between pigments of LH2 by the *ab-initio* transition density cube method. *J. Phys. Chem.* **102** (1998) 5378–5386.
112. J.N. Betts, D.N. Beratan, J.N. Onuchic, Mapping electron tunneling pathways: An algorithm that finds the "minimum length"/maximum coupling pathway between electron donors and acceptors in proteins. *J. Am. Chem. Soc.* **114** (1992) 4043–4046.
113. P. Siddarth, R.A. Marcus, Electron transfer reactions in proteins: An artificial intelligence approach to electronic coupling. *J. Phys. Chem.* **97** (1993) 2400–2405.
114. S.S. Skourtis, J.J. Regan, J.N. Onuchic, Electron transfer in proteins: A novel approach for the description of the donor–acceptor coupling. *J. Phys. Chem.* **98** (1994) 3379–3388.
115. J.N. Gehlen, I. Daizadeh, A.A. Stuchebrukhov, R.A. Marcus, Tunneling matrix element in Ru-modified blue copper proteins: pruning the protein in search of electron transfer pathways. *Inorg. Chim. Acta* **243** (1996) 271–282.
116. I.A. Balabin, J.N. Onuchic, Connection between simple models and quantum chemical models for electron-transfer tunneling matrix element calculations: A Dyson's equations-based approach. *J. Phys. Chem.* **100** (1996) 11573–11580.
117. C.-P. Hsu, R.A. Marcus, A sequential formula for electronic coupling in long range bridge-assisted electron transfer: Formulation of theory and application to alkanethiol monolayers. *J. Chem. Phys.* **106** (1997) 584–598.
118. C.C. Moser, J.M. Keske, K. Warncke, R.S. Farid, P.L. Dutton, Nature of biological electron-transfer. *Nature* **355** (1992) 796–802.
119. C.P. Page, C.C. Moser, X. Chen, P.L. Dutton, Natural engineering principles of electron tunneling in biological oxidation–reduction. *Nature* **402** (1999) 47–52.
120. D.N. Beratan, J.N. Betts, J.N. Onuchic, Protein electron-transfer rates set by the bridging secondary and tertiary structure. *Science* **252** (1991) 1285–1288.
121. A.A. Stuchebrukhov, Towards *ab-inito* theory of long-distance electron tunneling in proteins: Tunneling currents approach. *Adv. Chem. Phys.* **118** (2001) 1–44.
122. R. Langen, I-J. Chang, J.P. Germanas, J.H. Richards, J.R. Winkler, H.B. Gray, Electron tunneling in proteins: Coupling through a β-strand. *Science* **268** (1995) 1733–1735.
123. H.B. Gray, J.R. Winkler, Electron transfer in proteins. *Annu. Rev. Biochem.* **65** (1996) 537–561.

124. J. Eccles, B. Honig, Charged amino-acids as spectroscopic determinants for chlorophyll *in vivo*. *Proc. Natl. Acad. Sci. U.S.A.* **80** (1983) 4959–4962.
125. H.M. Damjanovic, H.M. Vaswani, P. Fromme, G.R. Fleming, Chlorophyll excitations in photosystem I of *Synechococcus elongatus*. *J. Phys. Chem. B* **106** (2002) 10251–10262.
126. B.A. Diner, E. Schlodder, P.J. Nixon, W.J. Coleman, F. Rappaport, J. Lavergne, W.F.J. Vermaas, D.A. Chisholm, Site-directed mutations ar D1-HIS198 and D2-HIS197 of Photosystem II in *Synechocystis* PCC 6803: Sites of primary charge separation and cation and triplet stabilization. *Biochemistry* **40** (2001) 9265–9281.
127. D. Spangler, G.M. Maggiora, L. Shipman, R.E. Christophersen, Stereoelectronic properties of photosynthetic and related systems. 1. *Ab–initio* quantum-mechanical ground state characterization of magnesium porphine, chlorin, and ethyl chlorophyllide *a*. *J. Am. Chem. Soc.* **99** (1977) 7470–7477.
128. J.N. Sturgis, B. Robert, The role of chromophore coupling in tuning the spectral properties of peripheral light-harvesting protein of purple bacteria. *Photosynth. Res.* **50** (1996) 5–10.
129. J.N. Sturgis, B. Robert, Pigment binding-site and electronic properties in light-harvesting proteins of purple bacteria. *J. Phys. Chem. B* **101** (1997) 7227–7231.
130. H. Witt, E. Schlodder, C. Teutloff, J. Niklas, E. Bordignon, D. Carbonera, S. Kohler, A. Labahn, W. Lubitz, Hydrogen bonding to P700: Site-directed mutagenesis of threonine A739 of photosystem I in *Chlamydomonas reinhardtii*. *Biochemistry* **41** (2002) 8557–8569.
131. A. Warshel, W.W. Parson, Spectroscopic properties of photosynthetic reaction centers. I. Theory. *J. Am. Chem. Soc.* **109** (1987) 6143–6152.
132. E. Gudowska-Nowak, M.D. Newton, J. Fajer, Conformational and environmental effects on bacteriochlorophyll optical spectra: Correlations of calculated spectra with structural results. *J. Phys. Chem.* **94** (1990) 5795–5801.
133. R.M. Pearlstein, R.P. Hemenger, Bacteriochlorophyll electronic-transition moment directions in bacteriochlorophyll *a*-protein. *Proc. Natl. Acad. Sci. U.S.A.* **75** (1978) 4920–4924.
134. R.M. Pearlstein, Theory of the optical spectra of the bacteriochlorophyll-*a* antenna protein trimer of *Prosthecochloris-aestuarii*. *Photosynth. Res.* **31** (1992) 213–226.
135. X. Lu, R.M. Pearlstein, Simulations of *Prosthecochloris* bacteriochlorophyll *a*-protein optical spectra improved by parametric computer search. *Photochem. Photobiol.* **57** (1993) 86–91.
136. D. Gülen, Interpretation of the excited-state structure of the Fenna–Matthews–Olson protein of the photosynthtetic pigment–protein complex of *Prosthecochloris-aestuarii* based on simultaneous simulation of the 4 K absorption, linear dichroism, and singlet–triplet absorption diffrence spectra: a possible excitonic explanation? *J. Phys. Chem.* **100** (1996) 17683–17689.
137. R.J.W. Louwe, J. Vrieze, A.J. Hoff, T.J. Aartsma, Towards an integral interpretation of the optical steady state spectra of the FMO-complex of *Prosthecochloris-aestuarii*. 2. Exciton simulations. *J. Phys. Chem. B* **101** (1997) 11280–11287.
138. S.I.E. Vulto, M.A. de Baat, R.J.W. Louwe, H.P. Permentier, T. Neef, M. Miller, H. van Amerongen, T.J. Aartsma, Exciton simulations of optical spectra of the FMO complex from the green sulfur bacterium *Chlorobium tepidum* at 6 K. *J. Phys. Chem. B* **102** (1998) 9577–9582.
139. M. Wendling, M.A. Przyjalgowski, D. Gülen, S.I.E. Vulto, T.J. Aartsma, R. van Grondelle, H. van Amerongen, The quantitative relationship between structure

and polarized spectroscopy in the FMO complex of *Prosthecochloris-aestuarii:* Refining experiments and simulations. *Photosynth. Res.* **71** (2002) 99–123.
140. J. Adolphs, T. Renger, How proteins tune excitation energies of pigments in photosynthetic antennae: Application to the FMO-complex of green sulfur bacteria. *Biophys. J.* **91** (2006) 2778–2797.
141. B. Rabenstein, G.M. Ullmann, E.-W. Knapp, Energetics of electron-transfer and protonation reactions of the quinones in the photosynthetic reaction center of *Rhodopseudomonas viridis*. *Biochemistry* **37** (1998) 2488–2495.
142. G.M. Ullmann, E.W. Knapp, Electrostatic models for computing protonation and redox equilibria in proteins. *Eur. Biophys. J.* **28** (1999) 533–550.
143. B. Rabenstein, G.M. Ullmann, E.-W. Knapp, Electron transfer between the quinones in the photosynthetic reaction center and its coupling to conformational changes. *Biochemistry* **39** (2000) 10487–10496.
144. H. Ishikita, G. Morra, E.-W. Knapp, Redox potential of quinones in photosynthetic reaction centers from *Rhodobacter spheroides:* Dependence on protonation of Glu-L212 and ASP-L213. *Biochemistry* **42** (2003) 3882–3892.
145. D. Bashford, M. Karplus, PKAS of ionizable groups in proteins-Atomic detail from a continuum electrostatic model. *Biochemistry* **29** (1990) 10219–10225.
146. B.R. Brooks, R.E. Bruccoleri, B.D. Olafson, D.J. States, S. Swaminathan, M. Karplus, CHARMM-A program for macromolecular energy, minimization and dynamics calculations. *J. Comput. Chem.* **4** (1983) 187–217.
147. B. Rabenstein (1999), Karlsberg online manual, http://lie.chemie.fu-berlin.de/karlsberg/.
148. H. Ishikita, W. Saenger, J. Biesiadka, B. Loll, E.W. Knapp, How photosynthetic reaction centers control oxidation power in chlorophyll pairs P680, P700, and P870. *Proc. Natl. Acad. Sci. U.S.A.* **103** (2006) 9855–9860.
149. D.R. Reichman, F.L.H. Brown, P. Neu, Cumulant expansion and the spin-boson problem. *Phys. Rev. E* **55** (1997) 2328–2337.
150. R.X. Xu, P. Cui, X.-Q. Li, Y. Mo, Y. Yan, Exact quantum master equations via the calculus on path integrals. *J. Chem. Phys.* **122** (2005) art. no. 041103.
151. M. Schröder, M. Schreiber, U. Kleinekathöfer, Calculation of absorption spectra for light-harvesting systems using non-Markovian approaches as well as modified Redfield theory. *J. Chem. Phys.* **126** (2007) art. no. 114102.
152. T. Renger, I. Trostmann, C. Theiss, M.E. Madjet, M. Richter, H. Paulsen, H.J. Eichler, A. Knorr, G. Renger, Refinement of a structural model of a pigment-protein complex by accurate optical lineshape theory and experiment. *J. Phys. Chem. B* (2007) in press.
153. F. Müh, M.E. Madjet, J. Adolphs, A. Abdurahman, B. Rabenstein, H. Ishikita, E.-W. Knapp, T. Renger, How proteins control excitation energy flow in light harvesting antennae. *Proc. Natl. Acad. Sci. USA* (submitted).

# III. Pigments

*Chapter 3*

# Chlorophylls

## Hugo Scheer

**Table of Contents**

| | | |
|---|---|---|
| 3.1 | Introduction | 103 |
| 3.2 | Functions | 104 |
| | 3.2.1 Light Absorption | 104 |
| | 3.2.2 Excitation Energy Transfer to Reaction Centers | 104 |
| | 3.2.3 Light-induced Electron Transfer | 105 |
| | 3.2.4 Quenching of Excitation Energy | 105 |
| | 3.2.5 Structure Stabilization | 106 |
| 3.3 | Structures of Chlorophyll Molecules | 107 |
| | 3.3.1 Chlorophylls c: the Porphyrin Type | 107 |
| | 3.3.2 Chlorophylls a, b, d: the Chlorin Type from Oxygenic Phototrophs | 109 |
| | 3.3.3 Bacteriochlorophylls c, d, e: the Chlorin Type from Anoxygenic Green Bacteria | 109 |
| | 3.3.4 Bacteriochlorophylls a, b, g: the Bacteriochlorin Type | 112 |
| | 3.3.5 Transmetalated Chlorophylls | 113 |
| | 3.3.6 "Minor" Chlorophylls | 113 |
| 3.4 | Spectroscopy | 114 |
| | 3.4.1 Optical Absorption Spectroscopy | 114 |
| | 3.4.2 Luminescence Spectroscopy | 117 |
| | 3.4.3 Circular Dichroism | 120 |
| | 3.4.4 Nuclear Magnetic Resonance Spectroscopy | 121 |
| | 3.4.5 Electron Spin Resonance Spectroscopy | 121 |
| | 3.4.6 Mass Spectrometry | 122 |
| | 3.4.7 Vibrational Spectroscopy | 122 |
| | 3.4.8 Electrochemistry | 123 |
| 3.5 | Biosynthesis | 124 |
| 3.6 | Concluding Remarks and Future Perspectives | 128 |
| References | | 129 |

## Abstract

Chlorophylls have several functions in photosynthesis: (1) in the light-harvesting antennas they efficiently absorb light and (2) transfer the excitation energy with minimum losses to the reaction centers, where (3) they act as primary electron donors and acceptors in light-induced charge separation across the photosynthetic membrane. In both types of complexes, they (4) contribute to the stabilization of the photosynthetic apparatus. Chlorophylls have also been found in other protein complexes, where less is known of their function. Pigment structures, biosynthetic pathways and spectroscopic properties are reviewed. Examples are given for strategies to study excitation energy transfer by the selective introduction of specifically modified chromophores. IUPAC numbering [1,2] is used throughout (Figure 1B).

## 3.1 Introduction

(Bacterio)Chlorophylls [(B)Chls] are cyclic tetrapyrroles that are ubiquitous in photosynthesis. They occur in most light-harvesting (LH) complexes [3] and in all reaction centers (RCs) [4]. In the former, they efficiently absorb light, and transfer the acquired electronic excitation energy with high quantum yield to the reaction centers (RCs) (for details, see Chapters 5–8). In all RCs, the primary donors are (B)Chls, which upon electronic excitation transfer an electron to the primary acceptor, which is also a (B)Chl, and further across the photosynthetic membrane via another Chl (type I RC) or the demetalated analogue, a (bacterio-)pheophytin ((B)Phe) (type II RC) to a quinone (for details, see Chapters 11–16) the sequence of events is probably slightly different in PS II-RC; (for a discussion see [5]). Chlorophylls have also been found in other complexes of photosynthetic organisms, where they have still unknown functions. Most notably is the presence of a Chl $a$ in the electrogenic cytochrome $b_6/f$ complex [6–9], and in several water-soluble chlorophyll-proteins [10–12]. In all photosynthetically active chlorophyll proteins, they are accompanied by carotenoids that, among other functions, accept and quench excess excitation energy from the chlorophylls [13]. There is evidence that under certain circumstances Chls can also degrade excess excitation energy in a yet poorly understood fashion [14,15]. In all chlorophyll–protein proteins, the pigments also contribute to the stabilization of the photosynthetic complexes [16–20].

The current chapter is a short review of the occurrence, structures and biosynthesis of chlorophylls, as well as on their spectroscopic properties in monodisperse solution, in aggregates, and in their native environment. For more comprehensive treatments, the reader is referred to the other chapters of this book and several other books, from which individual chapters are cited throughout this review [3,4,21–28].

## 3.2 Functions

### 3.2.1 Light Absorption

Antennas serve to increase the absorption range and cross-section of the RC, with reduced investment in protein biosynthesis. By varying the type and quantity of certain antenna complexes, light absorption can furthermore be adjusted to the prevailing light conditions [3]. Chlorophylls have intense absorptions in the blue and (near-infrared) red regions ($\varepsilon \approx 10^5$ M$^{-1}$ cm$^{-1}$), which in combination cover most of the photosynthetically useful spectrum (330–1050 nm). Chl $a$, $b$, $d$ and BChls $a$, $b$, $c$, $d$, $e$, $g$ cover the extremes of this range efficiently, with strong absorptions in the 330–480 nm and the 630–1050 nm ranges. The intervening "green gap" is filled by the absorptions of the c-chlorophylls (or of biliproteins or carotenoids). This is particularly important in aquatic environments, where green light often prevails and the overall light intensity is reduced.

### 3.2.2 Excitation Energy Transfer to Reaction Centers

Excitation energy has to be transferred from the site of original light absorption to the primary donor of the reaction center, generally via a considerable number of intervening chromophores over distances up to 50 Å. Three basic mechanisms are discussed for the efficient non-radiative transfer among the chromophores; in practice they are often mixed (for theoretical background, see Chapter 2 and [29–38]). Only at very short (contact) distances can excitation energy be transferred by electron exchange (Dexter mechanism). This transfer is of particular importance for triplet energy transfer between Chls and carotenoids [39–42]. Since electron exchange, like electron transfer, requires orbital overlap, it is critically dependent on very small geometric changes. It can also be mediated, via superexchange, by intervening chromophores with excited states of considerably higher energy. At intermediate distances (<2 nm), exciton coupling can occur: a cluster of two or more pigments is excited practically simultaneously. The excitation is delocalized and consequently spread over the ensemble [30,43–45]. At still longer distances ($\leq 10$ nm) only *Förster* transfer can operate efficiently, here the energy hops in discrete steps from one pigment to the other. This transfer mechanism is of particular importance in phycobiliproteins, where distances among chromophores are relatively large [46]. Both exciton and Förster mechanisms arise from dipolar couplings that depend on distance, relative orientations and spectral properties of the pigments (Chapter 2).

The quantum yield $\Phi_q$ of excitation energy transfer (EET) in unquenched chlorophyll antennas is generally close to 100% – for each quantum absorbed a reaction center is excited. This situation is typical for well-adapted conditions of low to intermediate light intensities. The energetic yield $\Phi_e$ depends on the energy gap between the originally excited chromophore and the trap, e.g., the primary donor. It is near 100% for the excitation into the $Q_Y$ band (see below) in *shallow antennas* that are nearly isoenergetic with the RC, as for example, in green plants. It can even be distinctly $>100\%$ in the core antennas, which generally absorb to the red of the RC. In these cases, the transfer is diffusive and the gained energy is of thermal origin (see [47]). Examples are *Blastochloris viridis* (antenna absorption at 1025 nm, RC at 980 nm, $\Phi_e \approx 105\%$) [48], *Ostreobium* (antenna $\leq 740$ nm, primary donor 700 nm, $\Phi_e \approx 105\%$) [49], and a purple sulfur bacterium provisionally called strain 970 (antenna 963 nm, RC 870 nm, $\Phi_e = 111\%$) [50]. In these antennas, EET is reversible, and limited kinetically by the charge-separation in the RC.

In *steep antennas*, the energy gap can be much larger, and $\Phi_e$ is reduced accordingly. Such an energy transfer is practically irreversible and helps to direct the excitation energy flow towards the RC. The $\Phi_e$ is particularly low whenever the antenna pigment is excited into a higher state. *Blastochloris viridis* is again an extreme example: when excited in the Soret band ($\sim 350$ nm), the transfer to the RC ($\lambda_{max} = 980$ nm) corresponds to a $\Phi_e$ as low as 35%.

*3.2.3 Light-induced Electron Transfer*

The primary donors of all reaction centers are chlorophylls *a* or in case of the cyanobacterium *Acaryochloris marina* Chl *d* (oxygenic photosynthesis) (Chapters 6, 14 and 16) or bacteriochlorophylls *a*, *b* or *g* (anoxygenic bacteria) (Chapter 12) [4]. Upon excitation, a stepwise electron transfer is induced across the photosynthetic membrane, which involves in the first steps neighboring (B)Chls and, in PSII-type RC, (bacterio-)pheophytins ((B)Phe). The process has been investigated in greatest detail in purple bacterial RC [51]. Here, the primary donor is a dimer ("*special pair*") of BChl *a* or *b*, which upon excitation transfers within $\sim 3$ ps an electron to a neighboring monomeric BChl *a* (or *b*), thus generating the primary radical pair, $BChl_2^{+\cdot}/BChl^{-\cdot}$. The electron is then transferred within $\sim 1$ ps on to a secondary acceptor, which is a bacteriopheophytin (BPhe) *a* (or *b*) that lacks the central Mg (Section 3.3.6). In the reaction center of PS II, the BChls are replaced by Chl *a*, the BPhe by pheophytin (Phe) *a*, but here the primary donor is probably not the special pair, but the monomeric Chl *a* [52]. Type I reaction centers (PS I, heliobacteria, green sulfur bacteria) lack the metal free (B)Phe, but have a chlorophyllous pigment (= Mg complex) at the same location. Here, the primary electron transfer generates from a heterodimer of Chl *a* and its epimer, Chl *a'* (PS I), or from a BChl g/BChl g' pair (heliobacteria) [53]. For a discussion of alternative primary events, the reader is referred to the literature [52].

*3.2.4 Quenching of Excitation Energy*

Excess energy in the antenna, or triplet energy in the RC, is generally quenched by transfer to carotenoids, and subsequent rapid internal conversion [39,54]. Only few examples are currently known for the quenching of excited states by Chls, but there may be more. One example is cation radicals. They have been generated artificially in purple bacterial LH complexes, but may also arise in vivo under saturating light conditions [14]. Another example are chlorosomes: in model aggregates devoid of carotenoids, a conformational(?) change can be induced by intense light pulses, which leads to excited state quenching [15]. It is tempting to anticipate such processes also in vivo.

### 3.2.5 Structure Stabilization

Chls contribute up to 40% (by weight) of light-harvesting chlorophyll proteins; obviously, therefore, they contribute to their structures or may even be a driving force for antenna assembly. Chl proteins are destabilized if Chls are removed by extraction [18] or by genetic manipulation of ligands to the central Mg (see, for example, [55]) and protected against degradation by the pigments [56]. In bacterial LH1, the thermodynamics of the assembly are influenced by changes of the central metal [57].

A particular organization factor derives from the rich aggregation behavior of (B)Chls both in organic [58,59] and microheterogeneous aqueous environments [60,61]. The physiological relevance of such aggregates had been dismissed with the detection and isolation of chlorophyll proteins [62–64]. However, chlorophyll oligomers are frequently found in photosynthetic complexes and their importance in energy and electron transfer has been recognized [53,65–76]. The geometries of such oligomers resemble in particular those found in (B)Chl oligomers formed in micellar aqueous media (see [60]). This led to a concept that chlorophyll interactions contribute to the organization of (B)Chl proteins, but these interactions are modified by the polypeptide for functional optimization (see [77,78]). Strong interactions among the chlorophylls have been substantiated in particular in bacterial antennas [45,59,79–82]. All this points to a considerable contribution of chlorophylls to the formation and stability of the light-harvesting pigment–protein complexes. Of particular importance is the avoidance of excited-state quenching: most (B)Chl aggregates are non-fluorescing, and even in chlorosome-type aggregates (see below) only a minor structural change has been proposed to generate quenching states [15].

The presence of only minor amounts of protein in the chlorosomes of green bacteria has revived the idea that chlorophyll-only aggregates are present and functional in vivo. In vitro aggregates of the BChls *c*, *d* or *e* are spectroscopically very similar to chlorosomes containing the respective pigments [59,83–85]. However, the CD spectrum of chlorosomes from *Chloroflexus aurantiacus* are changed by treatment with protease [86], indicating some influence of the protein on the structure. All chlorosome-generating pigments carry a $3^1$-OH group. Introduction of α-OH- and α-CO-groups at different pyrrole rings has been demonstrated as a general feature to promote aggregation of metalloporphyrins, -chlorins and -bacteriochlorins [87–92].

## 3.3 Structures of Chlorophyll Molecules

Chlorophylls are generally described as cyclic Mg-tetrapyrroles derived from protoporphyrin IX (Proto), in which the 13-propionic acid side chain is methylated and cyclized to give rise to the isocyclic ring E, and the 17-propionic acid side chain is esterified by a terpenoid alcohol like phytol (for nomenclature, see Figure 1B and [1,2,66,93]). Of these features, the only remaining universal one is the isocyclic five-membered ring; there are more or less abundant exceptions from the others. The central Mg is replaced by Zn in a group of purple bacteria while retaining the function [94], and type II RC contain metal-free pheophytins, which participate in charge separation [95,96]. The 17-propionic acid is free in most of the Chls c that are abundant in certain algae [97], or esterified with alcohols other than phytol in many photosynthetic bacteria, and last but not least the $13^2$-COOCH$_3$-group is missing in BChls c, d, e in the chlorosomes of green bacteria [84,98].

A distinguishing structural feature among the different Chls is the degree of unsaturation of the macrocycle, which is also a spectral determinant (Table 2). The Chls c of chromophyte algae and some prokaryotes are fully unsaturated porphyrins (Figure 1A); they absorb moderately in the 620 nm region and strongly in the 400–450 nm region. Chls a, b and d of oxygenic organisms and the BChls c, d and e of green anoxygenic bacteria (Figure 1B) are chlorins (17,18-dyhydroporphyrins); they have two intense absorptions at the edges of the visible spectral region (Vis) at 400–470 and 640–700 nm. Bacteriochlorophylls a, b and g of anoxygenic bacteria are bacteriochlorins (7,8,17,18-tetrahydroporphyrins) (Figure 1C), which absorb only weakly in the Vis, but have two intense absorptions outside, in the near-ultraviolet (UV) and the near-infrared (NIR).

*3.3.1 Chlorophylls c: the Porphyrin Type*

All c-type chlorophylls are porphyrins (Figure 1A). An important structural feature of most but not all Chls c is the free acrylic or propionic acid side-chain at C-17; accordingly they should properly be termed chlorophyllides (Chlide) c, with the ending "ide" characterizing the free acid. They are much more polar compounds than the esterified Chls, and widespread in algae that are sometimes summed up as "chromophytes" (Chrysophyceae, Raphidophyceae, Pheophyceae, Xanthophyceae, Bacillariophyceae, haptophyta, cryptophyta and dinophyta) [24,97,99]. There are also some prokaryotes members of the chlorophyll c family [100], where they contribute to the absorption of green light that is prevalent in many aquatic environments (for a discussion, see Chapter 22 and [24,101]).

Based mainly on improved chromatographic systems [102], several new Chls c have been identified over the past decade, and more can be expected in view of the variety of (particularly marine) photosynthetic organisms [97].

(a)

| Pigment | $R_1$ | $R_2$ | Remarks |
|---|---|---|---|
| Chl(ide) $c_1$ | $CH_3$ | $C_2H_5$ | 1 |
| Chl(ide) $c_2$ | $CH_3$ | $C_2H_3$ | 1 |
| Chl(ide) $c_3$ | $COOCH_3$ | $C_2H_{3/5}$ | 1 |
| PChl(ide) a | $CH_3$ | $C_2H_5$ | 2 |
| [8-Vinyl]-PChl(ide) a | $CH_3$ | $C_2H_3$ | 1,2,3 |

(b)

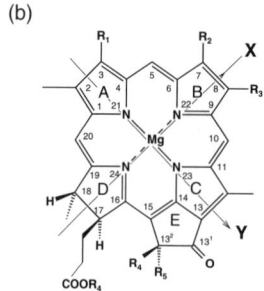

| Pigment | $R_1$ | $R_2$ | $R_3$ | $R_4$ | $R_5$ | $R_6$ |
|---|---|---|---|---|---|---|
| Chl a | $C_2H_3$ | $CH_3$ | $C_2H_5$ | H | $COOCH_3$ | Phy |
| Chl a' | $C_2H_3$ | $CH_3$ | $C_2H_5$ | $COOCH_3$ | H | Phy |
| Chlid a | $C_2H_3$ | $CH_3$ | $C_2H_5$ | H | $COOCH_3$ | H |
| Chl b | $C_2H_3$ | CHO | $C_2H_5$ | H | $COOCH_3$ | Phy |
| Chl d | CHO | $CH_3$ | $C_2H_5$ | H | $COOCH_3$ | Phy |
| [8-Vinyl]-Chl a | $C_2H_3$ | $CH_3$ | $C_2H_3$ | H | $COOCH_3$ | Phy |
| $8^2$-OH-Chl a | $C_2H_3$ | $CH_3$ | $C_2H_4$-OH | H | $COOCH_3$ | Phy |
| Phe a | $C_2H_3$ | $CH_3$ | $C_2H_5$ | H | $COOCH_3$ | Phy |

| Pigment | $R_1$ | $R_2$ | $R_3$ | $R_4$ | $R_5$ |
|---|---|---|---|---|---|
| BChl c | $CH_3$ | et,pr,ib,np | me,et | Farn,18:0,many others | $CH_3$ |
| BChl d | $CH_3$ | et,pr,ib,np | me,et | Farn,18:0,many others | H |
| BChl e | CHO | et,pr,ib,np | me,et | Farn,18:0,many others | $CH_3$ |

(c)

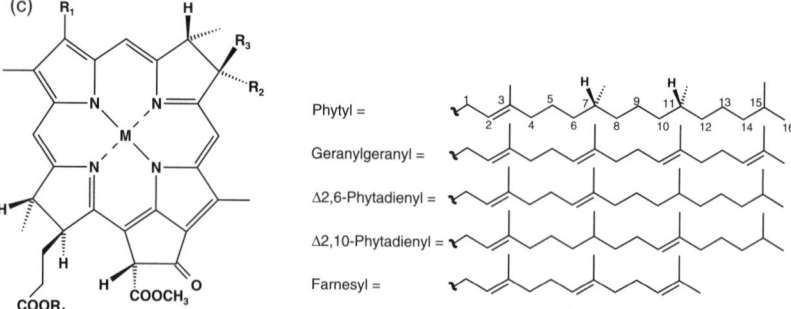

| Pigment | $R_1$ | $R_2$ | $R_3$ | $R_4$ | M |
|---|---|---|---|---|---|
| BChl a | $COCH_3$ | H | $C_2H_5$ | variable | Mg (or Zn) |
| BChl b | $COCH_3$ | | =CH-$CH_3$ | variable | Mg |
| BChl g | $C_2H_3$ | | =CH-$CH_3$ | variable | Mg |

# CHLOROPHYLLS

[8-Vinyl]-protochlorophyllide *a* (3,8-divinyl-pheoporphyrin *a*-Mg-monomethyl ester), which is a precursor of most other Chls and therefore probably phylogenetically old, is a light-harvesting pigment in symbiontic prokaryotes [103]. Esterified Chls *c* have been known for nearly 20 years [99]; their proposed structures include one that is covalently linked to a galactolipid [104].

*3.3.2 Chlorophylls a, b, d: the Chlorin Type from Oxygenic Phototrophs*

Chl *a* (Figure 1B) is the prototype textbook Chl; its structure was the first to be established [105] and it has been synthesized [106]. It is present in the RC and LH complexes of almost all oxygenic organisms (Tables 1 and 2). It is, however, almost always accompanied by other pigments that supplement its two intense ($\varepsilon \approx 10^5$ $M^{-1}$ $cm^{-1}$) but narrow absorptions at the edges of the visible spectrum ($\approx 460$ and $\approx 670$ nm). Green plants, green algae and type II cyanobacteria ("prochlorophytes") [107] contain Chl *b*, which reduces the "green gap" to the region 500–600 nm. Chl *d* has been identified as the major pigment in a Chl *c*-containing prochlorophyte, *Acaryochloris marina* [100]. It has distinctly red-shifted absorptions as compared with Chl *a*, and can replace the latter in the LH complexes, including the core antenna [108], in RCI [109,110] and probably even in RC II. Chl *b* can replace Chl *a* in LHC II [17,111] and at least partly in core antennas and reaction centers of cyanobacteria [112,113].

*3.3.3 Bacteriochlorophylls c, d, e: the Chlorin Type from Anoxygenic Green Bacteria*

Bchls *c*, *d* and *e* (Figure 1B) are the main constituents of chlorosomes, the extra-membraneous peripheral antennas of green bacteria [84,114]. Despite their names, these bacteriochlorophylls are chlorins and not bacteriochlorins. Their

---

**Figure 1.** Structures of chlorophylls (Chl) and bacteriochlorophylls (BChl). (a) Chlorophylls of the porphyrin-type. On the right-hand side, a novel hydrophobic chlorophyll c is shown that has been isolated from *Emiliana huxleyi* [104]. See part (b) for numbering. Note the distinction between chlorophylls (Chl, esterified at C-17$^3$, $R_3$ = esterifying alcohol) and chlorophyllides (Chlide, free C-17$^3$ acid group, $R_3$ – H), which is often blurred in the literature. Remarks: (1) Stereochemistry at C-13$^2$ unknown. (2) No double-bond in the C-17 side-chain. (3) This pigment is also referred to as "divinyl-PChlide a". (b) Chlorophylls of the chlorin type. Left: Plant chlorophylls (chlorins) with a single bond between C-17 and C-18. The structure of Phytol (Phy) is shown in (C). Note that Phe *a* lacks the central Mg. Numbering according to IUPAC [1,66], the *x*- and *y*-axes relevant to spectroscopy are indicated. Right: Bacterial chlorophylls of the chlorin type: Bacteriochlorophylls c, d, e. These pigments, which occur in chlorosomes, are also referred to as chlorobium chlorophylls in the older literature. Abbreviations: 18:0 = stearyl, et = ethyl, ib = isobutyl, np = neopentyl, pr = propyl, me = methyl. C-3$^1$ (marked by an asterisk) can occur in two epimeric configurations; the 3$^1$(*R*)-to-3$^1$(*S*) epimer ratio varies with the size of the C-8 substituent. (c) Chlorophylls of the bacteriochlorin-type, with single bonds between C-7/C-8 and C-17/C-18: bacteriochlorophylls a, b and g. Right-hand side: a selection of esterifying alcohols.

**Table 1.** Occurrence of chlorophylls (mass pigments bold **X**, minor pigments in brackets)

| Pigment | Chloroflexaceae | Chlorobiaceae | Heliobacteria | Purple bacteria | Cyanophyta I[b] | Cyanophyta II[b] | Glaucophyta (Cyanelles) | Rhodophyta | Chrysophyceae | Raphidophyceae | Pheophyceae | Xanthophyceae | Eustigmatophyceae | Bacillariophyceae (Diatoms) | Haptophyta | Cryptophyta | Dinophyta (Dinoflagellates)[c] | Euglenophyta | Chlorarachniophyta | Prasinophyceae | Chlorophyceae | Green plants |
|---|---|---|---|---|---|---|---|---|---|---|---|---|---|---|---|---|---|---|---|---|---|---|
| **Chlorophylls** | | | | | | | | | | | | | | | | | | | | | | |
| Chlorophyll a | | | | | **X** | **X** | **X** | **X** | **X** | **X** | **X** | **X** | **X** | **X** | **X** | **X** | **X** | **X** | **X** | **X** | **X** | **X** |
| [8-Vinyl]-chlorophyll a | | | | | | **X** | | | | | | | | | | | | | | | | |
| $8^2$-Hydroxy-chlorophyll a | | (x) | | | | | | | | | | | | | | | | | | | | |
| Chlorophyll b | | | | | | **X** | | | | | | | | | | | | **X** | **X** | **X** | **X** | **X** |
| [8-Vinyl]-chlorophyll b | | | | | | **X** | | | | | | | | | | | | | | | | |
| Chlorophyll $c_1$ | | | | | | | x | | **X** | **X** | **X** | (x) | | **X** | **X** | | | | | | | |
| Chlorophyll $c_2$ | | | | | | | | | **X** | **X** | **X** | (x) | | **X** | **X** | **X** | (x)[c] | | | | | |
| Chlorophyll $c_3$ | | | | | | | | | | | | | | | **X** | | (x)[c] | | | | | |
| Esterified chlorophyll c | | | | | | | | | | | | | | | | | | | | | | |
| Mg-[8-vinyl]-Protochlorophyllide a | | | | | | | | | | | | | | | | | | | | **X** | | |
| Chlorophyll d | | | | | (x) | $X^d$ | | | | | | | | | | | | | | | | |
| Bacteriochlorophyll a | **X** | **X** | | **X** | | | | | | | | | | | | | | | | | | |
| [Zn]-Bacteriochlorophyll a | | | | $X^d$ | | | | | | | | | | | | | | | | | | |
| Bacteriochlorophyll b | | | | **X** | | | | | | | | | | | | | | | | | | |
| Bacteriochlorophylls c | **X** | **X** | | | | | | | | | | | | | | | | | | | | |
| Bacteriochlorophylls d | **X** | **X** | | | | | | | | | | | | | | | | | | | | |
| Bacteriochlorophylls e | | **X** | | | | | | | | | | | | | | | | | | | | |
| Bacteriochlorophyll f | | | | | | | | | | | | | | | | | | | | | | |
| Bacteriochlorophyll g | | | **X** | | | | | | | | | | | | | | | | | | | |

[a]See Green and Anderson [64] for taxonomy of algae, in particular of the Heterokonts (Chrysophyceae, Raphidophyceae, Pheophyceae, Xanthophyceae, Eustigmatophyceae, Haptophyta).
[b]Cyanophyta I have the classical pigmentation (Chl a plus phycobilins). Cyanophyta II contain Chl b in addition to Chl a (or the respective [8-vinyl]-analogues), and few or no phycobilins.
[c]Pigmentation depends on endosymbiontic photosynthetic organisms. Besides dinophytes, cryptophytes, green algae or various heterokonts are known, the pigments can be useful as phylogenetic markers.
[d]Identified only in few species, but here the major pigment.

**Table 2.** Location, functions and major absorptions of photosynthetic pigments. LH = Light-harvesting, eT = electron transfer

| Pigments | Location | Function(s) | Absorption | | Reference |
|---|---|---|---|---|---|
| | | | In diethyl ether, $\lambda_{max}$ (nm) ($\epsilon$ $10^{-3}$ $M^{-1}$ $cm^{-1}$) | In vivo, $\lambda_{max}$ (nm) | |
| Chl $a$ | Antenna, reaction centers | LH + eT | 429(115), 661(90) | ≈440, ≈670 | [136] |
| Chl $a'$ | PS I reaction center | eT | 429(115), 661(90) | ≈440, ≈770 | |
| [8-Vinyl]-Chl $a$ | Antenna | LH | 435,660 | 442,666 | [152] |
| Phe $a$ | PS II reaction center | eT | 408(107), 668(53) | | [136] |
| Chl $b$ | Peripheral antenna | LH | 452(159), 642(57) | ≈460, ≈650 | [136] |
| [8-Vinyl]-Chl $b$ | Antenna | LH | 460,644 | 478,658 | [152] |
| Chl $c_1$[a] | Peripheral antenna | LH | 446(212), 629(24)[b] | ≈400, 550–630 | [136] |
| Chl $d$[e] | Antenna, reaction center | LH + eT | 447(87), 688(98) | ≈440, ≈690 | [323] |
| Phe $d$ | PS II reaction center | eT | 421(86), 692(72) | | [323] |
| Bchl $a$ | Antenna, reaction center | LH+eT | 357(75), 771(97) | <400, 800–960 | [136] |
| Bphe $a$ | Type II reaction center | eT | 358(114), 749(68) | | [136] |
| Bchl $b$ | Antenna, reaction center | LH + eT | 372(77), 91(106) | <400, 800–1020 | [323] |
| Bphe $b$[e] | Type II reaction center | ET | 398(1), 776(0.42)[d] | | [136] |
| Bchl $c$[c] | Peripheral antenna (chlorosomes) | LH | 429(112), 660(73) | ≈440, 640–760 | [136] |
| BChl $d$[c] | Peripheral antenna (chlorosomes) | LH | 423(117), 651(88) | ≈440, 640–750 | [136] |
| BChl $e$[c] | Peripheral antenna (chlorosomes) | LH | 476, 660(41) | | [324] |
| Bchl $g$ | Antenna/reaction center unit | LH + eT | 364(0.94), 767(1)[d] | <400, 780–850 | [136] |

[a] Spectra of other c-Chls and of Pchlide are similar.
[b] Acetone-pyridine = 100:1.
[c] Mixture of homologues.
[d] Relative absorptions.
[e] Major pigment in few species.

unifying structural features are a 3-CHOH-CH$_3$ substituent and the lack of the 13$^2$-COOCH$_3$ group of the isocyclic ring. BChls c and e carry a 20-CH$_3$ substituent; BChls e also carry the 7-CHO characteristic of Chl b. Otherwise, these BChls show remarkable structural variations. There is a prevalence of farnesol as esterifying alcohol, but several others have also been found [115]. Other variations are single (C-12, C-12$^1$, C-20) or even multiple methylations (C-8$^2$), and the occurrence of C-3$^1$ epimers (Figure 1B) [116,117]. Not all theoretically possible combinations of these features have (yet?) been found, but the phylogenetically rather restricted BChls c, d and e provide nonetheless over 50% of the currently known Chl structures. An understanding of the functional significance of these variations for the chlorosome, whose interior appears to be largely devoid of proteins, is currently a major challenge in chlorophyll research [15,83,89,118,119].

*3.3.4 Bacteriochlorophylls a, b, g: the Bacteriochlorin Type*

These three pigments from anoxygenic photosynthetic bacteria are true bacteriochlorins (=7,8,17,18-tetrahydroporphyrins), characterized by hydrogenation of the peripheral double bonds of rings B and D. In solutions, this type of pigments has the Q$_Y$-absorption band redshifted to 750–800 nm, and a blue-shifted Soret-band (<400 nm), thereby extending the absorptions in both regions beyond those of all other chlorophylls. In vivo, the Q$_Y$-band can be redshifted even up to 1020 nm (Table 2). The most widely distributed of these pigments is probably bacteriochlorophyll a (Bchl a, Figure 1C). It is present in RCs and the core-antennas of green and purple anoxygenic bacteria [48,98], as well as in the antennas of the purple bacteria [48]. In a few species, it is replaced by the structurally related BChl b, which carries an ethylidene substituent at C-8 (instead of the ethyl group in BChl a) [120,121]. Bchl g$_F$ (Figure 1C, the subscript refers to the esterifying alcohol, farnesol) is the major pigment of the strictly anaerobic Gram-positive heliobacteria [122], in both the light-harvesting complexes and the RC, which are integrated in the type I-RC of heliobacteria [123].

In certain purple bacteria, pigments with more highly unsaturated terpenoid alcohols can replace the BChl $a_p$ (the subscript "p" denotes phytol as esterifying alcohol) [124] or BChl $b_p$ [125]. The significance of such modified alcohols remains unclear. In monodisperse solution, the esterifying alcohols have practically no influence on the optical spectra. However, they profoundly affect aggregation of the pigments [126], which may have an effect on the stability and assembly of the pigment–protein complexes (see Section 3.4). Indications of this come from X-ray structures, where the alcohols are generally well defined [53,65,67,74,127–132]. In LH2 from *Rhodopseudomonas acidophila*, for example, the "phytyl-tails" show remarkable interactions among each other and with the carotenoids [69], and they also interact with lipids that have been found in several complexes [53,73,131,133,134].

## CHLOROPHYLLS

### 3.3.5 Transmetalated Chlorophylls

In the purple bacterium *Acidiphilium rubrum* and several related strains, up to 90% of the BChl has Zn instead of Mg as the central metal [94,135,136]. Probably, the acidity of the mine-ponds posed the evolutionary pressure responsible for a change of the central metal: [Zn]-BChl is much more stable towards acid than BChl; while the two pigments have otherwise quite similar chemical and photophysical properties [57,137–139]. The transmetalated pigment is therefore capable of functionally replacing BChl *a* in all pigment proteins and at all sites, including the primary donor, P870 [140]. The only other organism for which a Zn-tetrapyrrole, Zn-Proto, has been reported is the rhodophyte *Cyanidium caldarium* (*Galdieria sulphuraria*) [141]. It grows under very acidic conditions, too, but all its Chls contain Mg (Wolfgang Gross, private communication, 2003). It is currently not clear whether in *Acidiphilium* the Zn is introduced either by a specialized chelatase or by replacing an originally inserted Mg at a later biosynthetic stage (see [136]). Practically all subsequent enzymes of Chl biosynthesis accept both the Mg- and the Zn-pigments as substrates (see, e.g., [142]), and the Zn-pigments can replace the respective chlorophylls in all sites accessible to exchange or reconstitution (see [18,57,143]).

Chls with Hg, Cd, Ni, Cu or Pb replacing the central Mg have been isolated from several plants grown on media or at sites enriched in the respective metals [144]. These pigments may arise by spontaneous, non-enzymatic replacement of the labile Mg, which is not only possible in vitro with the free pigments but even in isolated light-harvesting complexes, at concentrations likely to exist within the cells. In these organisms, photosynthesis is strongly impaired [145], which is likely due to the rapid internal conversion of tetrapyrroles containing metals with unfilled d-shells [146]. Such pigments can act as "black holes", which efficiently quench any exciton that passes by. For example, [Ni]-BChl *a* shows internal conversion (IC) on a time-scale < 100 fs [147–150]: if it is incorporated in bacterial LH1 complexes [80,81] or RC [151] it can compete efficiently with energy transfer at time-scales down to 50 fs.

### 3.3.6 "Minor" Chlorophylls

The number of recognized chlorophylls is constantly increasing. In some cases already mentioned above, new chlorophylls functionally replace most of the "common" Chl of the respective organisms in both antenna and RC. An example is the presence of [8-vinyl]-Chls a and b as the most abundant pigments in *Prochlorococcus* species that live down to considerable depths ($\approx 100$ m) [152]. The functional significance of this substituent change is currently unclear: in the red spectral region they absorb only slightly differently from the corresponding Chls a and b bearing an 8-ethyl-group instead, but this may be significant with respect to the absorption band of water around 700 nm.

Small amounts of "unusual" Chls are often present in the RC. The metal-free pheophytin (Phe) *a* is located in the PSII-RC halfway across the membrane between the primary acceptor and the quinone $Q_A$ (Chapter 15 and [73]) and can be used to quantify PSII [153]. *Acaryochloris marina* contains, possibly, a Phe *d* instead ([154], but see [155]), and bacteriopheophytin (Bphe) *a* or *b* is similarly located in the related RC of purple bacteria [65,67,129]. Phe *b* can replace one Phe *a* in PSII-RC of cyanobacteria [113]. The redox potentials of pheophytins are ≈ 200 mV more positive than those of the respective chlorophylls [156], which helps them to serve as secondary acceptors in the electron transfer [157]. Type I-RCs contain *prime* Chls, the $13^2$(S)-epimers of the respective major chlorophylls. PSI of Chl *a*-containing organisms contain Chl *a'* [153], where is has been verified as one of the pigments of the special pair [53,158]. Chl *d'* is present in the Chl *d*-containing *Acaryochloris marina* [154], and heliobacteria contain BChl *g'* [159].

$8^2$-Hydroxy-Chl $a_F$ bearing a hydroxyethyl substituent at C-8 and esterified with farnesol has been identified in *Heliobacterium chlorum*; it is believed to function as primary acceptor $A_0$ [160]. Selective modifications of the esterifying alcohols have been found in two cases: Chl $a_{\Delta2,6}$ (esterified with $\Delta^{2,6}$-phytadienol) is present in the RCs from green bacteria, which are also likely to be of the type I [161]. In *Rhodospirillum rubrum*, the bacteriochlorophylls of the RC are esterified with phytol, and those in the antennas with geranylgeraniol [162].

Chl-enols have been implicated as components of P700 in PSI-RCs [163]. The second Chl of P700 is strongly distorted, but the recent 2.5 Å X-ray structure [53] is still inconclusive in this respect.

## 3.4 Spectroscopy

### 3.4.1 Optical Absorption Spectroscopy

The intense color of chlorophylls and the response of the spectra to structural modifications and environmental changes has made absorption spectroscopy one of the most widely used methods in chlorophyll research. It is simple, sensitive and relatively free of background noise, and time-resolution is possible down to the femtosecond ($10^{-15}$ s) range [164,165]. With high-intensity (laser) irradiation, optical transitions can be induced that involve more than one photon; no such processes are considered in this and the following sections. According to the four-orbital model of Gouterman [166], excitation of $D_{4h}$-symmetric metalloporphyrins results in two degenerate pairs of transitions, which are both accompanied by vibronic side bands. They give rise to the comparatively weak ($\varepsilon \approx 10^4$ $M^{-1}$ $cm^{-1}$) $Q_{0-0}$ band with a vibronic side band ($Q_{0-1}$) in the 500–600 nm region, and to the intense ($\varepsilon \approx 10^5$ $M^{-1}$ $cm^{-1}$) Soret or B-bands ($B_{0-0}$, $B_{0-1}$) near 400 nm (Figure 2; see Figure 3 for a Jablonski diagram depicting different electronic and vibrational levels and transitions among them). A lowering of the symmetry, like the introduction of the isocyclic ring E, lifts the degeneracy of both the Q and the B bands, and renders at the same time the visible Q-bands less forbidden. This increases the absorption of

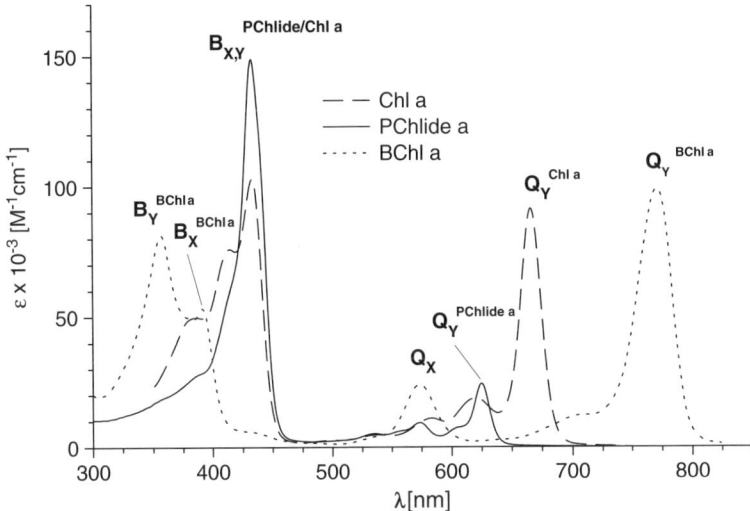

Figure 2. Absorption spectra of cyclic conjugated tetrapyrroles in monodisperse solutions: Influence of conjugation system on spectra. Shown are the spectra of porphyrin type (PChlide a = protochlorophyllide a), chlorin type (Chl a = chlorophyll a) and bacteriochlorin type (BChl a = bacteriochlorophyll a) with assignments of the major absorption bands according to the four-orbital model.

PChlide and c-type Chlides (which are all Mg-porphyrins containing the isocyclic ring E) in the green region 2–3-fold (Table 2, Figure 2), which is likely to be a major factor for the evolution of this structural signature of the chlorophylls.

The reduction of the porphyrin-macrocycle at C-17,18 in the chlorins, and additionally at C-7,8 in the bacteriochlorins, stepwise reduces the symmetry π-system even more; the intensities of the Q- and B-bands now become comparable. At the same, the more elongated shape of the π-system produces a redshift of one of the Q-bands ($Q_Y$) to 650–680 nm (chlorins) or even 750–800 nm (bacteriochlorins), thus increasing substantially light-harvesting in the visible or NIR region. The $Q_X$-band, which is oriented along the X-axis running through rings B and D [167], is less redshifted and less intense. In the chlorins (e.g., Chl a) the B-bands are split, too ($B_x$, $B_y$), but still overlap. The x/y-subscripts denote the orientation of this transition along the molecular Y- and X-axes running through rings A/C/E and B/D, respectively, as indicated in the Chl a formula in Figure 1(B). In the bacteriochlorins, all four bands predicted by MO theory are well separated – they even have moderately intense and prominent $Q_X$-bands. Scherz et al. have this investigated situation in detail, including the mixing of the transitions [60,137,168].

The absorption spectra can be considerably modified in situ. The most pronounced effect in nearly all photosynthetic complexes is a redshift of the $Q_y$ transition by up to 220 nm (2700 cm$^{-1}$), which is often accompanied by an increase of this band at the expense of the $Q_x$ and the B-bands. These effects arise (a) from interactions of the pigment with the surrounding protein or nearby lipids, which are often termed "site interactions" or "site shifts", and (b) from interactions with neighboring chromophores (pigment–pigment interaction). The two factors are not easily separated; furthermore, any change of the former can influence the latter. An added complexity is the time-scale: light absorption, energy transfer, charge separation, electron transfer, and dissipation of excess energy span a time regime from tens of femtoseconds (fs) to nanoseconds (ns). Therefore, the dynamics of these interactions have to be included in the description [30,42,43,45,81,169]. Considerable effort has been invested to understand these interactions on a molecular basis, by which the photosynthetic apparatus is fine-tuned (Chapters 2 and 16).

The structural characterization of many photosynthetic pigment–protein complexes has set the stage for directed modifications [53,65,67–76,127,131,170], which are often complemented by in vitro model studies [60,168,171–175]. Parametric changes of the redox potentials or absorption energies of defined chromophores are particularly valuable tools for such an analysis (Table 3). Three methods have proven particularly useful, of which only selected examples are given here. The first is manipulations of the chromophores' biosynthetic pathways. While more widely applied to manipulate carotenoids (Chapter 4 and [176–178]), they have only more recently been used to introduce modified chlorophylls [112,113]. The second approach is site-directed mutagenesis of the chromophore binding pocket. One target are those amino acids that are ligands to the central Mg. It is possible to exchange pheophytins for chlorophylls, or vice versa, by removing or introducing amino acids capable of ligating the central Mg. Care has to be taken, however, that the mutation does not create a void into which a chlorophyll can carry a small ligand like water (see, e.g., [179–182]). More subtle changes are possible if the original ligating amino acid (aa) is exchanged for another one by which the

**Table 3.** Adjustable properties of chromophores, and selected examples of their use in studying photosynthetic pigment–protein complexes

| Adjustable property | Probe | References |
|---|---|---|
| Excited state energy | Energy transfer (singlet and triplet) | [44,325] |
| | Excitonic coupling of chromophores | [326] |
| | Band assignments | [327,328] |
| Redox potentials | Electron transfer | [51,113,329,330] |
| | Creation of trapping sites | |
| Excited state dynamics | Energy transfer | [80,81,113,151] |
| | Creation of unusual excited states | |
| Functional groups | Interactions (pigment–pigment and pigment–protein) | [51,57,328] |
| | Redox potentials | |
| Isotope composition | Labeling | [266,331] |
| | Assignments (NMR, vibrational and X-ray spectra, neutron scattering) | |
| | Biosynthesis | |

ligation is modified. A recent example is an Asn-His exchange to the far-redshifted chlorophylls in LHCI-complexes (Roberto Bassi, personal communication, 2004). It is likely that excitonic interactions are modified by this exchange, by either a change in the inter-chromophore distance due to steric effects or by changing the electron density of the macrocycle. Partial charge transfer from ligands via the central atom to the macrocycle has been demonstrated [171,183,184].

Mutations of amino acids interacting with the peripheral groups have proven particularly valuable not only for changing the redox potential of chlorophylls but also their absorption spectra [170,185,186]. A pertinent example is mutations that interact with the 3-acetyl group of BChl $a$ in purple bacterial complexes [68,77,187]. Recently, more extensive mutations that inhibit the assembly of complexes have been used as a starting point to introduce individual amino acids and study their effect in rescuing the assembly and on the properties of the resulting complex. As an example, an individual H-bond to the isocyclic ring C-$13^1$ could be identified as driving the assembly, and thereby the excitonic coupling of BChls, in LH1 [188,189].

The third approach is the introduction of chemically modified chromophores, either by reconstitution or by exchange of chromophores [16,18,44,57,111,143,190,191]. Modified pigments can be either of natural origin or obtained by chemical modification of natural pigments (see [18,142,190,192–194] for leading references on chlorophyll modifications). By introducing pigments with increasingly blue-shifted absorptions, the monomeric nature and the absence of significant excitonic interactions have been demonstrated for BChl-B800 in the purple bacterial antenna, LH2 [44], and for the primary acceptor, BChl-B800 in reaction centers from the same organism [190]. On the other hand, long-range excitonic interactions over ~20 BChl have been deduced from the introduction of chromophores that, by their extremely short excited states, interfere with energy migration in LH1 [80,81]. Excitonic coupling in the peripheral antenna of PSII, viz. LHCII, has likewise been probed by exchanging Chl $a$ for Chl $b$, and vice versa (see [111]).

*3.4.2 Luminescence Spectroscopy*

Fluorescence has many of the advantages of optical absorption spectroscopy [195]. In analytical applications it is even more sensitive, down to the single molecule level [45], but requires care to avoid artifacts because of the sensitivity of fluorescence to environmental changes and to shading. This sensitivity has, though, been exploited widely in physiological studies. In solution, chlorophylls show intense fluorescence due to a radiative transition from the $S_1$ to the $S_0$ electronic state (Figure 3). It is only slightly redshifted as compared with the respective $Q_Y$-absorption (for the origin of this Stokes shift see caption of Figure 3). This intense fluorescence reflects the relatively long $S_1$-lifetimes (several ns) of this type of pigment, which is due to the rigid macrocycle and the light main group metal, Mg, in the center of the macrocycle (see [196]). The selection for these structural features has probably been a major factor in the success of (B)Chl-based photosynthesis. The intense fluorescence can be used for very sensitive detection of (B)Chls, e.g., in liquid chromatography [102,197]. Since fluorescence and de-excitation via internal conversion are complementary processes, it should be mentioned that the latter can be measured by thermal methods, including, in particular, photoacoustic spectroscopy [198].

Intersystem crossing (ISC) from $S_1$ can lead to the lowest triplet state $T_1$ and subsequent radiative recovery of the ground-state by emission of phosphorescence [199]. $T_1$ still contains $\approx 2/3$ of the energy of the $S_1$ state and has a very long lifetime (μs to ms), which render $T_1$ potentially very dangerous. In particular, it can generate reactive oxygen species: energy transfer to oxygen (which is a triplet in its ground state) is spin-allowed and leads to the generation of highly reactive singlet oxygen ($^1O_2$), and electron transfer to oxygen can generate superoxide or the highly reactive OH-radical (Figure 3). Solutions of (B)Chls therefore bleach very rapidly on irradiation in the presence of oxygen, and can also bleach other pigments [200–202]. This photodynamic action of (B)Chls and other tetrapyrroles is the basis of several insecticides [203], herbicides [204] and anti-tumor agents [205–209]. Replacement of the central metal by transition metals leads to a shortening of the $S_1$-lifetimes by several orders of magnitude, a corresponding shortening of the fluorescence, and is often accompanied by increased ISC. An exception is Zn, which is a central metal for BChl *a* in certain acidophilic purple bacteria ([94,139], while other metals are deleterious to photosynthesis [80,144,151]).

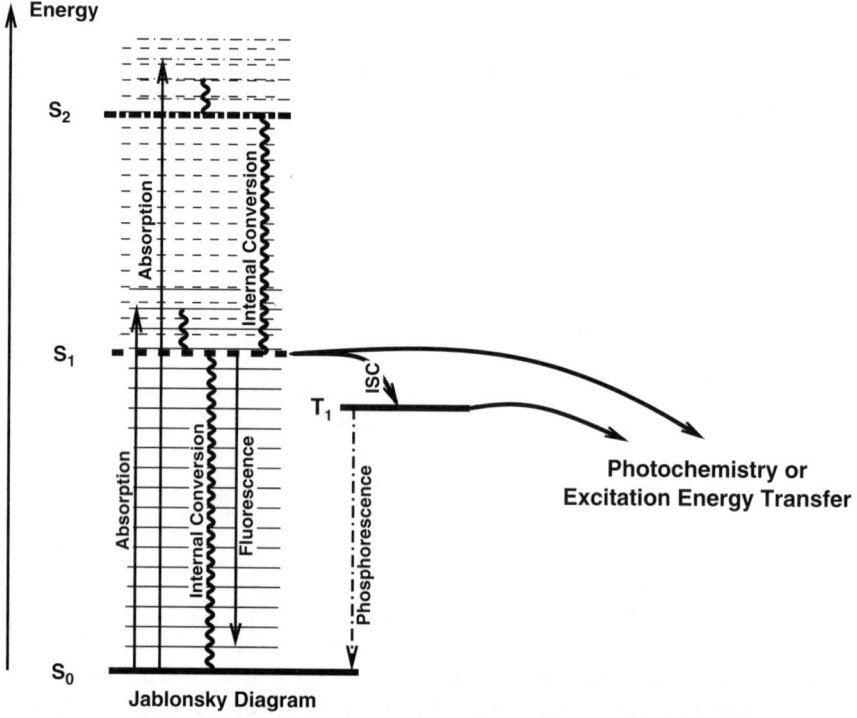

Jablonsky Diagram

Most (B)Chl aggregates have negligible fluorescence [126,210–212], due to a poorly understood process termed concentration quenching [196]. Exceptions are aggregates of BChl c, d and e and of related pigments that carry a hydroxy-group at C-$3^1$ and are devoid of the $13^2$-carbomethoxy group [85,92,119,213–216]. These aggregates are similar to those found in chlorosomes, the extra-membraneous antennas of green bacteria that are largely devoid of protein [84]. Fluorescence can be quenched, i.e., concentration quenching restored, in these aggregates [15] and in chlorosomes [98] by photochemical processes generating energy traps; further investigations of these processes may also lead to a better understanding of concentration quenching.

In photosynthesis, the $S_1$ excitation energy of (B)Chls is transduced into chemical energy within times that are short compared with the $S_1$ radiative

**Figure 3.** Jablonski diagram of chlorophylls: $S_0$ (———), $S_1$ (– – –) and $S_2$ (– · – ·) represent the electronic singlet energy levels. The lowest vibrational level is emphasized by heavy lines; the excited vibrational levels are marked by thin lines. Owing to the Franck–Condon principle, light absorption of the lowest vibrational level of $S_0$ leads to excitation in vibrationally excited levels of $S_1$ or $S_2$, which rapidly ($\leq$ps) relax to the lowest vibrational level of $S_1$. This state is relatively long-lived (ns). In solution, the ground state can be regained by three processes: (1) internal conversion, which can be envisioned by crossing to a high vibrational state of $S_0$ and subsequent vibrational relaxation processes, (2) fluorescence that by the Franck–Condon principle ends in a vibrationally excited state of $S_0$, which then quickly relaxes to the ground state by internal conversion, and (3) intersystem crossing (ISC) to the long-lived (μs–ms) lowest triplet state (generally termed $T_1$, but more appropriately termed $T_0$) and subsequent phosphorescence. The triplet level is split, usually there are two levels in the absence and three levels in the presence of a magnetic field. On the energy scale shown, this splitting is negligible. Modulation of the triplet relaxation by microwaves, which induce transitions among the triplet sublevels, is the basis to optically detected magnetic resonance. Heat production due to internal conversion processes can also be measured, e.g., by opto-acoustic spectroscopy. Provided there is a suitable partner, excitation energy transfer or photochemistry can occur from both $S_1$ and $T_0$. In photosynthesis, rapid energy transfer (antenna pigments) or electron transfer (primary donors or reaction centers) to suitably positioned acceptors occurs sufficiently rapid from $S_1$, such that (slow) ISC is negligible. If there are no such partners, $T_0$ can be populated by ISC. Owing to its long lifetime, the triplet can react directly with nearby molecules or generate, during encounters with the mobile $O_2$, reactive oxygen species by energy (singlet oxygen, $^1O_2$) or electron transfer ($O_2^-$, $H_2O_2$, OH·). In photosynthesis, triplets can be generated by charge recombination (radical pair mechanism) if electron transfer is blocked by over-reduction of the acceptor pool. The ensuing triplet energy transfer to carotenoids, directly or indirectly (via other chlorophylls), is a major protective mechanisms of the photosynthetic apparatus. Light absorption of excited states and stimulated fluorescence of $^1S$ are not included in this scheme. They are negligible under low intensity irradiation conditions, including photosynthesis, as are reactions between excited molecules. They occur, however, in laser spectroscopy, where they can provide important information on the photophysics of the pigments, and on the organization of the photosynthetic apparatus in situ. Vibrational spectroscopy involves transitions between vibrational levels, generally mainly the lowest ones of $S_0$.

lifetime; fluorescence is therefore reduced to low levels (<1%). It is still sufficient, however, to be used for remote detection of terrestrial or marine vegetation (see, e.g., Morel [217]). Moreover, as photosynthetic energy transduction, and thereby the $S_1$ lifetime, depends critically on the physiological status of photosynthetic organisms, fluorescence is widely used as a sensitive, non-invasive reporter in plant physiology and agriculture [27,218–223]. Complementary information can be derived from delayed luminescence [224] and thermoluminescence [225]: if the acceptor pools in photosynthesis are reduced, electron transport becomes inhibited. Excited singlet or triplet states of the primary donor can then be generated by charge recombination, or from other trapped high-energy states, leading to delayed fluorescence and phosphorescence, respectively (Figure 3). Triplet generation by charge recombination can also lead to photodynamic damage [226,227]. Carotenoids are potent quenchers of such triplets. Energy transfer from chlorophyll triplets generates the much safer carotenoid triplets: their energy is below that required for $^1O_2$ formation, and due to the flexibility of these chromophores their triplet lifetimes are comparably short. This quenching requires carotenoids of sufficiently low energy that are in contact distance with the donor or intermediate carriers, a situation that has been investigated in some detail in bacterial reaction centers [228,229].

Energy losses due to vibrational relaxation and internal conversion processes can be considered as loss channels competing with fluorescence and, in situ, with photosynthesis. These processes can be measured, and an energy balance obtained, by thermal methods. Under pulsed excitation conditions, optoacoustic spectroscopy is a particularly useful method that can be used with molecules in solution as well as with intact photosynthetic systems [198].

*3.4.3 Circular Dichroism*

Circular dichroism (CD) is a specialized optical technique applicable to dissymmetric molecules and assemblies, viz. structures lacking a plane of symmetry. Chlorophylls contain 1–5 asymmetric centers at the macrocycle, plus up to two additional ones at the esterifying alcohol, and they are therefore optically active. Chlorophylls and derivatives show CD, viz. optically active electronic absorptions in the Vis and NIR spectral region. This CD is weak in monodisperse solutions [230,231]; the π-system of a planar macrocycle is even expected to be CD inactive. The weak CD has been rationalized in a series of pheophorbides by a combination of chiral induction by the asymmetrically substituted carbons and by twist of the macrocycle generated by the chiral substituents that renders the π-system inherently dissymmetric. This optical activity has been used to study, for example, the *prime*-chlorophylls, viz. the $13^2$-epimers [232]. Yet to be explored is the optical activity of chlorophylls related to dissymmetric ligation of the central Mg [233,234]. Optical activity can also be generated in strong magnetic fields; this magnetic circular dichroism can yield information on the symmetry of molecular orbitals participating in the transition that is difficult to gain otherwise [235].

# CHLOROPHYLLS

Much larger optical activity is found in (B)Chl aggregates. In brief, two processes can be distinguished. Short-range excitonic interactions in small aggregates and chlorophyll proteins [58,236–238] and long-range interactions in large, ordered systems, including thylakoids [239] and chlorosomes [86,239]. The former can be treated theoretically rather well [240] and can give, in favorable cases, details of the geometries of interacting pigments [241]. The theory of complex long-range interactions is less understood, but it is nonetheless a useful tool to monitor long-range interactions [242].

*3.4.4 Nuclear Magnetic Resonance Spectroscopy*

In solution, nuclear magnetic resonance (NMR) spectroscopy is probably the single most powerful technique for structure elucidation of chlorophylls [243–245]. It requires relatively large amounts of sample material ($\geq 1$ µg for $^1$H NMR, 10–100-fold more for $^{13}$C and $^{15}$N NMR) but provides a wealth of information on through-bond (spin–spin coupling) and through-space interactions (nuclear Overhauser effect, ring-current induced shifts), allowing for a full structure analysis, including the conformation of substituents and ligands, and their dynamics in the µs range and longer. Through-space interactions have been used also to investigate interactions of chlorophylls with their environment, including solvent, other chlorophylls in aggregates, amino acids in chlorophyll proteins, etc. Here, the large, anisotropic shifts induced by the ring-current of the aromatic π-system have yielded important information on the relative orientation of the pigments in aggregates [243,246,247]. With the advent of high-resolution solid-state NMR spectroscopy, these investigations can now been extended to macromolecular systems such as the chlorosome [84,248].

NMR spectroscopy is also applied in biosynthetic studies using stable isotopes. They not only allow to trace the biosynthesis of any individual H or C but also give, through spin–spin coupling, information on the retention of neighbor-relationships during biosynthesis (for examples and leading references, see [249–251]).

*3.4.5 Electron Spin Resonance Spectroscopy*

Electron spin resonance (ESR) spectroscopy is used to study unpaired spins. Relevant examples for chlorophylls are (1) cation and anion radicals (= doublet states) as well as triplet states generated by charge separation or recombination processes that are central to photosynthesis (see [252–254]), and (2) transition metals replacing the central Mg [255,256] that can, for example, be used as reporters. Owing to its selectivity, the method can be applied with little background to whole organisms or crystallized chlorophyll proteins. Its spectral complexity due to multiple couplings has been reduced by double-resonance resonance techniques (electron–nucleus (ENDOR) [257], electron–electron (ELDOR), electron–photon (ODMR) [253]) and the application of high fields [258,259]. Like NMR, these methods can not only yield information on through-bond interactions, but also on through-space interactions over several nm. Examples for applications are the mapping of unpaired electrons over the dimeric primary donors of the different photosystems [260], or of the distances and orientations of reaction partners in electron transfer reactions [261,262]. The originally relatively slow method has been extended to time resolutions in the ns range [263].

*3.4.6 Mass Spectrometry*

In mass spectrometry, charged ions of a molecule of interest have to be generated in the gas phase. The mass-to-charge ratio of these ions is then analyzed by their interactions with electric or magnetic fields, or by their time-of-flight after pulsed acceleration. Various methods are available, for which the reader is referred to specialized literature [245]. The primary information obtained is the molecular mass. In combination with NMR and optical spectroscopy, this generally allows for a full structure assignment. The isotope pattern of the molecular ion is also an excellent indicator for the analysis of incorporated isotopes, or of central metals other than Mg [138]. Secondary information can be derived from the fragmentation pattern, which with suitable equipment can be followed by multiple mass spectroscopy ($MS^n$): a fragment ion is selected and subsequently investigated again by mass spectroscopy, a process that can be repeated again with a fragment of the first fragment, and so on. In favorable cases, this allows structural assignments based on optical and mass spectrometry alone, which require orders of magnitude less material than NMR spectroscopy. A further advantage of mass spectrometry is that it can be combined with high-resolution liquid chromatography techniques and is thus capable of analyzing complex mixtures. For leading references, the reader is referred to examples on structure elucidations of minor chlorophylls [102,136,245,264] and of chlorophyll-derived geoporphyrins [265].

Mass spectrometry is also applied in biosynthetic studies using, generally, stable isotopes. An example are studies directed at the origin of various oxygen atoms in chlorophylls from organisms adapted to varying levels of environmental oxygen [266].

*3.4.7 Vibrational Spectroscopy*

Vibrational spectra give information on molecular fragments, in chlorophylls in particular on the carbonyl groups and the methine bridges, and their interactions with the environment [267]. Hydrogen bonding to carbonyl groups can be monitored in solution, in aggregates and in situ, in chlorophyll-proteins or chlorosomes. The C=C stretching bands related to the methine bridges contain information on the ligation of the central Mg, which influences the rigidity and conformation of the macrocycle, and on distortions of the macrocycle. Isotope labeling is generally necessary for unequivocal band assignments [268]. With the advent of increasingly powerful and reliable computational methods [269], vibrational spectroscopy techniques are expected to gain still increasing importance. Also, non-bonding (through space) interactions via dipolar coupling of vibrations are, in principle, possible but to date no routine methods are available (as in NMR) that can be applied for their study.

Two techniques have been important in vibrational spectroscopy of chlorophylls, infrared (IR) spectroscopy [270] and Raman resonance spectroscopy [5,271,272]. IR spectroscopy is an absorption technique where IR radiation of suitable energy induces transitions between vibrational levels of the electronic ground state, $S_0$ (Figure 3). In Raman spectroscopy, irradiation with visible light leads to non-elastic scattering due to transfer of vibrational energy, thus giving rise to side-bands of the scattered beam whose distances from the exciting beam correspond to vibrational transitions. While the Raman process has generally a very low probability, it is enhanced by many orders of magnitude if the excitation wavelength is at (resonance Raman) or near (pre-resonance Raman) an absorption band of the molecule investigated; it can even be further enhanced under certain conditions [273]. Both methods allow kinetic studies down to sub-picosecond time resolution.

IR and Raman resonance spectroscopy have different selection rules, but in practice give similar information on molecules as large and complex as the chlorophylls. An important difference is, however, that Raman resonance "sees" only groups participating in the π-system. It is, therefore, "*blind*" to the $C17^3$=O bond of chlorophylls, and, in part, for the $C13^3$=O bond. It is also "blind" to protein and lipids and therefore highly selective for the colored chlorophylls and carotenoids, which can even be discriminated against each other by variation of the excitation wavelength. By the same token, however, Raman spectra obviously lack a large amount of information relevant to those parts of the chlorophylls that take no part in the π-system, and to the protein environment, which can only be gained by IR spectroscopy. Difference methods have been developed to overcome the huge background encountered; they are used in conjunction with selective, non-invasive perturbations such photo- or redox reactions (for examples, see [270,274]).

*3.4.8 Electrochemistry*

Electrochemical reactions of the macrocyclic π-system involve electron additions to the lowest unoccupied molecular orbitals, or electron abstractions from the highest occupied molecular orbital. Although they are strictly speaking not a spectroscopic method, they provide nonetheless complementary information to optical spectroscopy. To a first-order approximation, redox potentials are proportional to the electron density of the macrocycle. The higher its electron density, the more easily it is oxidized and the more difficult it is reduced. Electron density can be modified directly (1) by hydrogenation of the double bonds when going from the porphyrin to the chlorin to the bacteriochlorin [156], (2) by the central metal [137,275,276], and (3) peripheral substituents [156,277,278]. These effects can further be modulated by second-shell interactions, including H-bonding to conjugated C=O groups [77,78], conformational changes of such groups that change their conjugation to the macrocyclic π-system, or ligation to the central metal [137,168].

## 3.5 Biosynthesis

The first dedicated precursor of tetrapyrroles is 5-aminolevulinic acid (ALA), which can be formed by two different pathways (Figure 4A, reviewed in [279,280]). In the $C_{4+1}$ or Shemin-pathway operative in animals and purple bacteria, ALA is formed by condensation of glycine with succinyl-CoA, catalyzed by ALA-synthase [281]. In the $C_5$ pathway, it is formed from glutamate. The direct conversion of the $C_5$-skeleton into that of ALA remarkably involves tRNA$^{Glu}$ as a non-proteinogenic intermediate [280,282,283]. It is reduced to glutamate semialdehyde, which in turn is isomerized to ALA. Side-reactions of the labile intermediate are probably minimized by substrate channeling within a supercomplex of the enzymes involved [280]. This $C_5$ pathway is probably the more ubiquitous one – it operates in green algae [284] and green plants [250], and several anoxygenic photosynthetic bacteria, including *Chromatium* and *Prosthecochloris* [285,286].

Subsequent octamerization of ALA yields protoporphyrin IX (Proto) as the common precursor of most tetrapyrroles, including the chlorophylls (Fig 4B) [287]. In the first step, two molecules of ALA condense to give the monopyrrole, porphobilinogen. Four such pyrrole units are then successively grafted to a dipyrrolic "primer" by PBG-deaminase, yielding a covalently bound linear hexapyrrole, from which the linear tetrapyrrole, hydroxymethylbilane is released. The latter is the substrate for the uro'gen III cosynthase, which catalyses the cyclization to uroporphyrinogen (uro'gen) III, in a reaction involving the flip of ring D [288]. Uro'gen III is a branching point: one biosynthetic pathway, which is not considered here, leads to the Ni-containing F430, the Co-containing vitamin $B_{12,}$ and the Fe-containing siroheme [289,290]. The second branch [291] leads to protoporphyrin IX (proto), from which all other hemes, the bilins, and the Chls are derived. First, the four acetate side chains of uroporphyrinogen III are decarboxylated to yield coproporphyrinogen, and then the two propionic acid side chains of rings A and B to yield protophyrinogen IX. Owing to the interruption of conjugation at the methylene bridges, all tetrapyrroles up to this point are colorless, the first macrocyclic conjugated and colored product, Proto, is formed in the ensuing two-step oxidation.

An important aspect of this pathway is that porphyrinogens are easily oxidized to colored porphyrins. Since the latter are highly phototoxic and can generate reactive oxygen species, the pathway is tightly controlled, not only to maintain the intermediates at manageable levels and prevent their autoxidation to porphyrins other than the final Proto but also to generate Proto only in amounts and in cell compartments where it can be processed further without its accumulation. The main point of control in this process is the supply of

ALA. Both the $C_{4+1}$ and the $C_5$ pathways are regulated by feedback inhibition of late products of the pathway (reviewed in [251,279,280,292–295]). Heme and protochlorophyllide (Pchlide) have long been recognized as inhibitors, but more recently also Mg-Proto IX and its monomethyl-ester have been implicated in the feedback regulation of chlorophyll biosynthesis and nucleus-plastid communication [296,297].

From Proto, one important branch of tetrapyrroles, the Fe-branch that leads to hemes and bilins, is initiated by metalation with $Fe^{2+}$ [298]; it is not considered here. The second branch leading to the Chls is initiated by insertion of $Mg^{2+}$ (Figure 4B). It is considerably more complex than that of $Fe^{2+}$ and endergonic in an aqueous environment, the energy being supplied by ATP. Three gene products cooperate in the process [299,300] to yield Mg-protoporphyrin, which is then methylated regiospecifically at $C-13^3$ by S-adenosylmethionine [250].

The mechanism of the subsequent formation of ring E is still only partly elucidated. It requires the abstraction of six electrons (four at $C-13^1$, one each at $C-13^2$ and C-15 for the ring closure) and the introduction of one oxygen [301]. The requirement of vitamin $B_{12}$ suggests a radical mechanism for the cyclization [302]. The oxygen is provided by water under anaerobic conditions [303], while an oxygenase is involved instead in the oxygenic cyanobacteria, algae and green plants (and in purple bacteria under aerobic conditions) (see [266]). The resulting [8-vinyl]-PChlide is the first true chlorophyll, functional in light harvesting [103]. Little is known about the pathway from here to the other c-type chlorophylls. Some of the reactions have counterparts in other tetrapyrrole biosynthetic reactions like the oxygenation at $C-7^1$ to yield Chl $c_3$, but none of the enzymes have been identified to the author's knowledge.

All other Chls derive from Pchlide or [8-vinyl]-Pchlide (see below) by a regio- and stereoselective hydrogenation of the Δ17,18- double bond, which is catalyzed by two different protochlorophyllide oxidoreductases (POR). One class of POR is light-independent ("dark" POR) and appears to be ubiquitous in all photosynthetic organisms, with the exception of angiosperms. The three-subunit complex is related to nitrogenase, including the requirement of ferredoxin as reducing agent [304,305]. It is supplemented in many organisms, in angiosperms even replaced, by the NADPH and light-dependent enzymes, "light" POR, one of the few members of photoenzymes [306]. One of the isoenzymes, PORA, has been intensely studied. It forms a stable enzyme–substrate complex (PChlide-holochrome), which accumulates to substantial amounts in the etioplasts of dark-grown seedlings in the prolamellar bodies [307]. While Pchlide is highly phototoxic, like all intermediates beyond and including proto, the photoreactivity of the POR-Pchlide-NADPH complex reduces triplet formation and thus photosensitization. This ternary, light-activated complex therefore seems to provide a relatively safe store from which chlorophylls can be rapidly generated in greening plants [308]. The ternary POR-Pchlide-NADPH complex accumulating in the dark inhibits PChlide formation by feedback of ALA synthesis [294], and the Chlide $a$ formed as a product in the light is an activator for the formation of chlorophyll proteins [309].

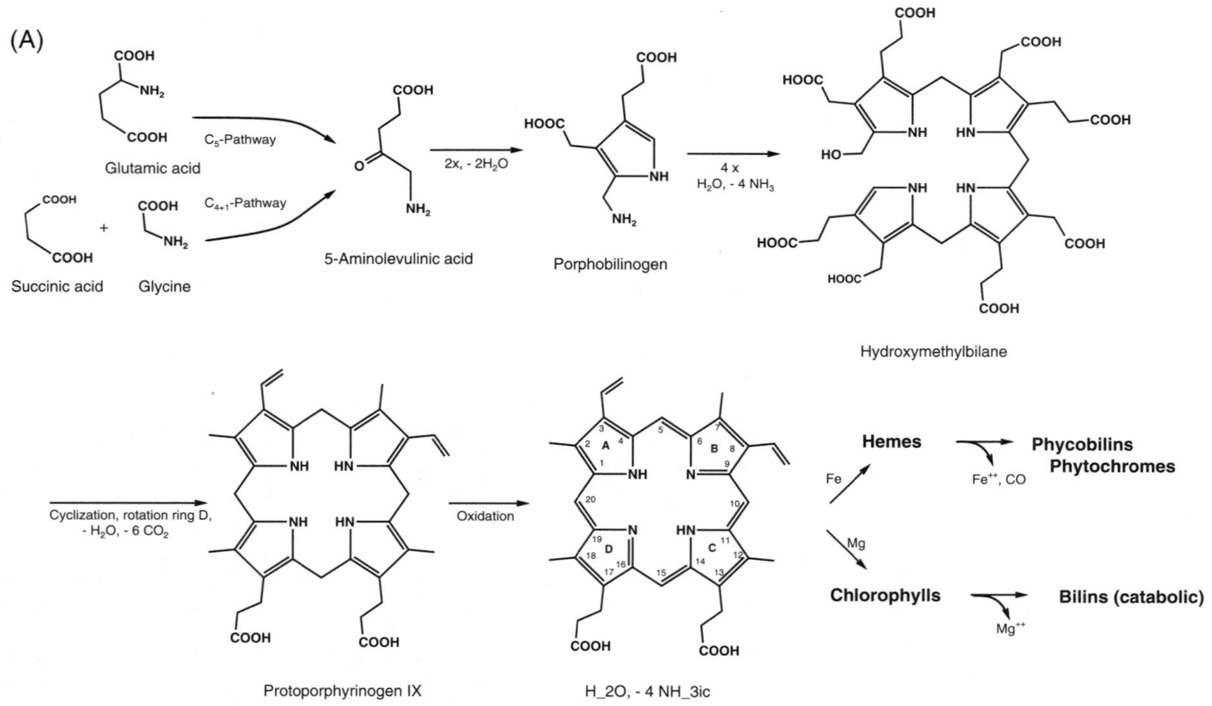

**Figure 4.** Overview of the biosynthesis of chlorophylls and bacteriochlorophylls. (A) The two pathways to 5-aminolevulinic acid (ALA), and the ensuing common pathway to protoporphyrin IX, the common intermediate for all chlorophylls and bilins, and for most hemes.

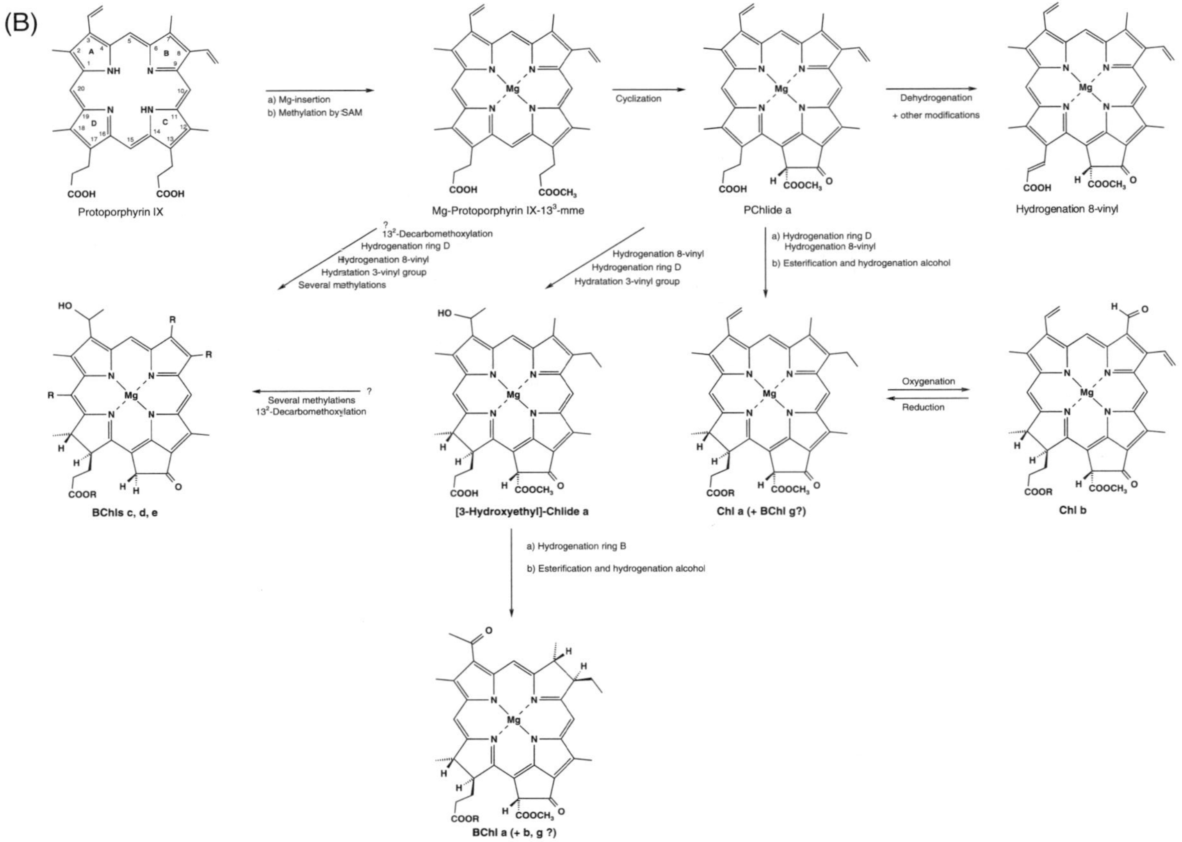

**Figure 4.** Overview of the biosynthesis of chlorophylls and bacteriochlorophylls. (B) Pathways from protoporphyrin IX to the different chlorophylls. Only major intermediates and chlorophylls are shown.

In green plants, the resulting Chlide *a* is esterified by geranyl-geranyl-pyrophosphate along with the hydrogenation of three of the four double-bonds of geranyl-geraniol, yielding Chl *a*, esterified with phytol as the final product [307]. Chl *b* is formed from Chl *a* by an oxygenase [310–312], and can be converted back into Chl *a* [313,314]; the latter reaction also occurs in higher plants before ring-opening during chlorophyll degradation [315].

Chl *a* and *b* come in two forms: in eukaryotes pigments are prevalent that carry a single vinyl group at C-3, while among the prokaryotes pigments from some rather abundant *Prochlorococcus* species carry a second one at C-8. In these [8-vinyl]-Chls (often termed "Divinyl-Chls") the two vinyl groups of Proto are preserved. A complex network of parallel but interconnected pathways has been proposed [316], leading from Proto to Chl *a* and *b*. It involves not only parallel 8-ethyl and 8-vinyl-branches, but also branches with free and esterified C-17 propionic acid side chains. The actual patterns of the favored pathways depend on the particular species and its physiological state. This would require a set of specific 8-vinyl reductases, or one enzyme that has a broad specificity. So far, only a single example has been studied, which is specific for reducing [8-vinyl]-PChlide to PChlide [317]. A network of parallel reactions with multiple connections also seems to exist for the conversion of geranyl-geraniol-pyrophosphate and Chlide a into Chl $a_P$ [318].

In anoxygenic bacteria, hydrogenation of ring D is followed by hydrogenation of ring B, by a variant of the "dark" POR. The ensuing final steps, viz. esterification and alcohol hydrogenation, appear to be basically similar to the corresponding reactions of Chls a and b in green plants and cyanobacteria [319], despite different specificities leading to variations in hydrogenation (and length) of the alcohols [320,321]. In *Rba. sphaeroides*, BchG catalyzes the esterification reaction [322].

Much less is known about the biosynthesis of the other bacteriochlorophylls. BChl *g* is formally an isomer of Chl *a* and could possibly derive biosynthetically from it by isomerization [122] to yield the 8-ethylidene substituent. A similar reaction would lead from [3-acetyl]-Chla to BChl *b*, but none of the required enzymes have been identified to the author's knowledge.

Considerable progress has been made recently in unraveling the biosynthesis of BChl *c*, *d* and *e*, following the genome sequencing for *Chl. tepidum*. Several enzymes could be cloned that are involved in the transfer of $CH_3$-groups from S-adenosylmethionine, and a scheme has been proposed in which the only major uncertainty is the positioning of the decarbomethoxylation event at $C-13^2$, as indicated by the two question-marked arrows in Figure 4(B) [114].

## 3.6 Concluding Remarks and Future Perspectives

Due to their optical properties, their importance in photosynthesis, their application as probes in plant physiology, ecology or geochemistry, and their only recently realized potential in photonics and in medicine, the biochemistry, biophysics, functions and applications of chlorophylls remain a fascinating and active field of research [28].

## References

1. G.P. Moss, IUPAC-IUB Joint Commission Biochemical Nomenclature (JCBN). Nomenclature of Tetrapyrroles. *Eur. J. Biochem.* **178** (1988) 277–328.
2. R.G. Moss. "IUPAC joint commission biochemical nomenclature (ICBN): The Nomenclature of Tetrapyrroles." 1986 Web page available at http://www.chem.qmul.ac.uk/iupac/tetrapyrrole/.
3. B. Green and W. Parson (eds.), *Light-Harvesting Antennas in Photosynthesis*, (2003), Kluwer, Dordrecht.
4. Deisenhofer and J.R. Norris (eds.), *The Photosynthetic Reaction Center*, (1993), Academic Press, New York.
5. G. Renger, A.-R. Holzwarth, Primary electron transfer. In: Photosystem II: The water/plastoquinone oxido-reductase, in: *Photosynthesis* (2005) (T. Wydrzynski, K. Satoh, eds.), Kluwer Academic Publishers, Dordrecht, pp. 139–175.
6. Y. Pierre, C. Breyton, Y. Lemoine, B. Robert, C. Vernotte, J.-L. Popot, On the presence and role of a molecule of chlorophyll $a$ in the cytochrome $b_6 f$ complex. *J. Biol. Chem.* **272** (1997) 21901–21908.
7. E.J. Peterman, S.O. Wenk, T. Pullerits, L.O. Palsson, R. van Grondelle, J.P. Dekker, M. Rögner, H. van Amerongen, Fluorescence and absorption spectroscopy of the weakly fluorescent chlorophyll a in cytochrome $b_6 f$ of *Synechocystis* PCC6803. *Biophys J.* **75** (1998) 389–398.
8. D. Stroebel, Y. Choquet, J.L. Popot, D. Picot, An atypical haem in the cytochrome $b_6 f$ complex. *Nature* **426** (2003) 413–418.
9. G. Kurisu, H. Zhang, J.L. Smith, W.A. Cramer, Structure of the cytochrome $b_6 f$ complex of oxygenic photosynthesis: Tuning the cavity. *Science* **302** (2003) 1009–1014.
10. K. Schmidt, C. Fufezan, A. Krieger-Liszkay, H. Satoh, H. Paulsen, Recombinant water-soluble chlorophyll protein from Brassica oleracea var. botrys binds various chlorophyll derivatives. *Biochemistry* **42** (2003) 7427–7433.
11. T. Noguchi, Y. Kamimura, Y. Inoue, S. Itoh, Photoconversion of a water-soluble chlorophyll protein from Chenopodium album: Resonance Raman and Fourier transform infrared study of protein and pigment structures. *Plant Cell Physiol.* **40** (1999) 305–310.
12. C. Reinbothe, H. Satoh, J.-P. Alcaraz, S. Reinbothe, A novel role of water-soluble chlorophyll proteins in the transitory storage of chlorophyllide. *Plant Physiol.* **134** (2004) 1355–1365.
13. H.A. Frank, A.J. Young, G. Britton and R.J. Cogdell (eds.), *The Photochemistry of Carotenoids*, (1999), Kluwer, Dordrecht.
14. C.J. Law, R.J. Cogdell, The effect of chemical oxidation on the fluorescence of the LH1 (B880) complex from the purple bacterium *Rhodobium marinum. FEBS Lett.* **432** (1998) 1–2.
15. Y. Kakitani, F.S. Rondonuwu, T. Mizoguchi, Y. Watanabe, Y. Koyama, Energy dissipations in chlorosomes: Emission from the Qy state following singlet–singlet and triplet–triplet annihilation reactions in the cylindrical aggregate and its

reversible dissociation into the piggy-back dimmers. *J. Phys. Chem. B* **107** (2003) 14545–14555.
16. F.G. Plumley, G.W. Schmidt, Light-harvesting chlorophyll a/b complexes: Interdependent pigment synthesis and protein assembly. *Plant Cell* **7** (1995) 689–704.
17. H. Paulsen, Chlorophyll a/b-binding proteins. *Photochem. Photobiol.* **62** (1995) 367–382.
18. H. Scheer, G. Hartwich, Bacterial reaction centers with modified tetrapyrrole chromophores, in: *Anoxygenic Photosynthetic Bacteria* (1995) (R. Blankenship, M.T. Madigan, C.E. Bauer, eds.), Kluwer, Dordrecht, pp. 649–663.
19. J.B. Todd, P.S. Parkes-Loach, J.F. Leykam, P.A. Loach, In vitro reconstitution of the core and peripheral light-harvesting complexes of *Rhodospirillum molischianum* from separately isolated components. *Biochemistry* **37** (1998) 17458–17468.
20. A. Näveke, K. Lapouge, J.N. Sturgis, G. Harwich, I. Simonin, H. Scheer, B. Robert, Resonance Raman spectroscopy of metal-substituted bacteriochlorophylls: Characterization of Raman bands sensitive to bacteriochlorin conformation. *J. Raman Spectrosc.* **28** (1997) 599–604.
21. L.P. Vernon and G.R. Seely, *The Chlorophylls*, (1966), Academic Press, New York.
22. H. Scheer, (ed.) in: *Chlorophylls* 1991, CRC Press, Boca Raton, FL.
23. J. Amesz and A.J. Hoff (eds.), *Biophysical Techniques in Photosynthesis*, (1996) Kluwer, Dordrecht.
24. S.W. Jeffrey, R.F.C. Mantoura and S.W.E. Wright, *Phytoplankton Pigments in Oceanography*, (1997) UNESCO Publications, Paris.
25. A.G. Smith and M. Witty (eds.), *Heme, Chlorophyll, and Bilins*, (2002) Humana Press, Totowa NJ.
26. K.M. Kadish, K.M. Smith, R. Guilard (eds.), *The Porphyrin Handbook*, Vol. 13: *Chlorophylls and Bilins: Biosynthesis, Synthesis and Degradation* 2002, Academic Press, Amsterdam.
27. G.C. Papageorgiou and Govindjee (ed.), *Chlorophyll a Fluorescence: a Signature of Photosynthesis*, ((2004)) Kluwer, Dordrecht.
28. B. Grimm, R. Porra, W. Rüdiger, H. Scheer (eds.), *Chlorophylls and Bacteriochlorophylls: Biochemistry, Biophysics, Functions and Applications* (2006), Springer, Berlin.
29. K. Sauer, Primary events and the trapping of energy, in: *Bioenergetics of Photosynthesis* (1975) (Govindjee, ed.) Academic Press, New York, pp. 115–181.
30. D. Leupold, H. Lokstein, H. Scheer, Excitation energy transfer between (bacterio)chlorophylls-The role of excitonic coupling, in: *Chlorophylls and Bacteriochlorophylls: Biochemistry, Biophysics, Functions and Applications* (2006) (B. Grimm, R. Porra, W. Rüdiger, H. Scheer, eds.), Springer, Berlin, pp. 413–430.
31. M. Stavola, D.L. Dexter, R.S. Knox, Electron-hole pair excitation in semiconductors via energy transfer from an external sensitizer. *Phys. Rev. B.* **31** (1985) 2277–2289.
32. S.H. Lin, W.Z. Xiao, W. Dietz, Generalized Forster-Dexter theory of photoinduced intramolecular energy transfer. *Phys. Rev. E.* **47** (1993) 3698–3706.
33. S. Faure, C. Stern, R. Guilard, P.D. Harvey, Role of the spacer in the singlet–singlet energy transfer mechanism (Forster vs Dexter) in cofacial bisporphyrins. *J. Am. Chem. Soc.* **126** (2004) 1253–1261.
34. A. Kimura, T. Kakitani, Theory of excitation energy transfer in the intermediate coupling case of clusters. *J. Phys. Chem. B* **107** (2003) 14486–14499.
35. T. Kakitani, A. Kimura, Empirical formula of exciton coherent domain in oligomers and application to LH2. *J. Phys. Chem. A* **106** (2002) 2173–2179.

36. X. Hu, T. Ritz, A. Damjanovic, F. Autenrieth, K. Schulten, Photosynthetic apparatus of purple bacteria. *Q. Rev. Biophys.* **35** (2002) 1–62.
37. X.J. Jordanides, G.D. Scholes, W.A. Shapley, J.R. Reimers, G.R. Fleming, Electronic couplings and energy transfer dynamics in the oxidized primary electron donor of the bacterial reaction center. *J. Phys. Chem. B* **108** (2004) 1753–1765.
38. B. Brueggemann, J.L. Herek, V. Sundstroem, T. Pullerits, V. May, Microscopic theory of exciton annihilation: Application to the LH2 antenna system. *J. Phys. Chem. B* **105** (2001) 11391–11394.
39. Y. Koyama, Y. Kakitani, Mechanisms of carotenoid-to-bacteriochlorophyll energy transfer in the light harvesting antenna complexes 1 and 2: Dependence on the conjugation length of carotenoids, in: *Chlorophylls and Bacteriochlorophylls: Biochemistry, Biophysics, Functions and Applications* (2006) (B. Grimm, R. Porra, W. Rüdiger, H. Scheer, eds.), Springer, Berlin, pp. 431–443.
40. L. Flamigni, A.M. Talarico, F. Barigelletti, M.R. Johnston, An unusual energy transfer process from free-base porphyrin guests to a zinc porphyrin host in self-assembled systems. *Photochem. Photobiol. Sci.* **1** (2002) 190–197.
41. Y. Koyama, M. Kuki, P.O. Andersson, T. Gillbro, Singlet excited states and the light-harvesting function of carotenoids in bacterial photosynthesis. *Photochem. Photobiol.* **63** (1996) 243–256.
42. G.R. Fleming, R. van Grondelle, Femtosecond spectroscopy of photosynthetic light-harvesting systems. *Curr. Opin. Struct. Biol.* **7** (1997) 738–748.
43. R. Van Grondelle, J.P. Dekker, T. Gillbro, V. Sundstrom, Energy transfer and trapping in photosynthesis. *Biochim. Biophys. Acta* **1187** (1994) 1–65.
44. J.L. Herek, N.J. Fraser, T. Pullerits, P. Martinsson, T. Polvika, H. Scheer, R.J. Cogdell, V. Sundström, Mechanism of B800 -> B850 energy transfer mechanism in bacterial LH2 complexes investigated by B800 pigment exchange. *Biophys. J.* **78** (2000) 2590–2596.
45. J. Köhler, T.J. Aartsma, Single molecule spectroscopy of pigment protein complexes from purple bacteria, in: *Chlorophylls and Bacteriochlorophylls: Biochemistry, Biophysics, Functions and Applications* (2006) (B. Grimm, R. Porra, W. Rüdiger, H. Scheer, eds.), Springer, Berlin, pp. 309–321.
46. M.P. Debreczeny, K. Sauer, J. Zhou, D.A. Bryant, Comparison of calculated and experimentally resolved rate constants for excitation energy transfer in C-phycocyanin. 2. Trimers. *J. Phys. Chem.* **99** (1995) 8420–8431.
47. H.W. Trissl, Long-wavelength absorbing antenna pigments and heterogeneous absorption bands concentrate excitons and increase absorption cross section. *Photosynth. Res.* **35** (1993) 247–263.
48. B. Robert, R. Cogdell, R. Van Grondelle, The light-harvesting system of purple bacteria, in: *Light-Harvesting Antennas in Photosynthesis*, (2003) (B. Green, W. Parson, eds.), Kluwer, Dordrecht, pp. 169–194.
49. D.C. Fork, A.W.D. Larkum, Light harvesting in the green alga *Ostreobium* sp., a coral symbiont adapted to extreme shade. *Marine Biol.* **103** (1989) 381–385.
50. H.P. Permentier, S. Neerken, J. Overmann, J. Amesz, A bacteriochlorophyll a antenna complex from purple bacteria absorbing at 963 nm. *Biochemistry* **40** (2001) 5573–5578.
51. S. Spörlein, W. Zinth, M. Meyer, H. Scheer, J. Wachtveitl, Primary electron transfer in modified bacterial reaction centers: Optimization of the first events in photosynthesis. *Chem. Phys. Lett.* **322** (2000) 454–464.
52. J.P. Dekker, R. Van Grondelle, Primary charge separation in photosystem II. *Photosynth. Res.* **63** (2000) 195–208.

53. P. Jordan, P. Fromme, H.T. Witt, O. Klukas, W. Saenger, N. Krauss, Three-dimensional structure of cyanobacterial photosystem I at 2.5A resolution. *Nature* **411** (2001) 909–917.
54. R. Bittl, E. Schlodder, I. Geisenheimer, W. Lubitz, R.J. Cogdell, Transient EPR and absorption studies of carotenoid triplet formation in purple bacterial antenna complexes. *J. Phys. Chem. B* **105** (2001) 5525–5535.
55. J.D. Olsen, J.N. Sturgis, W.H. Westerhuis, G.J. Fowler, C.N. Hunter, B. Robert, Site-directed modification of the ligands to the bacteriochlorophylls of the light-harvesting LH1 and LH2 complexes of *Rhodobacter sphaeroides*. *Biochemistry* **36** (1997) 12625–12632.
56. L.A. Eichacker, M. Helfrich, W. Rüdiger, B. Müller, Stabilization of chlorophyll a-binding apoproteins P700, CP47, CP43, D2, and D1 by chlorophyll a or Zn-pheophytin a. *J. Biol. Chem.* **271** (1996) 32174–32179.
57. K. Lapouge, A. Näveke, B. Robert, H. Scheer, J.N. Sturgis, Exchanging cofactors in the core antennae from purple bacteria: Structure and properties of Zn-bacteriophaeophytin containing LH1. *Biochemistry* **39** (2000) 1091–1099.
58. J.J. Katz, W. Oettmeier, J.R. Norris, Organization of antenna and photo-reaction centre chlorophylls on the molecular level. *Phil. Trans. Roy. Soc.* **273** (1976) 227–253.
59. B.-J. van Rossum, G.J. Boender, F.M. Mulder, T.S. Balaban, A. Holzwarth, K. Schaffner, S. Prytulla, H. Oschkinat, H.J.M. de Groot, Multidimensional CP-MAS $^{13}$C NMR of uniformly enriched chlorophyll. *Spectrochim. Acta* **54** (1998) 1167–1176.
60. A. Scherz, V. Rosenbach-Belkin, T.J. Michalski, D.L. Worcester, Chlorophyll aggregates in aqueous solutions, in: *Chlorophylls* (1991) (H. Scheer, ed.), CRC Press, Boca Raton, FL, pp. 237–268.
61. A. Agostiano, L. Catucci, G. Colafemmina, M. Della Monica, H. Scheer, Relevance of the chlorophyll phytyl chain on lamellar phase formation and organization. *Biophys. Chem.* **84** (2000) 189–194.
62. J.P. Thornber, Biochemical characterization and structure of pigment-proteins of photosynthetic organism, in: *Photosynthesis III: Photosynthetic Membranes and Light-Harvesting Systems* (1991) (L.A. Staehelin, C.J. Arntzen, eds.), Springer Verlag, Berlin, pp. 98–142.
63. J.P. Thornber, Thirty years of fun with antenna pigment–protein and photochemical reaction centers: A tribute to the people who have influenced my career. *Photosynth. Res.* **44** (1995) 3–22.
64. B. Green, J. Anderson, W.W. Parson, Photosynthetic membranes and their light-harvesting antennas, in: *Light-Harvesting Antennas in Photosynthesis* (2003) (B. Green, W. Parson, eds.), Kluwer, Dordrecht, pp. 1–28.
65. M. Schiffer, J.R. Norris, Structure and function of the photosynthetic reaction center of Rhodobacter sphaeroides, in: *The Photosynthetic Reaction Center* (1993) (J. Deisenhofer, J.R. Norris, eds.), Academic Press, New York, pp. 1–12.
66. J. Standfuss, A.C. Terwisscha van Scheftinga, M. Lamborghini, W. Kühlbrandt, Mechanisms of photoprotection and nonphotochemical quenching in pea light-harvesting complex at 2.5 A resolution. *EMBO J.* **24** (2005) 919–928.
67. J. Deisenhofer, H. Michel, Three-dimensional structure of the reaction center of Rhodopseudomonas viridis, in: *The Photosynthetic Reaction Center* (1993) (J. Deisenhofer, J.R. Norris, eds.), Academic Press, New York, pp. 541–558.
68. K. McLuskey, S.M. Prince, R.J. Cogdell, N.W. Isaacs, Crystallization and preliminary X-ray crystallographic analysis of the B800–820 light-harvesting complex

from *Rhodopseudomonas acidophila* strain 7050. *Acta Crystallogr., D. Biol. Cryst.* **55** (1999) 885–887.
69. A. Freer, S. Prince, K. Sauer, M. Papiz, A. Hawthornthwaite-Lawless, G. McDermott, R. Cogdell, N.W. Isaacs, Pigment–pigment interactions and energy transfer in the antenna complex of the photosynthetic bacterium *Rhodopseudomonas acidophila*. *Structure* **4** (1996) 449–462.
70. J. Koepke, X. Hu, C. Muenke, K. Schulten, H. Michel, The crystal structure of the light-harvesting complex II (B800–850) from *Rhodospirillum molischianum*. *Structure* **4** (1996) 581–597.
71. A. Ben-Shem, F. Frolow, N. Nelson, Crystal structure of plant photosystem I. *Nature* **426** (2003) 630–635.
72. A. Zouni, H.T. Witt, J. Kern, P. Fromme, N. Krauss, W. Saenger, P. Orth, Crystal structure of Photosystem II from *Synechococcus elongatus* at 3.8 A resolution. *Nature* **409** (2001) 739–743.
73. K.N. Ferreira, T.M. Iverson, K. Maghlaoui, J. Barber, S. Iwata, Architecture of the photosynthetic oxygen-evolving center. *Science* **303** (2004) 1831–1838.
74. Z. Liu, H. Yan, K. Wang, T. Kuang, J. Zhang, L. Gui, X. An, W. Chang, Crystal structure of spinach major light-harvesting complex at 2.72 A resolution. *Nature* **428** (2004) 287–292.
75. J. Kern, B. Loll, C. Luneberg, D. Difiore, J. Biesiadka, K.D. Irrgang, A. Zouni, Purification, characterisation and crystallisation of photosystem II from *Thermosynechococcus elongatus* cultivated in a new type of photobioreactor. *Biochim. Biophys. Acta* **1706** (2005) 147–157.
76. H. Rogl, R. Schodel, H. Lokstein, W. Kuhlbrandt, A. Schubert, Assignment of spectral substructures to pigment-binding sites in higher plant light-harvesting complex LHC-II. *Biochemistry* **41** (2002) 2281–2287.
77. D. Spiedel, A.W. Roszak, K. McKendrick, K.E. McAuley, P.K. Fyfe, E. Nabedryk, J. Breton, B. Robert, R.J. Cogdell, N.W. Isaacs, M.R. Jones, Tuning of the optical and electrochemical properties of the primary donor bacteriochlorophylls in the reaction centre from *Rhodobacter sphaeroides*: Spectroscopy and structure. *Biochim. Biophys. Acta* **1554** (2002) 75–93.
78. J.P. Allen, J.C. Williams, The influence of protein interactions on the properties of the bacteriochlorophyll dimer in reaction centers, in: *Chlorophylls and Bacteriochlorophylls. Biochemistry, Biophysics, Functions and Applications* (2006) (B. Grimm, R. Porra, W. Rüdiger, H. Scheer, eds.), Springer, Berlin, pp. 283–285.
79. D. Leupold, H. Stiel, J. Ehlert, F. Nowak, K. Teuchner, M. Bandilla, B. Ücker, H. Scheer, Photophysical characterization of the B800-depleted light harvesting complex B800 ->850nm. *Chem. Phys. Lett.* **301** (1999) 537–545.
80. L. Fiedor, D. Leupold, K. Teuchner, B. Voigt, C.N. Hunter, A. Scherz, H. Scheer, Excitation trap approach to analyze size and pigment–pigment coupling: Reconstitution of lh1 antenna of *Rhodobacter sphaeroides* with ni-substituted bacteriochlorophyll. *Biochemistry* **40** (2001) 3737–3747.
81. L. Fiedor, H. Scheer, N.C. Hunter, F. Tschirschwitz, B. Voigt, J. Ehlert, E. Nibbering, D. Leupold, T. Elsässer, Introduction of a 60 fs deactivation channel in the photosynthetic antenna LH1 by Ni-bacteriopheophytin *a*. *Chem. Phys. Lett.* **319** (2000) 145–152.
82. M. Matsushita, M. Ketelaars, A.M. van Oijen, J. Kohler, T.J. Aartsma, J. Schmidt, Spectroscopy on the B850 band of individual light-harvesting 2 complexes of *Rhodopseudomonas acidophila*. II. Exciton states of an elliptically deformed ring aggregate. *Biophys. J.* **80** (2001) 1604–1614.

83. R.E. Blankenship, J.M. Olson, M. Miller, Antenna complexes from green photosynthetic bacteria, in: *Anoxygenic Photosynthetic Bacteria* (1995) (R. Blankenship, M.T. Madigan, C.E. Bauer, eds.), Kluwer, Dordrecht, pp. 399–435.
84. I. DeBoer, H. DeGroot, MAS NMR of the chlorosomes, in: *Chlorophylls and Bacteriochlorophylls: Biochemistry, Biophysics, Functions and Applications* (2006) (B. Grimm, R. Porra, W. Rüdiger, H. Scheer, eds.), Springer, Berlin, 297–301.
85. M. Hirota, T. Moriyama, K. Shimada, M. Miller, J.M. Olson, K. Matsuura, High degree of organization of bacteriochlorophyll c in chlorosome-like aggregates spontaneously assembled in aqueous solution. *Biochim. Biophys. Acta* **1099** (1992) 271–274.
86. G. Niedermeier, H. Scheer, R. Feick, The functional role of protein in the organization of bacteriochlorophyll c in chlorosomes of *Chloroflexus aurantiacus*. *Eur. J. Biochem.* **204** (1992) 685–692.
87. S. Yagai, T. Miyatake, H. Tamiaki, Self-assembly of synthetic 8(1)-hydroxychlorophyll analogues. *J. Photochem. Photobiol. B* **52** (1999) 74–85.
88. S. Yagai, T. Miyatake, Y. Shimono, H. Tamiaki, Supramolecular structure of self-assembled synthetic zinc-13(1)-oxo- chlorins possessing a primary, secondary or tertiary alcoholic 3(1)-hydroxyl group: Visible spectroscopic and molecular modeling studies. *Photochem. Photobiol.* **73** (2001) 153–163.
89. M. Kunieda, T. Mizoguchi, H. Tamiaki, Diastereoselective self-aggregation of synthetic 3-(1-hydroxyethyl)-bacteriopyrochlophyll-a as a novel photosynthetic antenna model absorbing near the infrared regions. *Photochem. Photobiol.* **79** (2004) 55–61.
90. H. Tamiaki, H. Kitamoto, T. Watanabe, R. Shibata, Self-aggregation of synthetic protobacteriochlorophyll-d derivatives. *Photochem. Photobiol.* **81** (2005) 170–176.
91. I. de Boer, J. Matysik, M. Amakawa, S. Yagai, H. Tamiaki, A.R. Holzwarth, H.J. de Groot, MAS NMR structure of a microcrystalline cd-bacteriochlorophyll d analogue. *J. Am. Chem. Soc.* **125** (2003) 13374–13375.
92. T.S. Balaban, M. Linke-Schaetzel, A.D. Bhise, N.a.R.C. Vanthuyne, Green self-assembling porphyrins and chlorins as mimics of the natural bacteriochlorophylls c,d, and e. *Eur. J. Org. Chem.* (2004), 3919–3930.
93. IUPAC-IUB Joint commission biochemical nomenclature (ICBN), Tetrapyrroles, *Pur. Appl. Chem.* **51**, (1979), 2251.
94. N. Wakao, N. Yokoi, N. Isoyama, A. Hiraishi, K. Shimada, M. Kobayashi, H. Kise, M. Iwaki, S. Itoh, S. Takaichi, Y. Sakurai, Discovery of natural photosynthesis using Zn containing bacteriochlorophyll in an aerobic bacterium *Acidiphilium rubrum*. *Plant Cell Physiol.* **37** (1996) 889–893.
95. W.W. Parson, Electron transfer in reaction centers, in: *Chlorophylls* (1991) (H. Scheer, ed.), CRC Press, Boca Raton, FL, pp. 1153–1180.
96. W.W. Parson, A. Warshel, Simulations of electron transfer in bacterial reaction centers, in: *The Photosynthetic Reaction Center* (1993) (J. Deisenhofer, J.R. Norris, eds.), Academic Press, New York, pp. 23–48.
97. M. Zapata, J.L. Garrido, S.W. Jeffrey, Chlorophyll c pigments: Current status, in: *Chlorophylls and Bacteriochlorophylls: Biochemistry, Biophysics, Functions and Applications* (2006) (B. Grimm, R. Porra, W. Rüdiger, H. Scheer, eds.), Springer, Berlin, pp. 39–53.
98. B. Blankenship, K. Matsuura, Antenna complexes from green photosynthetic bacteria, in: *Light-Harvesting Antennas in Photosynthesis* (2003) (B. Green, W. Parson, eds.), Kluwer, Dordrecht, pp. 195–217.

99. J.L. Stauber, S.W. Jeffrey, Photosynthetic pigments in fifty-one species of marine diatoms. *J. Phycol.* **24** (1988) 158–172.
100. H. Miyashita, K. Adachi, N. Kurano, H. Ikemoto, M. Chihara, S. Miyachi, Pigment composition of a novel oxygenic photosynthetic prokaryote containing chlorophyll *d* as the major chlorophyll. *Plant Cell Physiol.* **38** (1997) 274–281.
101. A.W.D. Larkum, The evoluition of chlorophylls and photosynthesis, in: *Chlorophylls and Bacteriochlorophylls: Biochemistry, Biophysics, Functions and Applications* (2006) (B. Grimm, R. Porra, W. Rüdiger, H. Scheer, eds.), Springer, Berlin, pp. 109–121.
102. J.L. Garrido, M. Zapata, Chlorophyll analysis by new HPLC methods, in: *Chlorophylls and Bacteriochlorophylls: Biochemistry, Biophysics, Functions and Applications* (2006) (B. Grimm, R. Porra, W. Rüdiger, H. Scheer, eds.), Springer, Berlin, pp. 108–121.
103. M. Helfrich, A. Ross, G.C. King, A.G. Turner, A.W.D. Larkum, Identification of (8-vinyl)-protochlorophyllide a in phototrophic prokaryotes and algae: Chemical and spectroscopic properties. *Biochim. Biophys. Acta* **1410** (1999) 262–272.
104. J.L. Garrido, J. Otero, M.A. Maestro, M. Zapata, The main nonpolar chlorophyll c from *Emiliana huxleyi* (Prymnesiophyceae) is a chlorophyll $c_2$-monogalactosyldiacylglyceride ester: A mass spectrometry study. *J. Phycol.* **36** (2000) 497–505.
105. H. Fischer, H. Orth, Die Chemie des Pyrrols, Vol. II, 2nd Half, (1940) in. *Leipzig: Akademische Verlagsgesellschaft*, Leipzig, reprinted 1968, Johnson Reprint corporation, New York.
106. R.B. Woodward, Totalsynthese des chlorophylls. *Angew. Chem.* **72** (1960) 651–662.
107. R. Goericke, D.J. Repeta, Chlorophylls a and b and divinyl chlorophylls a and b in the open subtropical North Atlantic ocean. *Mar. Ecol.: Prog. Ser.* **101** (1993) 307–313.
108. M. Chen, R.G. Hiller, C.J. Howe, A.W. Larkum, Unique origin and lateral transfer of prokaryotic chlorophyll-b and chlorophyll-d light-harvesting systems. *Mol. Biol. Evol.* **22** (2005) 21–28.
109. M. Akiyama, H. Miyashita, H. Kise, T. Watanabe, M. Mimuro, S. Miyachi, M. Kobayashi, Quest for minor but key chlorophyll molecules in photosynthetic reaction centers-Unusual pigment composition in the reaction centers of the chlorophyll d dominated cyanobacterium *Acaryochloris marina*. *Photosynth. Res.* **74** (2002) 97–107.
110. S. Kumazaki, K. Abiko, I. Ikegami, M. Iwaki, S. Itoh, Energy equilibration and primary charge separation in chlorophyll d-based photosystem I reaction center isolated from Acaryochloris marina. *FEBS Lett.* **530** (2002) 153–157.
111. H. Paulsen, Reconstitution and pigment exchange, in: *Chlorophylls and Bacteriochlorophylls: Biochemistry, Biophysics, Functions and Applications* (2006) (B. Grimm, R. Porra, W. Rüdiger, H. Scheer, eds.), Springer, Berlin, pp. 375–385.
112. H. Xu, D. Vavilin, W. Vermaas, Chlorophyll b can serve as the major pigment in functional photosystem II complexes of cyanobacteria. *Proc. Natl. Acad. Sci. U.S.A.* **98** (2001) 14168–14173.
113. D. Vavilin, H. Xu, S. Lin, W. Vermaas, Energy and electron transfer in photosystem II of a chlorophyll b-containing *Synechocystis* sp. PCC 6803 mutant. *Biochemistry* **42** (2003) 1731–1746.
114. N.U. Friegaard, A.G.M. Chew, J.A. Maresca, D.A. Bryant, Bacteriochlorophyll biosynthesis in green bacteria, in: *Chlorophylls and Bacteriochlorophylls:*

*Biochemistry, Biophysics, Functions and Applications* (2006) (B. Grimm, R. Porra, W. Rüdiger, H. Scheer, eds.), Springer, Berlin, pp. 201–221.

115. M.B. Caple, H.-C. Chow, C.E. Strouse, Photosynthetic pigments of green sulfur bacteria (the esterifying alcohols of bacteriochlorophylls c from *Chlorobium limicola*). *J. Biol. Chem.* **253** (1978) 6730–6737.
116. K.M. Smith, D.J. Simpson, Stereochemistry of the bacteriochlorophyll e homologues. *J. Chem. Soc. Chem. Commun.* (1986), 1682–1684.
117. H. Tamiaki, S. Takeuchi, R. Tanikaga, S. Balaban, A. Holzwarth, K. Schaffner, Diastereoselective control of aggregation of $3^1$-epimeric zinc methyl bacteriopheophorbides d in apolar solvents. *Chem. Lett.* (1994), 401–402.
118. Y. Saga, H. Tamiaki, Comparison between chlorosomes containing bacteriochlorophyll-c and chlorosomes containing bacteriochlorophyll-d isolated from two substrains of green sulfur photosynthetic bacterium *Chlorobium vibrioforme* NCIB 8327. *J. Photochem. Photobiol. B* **75** (2004) 89–97.
119. H. Tamiaki, H. Kitamoto, A. Nishikawa, T. Hibino, R. Shibata, Determination of 3(1)-stereochemistry in synthetic bacteriochlorophyll-d homologues and self-aggregation of their zinc complexes. *Bioorg. Med. Chem.* **12** (2004) 1657–1666.
120. H. Scheer, W.A. Svec, B.T. Cope, M.H. Studier, R.G. Scott, J.J. Katz, Structure of bacteriochlorophyll b. *J. Am. Chem. Soc.* **96** (1974) 3714–3716.
121. N. Risch, Bacteriochlorophyll b-Determination of its configuration by nuclear Overhauser effect difference spectroscopy. *J. Chem. Res.* (1981), 116–117.
122. T.J. Michalski, J.E. Hunt, M.K. Bowman, U. Smith, K. Bardeen, H. Gest, J.R. Norris, J.J. Katz, Bacteriopheophytin g-Properties and some speculations on a possible primary role for bacteriochlorophyll b and g in the biosynthesis of chlorophylls. *Proc. Natl. Acad. Sci. U.S.A.* **84** (1987) 2570–2574.
123. J. Amesz, The antenna-reaction center complex of heliobacteria, in: *Anoxygenic Photosynthetic Bacteria.* (1995) (R. Blankenship, M.T. Madigan, C.E. Bauer, eds.), Kluwer, Dordrecht, pp. 687–697.
124. J.J. Katz, H.H. Strain, A.C. Harkness, M.H. Studier, W.A. Svec, T.R. Janson, B.T. Cope, Esterfying alcohols in the chlorophylls of purple photosynthetic bacteria. A new chlorophyll, bacteriochlorophyll (Gg), *all-trans* geranylgeranyl bacteriochlorophyllide a. *J. Am. Chem. Soc.* **94** (1972) 7938–7939.
125. R. Steiner, W. Schäfer, I. Blos, H. Wieschhoff, H. Scheer, Δ2,10-phytodienol as esterifying alcohol of bacteriochlorophyll b from *Ectothiorhodospira halochloris*. *Z. Naturforsch.* **36c** (1981) 417–420.
126. H. Scheer, B. Paulke, J. Gottstein, Long-wavelength absorbing forms of bacteriochlorophylls. II. Structural requirements for formation in Triton X100 micelles and in aqueous methanol and acetone, in: *Optical Properties and Structure of Tetrapyrrols* (1985) (G. Blauer, H. Sund, eds.), De Gruyter, London, pp. 507–521.
127. D.E. Tronrud, B.W. Matthews, Refinement of the structure of a water-soluble antenna complex from green photosynthetic bacteria by incorporation of the chemically determined amino acid sequence, in: *The Photosynthetic Reaction Center* (1993) (J. Deisenhofer, J.R. Norris, eds.), Academic Press, New York, Vol. I, pp. 13–22.
128. K.E. McAuley-Hecht, P.K. Fyfe, J.P. Ridge, S.M. Prince, C.N. Hunter, N.W. Isaacs, R.J. Cogdell, M.R. Jones, Structural studies of wild-type and mutant reaction centers from an antenna-deficient strain of *Rhodobacter sphaeroides*: Monitoring the optical properties of the complex from bacterial cell to crystal. *Biochemistry* **37** (1998) 4740–4750.

129. T.O. Yeates, H. Komiya, A. Chirino, D.C. Rees, J.P. Allen, G. Feher, Structure of the reaction center from *Rhodobacter sphaeroides* R26 and 2.4.1: Protein-cofactor (bacteriochlorophyll, bacteriopheophytin and carotenoid) interactions. *Proc. Natl. Acad. Sci. U.S.A.* **85** (1988) 7993–7997.
130. G. McDermott, S.M. Prince, A.A. Freer, A.M. Hawthornthwaite-Lawless, M.Z. Papiz, R.J. Cogdell, N.W. Isaacs, Crystal structure of an integral membrane light-harvesting complex from photosynthetic bacteria. *Nature* **374** (1995) 517–521.
131. E. Hofmann, P.M. Wrench, F.P. Sharples, R.G. Hiller, W. Welte, K. Diederichs, Structural basis of light-harvesting by carotenoids: Peridinin-chlorophyll-protein from *Amphidinium carterae*. *Science* **272** (1996) 1788–1791.
132. U. Ermler, G. Fritzsch, S.K. Buchanan, H. Michel, Structure of the photosynthetic reaction centre from *Rhodobacter sphaeroides* at 2.65 Ångstrom resolution: Cofactors and protein-cofactor interactions. *Structure* **2** (1994) 925–936.
133. G. McDermott, S.M. Prince, A.A. Freer, A.M. Hawthornthwaite-Lawless, M.Z. Papiz, R.J. Cogdell, N.W. Isaacs, Crystal structure of an integral membrane light-harvesting complex from photosynthetic bacteria. *Nature* **374** (1995) 517–521.
134. J. Biesiadka, B. Loll, J. Kern, K.-D. Irrgang, A. Zouni, Crystal structure of cyanobacterial photosystem II at 3.2. ANG. Resolution: A closer look at the Mn cluster. *Phys. Chem. Chem. Phys.* **6** (2004) 4733–4736.
135. M. Kobayashi, M. Akiyama, T. Watanabe, H. Kano, Exotic chlorophylls as key components of photosynthesis. *Curr. Top. Plant Biol.* **1** (1999) 17–35.
136. M. Kobayashi, M. Akiyama, H. Kise, T. Watanabe, Unusual terapyrrole pigments of photosynthetic antennas and reaction centers: Specially tailored chlorophylls, in: *Chlorophylls and Bacteriochlorophylls: Biochemistry, Biophysics, Functions and Applications* (2006) (B. Grimm, R. Porra, W. Rüdiger, H. Scheer, eds.), Springer, Berlin, pp. 323–335.
137. D. Noy, L. Fiedor, G. Hartwich, H. Scheer, A. Scherz, Metal-substituted bacteriochlorophylls. 2. Changes in redox potentials and electronic transition energies are dominated by intramolecular electrostatic interactions. *J. Am. Chem. Soc.* **120** (1998) 3684–3693.
138. G. Hartwich, L. Fiedor, I. Simonin, E. Cmiel, W. Schaefer, D. Noy, A. Scherz, H. Scheer, Metal-substituted bacteriochlorophylls. 1. Preparation and influence of metal and coordination on spectra. *J. Am. Chem. Soc.* **120** (1998) 3675–3683.
139. M. Kobayashi, M. Akiyama, M. Yamamura, H. Kise, N. Wakao, N. Ishida, M. Koizumi, H. Kano, T. Watanabe, Comparison of physicochemical properties of metallobacteriochlorophylls and metallochlorophylls. *Z. Physik. Chem.* **213** (1999) 207–214.
140. M. Akiyama, M. Kobayashi, H. Kise, M. Hara, N. Wakao, K. Shimada, Pigment composition of the reaction center complex isolated from an acidophilic bacterium *Acidiphilium rubrum* grown at pH 3.5. *Photomed. Photobiol.* **20** (1998) 85–87.
141. K. Csatorday, R. MacColl, D.S. Berns, Accumulation of protoporphyrin IX and zinc protoporphyrin IX in *Cyanidium caldarium*. *Proc. Natl. Acad. Sci. U.S.A.* **78** (1981) 1700–1702.
142. S. Schoch, M. Helfrich, B. Wiktorsson, C. Sundqvist, W. Rüdiger, M. Ryberg, Photoreduction of zinc-protopheophorbide b with NADPH-protochlorophyllide oxidoreductase from etiolated wheat (*Triticum aestivum L.*). *Eur. J. Biochem.* **229** (1995) 291–298.
143. C.M. Davis, P.S. Parkes-Loach, C.K. Cook, K.A. Meadows, M. Bandilla, H. Scheer, P.A. Loach, Comparison of the structural requirements for bacteriochlorophyll binding in the core light-harvesting complexes of *Rhodospirillum*

*rubrum* and *Rhodobacter sphaeroides* using reconstitution methodology with bacteriochlorophyll analogs. *Biochemistry* **35** (1996) 3072–3084.
144. H. Küpper, F.C. Küpper, M. Spiller, [Heavy metal]-chlorophylls formed in vivo during heavy metal stress and degradation products formed during digestion, extraction and storage of plant material, in: *Chlorophylls and Bacteriochlorophylls: Biochemistry, Biophysics, Functions and Applications* (2006) (B. Grimm, R. Porra, W. Rüdiger, H. Scheer, eds.), Springer, Berlin, pp. 67–77.
145. V. Caspi, M. Droppa, G. Horvath, S. Malkin, J.B. Marder, V.I. Raskin, The effect of copper on chlorophyll organization during greening of barley leaves. *Photosynth. Res.* **62** (1999) 165–174.
146. H. Küpper, F. Küpper, M. Spiller, In situ detection of heavy metal substituted chlorophylls in water plants. *Photosynth. Res.* **58** (1998) 123–133.
147. K. Teuchner, H. Stiel, D. Leupold, A. Scherz, D. Noy, I. Simonin, G. Hartwich, H. Scheer, Fluorescence and excited state absorption in modified pigments of bacterial photosynthesis: A comparative study of metal-substituted bacteriochlorophylls a. *J. Lumin.* **72–74** (1997) 612–614.
148. D. Noy, V. Brumfeld, I. Ashur, R. Yerushalmi, H. Scheer, Axial ligand coordination and photodissociation of nickel substituted bacteriochlorophyll a, in: *Photosynthesis: Mechanisms and Effects* (1998) (G. Garab, ed.), Kluwer, Dordrecht, pp. 4225–4228.
149. C. Musewald, G. Hartwich, F. Pöllinger-Dammer, H. Lossau, H. Scheer, M.E. Michel-Beyerle, Time resolved spectral investigation of bacteriochlorophyll a and its transmetalled derivatives [Zn]-bacteriochlorophyll a and [Pd]-bacteriochlorophyll a. *J. Phys. Chem. B* **102** (1999) 8336–8342.
150. C. Musewald, G. Hartwich, H. Lossau, P. Gilch, F. Pöllinger-Dammer, H. Scheer, M.E. Michel-Beyerle, Ultrafast photophysics and photochemistry of (Ni)-bacteriochlorophyll a. *J. Phys. Chem. B* **103** (1999) 7055–7060.
151. G. Hartwich, M. Friese, H. Scheer, A. Ogrodnik, M.E. Michel-Beyerle, Ultrafast internal conversion in 13(2)-OH-Ni-bacteriochlorophyll in reaction centers of *Rhodobacter sphaeroides* R26. *Chem. Phys.* **197** (1995) 423–434.
152. R. Goericke, D. Repeta, The pigments of *Prochlorococcus marinus:* The presence of divinyl-chlorophyll a and b in a marine prokaryote. *Limnol. Oceanogr.* **37** (1992) 425–433.
153. M. Kobayashi, T. Watanabe, M. Nakazato, I. Ikegami, T. Hiyama, T. Matsunaga, Chlorophyll a'/P700 and pheophytin a/P680 stoichiometries in higher plants and cyanobacteria determined by HPLC analysis. *Biochim. Biophys. Acta* **936** (1988) 81–89.
154. M. Akiyama, H. Miyashita, H. Kise, T. Watanabe, S. Miyachi, M. Kobayashi, Detection of chlorophyll d' and pheophytin a in a chlorophyll d- dominating oxygenic photosynthetic prokaryote *Acaryochloris marina*. *Anal. Sci.* **17** (2001) 205–208.
155. M.R. Razeghifard, M. Chen, J.L. Hughes, J. Freeman, E. Krausz, T. Wydrzynski, Spectroscopic studies of photosystem II in chlorophyll d-containing *Acaryochloris marina*. *Biochemistry* **44** (2005) 11178–11187.
156. T. Watanabe, M. Kobayashi, Electrochemistry of chlorophylls, in: *Chlorophylls* (1991) (H. Scheer, ed.) CRC Press, Boca Raton, FL, pp. 287–316.
157. S. Schmidt, T. Arlt, P. Hamm, H. Huber, T. Nägele, J. Wachtveitl, W. Zinth, M. Meyer, H. Scheer, Primary electron-transfer dynamics in modified bacterial reaction centers containing pheophytin a instead of bacteriopheophytin a. *Spectrochim. Acta A* **51** (1995) 1565–1578.

158. O. Klukas, W.-D. Schubert, P. Jordan, N. Krauß, P. Fromme, H.T. Witt, W. Saenger, Photosystem I, an improved model of the stromal subunits PsaC, PsaD, and PsaE. *J. Biol. Chem.* **274** (1999) 7351–7360.
159. M. Kobayashi, E.J. Vandemeent, C. Erkelens, J. Amesz, I. Ikegami, T. Watanabe, Bacteriochlorophyll g epimer as a possible reaction center component of *Heliobacteria*. *Biochim. Biophys. Acta* **1057** (1991) 89–96.
160. E.J. Van de Meent, M. Kobayashi, C. Erkelens, P.A. van Veelen, J. Amesz, zT. Watanabe, Identification of $8^1$-hydroxychlorophyll *a* as a functional reaction center pigment in *Heliobacteria*. *Biochim. Biophys. Acta* **1058** (1991) 356–362.
161. M. Kobayashi, H. Oh-oka, S. Akutsu, M. Akiyama, K. Tominaga, H. Kise, F. Nishida, T. Watanabe, J. Amesz, M. Koizumi, N. Ishida, H. Kano, The primary electron acceptor of green sulfur bacteria, bacteriochlorophyll 663, is chlorophyll a esterified with delta 2,6-phytadienol. *Photosynth. Res.* **63** (2000) 269–280.
162. E. Walter, J. Schreiber, E. Zass, A. Eschenmoser, Bakteriochlorophyll $a_{GG}$ und bakteriophäophytin $a_P$ in den photosynthetischen Reaktionszentren von *Rhodospirillum rubrum* G9. *Helv. Chim. Acta* **62** (1979) 899–920.
163. M.R. Wasielewski, J.R. Norris, L.L. Shipman, C.P. Lin, W.A. Svec, Monomeric chlorophyll a enol-Evidence for its possible role as the primary electron donor in photosystem I of plant photosynthesis. *Proc. Natl. Acad. Sci. U.S.A.* **78** (1981) 2957–2961.
164. R. Jimenez, G.R. Fleming, Ultrafast spectroscopy of photosynthetic systems, in: *Biophysical Techniques in Photosynthesis* (1996) (J. Amesz, A.J. Hoff, eds.), Kluwer, Dordrecht.
165. J. Wachtveitl, W. Zinth, Electron transfer in photosynthetic reaction centers, in: *Chlorophylls and Bacteriochlorophylls: Biochemistry, Biophysics, Functions and Applications* (2006) (B. Grimm, R. Porra, W. Rüdiger, H. Scheer, eds.), Springer, Berlin, pp. 445–459.
166. C. Weiss, Optical spectra of chlorophylls, in: *The Porphyrins* (1978) (D. Dolphin, ed.), Academic Press, New York, Vol. III, pp. 211–224.
167. S.G. Boxer, A. Kuki, K.A. Wright, B.A. Katz, N. Xuong, Oriented properties of the chlorophylls-Electronic absorption-spectroscopy of orthorhombic pyrochlorophyllide alpha-apomyglobin single-crystals. *Proc. Natl. Acad. Sci. U.S.A.* **79** (1982) 1121–1125.
168. R. Yerushalmi, I. Ashur, A. Scherz, Metal-substituted bacteriochlorophylls: Novel molecular tools, in: *Chlorophylls and Bacteriochlorophylls: Biochemistry, Biophysics, Functions and Applications* (2006) (B. Grimm, R. Porra, W. Rüdiger, H. Scheer, eds.), Springer, Berlin, pp. 495–506.
169. G. Trinkunas, J.L. Herek, T. Polivka, V. Sundstrom, T. Pullerits, Exciton delocalization probed by excitation annihilation in the light-harvesting antenna LH2. *Phys. Rev. Lett.* **86** (2001) 4167–4170.
170. A. Ivancich, K. Artz, J.C. Williams, J.P. Allen, T.A. Mattioli, Effects of hydrogen bonds on the redox potential and electronic structure of the bacterial primary electron donor. *Biochemistry* **37** (1998) 11812–11820.
171. D. Noy, C.C. Moser, P.L. Dutton, Bacteriochlorophyll protein maquettes, in: *Chlorophylls and Bacteriochlorophylls: Biochemistry, Biophysics, Functions and Applications* (2006) (B. Grimm, R. Porra, W. Rüdiger, H. Scheer, eds.), Springer, Berlin, pp. 348–363.
172. L.L. Eggink, J.K. Hoober, Chlorophyll binding to peptide maquettes containing a retention motif. *J. Biol. Chem.* **275** (2000) 9087–9090.

173. H.K. Rau, H. Snigula, A. Struck, B. Robert, H. Scheer, W. Haehnel, Design, synthesis and properties of synthetic chlorophyll proteins. *Eur. J. Biochem.* **268** (2001) 3284–3295.
174. M. Nango, Molecular assembly of bacteriochlorophyll complexes using synthetic light-harvesting (LH) model polypeptides, in: *Chlorophylls and Bacteriochlorophylls: Biochemistry, Biophysics, Functions and Applications* (2006) (B. Grimm, R. Porra, W. Rüdiger, H. Scheer, eds.), Springer, Berlin, pp. 365–373.
175. A. Kashiwada, H. Watanabe, T. Tanaka, M. Nango, Molecular assembly of zinc bacteriochlorophyll *a* by synthetic hydrophobic 1α-helix polypeptides. *Chem. Lett.* (2000), 24–25.
176. G. Sandmann, H. Scheer, Chloroplast pigments: Chlorophylls and carotenoids, in: *Photosynthesis-A Comprehensive Treatise* (1998) (A.S. Raghavendra, ed.) Cambridge University Press, Cambridge, pp. 44–57.
177. S. Takaichi, Carotenoids and carotenogenesis in anoxygenic photosynthetic bacteria, in: *The Photochemistry of Carotenoids* (1999) (H.A. Frank, A.J. Young, G. Britton, R.J. Cogdell, eds.), Vol. 8 of *Advances in Photosynthesis* (series editor Govindjee), Kluwer, Dordrecht, pp. 39–69.
178. D. Della-Penna, Biosynthetic pathways and the distribution of carotenoids in photosynthetic organisms, in: *The Photochemistry of Carotenoids* (1999) (H.A. Frank, A.J. Young, G. Britton, R.J. Cogdell, eds.), Vol. 8 of *Advances in Photosynthesis* (series editor Govindjee), Kluwer, Dordrecht, pp. 21–37.
179. W.J. Coleman, D.C. Youvan, Spectroscopic analysis of genetically modified photosynthetic reaction centers. *Annu. Rev. Biophys. (Biophys. Chem.)* **19** (1990) 333–367.
180. W.J. Coleman, T.A. Mattioli, D.C. Youvan, A.W. Rutherford, Site directed mutations near the L-subunit D-helix of the purple bacterial reaction center: A partial model for the primary donor of photosystem II. *Biochemistry* **36** (1997) 2178–2187.
181. H.A. Frank, J. Innes, M. Aldema, R. Neumann, C.C. Schenck, Triplet state EPR of reaction centers from the His(L173) ->Leu(L173) mutant of *Rhodobacter sphaeroides* with contains a heterodimer primary donor. *Photosynth. Res.* **38** (1993) 99–109.
182. G.Z. Shen, W.F. Vermaas, Mutation of chlorophyll ligands in the chlorophyll-binding CP47 protein as studied in a *Synechocystis sp.* PCC 6803 photosystem I-less background. *Biochemistry* **33** (1994) 7379–7388.
183. A.J. Matysik, C. Soede-Huijbregts, M. Baldus, J. Raap, J. Lugtenburg, P. Gast, H.J. van Gorkom, A.J. Hoff, H.J.M. de Groot, Ultra high field MAS NMR dipolar correlation spectroscopy of the histidine residues in light-harvesting complex II from photosynthetic bacteria reveals partial internal charge transfer in the B850/His complex. *J. Am. Chem. Soc.* **123** (2001) 4803–4809.
184. R. Yerushalmi, D. Noy, K.K. Baldridge, A. Scherz, Mutual control of axial and equatorial ligands; model studies with [Ni]-bacteriochlorophyll a. *J. Am. Chem. Soc.* **124** (2002) 8406–8415.
185. E. Nabedryk, J. Breton, J.C. Williams, J.P. Allen, M. Kuhn, W. Lubitz, FTIR characterization of the primary electron donor in double mutants combining the heterodimer HL(M202) with the LH(L131), HF(L168), FH(M197), or LH(M160) mutations. *Spectrochim. Acta A* **54** (1998) 1219–1230.
186. G.J.S. Fowler, G.D. Sockalingum, B. Robert, C.N. Hunter, Blue shifts in bacteriochlorophyll absorbance correlate with changed hydrogen bonding patterns in light-harvesting 2 mutants of *Rhodobacter sphaeroides* with alterations at alpha-Tyr-44 and alpha-Tyr-45. *Biochem. J.* **299** (1994) 695–700.

187. J.N. Sturgis, V. Jirsakova, F. Reiss-Husson, R.J. Cogdell, B. Robert, Structure and properties of the bacteriochlorophyll binding site in peripheral light-harvesting complexes of purple bacteria. *Biochemistry* **34** (1995) 517–523.
188. A. Garcia-Martin, L. Kwa, M. vonJan, P. Braun, Assembly of novel bacteriochlorophyll proteins in the native lipid environment, in: *Chlorophylls and Bacteriochlorophylls: Biochemistry, Biophysics, Functions and Applications* (2006) (B. Grimm, R. Porra, W. Rüdiger, H. Scheer, eds.), Springer, Berlin, pp. 387–396.
189. L.G. Kwa, A. Garcia-Martin, A.P. Vegh, B. Strohmann, B. Robert, P. Braun, Hydrogen bonding in a model bacteriochlorophyll-binding site drives assembly of light harvesting complex. *J. Biol. Chem.* **279** (2004) 15067–15075.
190. H. Scheer, A. Struck, Bacterial reaction centers with modified tetrapyrrole chromophores, in: *The Photosynthetic Reaction Center* (1993) (J. Deisenhofer, J.R. Norris, eds.), Academic Press, New York, pp. 157–193.
191. A. Pascal, M. Gastaldelli, S. Ceoldo, R. Bassi, B. Robert, Pigment conformation and pigment–protein interactions in the reconstituted Lhcb4 antenna protein. *FEBS Lett.* **492** (2001) 54–57.
192. M.O. Senge, A. Wiehe, C. Ryppa, Synthesis, reactivity and structure of chlorophylls, in: *Chlorophylls and Bacteriochlorophylls: Biochemistry, Biophysics, Functions and Applications* (2006) (B. Grimm, R. Porra, W. Rüdiger, H. Scheer, eds.), Springer, Berlin, pp. 27–37.
193. H. Scheer, Chemistry and spectroscopy of chlorophylls, in: *Handbook of Organic Photochemistry and Photobiology: Section II: Photobiology* (2004) (W.M. Horspool, F. Lenci, eds.), CRC Press, Boca Raton, FL, pp. 117:1–16.
194. T. Miyatake, T. Oba, H. Tamiaki, Pure and scrambled self-aggregates prepared with zinc analogues of bacteriochlorophylls c and d. *Chembiochem* **2** (2001) 335–342.
195. K. Sauer, M. Debreczeny, Fluorescence, in: *Biophysical Techniques in Photosynthesis* (1996) (J. Amesz, A.J. Hoff, eds.), Kluwer, Dordrecht, pp. 41–62.
196. H. Scheer, An overview of chlorophylls and bacteriochlorophylls, in: *Chlorophylls and Bacteriochlorophylls: Biochemistry, Biophysics, Functions and Applications* (2006) (B. Grimm, R. Porra, W. Rüdiger, H. Scheer, eds.), Springer, Berlin, 1–26.
197. H. Scheer, Chlorophylls: Chromatographic methods for the separation of chlorophylls, in: *Chlorophylls* (1988) (H.-P. Köst, ed.), CRC Press, Boca Raton, FL, pp. 235–307.
198. S. Malkin, The photoacoustic method in photosynthesis--Monitoring and analysis of phenomena which lead to pressure changes following light excitation, in: *Biophysical Techniques in Photosynthesis* (1996) (J. Amesz, A.J. Hoff, eds.), Kluwer, Dordrecht, pp. 191–208.
199. A.W.H. Mau, M. Puza, Phosphorescence of chlorophylls. *Photochem. Photobiol.* **25** (1977) 601–603.
200. J. Fiedor, L. Fiedor, R. Haessner, H. Scheer, Stable mono- and di-endoperoxides of β-carotene as products of photosensitized oxygenation. *Biochim. Biophys. Acta* **1709** (2005) 1–4.
201. J. Fiedor, L. Fiedor, N. Kammhuber, A. Scherz, H. Scheer, Photodynamics of the bacteriochlorophyll-caroteinoid system. 2. Influence of central metal, solvent and ß-carotene on photobleaching of bacteriochlorophyll derivatives. *Photochem. Photobiol.* **76** (2002) 145–152.
202. J. Fiedor, L. Fiedor, J. Winkler, A. Scherz, H. Scheer, Photodynamics of the bacteriochlorophyll-caroteinoid system. 1. Bacteriochlorophyll-photosensitized oxygenation of β-carotene in acetone. *Photochem. Photobiol.* **74** (2001) 64–71.

203. C.A. Rebeiz, L.J. Gut, K. Lee, J.A. Juvik, C.C. Rebeiz, C.E. Bouton, Photodynamics of porphyric insecticides. *Crit. Rev. Plant Sci.* **14** (1995) 329–366.
204. C.A. Rebeiz, K.N. Reddy, U.B. Nandihalli, J. Velu, Tetrapyrrole-dependent photodynamic herbicides. *Photochem. Photobiol.* **52** (1990) 1099–1118.
205. J.D. Spikes, J.C. Bommer, Chlorophyll and related pigments as photosensitizers in biology and medicine, in: *Chlorophylls* (1991) (H. Scheer, ed.), CRC Press, Boca Raton, FL, pp. 1181–1204.
206. R.K. Pandey, Recent advances in photodynamic therapy. *J. Porph. Phthalocyan.* **4** (2000) 368–373.
207. J.G. Moser (ed.), *Photodynamic Tumor Therapy: 2nd and 3rd Generation Photosensitizers*, (1998) OPA, Amsterdam.
208. A. Brandis, Y. Salomon, A. Scherz, Bacteriochlorophyll sensitizers in photodynamic therapy, in: *Chlorophylls and Bacteriochlorophylls: Biochemistry, Biophysics, Functions and Applications* (2006) (B. Grimm, R. Porra, W. Rüdiger, H. Scheer, eds.), Springer, Berlin, pp. 485–494.
209. A. Brandis, Y. Salomon, A. Scherz, Chlorophyll sensitizers in photodynamic therapy, in: *Chlorophylls and Bacteriochlorophylls: Biochemistry, Biophysics, Functions and Applications* (2006) (B. Grimm, R. Porra, W. Rüdiger, H. Scheer, eds.), Springer, Berlin, pp. 461–483.
210. J.R. Norris, H. Scheer, J.J. Katz, Models for antenna and reaction center chlorophylls. *Ann. New York Acad. Sci.* **244** (1975) 260–280.
211. J.J. Katz, M.K. Bowman, T.J. Michalski, D.L. Worcester, Chlorophyll aggregation: Chlorophyll-water micelles as models for in vivo long-wavelength chlorophyll, in: *Chlorophylls* (1991) (H. Scheer, ed.), CRC Press, Boca Raton, FL, pp. 211–236.
212. A. Scherz, W.W. Parson, Oligomers of bacteriochlorophyll and bacteriopheophytin with spectroscopic properties resembling those found in photosynthetic bacteria. *Biochim. Biophys. Acta* **766** (1984) 653–665.
213. T. Oba, H. Tamiaki, Molecular requirement of chlorosomal chlorophylls. Self-organization of a chlorophyll derivative possessing a hydroxyl group at ring II. *Photochem. Photobiol.* **67** (1998) 295–303.
214. T.S. Balaban, A.R. Holzwarth, K. Schaffner, G.-J. Boender, H.J.M. de Groot, CP-MAS 13C-NMR dipolar correlation spectroscopy of 13C-enriched chlorosomes and isolated bacteriochlorophyll c aggregates of *Chlorobium tepidum*: The self-organization of pigments is the main structural feature of chlorosomes. *Biochemistry* **34** (1995) 15259–15266.
215. P.L. Cheng, P.A. Liddell, S.X.C. Ma, R.E. Blankenship, Properties of zinc and magnesium methyl bacteriopheophorbide-d and their aggregates. *Photochem. Photobiol.* **58** (1993) 290–295.
216. K. Uehara, M. Mimuro, Y. Ozaki, J.M. Olson, The formation and characterization of the in vitro polymeric aggregates of bacteriochlorophyll c homologs from *Chlorobium limicola* in aqueous suspension in the presence of monogalactosyl diglyceride. *Photosynth. Res.* **41** (1994) 235–243.
217. A. Morel, How oceanic chlorophylls are monitored from space, in: *Chlorophylls and Bacteriochlorophylls: Biochemistry, Biophysics, Functions and Applications* (2006) (B. Grimm, R. Porra, W. Rüdiger, H. Scheer, eds.), Springer, Berlin, pp. 521–534.
218. L. Nedbal, M. Koblizek, Chlorophyll fluorescence as a reporter, in: *Chlorophylls and Bacteriochlorophylls: Biochemistry, Biophysics, Functions and Applications* (2006) (B. Grimm, R. Porra, W. Rüdiger, H. Scheer, eds.), Springer, Berlin, pp. 507–519.

219. G. Renger, U. Schreiber, Practical applications of fluorometric methods to algae and higher plants, in: *Light Emission by Plants and Bacteria* (1986) (D.C. Fork, Govindjee, J. Amesz, eds.), Academic Press, New York, pp. 587–619.
220. U. Schreiber, Chlorophyll fluorescence yield changes as a tool in plant physiology. I. The measuring system. *Photosynth. Res.* **4** (1983) 361–373.
221. K.K. Karukstis, Chlorophyll fluorescence as a physiological probe of the photosynthetic apparatus, in: *Chlorophylls* (1991) (H. Scheer, ed.), CRC Press, Boca Raton, FL, pp. 769–796.
222. O.H. Sayed, Chlorophyll fluorescence as a tool in cereal crop research. *Photosynthetica* **41** (2003) 321–330.
223. J.R. DeEll and P.M.A. Toivonen (eds.), *Practical Applications of Chlorophyll Fluorescence in Plant Biology*, (2003) Kluwer, Dordrecht.
224. A.A. Krasnovskii, N.N. Lebedev, F.F. Litvin, Phosphorescence and delayed fluorescence of chlorophyll and its precursors in solutions, leaves and chloroplasts at 77 degK. *Stud. Biophys.* **65** (1977) 81–89.
225. Y. Inoue, Photosynthetic thermoluminescence as a simple probe of photosystem II electron transport, in: *Biophysical Techniques in Photosynthesis* (1996) (J. Amesz, A.J. Hoff, eds.), Kluwer, Dordrecht, pp. 93–108.
226. R. Dedic, A. Svoboda, J. Psencik, L. Lupinkova, J. Komenda, J. Hala, Time and spectral resolved phosphorescence of singlet oxygen and pigments in photosystem II particles. *J. Lumin.* **102–103** (2003) 313–317.
227. A.A. Krasnovsky, Jr., O.B. Belyaeva, Yu.V. Kovalev, N.V. Ignatov, F.F. Litvin, Phosphorescence of intermediates of the terminal stage of chlorophyll biosynthesis in plants. *Biochemistry (Moscow)* **64** (1999) 587–591.
228. H.A. Frank, V. Chynwat, A. Posteraro, G. Hartwich, M. Meyer, I. Simonin, H. Scheer, Triplet state energy transfer between the primary donor and the carotenoid in *Rhodobacter sphaeroides R26.1* reaction centers exchanged with modified bacteriochlorophyll pigments and reconstituted with spheroidene. *Photochem. Photobiol.* **64** (1996) 823–831.
229. A. Angerhofer, F. Bornhäuser, V. Aust, G. Hartwich, H. Scheer, Triplet energy transfer in bacterial photosynthetic reaction centers. *Biochim. Biophys. Acta* **1365** (1998) 404–420.
230. C. Houssier, K. Sauer, Circular dichroism and magnetic circular dichroism of chlorophyll and protochlorophyll pigments. *J. Am. Chem. Soc.* **92** (1970) 779–791.
231. H. Wolf, H. Scheer, Stereochemistry and chiroptic properties of pheophorbides and related compounds. *Ann. New York Acad. Sci.* **206** (1973) 549–567.
232. P.H. Hynninen, G. Sievers, Conformations of chlorophyll a and a' and their magnesium-free derivatives as revealed by circular-dichroism and proton-magnetic resonance. *Z. Naturforsch. B* **36** (1981) 1000–1009.
233. T.S. Balaban, P. Fromme, A.R. Holzwarth, N. Krauß, V.I. Prokhorenko, Relevance of diastereotopic ligation of magnesium atoms of chlorophylls in photosytem I. *Biochim. Biophys. Acta* **1556** (2002) 197–207.
234. T. Oba, H. Tamiaki, Which side of the P-macrocycle plane of (bacterio)chlorophylls is favored for binding of the fifth ligand? *Photosynth. Res.* **74** (2002) 1–10.
235. M. Umetsu, Z.Y. Wang, T. Nozawa, New developments in magnetic circular dichroism application on biological pigments. New approaches to clarification of coordination and aggregation states of chlorophylls and bacteriochlorophylls. *Seibutsu Butsuri* **38** (1998) 197–202.
236. R.J. Cogdell, H. Scheer, Circular dichroism of light-harvesting complexes from purple photosynthetic bacteria. *Photochem. Photobiol.* **42** (1985) 669–678.

237. J.D. Bolt, C.N. Hunter, R.A. Niederman, K. Sauer, Linear and circular-dichroism and fluorescence polarization of the B875 light-harvesting bacteriochlorophyll-protein complex from *Rhodopseudomonas sphaeroides*. *Photochem. Photobiol.* **34** (1981) 653–656.
238. K. Sauer, Circular dichroism and optical rotatory dispersion of photosynthetic organelles and their component pigments. *Methods Enzymol.* **24** (1972) 206–217.
239. G. Garab, J. Kieleczawa, J.C. Sutherland, C. Bustamante, G. Hind, Organization of pigment–protein complexes into macrodomains in the thylakoid membranes of wild-type and chlorophyll b-less mutant of barley as revealed by circular dichroism. *Photochem. Photobiol.* **54** (1991) 273–282.
240. A. Scherz, W.W. Parson, Exciton interaction in dimers of bacteriochlorophyll and related molecules. *Biochim. Biophys. Acta* **766** (1984) 666–678.
241. G.M. Gazit, *Studies of Structural Motifs in Bacterial Reaction Centers by Computer Modeling*, (1994) Weizmann Institut, Rehovot, Israel, 25 pp.
242. G. Garab, Linear and circular dichroism, in: *Biophysical Techniques in Photosynthesis* (1996) (J. Amesz, A.J. Hoff, eds.) Kluwer, Dordrecht, pp. 11–40.
243. H. Scheer, J.J. Katz, Nuclear magnetic resonance spectroscopy of porphyrins and metalloporphyrins, in: *Porphyrins and Metalloporphyrins* (1975) (K.M. Smith, ed.), Elsevier, New York, pp. 399–524.
244. R.J. Abraham, A.E. Rowan, Nuclear magnetic resonance spectroscopy of chlorophyll, in: *Chlorophylls* (1991) (H. Scheer, ed.) CRC Press, Boca Raton, FL, pp. 797–834.
245. M. Kobayashi, M. Akiyama, H. Kano, H. Kise, Spectroscopy and structure determination, in: *Chlorophylls and Bacteriochlorophylls: Biochemistry, Biophysics, Functions and Applications* (2006) (B. Grimm, R. Porra, W. Rüdiger, H. Scheer, eds.), Springer, Berlin, pp. 79–94.
246. J.J. Katz, R.C. Dougherty, L.J. Boucher, Infrared and nuclear magnetic resonance spectroscopy of chlorophyll, in: *The Chlorophylls* (1966) (L.P. Vernon, G.R. Seely, eds.), Academic Press, New York, pp. 185–251.
247. J.J. Katz, C.E. Brown, Nuclear magnetic resonance spectroscopy of chlorophylls and corrins. *Bull. Magn. Res.* **5** (1983) 3–49.
248. H.J.M. de Groot, Magic angle spinning nuclear magnetic resonance of photosynthetic components, in: *Biophysical Techniques in Photosynthesis* (1996) (J. Amesz, A.J. Hoff, eds.), Kluwer, Dordrecht, pp. 299–316.
249. R.C. Dougherty, H.L. Crespi, H.H. Strain, J.J. Katz, NMR studies of plant biosynthesis. Bacteriochlorophyll. *J. Am. Chem. Soc.* **88** (1966) 2854–2855.
250. R.J. Porra, O. Klein, P.E. Wright, The proof by 13C-nuclear magnetic resonance spectroscopy of the predominance of the $C_5$-pathway over the shemin pathway in chlorophyll biosynthesis and the formation of the methyl ester group of chlorophyll from glycine. *Eur. J. Biochem.* **130** (1983) 509–516.
251. A.R. Battersby, F.J. Leeper, Biosynthesis of the pigments of life: Mechanistic studies on the conversion of porphobilinogen to uroporphyrinogen III. *Chem. Rev.* **90** (1990) 1261–1274.
252. A. Angerhofer, Chlorophyll triplets and radical pairs, in: *Chlorophylls* (1991) (H. Scheer, ed.), CRC Press, Boca Raton, FL, pp. 945–992.
253. A.J. Hoff, Optically detected magnetic resonance (ODMR) of triplet states in photosynthesis, in: *Biophysical Techniques in Photosynthesis* (1996) (J. Amesz, A.J. Hoff, eds.), Kluwer, Dordrecht, pp. 277–298.
254. W. Lubitz, EPR and ENDOR studies of chlorophyll cation and anion radicals, in: *Chlorophylls* (1991) (H. Scheer, ed.), CRC Press, Boca Raton, FL, pp. 903–944.

255. P.W. Lau, W.C. Lin, Electron spin resonance and electronic structure of metalloporphyrins. *J. Inorg. Nucl. Chem.* **37** (1975) 2389–2398.
256. M. Hugerat, A. van der Est, E. Ojadi, L. Biczok, H. Linschitz, H. Levanon, D. Stehlik, Transient EPR studies of ion-paired metalloporphyrin heterodimers. *J. Phys. Chem.* **100** (1996) 495–500.
257. W. Lubitz, F. Lendzian, ENDOR spectroscopy, in: *Biophysical Techniques in Photosynthesis* (1996) (J. Amesz, A.J. Hoff, eds.), Kluwer, Dordrecht, pp. 255–276.
258. P.J. Bratt, E. Ringus, A. Hassan, H. van Tol, A.-L. Maniero, L.-C. Brunel, M. Rohrer, C. Bubenzer-Hange, H. Scheer, A. Angerhofer, EPR on biological samples beyond the limits of superconducting magnets-the primary donor cation of purple bacterial photosynthesis. *J. Phys. Chem. B* **103** (1999) 10973–10977.
259. A.J. Hoff, Magnetic resonance: an introduction, in: *Biophysical Techniques in Photosynthesis* (1996) (J. Amesz, A.J. Hoff, eds.), Kluwer, Dordrecht, pp. 209–210.
260. W. Lubitz, F. Lendzian, M. Plato, H. Scheer, K. Mobius, The bacteriochlorophyll a cation radical revisited. An ENDOR and TRIPLE resonance study. *Appl. Magn. Res.* **13** (1997) 531–551.
261. S.G. Zech, J. Kurreck, G. Renger, W. Lubitz, R. Bittl, Determination of the distance between and in photosystem II by pulsed EPR spectroscopy on light-induced radical pairs. *FEBS Lett.* **442** (1999) 79–82.
262. S.G. Zech, J. Kurreck, H.-J. Eckert, G. Renger, W. Lubitz, R. Bittl, Pulsed EPR measurement of the distance between and in photosystem II. *FEBS Lett.* **414** (1997) 454–456.
263. H. Levanon, Time-resolved electron paramagnetic resonance spectroscopy--Principles and application, in: *Biophysical Techniques in Photosynthesis* (1996) (J. Amesz, A.J. Hoff, eds.), Kluwer, Dordrecht, pp. 211–234.
264. R.R. Bidigare, M.C.I. Kennicutt, M.E. Ondrusek, M.D. Keller, R.R.L. Guillard, Novel chlorophyll-related compounds in marine phytoplankton: distributions and geochemical implications. *Energy Fuels* **4** (1990) 653–657.
265. B. Keely, Geochemistry of chlorophylls, in: *Chlorophylls and Bacteriochlorophylls: Biochemistry, Biophysics, Functions and Applications* (2006) (B. Grimm, R. Porra, W. Rüdiger, H. Scheer, eds.), Springer, Berlin, pp. 535–561.
266. R.J. Porra, H. Scheer, $^{18}O$ and mass spectrometry in chlorophyll research: derivation and loss of oxygen atoms at the periphery of the chlorophyll macrocycle during biosynthesis, degradation and adaptation. *Photosynth. Res.* **66** (2001) 159–175.
267. T.M. Cotton, P.A. Loach, J.J. Katz, K.H. Ballschmiter, Studies of chlorophyll-chlorophyll and chlorophyll-ligand interactions. *Photochem. Photobiol.* **27** (1976) 735.
268. H. Morishita, H. Tamiaki, Synthesis and vibrational spectroscopic study of selectively $3^{1-18}O$-labelled chlorophyll derivatives. *J. Photosci.* **9** (2002) 356–358.
269. M. Chen, H. Zeng, A.W. Larkum, Z.L. Cai, Raman properties of chlorophyll d, the major pigment of *Acaryochloris marina*: Studies using both Raman spectroscopy and density functional theory. *Spectrochim. Acta A Mol. Biomol. Spectrosc.* **60** (2004) 527–534.
270. W. Mäntele, Infrared and Fourier-transform infrared spectroscopy, in: *Biophysical Techniques in Photosynthesis* (1996) (J. Amesz, A.J. Hoff, eds.), Kluwer, Dordrecht, pp. 137–160.
271. M. Lutz, W. Mäntele, Vibrational spectroscopy of chlorophylls, in: *Chlorophylls* (1991) (H. Scheer, ed.), CRC Press, Boca Raton, FL, pp. 855–902.
272. B. Robert, Resonance Raman studies in photosynthesis - Chlorophyll and carotenoid molecules, in: *Biophysical Techniques in Photosynthesis* (1996) (J. Amesz, A.J. Hoff, eds.), Kluwer, Dordrecht, pp. 161–176.

273. R. Picorel, G. Chumanov, E. Torrado, T.M. Cotton, M. Seibert, Surface-enhanced resonance Raman scattering spectroscopy of plant photosystem II reaction centers excited on the red-edge of the $Q_y$ band. *J. Phys. Chem. B* **102** (1998) 2609–2613.
274. J. Breton, Fourier Transform infrared spectroscopy of primary electron donors in type I photosynthetic reaction centers. *Biochim.Biophys. Acta* **1507** (2001) 180–193.
275. C. Geskes, G. Hartwich, H. Scheer, W. Mäntele, J. Heinze, Electrochemical and spectroelectrochemical investigation of metal-substituted bacteriochlorophyll a. *J. Am. Chem. Soc.* **117** (1995) 7776–7783.
276. J.-H. Fuhrhop, The oxidation states and reversible redox reactions of metalloporphyrins. *Struct. Bond.* **18** (1974) 2–62.
277. S.M. LeCours, S.G. DiMagno, M.J. Therien, Exceptional electronic modulation of porphyrins through meso-arylethynyl-groups. Electronic spectroscopy, electronic structure and electrochemistry of [5,15,-bis[(aryl)ethynyl]-10,20-diphenylporphinato]zinc(II) complexes. X-ray crystal structures of [5,15-bis(4-fluorophenyl)ethynyl]-10,20-diphenylporphinato]zinc(II) and 5,15-bis[(4-methoxyphenyl)ethynyl]-10,20-diphenylporphyrin. *J. Am. Chem. Soc.* **118** (1996) 11854–11864.
278. J.G. Goll, K.T. Moore, A. Ghosh, M.J. Therien, Synthesis, structure electronic spectroscopy, photophysics, electrochemistry and X-ray photoelectron spectroscopy of highly-electron-deficient [5,10,15,20-tetrakis(perfluoroalkyl)porphinato]zinc(II) complexes and their free base derivatives. *J. Am. Chem. Soc.* **118** (1996) 8344–8354.
279. S.I. Beale, Biosynthesis of aminolevulinic acid, in: *Chlorophylls and Bacteriochlorophylls: Biochemistry, Biophysics, Functions and Applications* (2006) (B. Grimm, R. Porra, W. Rüdiger, H. Scheer, eds.), Springer, Berlin, pp. 147–158.
280. D. Jahn, J. Moser, W.-D. Schubert, D.W. Heinz, Transfer RNA-dependent aminolevulinic acid formation: structure and function of glutamyl-TRNA synthetase, reductase and glutamate-1-semialdehyde-2,1-aminomutase, in: *Chlorophylls and Bacteriochlorophylls: Biochemistry, Biophysics, Functions and Applications* (2006) (B. Grimm, R. Porra, W. Rüdiger, H. Scheer, eds.), Springer, Berlin, pp. 159–171.
281. J. Wittenberg, D. Shemin, The location in protoporphyrin of the carbon atoms derived from the α-carbon of glycine. *J. Biol. Chem.* **185** (1950) 103–116.
282. C.G. Kannangara, R.V. Andersen, B. Pontoppidan, R. Willows, D. v. Wettstein, Enzymic and mechanistic studies on the conversion of glutamate to 5-aminolaevulinate, in: *The Biosynthesis of the Tetrapyrrole Pigments*. 1994, Ciba Foundation Symposium 180 Wiley, Chichester, pp. 3–25.
283. D. Vonwettstein, S. Gough, C.G. Kannangara, Chlorophyll biosynthesis. *Plant Cell* **7** (1995) 1039–1057.
284. T. Oh-hama, H. Seto, S. Miyachi, $^{13}$C-nuclear magnetic resonance studies of the biosynthesis of 5-aminolevulinic acid destined for chlorophyll formation in dark-grown *Scenedesmus obliquus*. *Plant Sci.* **42** (1985) 153–158.
285. T. Oh-Hama, H. Seto, S. Miyachi, $^{13}$C NMR evidenceof bacteriochlorophyll a formation by the $C_5$ pathway in Chromatium. *Arch Biochem. Biophys.* **246** (1986) 192–198.
286. T. Oh-Hama, H. Seto, S. Miyachi, $^{13}$C NMR evidence for bacteriochlorophyll c formation by the $C_5$ pathway in green sulfur bacterium, *Prosthecochloris*. *Eur. J. Biochem.* **159** (1986) 189–194.
287. Yaronskaya, B. Grimm, Intermediate steps to PChlide, in: *Chlorophylls and Bacteriochlorophylls: Biochemistry, Biophysics, Functions and Applications* (2006) (B. Grimm, R. Porra, W. Rüdiger, H. Scheer, eds.), Springer, Berlin, pp. 173–188.

288. F.J. Leeper, The evidence for a spirocyclic intermediate in the formation of uroporphyrinogen III by cosynthase, in: *The Biosynthesis of Tetrapyrrole Pigments* (1994) (D.J. Chadwick, K. Ackrill, eds.), John Wiley and Sons, Chichester, pp. 111–123.
289. I. Scott, C.A. Roessner, P.J. Santander, Genetic and mechanistic exploration of the two pathways of vitamin B12 biosynthesis, in: *The Porphyrin Handbook* (K.M. Kadish, K.M. Smith, R. Guilard, eds.) Vol. 12, *The Iron and Cobalt Pigments: Biosynthsis, Structure, Degradation* (2002), Academic Press, Amsterdam, pp. 211–228.
290. W.W. Ragsdale, Biochemistry of methyl-CoM reductase and coenzyme F430, in: *The Porphyrin Handbook* (K.M. Kadish, K.M. Smith, R. Guilard, eds.), Vol. 11, *Bioinorganic and Bioorganic Chemistry* (2002), Academic Press, Amsterdam, pp. 205–228.
291. M. Akhtar, Coproporphyrinogen III and protoporphyrinogen IX oxidases, in: *The Porphyrin Handbook* (K.M. Kadish, K.M. Smith, R. Guilard, eds.), Vol. 12, *The Iron and Cobalt Pigments: Biosynthsis, Structure, Degradation* (2002), Academic Press, Amsterdam, pp. 75–92.
292. S.I. Beale, J.D. Weinstein, Biochemistry and regulation of photosynthetic pigment formation in plants and algae, in: *Biosynthesis of Tetrapyrroles* (1991) (P.M. Jordan, ed.), Elsevier, Amsterdam-London-New York-Tokyo, pp. 155–235.
293. F.J. Leeper, Intermediate steps in the biosynthesis of chlorophylls, in: *Chlorophylls* (1991) (H. Scheer, ed.), CRC Press, Boca Raton, FL, pp. 407–432.
294. S.I. Beale, Enzymes of chlorophyll biosynthesis. *Photosynth. Res.* **60** (1999) 43–73.
295. B. Grimm, Regulatory mechanisms of eukaryotic tetrapyrrole biosynthesis, in: *The Porphyrin Handbook* (K.M. Kadish, K.M. Smith, R. Guilard, eds.), Vol. 12, *The Iron and Cobalt Pigments: Biosynthsis, Structure, Degradation* (2002), Academic Press, Amsterdam, pp. 1–32.
296. N. La Rocca, N. Rascio, U. Oster, W. Rüdiger, Amitrole treatment of etiolated barley seedlings leads to deregulation of tetrapyrrole synzhesis and to reduced expression of *Lhc* and *RbsC* genes. *Planta* **213** (2001) 101–108.
297. A. Kropat, U. Oster, W. Rüdiger, C.F. Beck, Chloroplast signalling in the light-induction of nuclear HSP70 genes requires the accumulation of chlorophyll precursors and their accessibility to cytoplasm/nucleus. *The Plant J.* **24** (2000) 523–531.
298. H.A. Dailey, T.A. Dailey, Ferrochelatase, in: *The Porphyrin Handbook* (K.M. Kadish, K.M. Smith, R. Guilard, eds.), Vol. 12. *The Iron and Cobalt Pigments: Biosynthsis, Structure, Degradation* (2002), Academic Press, Amsterdam, pp. 93–122.
299. P.E. Jensen, L.C.D. Gibson, C.N. Hunter, Determinants of catalytic activity with the use of purified I, D and H subunits of the magnesium protoporphyrin IX chelatase from *Synechocystis* PCC 6803. *Biochem. J.* **334** (1998) 335–3344.
300. R.D. Willows, M. Hansson, Mechanism, structure and regulation of magnesium chelatase, in: *The Porphyrin Handbook* (K.M. Kadish, K.M. Smith, R. Guilard, eds.), Vol. 13, *Chlorophylls and Bilins: Biosynthesis, Synthesis and Degradation* (2002), Academic Press, Amsterdam, pp. 1–48.
301. D.W. Bollivar, Intermediate steps in chlorophyll biosynthesis: Methylation and cyclization, in: *The Porphyrin Handbook* (K.M. Kadish, K.M. Smith, R. Guilard, eds.), Vol. 13, *Chlorophylls and Bilins: Biosynthesis, Synthesis and Degradation* (2002) Academic Press, Amsterdam, pp. 49–70.
302. S.P. Gough, B.O. Petersen, J.O. Duus, Anaerobic chlorophyll isocyclic ring formation in *Rhodobacter capsulatus* requires a cobalamin cofactor. *Proc. Natl. Acad. Sci. U.S.A.* **97** (2000) 6908–6913.

303. R.J. Porra, W. Schäfer, I. Katheder, H. Scheer, N. Gad'on, G. Drews, Evidence for two different pathways for the formation of isocyclic ring e of bacteriochlorophyll a in *Rhodobacter sphaeroides* and *Roseobacter denitrificans* using $^{18}$O-labelling and mass spectrometry, in: *Photosynthesis: From Light to Biosphere* (1995) (P. Mathis, ed.), Kluwer, Dordrecht, pp. 881–885.
304. Y. Fujita, C.E. Bauer, The light-independent protochlorophyllide reductase: A nitrogenase-like enzyme catalyzing a key reaction for greening in the dark, in: *The Porphyrin Handbook* (K.M. Kadish, K.M. Smith, R. Guilard, eds.), Vol. 13, *Chlorophylls and Bilins: Biosynthesis, Synthesis and Degradation* (2002), Academic Press, Amsterdam, pp. 109–156.
305. Y. Fujita, C.E. Bauer, Reconstitution of light-independent protochlorophyllide reductase from purified Bch1 and Bchn-Bchb subunits-in vitro confirmation of nitrogenase-like features of a bacteriochlorophyll biosynthesis enzyme. *J. Biol. Chem.* **275** (2000) 23583–23588.
306. H.Y. Adamson, R.G. Hiller, J. Walmsley, Protochlorophyllide reduction and greening in angiosperms: An evolutionary perspective. *J. Photochem. Photobiol.* **41** (1997) 201–221.
307. W. Rüdiger, The last steps of chlorophyll synthesis, in: *The Porphyrin Handbook* (K.M. Kadish, K.M. Smith, R. Guilard, eds.), Vol. 13, *Chlorophylls and Bilins: Biosynthesis, Synthesis and Degradation* (2002), Academic Press, Amsterdam, pp. 71–108.
308. W.T. Griffiths, Protochlorophyllide photoreduction, in: *Chlorophylls* (1991) (H. Scheer, ed.), CRC Press, Boca Raton, FL, pp. 433–450.
309. L. Eichacker, H. Paulsen, W. Rüdiger, Synthesis of chlorophyll a regulates translation of chlorophyll a apoproteins P700, CP47, CP43 and D2 in barley etioplasts. *Eur. J. Biochem.* **205** (1992) 17–24.
310. M.A. Schneegurt, S.I. Beale, Origin of the chlorophyll b formyl oxygen in *Chlorella vulgaris*. *Biochemistry* **31** (1992) 11677–11683.
311. R.J. Porra, W. Schäfer, E. Cmiel, I. Katheder, H. Scheer, Derivation of the formyl-group oxygen of chlorophyll *b* from molecular oxygen in greening leaves of a higher plant (*Zea mays*). *FEBS Lett.* **323** (1993) 31–34.
312. U. Oster, R. Tanaka, A. Tanaka, W. Rudiger, Cloning and functional expression of the gene encoding the key enzyme for chlorophyll b biosynthesis (Cao) from *Arabidopsis thaliana*. *Plant J.* **21** (2000) 305–310.
313. V. Scheumann, H. Ito, A. Tanaka, S. Schoch, W. Rüdiger, Substrate specificity of chlorophyll(Ide) b reductase in etioplasts of barley (*Hordeum vulgare L.*). *Eur. J. Biochem.* **242** (1996) 163–170.
314. H. Ito, T. Ohtsuka, A. Tanaka, Conversion of chlorophyll *b* to chlorophyll *a* via 7-hydroxymethyl chlorophyll. *J. Biol. Chem.* **271** (1996) 1475–1479.
315. P. Folly, N. Engel, Chlorophyll b to chlorophyll a conversion precedes chlorophyll degradation in *Hordeum vulgare L. J. Biol. Chem.* **274** (1999) 21811–21816.
316. C.A. Rebeiz, S.M. Wu, M. Kuhadja, H. Daniell, E.J. Perkins, Chlorophyll a biosynthetic routes and chlorophyll a chemical heterogeneity in plants. *Mol. Cell. Biochem.* **57** (1983) 97–125.
317. J.Y. Suzuki, C.E. Bauer, Altered monovinyl and divinyl protochlorophyllide pools in BchJ mutants of *Rhodobacter capsulatus* - Possible monovinyl substrate discrimination of light-independent protochlorophyllide reductase. *J. Biol. Chem.* **270** (1995) 3732–3740.
318. W. Rüdiger, Biosynthesis of tetrapyrroles in plants. *Naturwissenschaften* **80** (1993) 353–360.

319. G.W. Naylor, H.A. Addlesee, L.C.D. Gebson, C.N. Hunter, The photosynthesis gene cluster of *Rhodobacter sphaeroides*. *Photosynth. Res.* **62** (2000) 121–139.
320. M.O. Senge, K.M. Smith, Biosynthesis and structures of the bacteriochlorophylls, in: *Anoxygenic Photosynthetic Bacteria* (1995) (R. Blankenship, M.T. Madigan, C.E. Bauer, eds.), Kluwer, Dordrecht, pp. 137–151.
321. A.J. Biel, Genetic analysis and regulation of bacteriochlorophyll biosynthesis, in: *Anoxygenic Photosynthetic Bacteria* (1995) (R. Blankenship, M.T. Madigan, C.E. Bauer, eds.), Kluwer, Dordrecht, pp. 1125–1134.
322. H.A. Addlesee, L. Fiedor, C.N. Hunter, Physical mapping of *BchG*, Orf427, and Orf177 in the photosynthesis gene cluster of *Rhodobacter sphaeroides:* Functional assignment of the bacteriochlorophyll synthetase gene. *J. Bacteriol.* **182** (2000) 3175–3182.
323. J.H.C. Smith, A. Benitez, Chlorophylls: Analysis in plant materials, in: *Methods of Plant Analysis* (1995) (K. Paech, M. Tracey, eds.), Springer, Berlin, pp. 142–196.
324. C.M. Borrego, J.B. Arellano, C.A. Abella, T. Gillbro, J. Garcia-Gil, The molar extinction coefficient of bacteriochlorophyll *e* and the pigment stoichiometry in *Chlorobium phaeobacteroides*. *Photosynth. Res.* **60** (1999) 257–264.
325. R. Farhoosh, V. Chynwat, R. Gebhard, J. Lugtenburg, H.A. Frank, Triplet energy transfer between the primary donor and carotenoids in *Rhodobacter sphaeroides R 26-1* reaction centers incorporated which spheroidene analogs having different extents of pi-electron conjugation. *Photochem. Photobiol.* **66** (1997) 97–104.
326. A. Struck, E. Cmiel, I. Katheder, H. Scheer, Modified reaction centers from *Rhodobacter sphaeroides* R 26. 2. Bacteriochlorophylls with modified C-3 substituents at sites $B_A$ and $B_B$. *FEBS Lett.* **268** (1990) 180–184.
327. G. Hartwich, H. Scheer, V. Aust, A. Angerhofer, Absorption and ADMR studies on bacterial photosynthetic reaction centres with modified pigments. *Biochim. Biophys. Acta* **1230** (1995) 97–113.
328. V.H. Schmid, P. Thome, W. Ruhle, H. Paulsen, W. Kühlbrandt, H. Rogl, Chlorophyll b is involved in long-wavelength spectral properties of light-harvesting complexes LHC I and LHC II. *FEBS Lett.* **499** (2001) 27–31.
329. M. Friese, G. Hartwich, A. Ogrodnik, H. Scheer, M.E. Michel-Beyerle, No change of primary charge separation rate on lowering the energy of $P^+B^-$ by exchanging $13^2$-OH-Ni-BChl *a* for the accessory BChl *a*. *Biophys. J.* **68** (1995) A367.
330. J.T.M. Kennis, A.Y. Shkuropatov, I.H.M. vanStokkum, P. Gast, A.J. Hoff, V.A. Shuvalov, T.J. Aartsma, Formation of a long-lived $P^+B_A^-$ state in plant pheophytin-exchanged reaction centers of *Rhodobacter sphaeroides* R26 at low temperature. *Biochemistry* **36** (1997) 16231–16238.
331. T.A. Egorova-Zachernyuk, B. van Rossum, G.J. Boender, E. Franken, J. Ashurst, J. Raap, P. Gast, A.J. Hoff, H. Oschkinat, H.J. de Groot, Characterization of pheophytin ground states in Rhodobacter sphaeroides R26 photosynthetic reaction centers from multispin pheophytin enrichment and 2-D $^{13}C$ MAS NMR dipolar correlation spectroscopy. *Biochemistry* **36** (1997) 7513–7519.

*Chapter 4*

# Photophysical Properties and Light-Harvesting and Photoprotective Functions of Carotenoids in Bacterial Photosynthesis: Structural Selections

## Yasushi Koyama, Yoshinori Kakitani and Yasutaka Watanabe

### Table of Contents

| | | |
|---|---|---|
| 4.1 | Introduction............................................................ | 153 |
| 4.2 | Carotenoid Species in Anoxygenic Purple Bacteria: Natural Selection of Car Structures.......................... | 154 |
| 4.3 | Light-Harvesting Function......................................... | 157 |
| | 4.3.1 Singlet Excited States....................................... | 157 |
| | 4.3.2 Electronic Conversions Among the Singlet and Triplet States............................................. | 159 |
| | 4.3.3 Transition Dipole Moments of the Singlet States......... | 164 |
| | 4.3.4 Vibrational Relaxations..................................... | 167 |
| | 4.3.5 Electronic Conversions, Electronic Transitions and Vibrational Relaxations Identified by Time-Resolved Raman Spectroscopy................................. | 168 |
| | 4.3.6 Car-to-BChl Singlet-Energy Transfer in Antenna Complexes.................................................. | 172 |
| 4.4 | Photoprotective Function........................................... | 176 |
| | 4.4.1 Dependence of the Triplet-Energy and the Photoprotective Function of Cars on the Length of the Conjugated Chain........... | 177 |
| | 4.4.2 Rapid 15-Cis to All-Trans Isomerization in Cars Upon Triplet Excitation: the Role of the Triplet-Excited Region... | 179 |
| | 4.4.3 Structure of the RC-Bound 15-cis-Spheroidene in the $T_1$ State............................................ | 180 |

  4.4.4 Conformational Changes in the RC-Bound $T_1$ Spheroidene: Evidence for the Hypothetical Mechanism of Triplet-Energy Dissipation .......................... 183
4.5 Reasons for the Natural Selection of the Car Structures .......... 189
  4.5.1 Selection of A Shorter Conjugated Chain in the All-Trans Configuration by Cars in the Antenna Complexes. ......... 189
  4.5.2 Selection of A Longer Conjugated Chain in the 15-cis Configuration by Cars in the RC. ..................... 191
4.6 Concluding Remarks and Future Perspectives ................ 192
4.7 Other Proposals ....................................... 193
  4.7.1 Newly-Identified Singlet States. ....................... 193
  4.7.2 Mechanism of Photoprotection by 15-cis Carotenoids in the Reaction Center .............................. 194
Acknowledgements ........................................ 195
Bibliography .............................................. 195
 I. Reviews on Carotenoids in Photosynthesis ................. 195
 II. The Light-Harvesting Function. ......................... 196
 III. The Photoprotective Function. ......................... 196
References................................................ 196

## Abstract

The reasons for the natural selection of the length and the configuration of the conjugated chain of carotenoids bound to the antenna and the reaction-center complexes, in purple photosynthetic bacteria, are presented. In the antenna complexes, carotenoids select a shorter conjugated chain in the all-trans configuration whereas the reaction center has a longer conjugated chain in the 15-cis configuration, for the light-harvesting and the photoprotective functions, respectively. Natural selection of the carotenoid structures by the pigment–protein complexes is explained in terms of the energetics and dynamics of the carotenoid and bacteriochlorophyll molecules in the singlet- and triplet-excited states: a shorter conjugated chain in the all-trans configuration is advantageous for the carotenoid-to-bacteriochlorophyll singlet-energy transfer through multiple channels, whereas a longer conjugated chain in the 15-cis configuration is favored in quenching triplet bacteriochlorophyll and dissipating the triplet energy through the rotational motion around the central-cis double bond.

## 4.1 Introduction

(Bacterio)chlorophylls ((B)Chls) and carotenoids (Cars) are the most abundant natural pigments. Apart from their key function in the photosynthetic apparatus Cars are found in virtually all living organisms. With respect to their role outside photosynthesis, Cars play a key role in protective mechanisms by quenching of reactive oxygen species (ROS), which is most likely of high relevance in defense against several diseases. In addition the most abundant Car species β-carotene is the precursor of retinal as the key pigment of the light-mediated information transfer through the process of vision.

In keeping with the scope of this book we restrict our description to the photophysical processes of Cars that are exclusively related to the primary processes of photosynthesis. Photosynthesizing organisms are illuminated with light of different intensities and a spectral distribution. Therefore, suitable adaptation mechanisms are required that have to satisfy two functions: (a) at low photon flux rates the few quanta have to be collected and the electronically excited states formed by light absorption efficiently funneled to the photochemically active pigment in the reaction center (RC) and (b) under light stress the superfluous population of electronic excitation has to be channeled into pathways for harmless non-radiative dissipation to suppress photodynamic degradation reactions. To achieve this goal, special pigment–protein complexes were developed that act as antenna systems for light harvesting. Interestingly, during the evolution of the great variety of photosynthesizing organisms the structure of antenna complexes was quite substantially modified whereas that of the RCs remained much more conserved (Chapter 22).

Cars are essential constituents of these pigment–protein complexes that participate in both functions [1–6] by (i) acting as accessory pigments that enhance, via singlet–singlet excitation energy transfer, the spectral efficiency of light harvesting and (ii) exerting an indispensable protection role in a twofold manner, *i.e.*, dissipation of harmful (bacterio)chlorophyll triplets ($^3$(B)Chl) via triplet–triplet energy transfer and, simultaneously, acting as highly efficient quencher of the very reactive singlet oxygen that is formed through a reaction sensitized by $^3$(B)Chl.

To illustrate the details of the photophysical properties and their relation to the dual function of Car we concentrate in this chapter on the species that are present in anoxygenic purple bacteria. These organisms synthesize a group of integral membrane pigment–protein complexes that are involved in the exploitation of solar radiation as Gibbs energy source for their photoautotrophic growth. In general, two types of supramolecular complexes can be distinguished, called LH1 and LH2 (LH = light harvesting complex). Both are characterized by circular structures of pigment protein subunits that are described in detail in Chapter 5. LH1 and LH2 absorb light and transfer the electronic excitation energy to the photochemically active pigment P in the RC, where charge separation takes place.

The complex LH1 contains the RC inside a ring of antenna pigment–proteins, while LH2 forms a similar ring but lacks the RC, thus acting as a pure antenna system. Complexes LH1, including the RC and LH2, contain Cars as essential constituents that exert both functions, *i.e.*, participation in light harvesting and protection against photodynamic attack.

The first part of this chapter describes the photophysical behavior of the Cars of purple bacteria. Based on these properties an explanation is offered for the selection of Cars of different conjugation lengths in anoxygenic photosynthetic purple bacteria.

## 4.2 Carotenoid Species in Anoxygenic Purple Bacteria: Natural Selection of Car Structures

Figure 1 shows the biosynthetic pathways of Cars in *Rubrivivax* (*Rvi.*) *gelatinosus*. This organism has both spheroidene and spirilloxanthin pathways in carotenogenesis, and therefore, a wide variety of choices to manipulate the conjugation length of Cars by varying the number $n$ of conjugated double bonds that are in the range $n = 9$–13. Under semiaerobic conditions, it produces mono- and di-keto derivatives to increase the conjugation length by one or two additional double bond(s) ($n = 13 \rightarrow 13 + 1$ and $13 + 2$, for example). However, ordinary anoxygenic purple bacteria have either the spheroidene or the spirilloxanthin pathway. Concerning strains that are discussed in this chapter, *Rhodobacter* (*Rb.*) *sphaeroides* has the spheroidene pathway, whereas *Rhodospirillum* (*Rsp.*) *rubrum*, *Rsp. molischianum* and *Rhodopseudomonas* (*Rps.*) *acidophila* have the spirilloxanthin pathway. The composition of Cars changes, depending on the culturing conditions. After prolonged culturing, the final products, spheroidene and spirilloxanthin, tend to be accumulated. In a mutant, in which an enzyme is deleted, a particular Car can accumulate; in *Rb. sphaeroides* G1C, for example, only neurosporene is produced. The number of

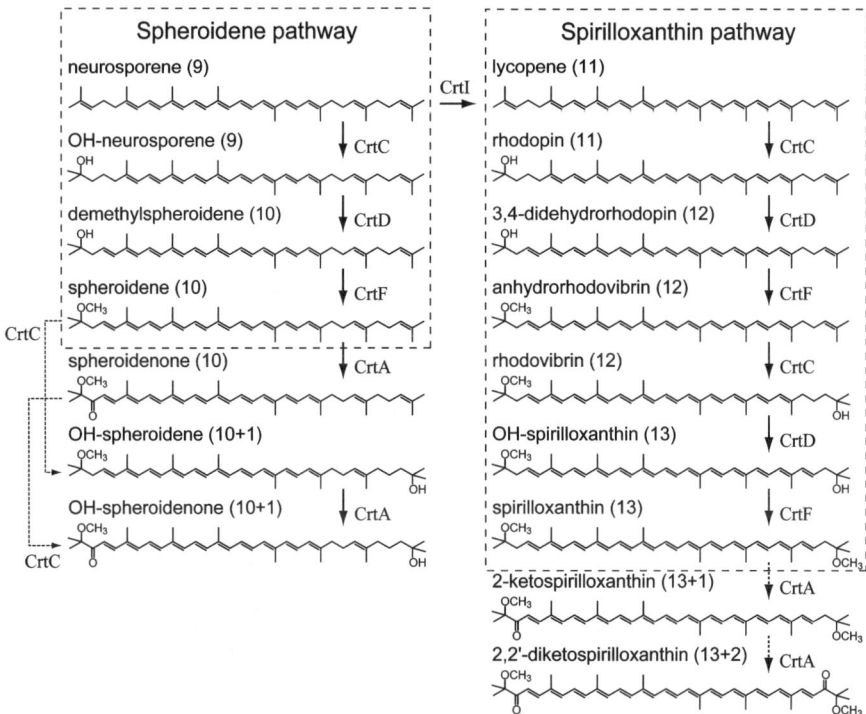

**Figure 1.** Biosynthetic pathways of Cars in *Rvi. gelatinosus*. This organism has both the spheroidene and the spirilloxanthin pathways in carotenogenesis, and therefore, a wide variety of Cars having numbers of conjugated double bonds in the range of $n = 9$–13 ($n$ for the corresponding molecules is given in parenthesis). Under semiaerobic conditions, it produces mono- and di-keto derivatives to further increase the conjugation length. *Rb. sphaeroides* has only the spheroidene pathway, whereas *Rsp. rubrum*, *Rsp. molischianum* and *Rps. acidophila* have the spirilloxanthin pathway.

enzymes is limited, and each of them is responsible for a particular structural transformation.

In Figure 2 the abundance of Cars in *Rvi. gelatinosus* are classified by the total $n$ value of the molecules. The structure of each Car in the extract from the pigment–protein complexes was determined by mass spectrometry and $^1$H NMR spectroscopy [Kakitani et al., *Biochemistry* in press]. Clearly, in both cultures, Cars having a shorter chain are preferentially bound to LH2, whereas those having a longer conjugated chain bind to the RC.

Figure 3 shows the configurations of Cars bound to LH2 and RC in purple bacteria. In those strains only a single major Car is available for both pigment–protein complexes. The trans and cis configurations were determined by $^1$H NMR spectroscopy of Cars extracted from LH2 and the RC [7–9]. In all three strains of purple bacteria, the all-trans configuration is selected by LH2, whereas the 15-cis configuration is selected by RC.

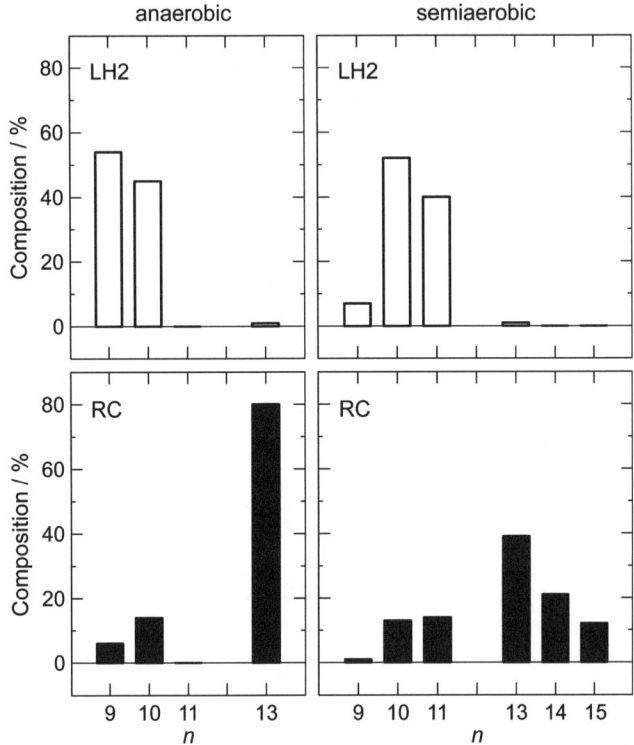

**Figure 2.** Selective binding of Cars with a shorter chain of conjugated double bonds to the LH2 and Cars with a longer chain of conjugated double bonds bind to the RC, in *Rvi. gelatinosus* grown under anaerobic and semiaerobic conditions. Cars are classified by the total number of conjugated double bonds ($n$), including both C=C and C=O bonds.

In relation to the major functions of Cars in LH2 and the RC, the above results lead us to the idea of natural selection of the Car structures: in LH2, a shorter conjugated chain in the all-trans configuration is selected for the light-harvesting function, whereas in the RC a longer conjugated chain in the 15-cis configuration is used for the photoprotective function.

On the basis of our present stage of understanding, the physiological reasons for the above-mentioned natural selections will be explained in terms of energetics and dynamics of the Car and BChl molecules in the singlet and triplet excited states, both of which depend on the length and the configuration of the conjugated chain. We prefer a pictorial presentation, letting figures and tables tell the story by themselves, thus making the text as short as possible. To reduce the number of figures, no raw spectral data will be presented, except when they are absolutely necessary.

We aim to present a simple, consistent picture, under the present title, mainly based on our own results. For a more general and objective overview in this particular field, readers are encouraged to examine references given in the Bibliography.

# PHOTOPHYSICAL PROPERTIES AND LIGHT-HARVESTING 157

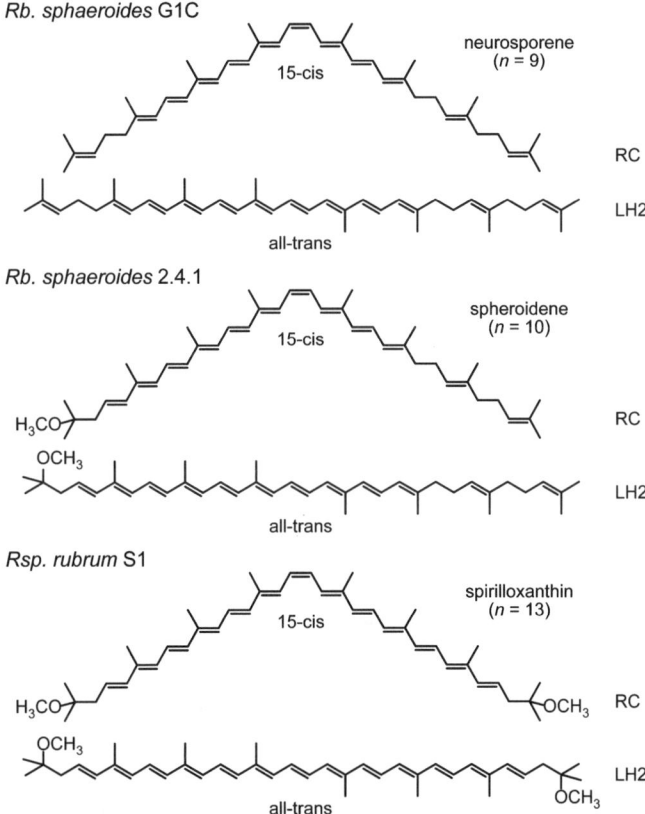

**Figure 3.** The 15-cis configuration of Cars bound to the RC and the all-trans configuration of Cars bound to the LH2 of *Rb. sphaeroides* G1C, *Rb. sphaeroides* 2.4.1 and *Rsp. rubrum* S1, containing neurosporene, spheroidene and spirilloxanthin, respectively, as the major component.

## 4.3 Light-Harvesting Function

The first topic to be discussed is the light-harvesting function of all-trans Cars in the LH2 and LH1 antenna complexes. Here, we will include a newly-found singlet state, $1B_u^-$, which led us to re-draw the picture of excited singlet–singlet-energy transfer from Car to BChl. First, we describe the intrinsic excited-state properties of all-trans Cars in solution, and then present the detailed mechanisms of the Car-to-BChl singlet-energy transfer in the antennas.

### 4.3.1 Singlet Excited States

Figure 4 (upper part) shows an energy diagram for the low-lying singlet states of Cars with different conjugation length, including the states $1B_u^+$, $3A_g^-$, $1B_u^-$ and $2A_g^-$, which were determined by measurements of resonance-Raman

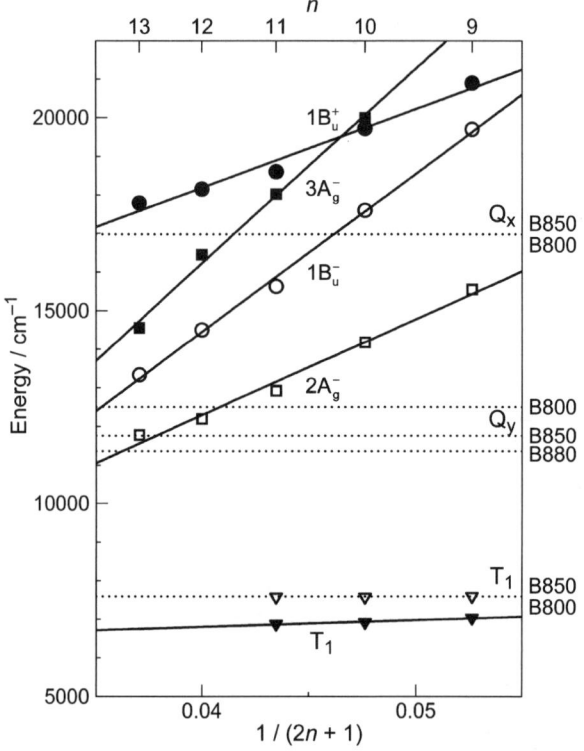

**Figure 4.** Energies of the singlet-excited states $1B_u^+$, $3A_g^-$, $1B_u^-$ and $2A_u^-$ determined by measurement of resonance-Raman excitation profiles for crystalline mini-9-β-carotene, spheroidene, lycopene, anhydrorhodovibrin and spirilloxanthin [10–12], and those of the $T_1$ ($1^3B_u$) state determined by high-sensitivity emission spectroscopy for neurosporene, spheroidene and rhodopin + lycopene bound to the LH2 complexes from *Rb. sphaeroides* G1C, *Rb. sphaeroides* 2.4.1 and *Rsp. molischianum* [35]. For comparison, energies of the $Q_x$ and $Q_y$ transitions and of the $T_1$ state of BChls in LH2 and LH1 complexes are shown as dotted lines.

excitation profiles (RREPs); the $1B_u^-$ [10,11] and $3A_g^-$ [12] states were discovered only relatively recently. Figure 5 shows a set of Cars used for the RREP measurements, including mini-9-β-carotene, spheroidene, lycopene, anhydrorhodovibrin and spirilloxanthin with $n = 9$–13, respectively, conjugated double bonds. All the state energies of these molecules (shown in Figure 4) decrease linearly as functions of $1/(2n + 1)$ when $n$ increases. Notably, the slopes of the linear relations for the $2A_g^-$, $1B_u^-$ and $3A_g^-$ states are characterized by a ratio of 2:3.1:3.8. This finding is in excellent agreement with the ratio of 2:3.1:3.7 obtained by theoretical calculations of the state energies for shorter polyenes ($n = 5$–8) [13] and provides a firm basis for the assignment of the newly found excited states. The $Q_x$ and $Q_y$ states of BChls in the LH2 (B800 and B850) and the LH1 (B880) complexes are shown for comparison. The dependence of the state ordering on $n$ indicates that electronic conversions within Cars as well as

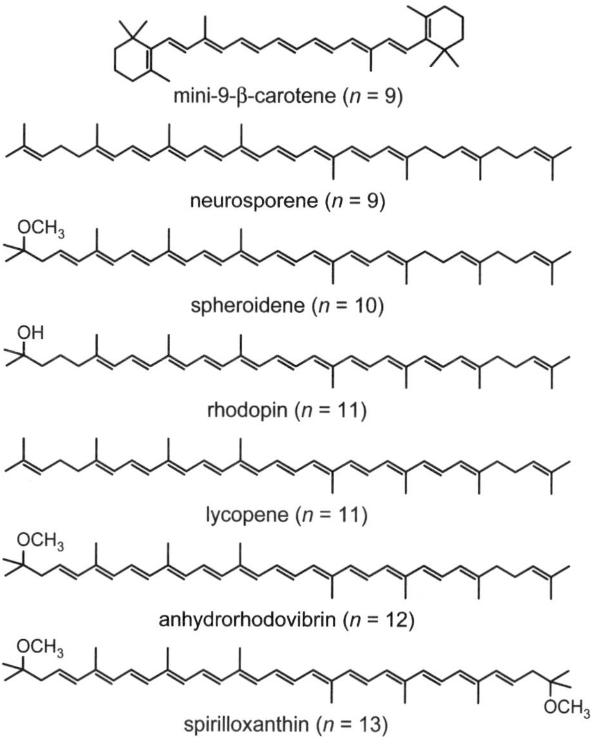

**Figure 5.** Structures of typical Cars described in this chapter.

the mechanism of singlet-energy transfer from Cars to BChl must vary from one Car to another.

*4.3.2 Electronic Conversions Among the Singlet and Triplet States*

The state ordering (Figure 4) shows that, when the Car molecule is excited to the $1B_u^+$ state by absorption of a photon, the next energetically lower lying electronic state to convert into is the $1B_u^-$ state for Cars with $n=9$ and 10, whereas it is the $3A_g^-$ state for Cars having $n=11$–13. The mode of conversion of the state $1B_u^+$ will depend on this energetic ladder of states and, therefore, these two groups of Cars are expected to exhibit different time-resolved spectra in the very initial stage after electronic excitation. Figure 6 shows species-associated difference spectra (SADS). The results were obtained by singular-value decomposition (SVD) followed by global fitting (using a sequential model) of the data matrices gathered from near-infrared, subpicosecond time-resolved absorption spectroscopy of the same set of Cars, except for mini-9-β-carotene which was replaced by neurosporene [14]. The SADS of the initially populated state $1B_u^+$ are the same, but those of the subsequent states ($1B_u^-$ or $3A_g^-$) are completely different between the two groups of Cars. The time-dependent changes in population are also different between the two

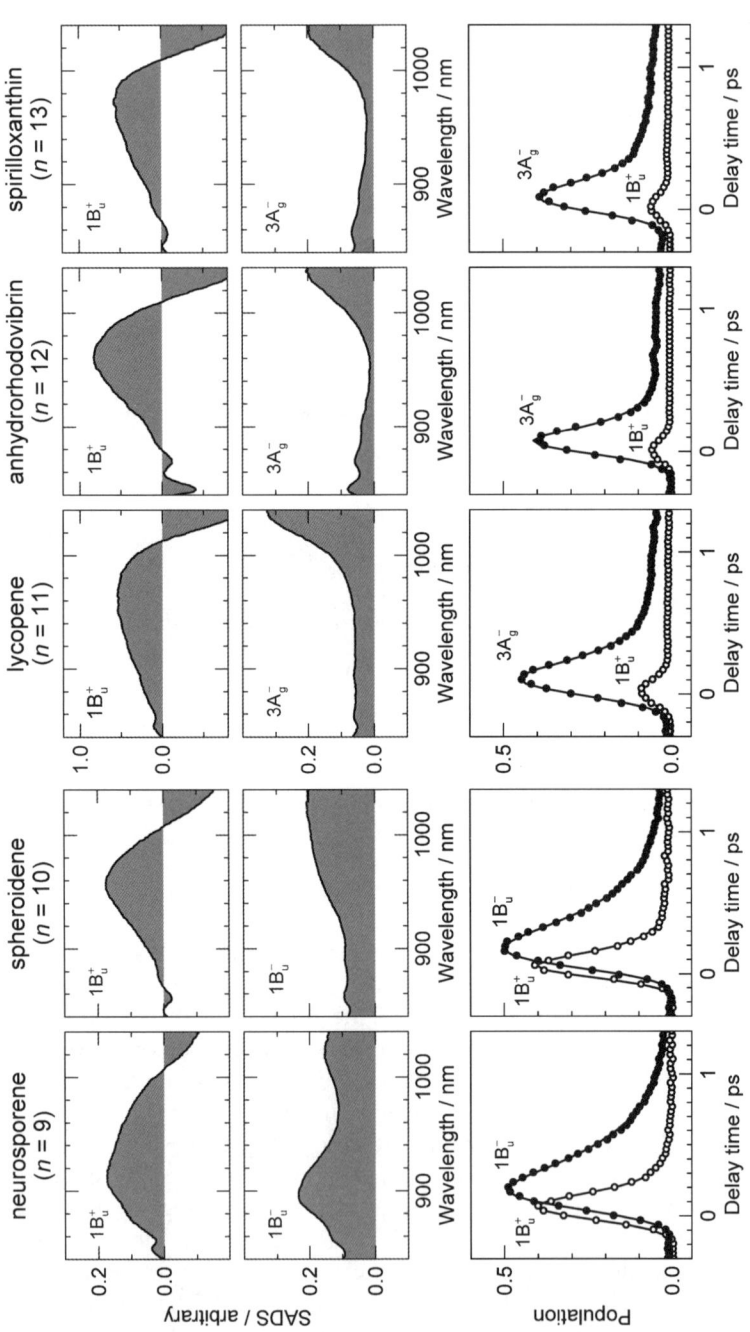

Figure 6. Species-associated difference spectra (SADS) (upper panel) and transient populations (bottom panels) of the states $1B_u^+$, $1B_u^-$ and $3A_g^-$ states gathered from the singular-value decomposition (SVD) and global-fitting analyses of near-infrared, subpicosecond time-resolved absorption spectra of neurosporene, spheroidene, lycopene, anhydrorhodovibrin and spirilloxanthin in $n$-hexane or in a mixture of $n$-hexane and benzene [14].

**Table 1.** Dependence of the $1B_u^+$, $1B_u^-$ and $2A_g^-$ lifetimes (ps) on the number of conjugated double bonds ($n$) [14,15]

|         | Neurosporene ($n=9$) | Spheroidene ($n=10$) | Lycopene ($n=11$) | Anhydrorhodovibrin ($n=12$) | Spirilloxanthin ($n=13$) |
|---------|---------|---------|---------|---------|---------|
| $1B_u^+$ | 0.10 | 0.10 | 0.02 | 0.01 | 0.01 |
| $1B_u^-$ | 0.24 | 0.23 | – | – | – |
| $3A_g^-$ | – | – | 0.15 | 0.10 | 0.10 |
| $2A_g^-$ | 24.0 | 8.9 | 3.9 | 2.2 | 1.4 |

groups. Table 1 summarizes data of the lifetimes of states $1B_u^+$, $1B_u^-$ and $2A_g^-$ and their dependence on the number $n$ of conjugated double bonds. An inspection of Table 1 reveals that the $1B_u^+$ lifetime decreases from 100 fs down to 10 fs when $n$ increases from 9 to 13. Furthermore, the lifetimes of state $1B_u^-$ for Cars with $n=9$ and 10 are longer than those of $3A_g^-$ for $n=11$–13 and tend to decrease for both states when $n$ increases. In comparison to these rather short lifetimes the corresponding values for state $2A_g^-$, directly determined by the decay profiles in the visible region, are much longer and decrease from 24 ps all the way down to 1.4 ps with increasing $n$.

The energy diagram of Figure 4 reveals that all the Cars share the states $1B_u^-$ and $2A_g^-$ on the lower energy side of the $1B_u^+$ state. Figure 7 shows, in the top panels, the spectral patterns identified as the SADS gathered from SVD and global-fitting analyses of visible, subpicosecond time-resolved absorption spectra of the same set of Cars with $n=9$–13 [15]. They include stimulated emission from the optically active $1B_u^+$ state, a broad transient absorption from the $1B_u^-$ state and a sharp transient absorption from the $2A_g^-$ state, both accompanying the bleaching of the ground-state absorption, and an interference pattern between the vibrational progressions, originating from the bleaching of the ground-state absorption and the transient absorption due to a newly discovered triplet state, *i.e.*, the $T_2$ state with $A_g$ symmetry. To obtain a perfect global fit (see the lower two panels for the almost complete overlap between the observed noisy time profiles and the smooth fitting curves), it was essential to introduce a branched relaxation scheme from the $1B_u^-$ singlet state down to both the singlet state $2A_g^-$ and the triplet state $T_2$.

Figure 8 shows the relaxation scheme used for the SVD and global-fitting analyses, which includes the singlet-to-singlet conversion of $1B_u^+ \rightarrow 1B_u^- \rightarrow 2A_g^- \rightarrow 1A_g^-$, the singlet-to-triplet conversion of $1B_u^- \rightarrow T_2(1^3A_g)$, and the triplet-to-triplet conversion of $T_2 \rightarrow T_1(1^3B_u)$. The $T_2 \rightarrow T_1$ conversion was spectroscopically identified at longer delay times (data not shown). The time constants of the $1B_u^- \rightarrow 2A_g^-$ and $2A_g^- \rightarrow 1A_g^-$ conversions as well as those of the $1B_u^- \rightarrow T_2$ conversion followed the energy-gap law.

This energy-gap law, first proposed by Englman and Jortner [16], can be expressed by a pair of equations [17]:

$$k = \frac{2\pi}{\hbar} C^2 \frac{1}{\sqrt{2\pi(\Delta E)\hbar\omega}} \exp(-1/2\Delta^2) \exp\left(-\frac{\gamma(\Delta E)}{\hbar\omega}\right) \quad (1)$$

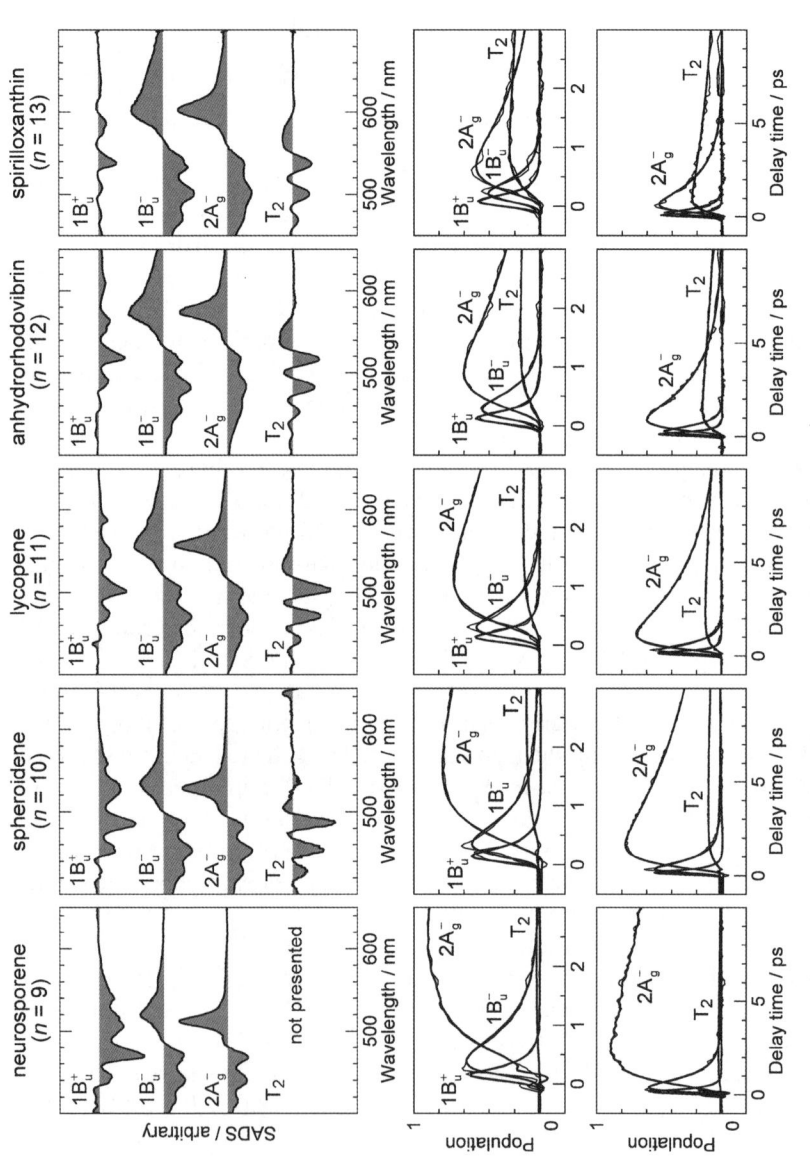

**Figure 7.** SADS (top panels) and transient populations (bottom two panels) for the $1B_u^+$, $1B_u^-$ and $2A_g^-$ singlet-excited states and the $T_2$ ($1^3A_g$) state, obtained by SVD and global-fitting analyses of the visible, subpicosecond time-resolved spectra of neurosporene, spheroidene, lycopene, anhydrorhodovibrin and spirilloxanthin in the visible region [15] (see Figure 8 for the relaxation scheme).

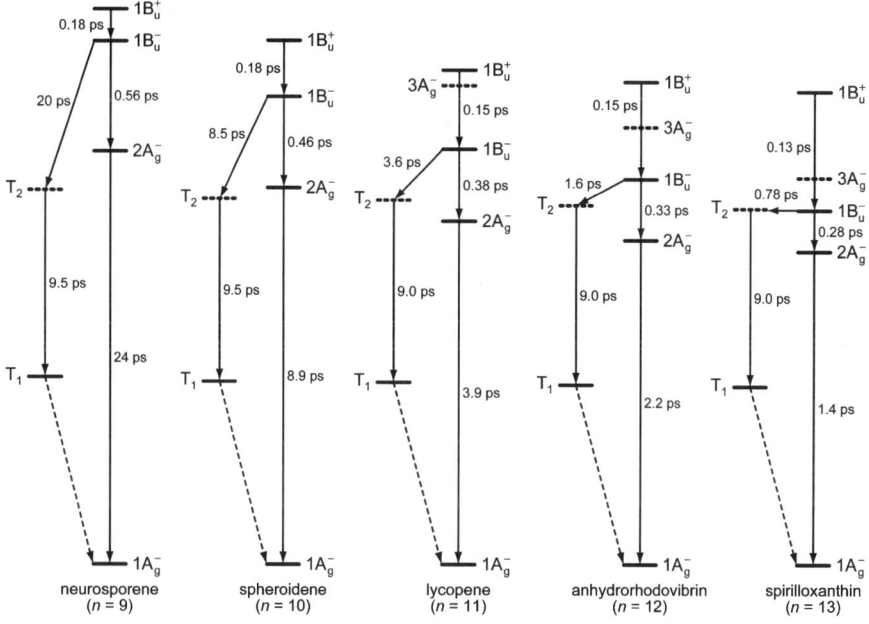

**Figure 8.** A branched relaxation scheme, including singlet-to-singlet, singlet-to-triplet and triplet-to-triplet electronic conversions, that was revealed by the SVD and global-fitting analyses of the data matrices obtained by visible, subpicosecond time-resolved absorption spectroscopy of neurosporene, spheroidene, lycopene, anhydrorhodovibrin and spirilloxanthin (see Figure 7 for the fitting results).

$$\gamma = \ln \frac{2(\Delta E)}{\Delta^2 \hbar \omega} - 1 \qquad (2)$$

where $k$ is the rate constant of the transition, $C$ is the vibronic coupling constant, $\Delta E$ is the energy gap, $\hbar \omega$ is the frequency of the accepting mode, $\Delta$ is the shift of potential minimum along the coordinate of the accepting mode. A normal mode that gives rise to the largest $C$ is called "the promoting mode" and the other normal mode giving rise to the largest $\Delta$ is called "the accepting mode" (see [17] for details). Roughly speaking, as the essence of the energy-gap law, the transition rate is inversely proportional to the exponential of the energy gap.

The $3A_g^-$ state that should appear immediately after excitation to the $1B_u^+$ state in Cars with $n = 11$–13 could not be detected by visible time-resolved absorption spectroscopy using 120 fs pump and probe pulses. A most likely explanation for this failure is the possibility that the difference spectra from the $3A_g^-$ state are completely blurred by the strong stimulated emission from the $1B_u^+$ state.

Experimental evidence for this idea was obtained in the case of the $3A_g^-$ state of spirilloxanthin ($n = 13$), which could actually be identified by visible time-resolved absorption spectroscopy using 5-fs pump–probe pulses [18]. Figure 9 shows a set of SADS and the time-dependent changes in the populations of the

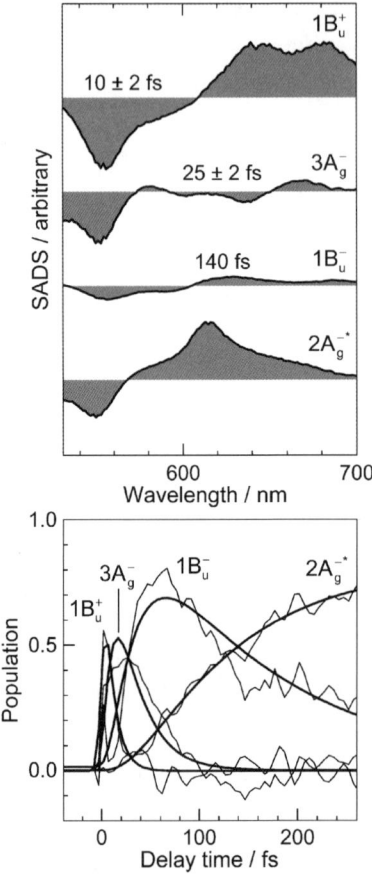

**Figure 9.** SADS (upper panel) and transient populations (lower panel) of the states $1B_u^+$, $3A_g^-$, $1B_u^-$ and $2A_g^-$ of spirilloxanthin in tetrahydrofuran [18]. Spectral data for the SVD and global-fitting analysis were obtained by using 5-fs pump–probe pulses.

states $1B_u^+$, $3A_g^-$, $1B_u^-$ and $2A_g^{-*}$ (here, the $2A_g^{-*}$ state indicates a "hot" $2A_g^-$ state where vibrational relaxation is not completed yet). In this case the sequential conversion of the electronic states $1B_u^+ \to 3A_g^- \to 1B_u^- \to 2A_g^-$ is clearly identified. The results show that near-infrared time-resolved absorption spectroscopy correctly determined the $1B_u^+$ lifetime, but overestimated the $3A_g^-$ lifetime (Table 1).

*4.3.3 Transition Dipole Moments of the Singlet States*

According to the selection rule based on Pariser's signs, + and −, that was applied to the approximate $C_{2h}$ symmetry of the all-trans conjugated chain, optical dipole transitions are allowed (forbidden) between a pair of electronic states having different signs (the same sign) (see [19,20]). Therefore, concerning the optical transitions to the ground $1A_g^-$ state, they are allowed from the $1B_u^+$ state but forbidden from the states $1B_u^-$, $3A_g^-$ and $2A_g^-$. Theoretically, the transition dipole moment of the $1B_u^+$ state can have a nonzero value, whereas those of the pure $1B_u^-$, $3A_g^-$ and $2A_g^-$ states should be zero.

In practice, however, high-sensitivity emission spectroscopy of the set of Cars having $n = 10$–$13$ revealed that both the $1B_u^-$ and $2A_g^-$ states do fluoresce [21–23]. Table 2 summarizes the relative quantum yields ($\Phi$) that were determined from the fluorescence spectra (see Table 2 of [24] for details). Since we have already determined the lifetimes ($\tau$) and the state energies ($\bar{\nu}$) of the relevant singlet-excited states, the relative transition dipole moments ($\mu$) can be calculated by using eqn. (3) [25]:

$$\frac{\mu_{1B_u^-}}{\mu_{1B_u^+}} \approx \left( \frac{\phi_{1B_u^-} \cdot \tau_{1B_u^+} \cdot E_{1B_u^+}^3}{\phi_{1B_u^+} \cdot \tau_{1B_u^-} \cdot E_{1B_u^-}^3} \right)^{\frac{1}{2}} \quad (3)$$

The values obtained and summarized under the title of $\mu$ in Table 2 indicate that the "optically-forbidden" $1B_u^-$ and $2A_g^-$ states are partially optically-allowed due to the mixing with the strongly optically-allowed $1B_u^+$ state, the extent of which depends on the energy gap between the relevant states (see below).

If we take the $1B_u^-$ state as an example, the real wavefunction of this state, $\Psi_{1B_u^-}$, can be expressed as a linear combination of the unperturbed wavefunctions, $\Psi_{1B_u^-}^{(0)}$ and $\Psi_{1B_u^+}^{(0)}$, by the use of the mixing parameter, $P_{1B_u^+/1B_u^-}$, as:

$$\Psi_{1B_u^-} = \Psi_{1B_u^-}^{(0)} + \Psi_{1B_u^+}^{(0)} \times P_{1B_u^+/1B_u^-} \quad (4)$$

Based on first-order perturbation theory, the ratio $P_{1B_u^+/1B_u^-}$ can be defined as:

$$P_{1B_u^+/1B_u^-} = \frac{\langle \Psi_{1B_u^+}^{(0)} | V | \Psi_{1B_u^-}^{(0)} \rangle}{E_{1B_u^-} - E_{1B_u^+}} \quad (5)$$

where $V$ is the perturbation that destroys the $C_{2h}$ symmetry of the conjugated chain. By the use of this equation, we can express the transition dipole moment of the $1B_u^-$ state and the ratio of the $1B_u^+$ and $1B_u^-$ transition moments by eqns. (6) and (7), respectively (note that $\mu_{1B_u^-}^{(0)} = 0$ due to the selection rule):

$$\mu_{1B_u^-} = \mu_{1B_u^-}^{(0)} + \mu_{1B_u^+}^{(0)} \times P_{1B_u^+/1B_u^-} \quad (6)$$

$$P_{1B_u^+/1B_u^-} = \frac{\mu_{1B_u^-}}{\mu_{1B_u^+}} \quad (7)$$

In the case of neurosporene, however, the energy difference between the states $1B_u^+$ and $1B_u^-$ is almost one vibrational quantum of the carbon–carbon stretching mode (Figure 4) and, therefore, their vibrational progression peaks are overlapping with each other. Under these circumstances it was necessary to *time-resolve* the pair of vibrational progressions by subpicosecond fluorescence up-conversion spectroscopy [24]. Here, we excited the molecule specifically to

**Table 2.** Relative quantum yields of fluorescence ($\Phi$) [23,24] and mixing parameters ($P$) [24] concerning the $1B_u^+$, $1B_u^-$ and $2A_g^-$ singlet-excited states, lifetimes ($\tau$) [14,15], state energies ($\bar{\nu}$) [21–23], transition dipole moments ($\mu$) [24] and molar extinction coefficients at the $1B_u^+ \leftarrow 1A_g^-$ absorption maximum ($\varepsilon$) [Qian et al., unpublished results], for carotenoids having $n = 10$–13. Equations in deriving the relevant parameters are shown in the text

| Carotenoid ($n$) | $\Phi_l/\%$ | | | $\tau_l/\text{ps}$ | | | $\bar{\nu}/\text{cm}^{-1}$ | | | $\varepsilon/\text{M}^{-1}\text{cm}^{-1}$ | $\mu/\text{D}$ | | | $|P|$ | |
|---|---|---|---|---|---|---|---|---|---|---|---|---|---|---|---|
| | $\frac{1B_u^-}{1B_u^+}$ | $\frac{2A_g^-}{1B_u^+}$ | | $1B_u^+$ | $1B_u^-$ | $2A_g^-$ | $1B_u^+$ | $1B_u^-$ | $2A_g^-$ | $1B_u^+$ | $1B_u^+$ | $1B_u^-$ | $2A_g^-$ | $\frac{1B_u^-}{1B_u^+}$ | $\frac{2A_g^-}{1B_u^+}$ |
| Spheroidene (10) | 17.1 | 3.3 | | 0.10 | 0.46 | 8.9 | 20300 | 17800 | 14200 | 173600 | 15.6 | 3.75 | 0.52 | 0.23 | 0.03 |
| Lycopene (11) | 4.2 | 1.9 | | 0.02 | 0.38 | 3.9 | 19600 | 16000 | 13300 | 181500 | 17.2 | 1.16 | 0.30 | 0.07 | 0.02 |
| Anhydrorhodovibrin (12) | 3.2 | 3.1 | | 0.01 | 0.33 | 2.2 | 19200 | 14900 | 12500 | 171000 | 17.4 | 0.88 | 0.39 | 0.05 | 0.02 |
| Spirilloxanthin (13) | 1.4 | 1.2 | | 0.01 | 0.28 | 1.4 | 18900 | 13600 | 11900 | 151000 | 16.8 | 0.71 | 0.31 | 0.04 | 0.02 |

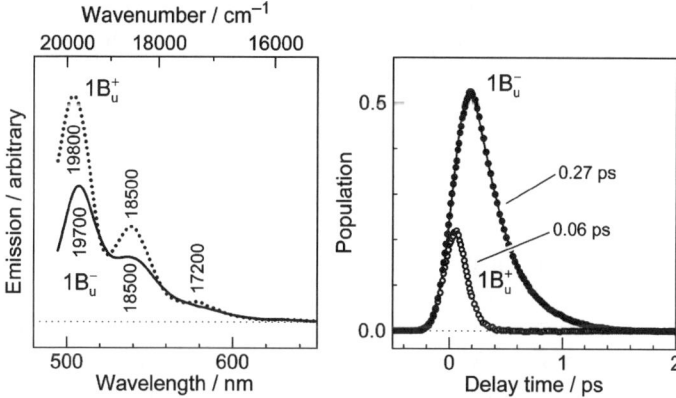

**Figure 10.** Species-associated fluorescence spectra (SAFS) and transient in populations of the states $1B_u^+$ and $1B_u^-$ of neurosporene in $n$-hexane gathered from results of SVD and global-fitting analysis of the data matrix obtained by subpicosecond time-resolved, fluorescence up-conversion spectroscopy [24].

the $1B_u^+(0)$ state to avoid complications due to vibrational relaxation in this particular electronic state. Figure 10 shows the results of the SVD and global-fitting analysis: the $1B_u^+$ and $1B_u^-$ vibrational progressions almost overlap completely after a shift by one vibrational quantum, as anticipated. However, they could be time-resolved for both states and their lifetimes were determined to be 60 and 270 fs, respectively. Assuming the same vibrational structure, the mixing parameter ($P_{1B_u^+/1B_u^-} = \mu_{1B_u^-}/\mu_{1B_u^+}$) was evaluated to be as high as 0.56 in this particular case of neurosporene with $n=9$.

*4.3.4 Vibrational Relaxations*

As shown in Section 4.3.2, electronic conversions in Cars generally take place very rapidly among the singlet-excited states that are located close by. Therefore, vibrational relaxation is not necessarily faster than electronic conversion, but takes place on a similar or even longer time scale.

Picosecond time-resolved absorption spectra of lycopene ($n=11$) in the $2A_g^-$ state exhibited the vibrational structures of the $v_1$ and $v_2$ (C=C and C–C stretching, respectively) modes, and the relative intensity of each peak changed with time, thus reflecting vibrational relaxation [26]. The rate constants $k_{v_1}$ and $k_{v_2}$ of vibrational relaxation between the levels $v=1$ to $v=0$ for the modes $v_1$ and $v_2$ relative to that of the electronic $2A_g^- \rightarrow 1A_g^-$ transition ($K_{v_1}/k$ and $K_{v_2}/k$) were determined by spectral simulation to be 0.6 and 0.3, respectively, in quinoline, and 0.2 and 1.6 in $CS_2$. Thus, the vibrational relaxations were always slower than the decay of the $2A_g^-$ state, except for the case of the $v_2$ mode in $CS_2$. In contrast, vibrational relaxations of the higher vibrational levels should be much faster, because the rate of vibrational relaxation from the $v=l$ to the $v=l-1$ level is proportional to $l$ [27].

To examine vibrational relaxations in the $1B_u^+$ state, subpicosecond Kerr-gate fluorescence spectroscopy was performed for neurosporene and spheroidene in $n$-hexane upon 400 nm excitation to the $1B_u^+$ state in the vibronic levels, $v=2$ and $v=3$, designated as $1B_u^+(2)$ and $1B_u^+(3)$, respectively [28]. Figure 11 shows the results of SVD and global-fitting analyses of the fluorescence data matrices, including the species-associated fluorescence spectra (SAFS) in the top panels and the time-dependent changes of the populations of the first and the second components ("component I" and "component II") in the middle panels. Furthermore, the bottom panels present stimulated fluorescence spectra for the transitions from vibrational levels $v=1$ and $v=0$ of state $1B_u^+$ to the vibrational level $v=0$, 1, 2 and 3 of the electronic state $1A_g^-$. These spectra were gathered from calculations of Franck–Condon overlaps. A comparison of the SAFS (top panels) with the simulated fluorescence spectra (bottom panels) of both Cars reveals that components I and II can be ascribed to fluorescence emission from the vibronic levels $1B_u^+(1)$ and $1B_u^+(0)$, respectively. Abnormally high intensities in SAFS of components I and II in the region of the $1B_u^+(1) \to 1A_g^-(2)$ and $1B_u^+(0) \to 1A_g^-(1)$ transitions can be ascribed to overlap with the $1B_u^-(0) \to 1A_g^-(0)$ transition (see the arrows in the top panels). In other words, overlap between the $1B_u^+$ and $1B_u^-$ fluorescence progressions needs to be considered in more rigorous simulations.

Thus, the lifetimes of the $1B_u^+(1)$ states, which were found to be 50 fs for neurosporene and 25 fs for spheroidene, can be attributed to vibrational relaxation from the $v=1$ to the $v=0$ level in the electronic state $1B_u^+$. Surprisingly, the lifetimes of the $1B_u^+(0)$ fluorescence, *i.e.*, 260 fs for both neurosporene and spheroidene, do not agree with the time constant of the transitions of the electronic states $1B_u^+ \to 1B_u^-$, *i.e.*, 60 fs, but rather correspond with the time constant of the transition of the electronic states $1B_u^- \to 2A_g^-$, which is characterized by a value of 270 fs (Figure 10). These results can be explained in terms of the strong mixing between electronic states $1B_u^-$ and $1B_u^+$ described in Section 4.3.3. If there exists such a mixing [eqn. (4)], the $1B_u^+$ fluorescence can take place as long as the $1B_u^-$ state remains. This is a unique property of the $1B_u^+$ and $1B_u^-$ states, which are energetically close together in Cars with shorter conjugated chains ($n=9$ and 10).

*4.3.5 Electronic Conversions, Electronic Transitions and Vibrational Relaxations Identified by Time-Resolved Raman Spectroscopy*

Stimulated Raman scattering using a pair of photons, *i.e.*, a monochromatic picosecond pulse for Raman pump and a white-continuum subpicosecond pulse for Raman probe [29], could overcome "the optical-transform limit" (11.2 cm$^{-1}$ ps) in the spontaneous Raman process using a single photon [30]. Actually, we could obtain a 220 fs time resolution and a 32 cm$^{-1}$ spectral resolution [31]. Figure 12 presents subpicosecond time-resolved Raman spectra of neurosporene ($n=9$) in $n$-hexane. The Car molecule was excited with a 120-fs pulse at 397 nm, leading to the transition into state $1B_u^+(3)$ [31]. At negative delay times, the ground-state Raman spectrum is seen where the peaks marked

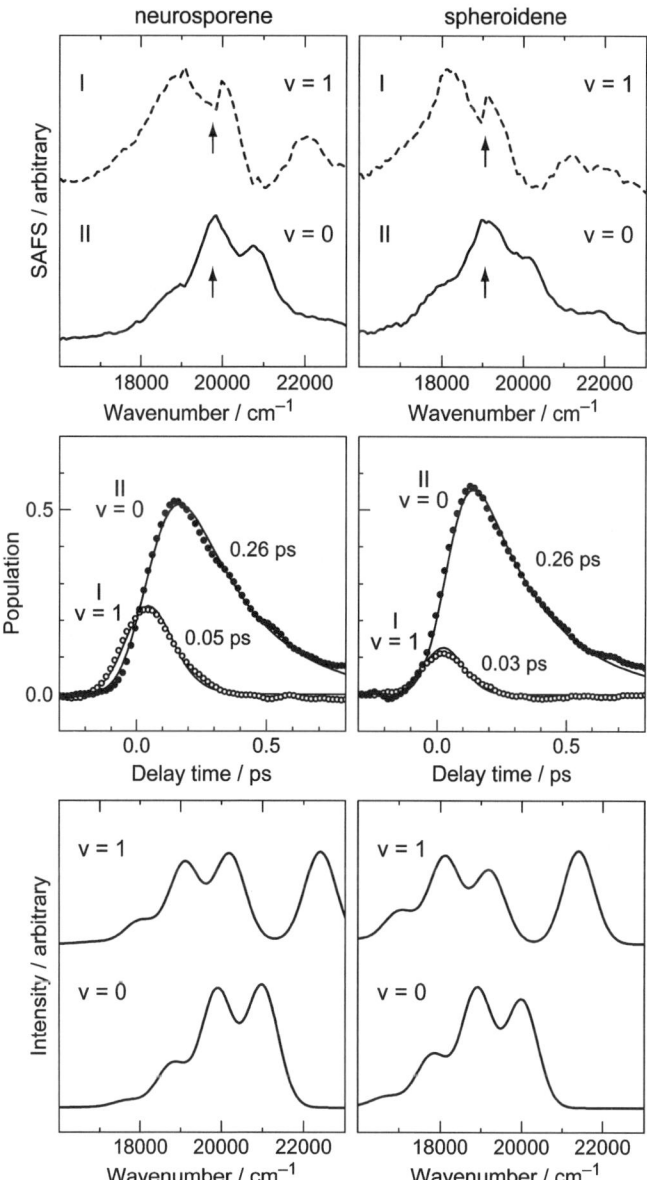

**Figure 11.** SAFS (top panels) and transient populations (middle panels) of the first and the second components in the time scale (component I and component II), gathered from SVD and global-fitting analyses of subpicosecond time-resolved fluorescence spectra obtained by Kerr-gate fluorescence spectroscopy of neurosporene and spheroidene in $n$-hexane [28]. For comparison the bottom panels present fluorescence spectra simulated by calculations of the Franck–Condon overlap for transitions from the levels $v=1$ and $v=0$ of the $1B_u^+$ state down to the levels $v=0$, 1, 2 and 3 of the $1A_g^-$ state.

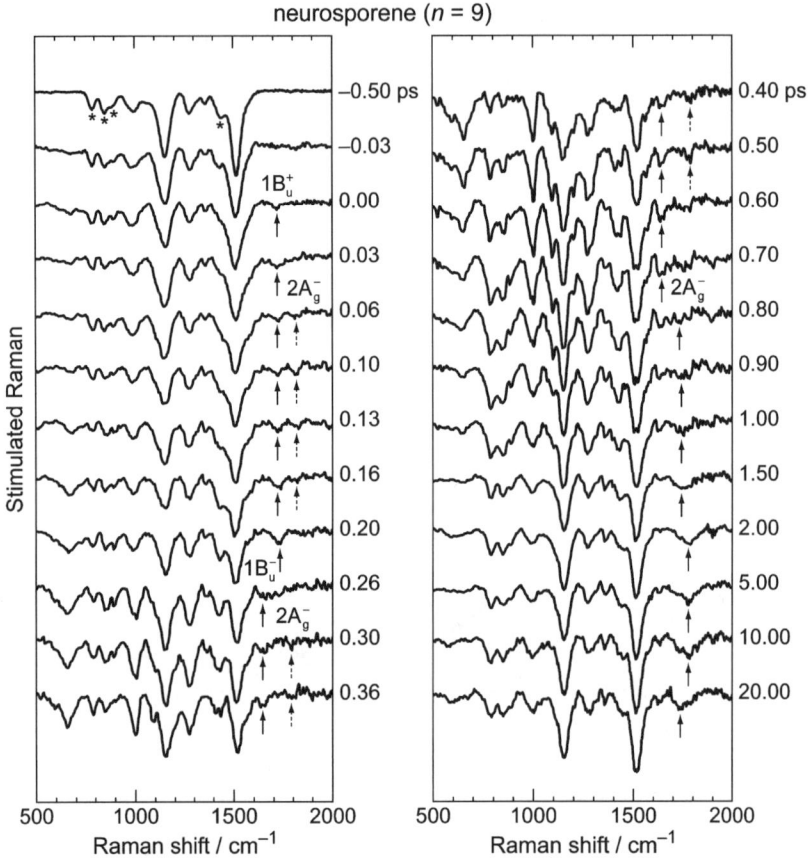

**Figure 12.** Subpicosecond time-resolved Raman spectra of neurosporene in *n*-hexane [31]. Key Raman lines indicated by arrows. See text for details.

by an asterisk are due to the solvent *n*-hexane. Upon excitation to the $1B_u^+(3)$ level (0 fs), a new C=C stretching Raman line (1725 cm$^{-1}$) appears, accompanying the broadening of the entire Raman profile. This Raman line can be definitely assigned to the electronic state $1B_u^+$ of the Car molecule that is formed by the monochromatic laser pulse. At around 260 fs, another C=C stretching Raman line (1645 cm$^{-1}$) appears, accompanying a complicated spectral pattern in the lower finger-print region, which can be assigned to the state $1B_u^-$ according to the energetic order of electronic states shown in Figure 4. At around 900 fs, a third C=C stretching Raman line (1730–1760 cm$^{-1}$) appears in the very high frequency region with a simplified spectral pattern in the finger-print region. The extraordinary high frequency of this $a_g$-type C=C stretching Raman line can be ascribed to vibronic coupling with the $1A_g^-$ state [17]. Therefore, this Raman line can be definitely assigned to the $2A_g^-$ state. Thus, the order of electronic transitions of $1B_u^+ \rightarrow 1B_u^- \rightarrow 2A_g^- \rightarrow (1A_g^-)$ has been established by these experiments.

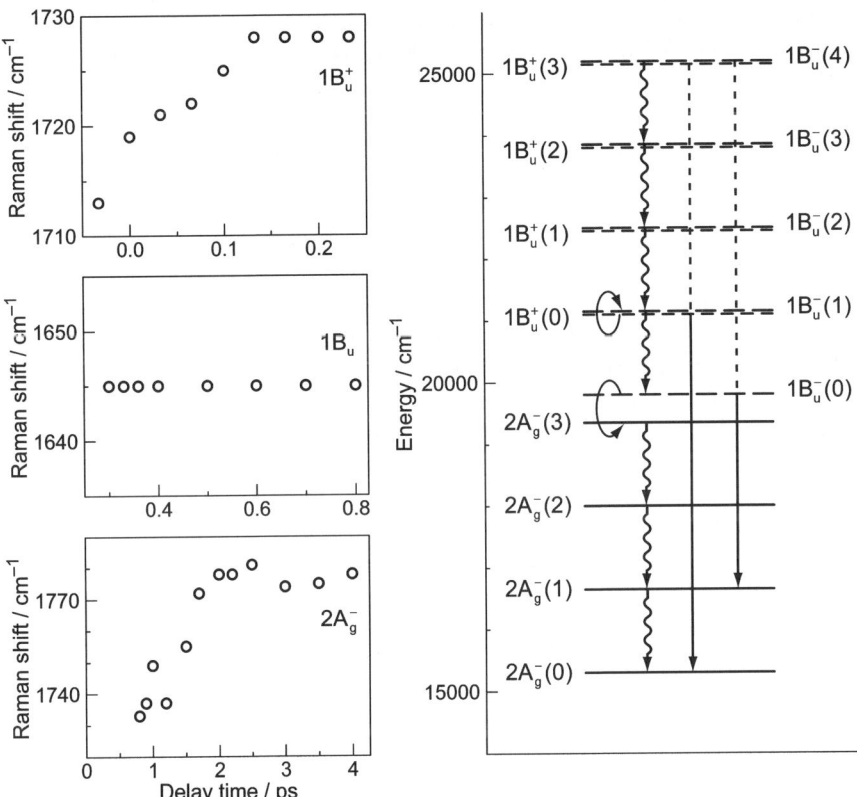

**Figure 13.** Time-dependent changes of the frequencies of the key C=C stretching Raman lines of the excited singlet states $1B_u^+$, $1B_u^-$ and $2A_g^-$ (left-hand panels) and scheme (right-hand frame) of their vibrational relaxation (wavy arrows), internal conversion (rounded arrows) and radiative transitions (straight arrows) [31].

The time-resolved Raman spectra also show that the key Raman lines of the states $1B_u^+$ and $1B_u^-$ accompany the key Raman line of the $2A_g^-$ state, when the intensities of the former two lines are the highest. These results indicate that the (radiative) electronic transitions $1B_u^+ \to 2A_g^-$ and $1B_u^- \to 2A_g^-$ take place in addition to the above (non-radiative) electronic conversions. The pair of radiative transitions is shown on the right-hand-side of Figure 13. The vibronic origin of these transitions has not yet been clarified.

The panels on the left-hand-side of Figure 13 show the time-dependent changes in the frequencies of all of the key Raman lines of the electronic states $1B_u^+$, $1B_u^-$ and $2A_g^-$. The shift of the Raman lines to the higher frequencies can be ascribed to vibrational relaxation in an anharmonic potential. The shift to higher-frequencies of the Raman line is clearly seen for the $1B_u^+$ and $2A_g^-$ states, but is absent in the $1B_u^-$ state. The vibronic level diagram on the right-hand-side shows that three steps of vibrational relaxation can take place in the electronic states $1B_u^+$ and $2A_g^-$, whereas there is only one step of vibrational relaxation in the state $1B_u^-$. Thus, the presence or absence of the high-frequency shift can be nicely explained in terms of the presence or absence of the stepwise vibrational relaxations.

*4.3.6 Car-to-BChl Singlet-Energy Transfer in Antenna Complexes*

The overall efficiency of the Car-to-BChl singlet–singlet excitation-energy transfer can be determined by a comparison of the intensities of the $1B_u^+(0) \leftarrow 1A_g^-(0)$ transition between the fluorescence-excitation and the electronic-absorption spectra (after normalization of the peak of the $Q_x \leftarrow S_0$ transition, for example). By this method, the overall efficiency was determined to be 92, 89, 53 and 56% for the LH2 complexes from *Rb. sphaeroides* G1C, *Rb. sphaeroides* 2.4.1, *Rsp. molischianum* and *Rps. acidophila* strain 10050, containing neurosporene ($n=9$), spheroidene ($n=10$), rhodopin + lycopene (3:1; both $n=11$) and rhodopin glucoside ($n=11$), respectively [32].

To explain the sharp drop from about 90% to 55% in the singlet-energy transfer efficiency when the number of conjugated double bonds increases from 10 to 11 in terms of the energetics and the dynamics of Car and BChl, visible and near-infrared subpicosecond time-resolved absorption spectroscopy was applied to the above set of LH2 complexes and the data matrices were analyzed by SVD and global fitting [32]. Figure 14 summarizes the results. The top panels show a set of SADS. They include stimulated emission from the $1B_u^+$ state, a broad and a sharp transient absorption from the $1B_u^-$ and $2A_g^-$ states, respectively (both accompanying the bleaching of the $1B_u^+ \leftarrow 1A_g^-$ absorption) and an interference pattern between the $T_n \leftarrow T_1$ transient absorption and the bleaching of the ground-state absorption. Here the difference spectral pattern of the $T_1$ state can be contrasted with that of the $T_2$ state presented in Figure 7. The middle panels show the time courses of the transient populations of states $1B_u^+$, $1B_u^-$, $2A_g^-$ and $T_1$. The time-dependent profiles reveal that both the $2A_g^-$ and the $T_1$ states are generated from the $1B_u^-$ state. These signals reflect the input of the singlet energy into the channels of Car-to-BChl excitation energy transfer. The bottom panels present the fits to the bleaching of the $Q_y$ absorption, reflecting the output of the singlet energy from those channels, *i.e.*, the arrival of the electronic excitation at BChl.

In the analyses, the time constants of the transition within the ladder of electronically excited singlet states of Car and BChl determined in solution were used to calculate the time constants of the three channels of singlet-energy transfer, *i.e.*, $1B_u^+ \to Q_x$, $1B_u^- \to Q_x$ and $2A_g^- \to Q_y$. Likewise, in this way the rate of singlet-to-triplet conversion, $1B_u^- \to T_1$, was also determined. The results are schematically summarized in Figure 15. An inspection of this data reveals (i) the $1B_u^+$ channel is always open, and it tends to speed up with increasing $n$; (ii) the $1B_u^-$ channel is open and speeds up slightly on going from $n=9$ to $n=10$; however, it becomes closed when $n$ increases from 10 to 11, probably due to uphill energy transfer; (iii) the $2A_g^-$ channel slows down on going from $n=9$ to $n=10$ and is practically closed for the Cars with $n=11$. A speculative explanation of this feature is that the energy gap between the $2A_g^-$ and the $Q_y$ states is

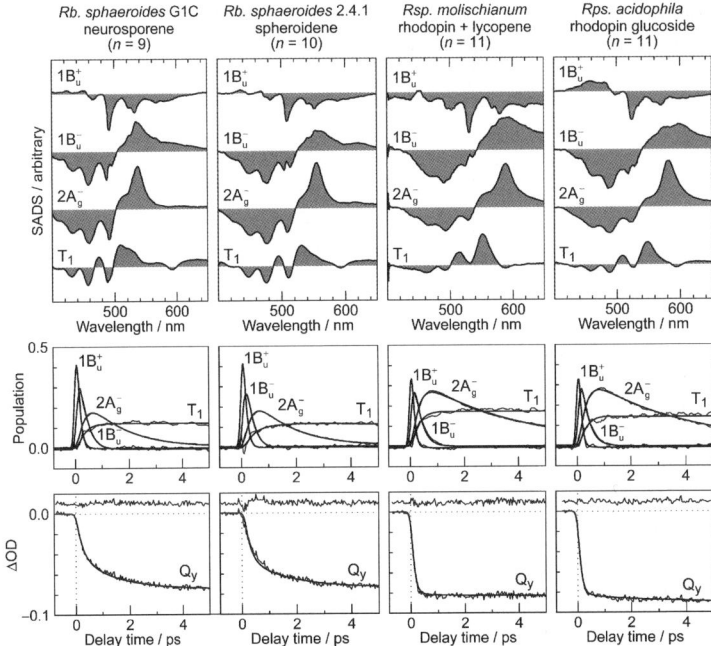

**Figure 14.** SADS (top panels) and transient population (middle panels) of the excited singlet states $1B_u^+$, $1B_u^-$ and $2A_g^-$ and the triplet state $T_1$ ($1^3B_u$) of neurosporene, spheroidene, rhodopin + lycopene, and rhodopin glucoside bound to the LH2 complexes from *Rb. sphaeroides* G1C, *Rb. sphaeroides* 2.4.1, *Rsp. molischianum* and *Rps. acidophila*, respectively [32]. The spectral data matrices obtained by visible, subpicosecond time-resolved absorption spectroscopy were analyzed by SVD and global fitting within the framework of the scheme shown in Figure 15. Fittings to the bleaching profile of the $Q_y$ absorption of BChl (bottom panels) are also shown, together with the residuals.

too small to facilitate singlet-energy transfer from the vibronic level $v=1$ before completing the last step of vibrational relaxation [see Section 4.3.4 for the slow vibrational relaxation from $v=1$ to $v=0$ in the $2A_g^-$ state, and Figure 11 (bottom panel) for Franck–Condon overlap starting from the levels $v=1$ and $v=0$].

Table 3(a) compiles the results of calculations of the excited singlet state energy flow through the three individual channels by using the time constants listed in Figure 15. In the LH2 complexes containing neurosporene and spheroidene ($n=9$ and 10), all the $1B_u^+$, $1B_u^-$ and $2A_g^-$ channels are open. In the LH2 complexes containing rhodopin + lycopene or rhodopin glucoside ($n=11$), however, only the $1B_u^+$ channel is open and the $1B_u^-$ and $2A_g^-$ channels are practically closed. The sum of the three channels represents the overall efficiency of the singlet–singlet excitation energy transfer of Car-to-BChl for each LH2. The numbers obtained, *i.e.*, 88, 84, 51 and 54%, are in good agreement with the values, *i.e.*, 92, 89, 53 and 56%, respectively, determined by comparison of the fluorescence excitation and electronic absorption spectra.

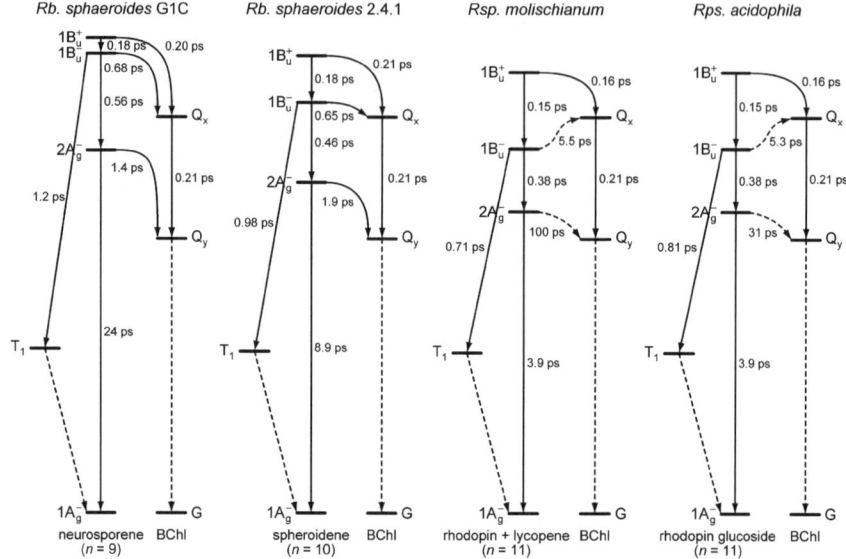

**Figure 15.** Kinetic scheme of electronic conversion of Cars and singlet–singlet energy-transfer to BChl. The time constants of Car-to-BChl singlet–singlet excitation energy transfer through the channels $1B_u^+ \to Q_x$, $1B_u^- \to Q_x$ and $2A_g^- \to Q_y$ and of the $1B_u^- \to T_1$ singlet-to-triplet conversion in Car were determined by fitting of the data shown in the middle and bottom panels of Figure 14, using values determined in solution.

**Table 3.** Efficiencies $\Phi$ (%) of Car-to-BChl singlet-energy transfer through the $1B_u^+$, $1B_u^-$ and $2A_g^-$ channels and those of the $1B_u^-$-to-$T_1$ singlet-to-triplet conversion in Cars as determined by the SVD and global-fitting analyses of subpicosecond time-resolved, spectral data matrices. The overall efficiencies that were determined by comparison of the fluorescence-excitation and electronic-absorption spectra are also shown

| Carotenoid (n) | $\Phi$ ($1B_u^+$) | $\Phi$ ($1B_u^-$) | $\Phi$ ($2A_g^-$) | $\Phi$ (sum) | $\Phi$ ($T_1$) | $\Phi$ (obs) |
|---|---|---|---|---|---|---|
| (a) Native LH2 complexes [32] | | | | | | |
| Neurosporene (9)[a] | 48 | 19 | 22 | 88 | 10 | 92 |
| Spheroidene (10)[b] | 46 | 18 | 20 | 84 | 12 | 89 |
| Rhodopin + lycopene (11)[c] | 48 | 2 | 1 | 51 | 17 | 53 |
| Rhodopin glucoside (11)[d] | 48 | 2 | 4 | 54 | 16 | 56 |
| (b) Reconstituted LH1 complexes [33] | | | | | | |
| Neurosporene (9) | 47 | 11 | 20 | 78 | 19 | – |
| Spheroidene (10) | 47 | 9 | 19 | 75 | 20 | – |
| Lycopene (11) | 41 | 2 | 3 | 46 | 27 | – |
| Anhydrorhodovibrin (12) | 39 | 0 | 1 | 40 | 29 | – |
| Spirilloxanthin (13) | 35 | 0 | 1 | 36 | 31 | – |

In the LH2 from
[a] *Rb. sphaeroides* G1C,
[b] *Rb. sphaeroides* 2.4.1,
[c] *Rsp. molischianum* and
[d] *Rps. acidophila*.

A set of Cars including neurosporene, spheroidene, lycopene, anhydrorhodovibrin and spirilloxanthin having $n=9$–13, respectively, were incorporated into the LH1 complex from *Rsp. rubrum* G9 (a carotenoidless mutant), and the same time-resolved absorption spectroscopy and analytical methods were applied as described for LH2 [33]. Figure 16 presents the results. The top and middle panels exhibit the SADS and the time course of the transient populations, respectively, of the electronic states $1B_u^+$, $1B_u^-$, $2A_g^-$ and $T_1$ after flash excitation. The bottom panels show the fits to the time profiles of the $Q_y$ bleaching. Comparison with Figure 14 reveals that the results are similar to those obtained for the LH2 complexes. Figure 17 shows, in analogy to Figure 15, a schematic representation of the time constants for singlet–singlet energy transfer from excited Car to BChl through the $1B_u^+$, $1B_u^-$ and $2A_g^-$ channels, and that of the singlet-to-triplet conversion within Car. Based on this data it can be concluded: (i) the $1B_u^+$ channel slows down slightly when $n$ increases from 9 to 13, (ii) the $1B_u^-$ channel also slightly slows down on going from $n=9$ to $n=10$, but is completely closed for $n=11$–13, and (iii) the $2A_g^-$ channel somewhat speeds up for $n$ increasing from 9 to 10, but becomes completely closed for $n=11$–13.

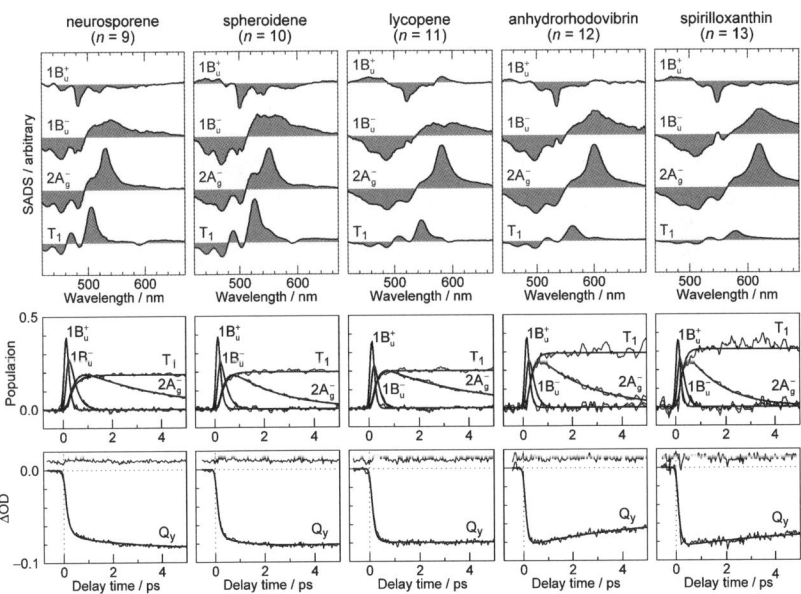

**Figure 16.** SADS (top panels) and transient populations (middle panels) of the states $1B_u^+$, $1B_u^-$, $2A_g^-$ and $T_1$ of neurosporene, spheroidene, lycopene, anhydrorhodovibrin and spirilloxanthin that were incorporated into the LH1 from *Rsp. rubrum* G9 (a carotenoidless mutant) [33]. Spectral data matrices were obtained by visible, subpicosecond time-resolved absorption spectroscopy, and analyzed by SVD and global fitting within the framework of the schemes shown in Figure 17. Fittings to the time profiles of the $Q_y$ bleaching (bottom panels), recorded in the near-infrared region, are also shown with the residuals.

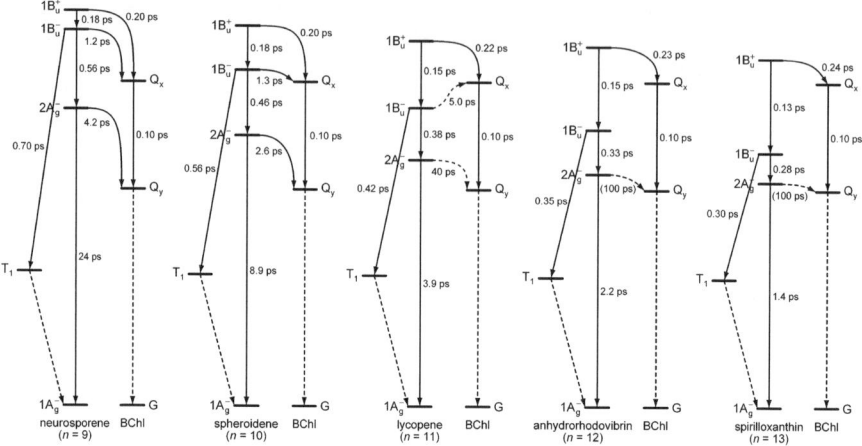

**Figure 17.** Kinetic schemes of electronic conversion in Cars and singlet–singlet-energy transfer to BChl. Time constants were obtained by the same strategy as described in Figure 15. The fitting results are shown in Figure 16.

From the results the efficiency can be determined of excited singlet state energy flow through the individual $1B_u^+$, $1B_u^-$ and $2A_g^-$ channels. The data summarized in Table 3(b) reveal that all three channels are open for $n=9$ and 10, whereas only the $1B_u^+$ channel is open for $n=11-13$.

The sum of the three individual channels of each Car leads to values of 78, 75, 46, 40 and 36% for the molecules with $n=9-13$, respectively. As in the case of LH2 (Table 3(a)), here, again, a drastic drop is obtained for the excited singlet-energy transfer from Car to BChl when the number of conjugated double bonds increases from 10 to 11. Comparison of the data in Table 3(a) and (b) also indicates that, in general, the energy-transfer efficiencies are lower in LH1 than in LH2. In contrast, the yield of the $T_1$ state is much larger in LH1 than in LH2. This phenomenon probably reflects the different conformation in the conjugated chain (Section 4.7).

## 4.4 Photoprotective Function

Among the different pathways of singlet state decay of (B)Chls in photosynthetic organisms one reaction is of potential danger, *i.e.*, the formation of $^3$(B)Chl either via intersystem crossing or the reversal of electron transfer reactions leading to population of the triplet radical pair and subsequent transition into the triplet state of the photoactive pigment (in the case of anoxygenic purple bacteria this is the state $^3$P of the special pair P). In general, (B)Chl triplets give rise to sensitized generation of singlet oxygen – a very reactive species that damages the system. Therefore, singlet oxygen formation must be suppressed. Cars are unique in protection because they act in a twofold

PHOTOPHYSICAL PROPERTIES AND LIGHT-HARVESTING

manner: (i) by efficient quenching of $^3$(B)Chl via triplet-energy transfer to Cars (in the case of $^3$P this process occurs through the accessory BChl, $B_M$, followed by triplet-energy dissipation at 15-cis Car, see [34]) and (ii) by quenching of singlet oxygen under triplet carotenoid ($^3$Car) formation. In both cases the populated $^3$Car states rapidly decay via radiationless transition into the ground state (for further information on the protective role of Cars, see [5,6]).

In this chapter we concentrate on a particular point, *i.e.*, the quenching of $^3$P by Cars in the RCs of anoxygenic purple bacteria (interestingly, an analogous reaction does not take place in Photosystem II of oxygen evolving organisms, see Chapter 16). At first, it will be shown that the photoprotective function of Cars having a longer chain of conjugated double bonds is more efficient than of those having a shorter chain, due to the dependence on this conjugation length of both the $T_1$ energies and the protective function to photo-oxidation of BChls. Secondly, we will present experimental evidence supporting a hypothetical mechanism of triplet-energy dissipation by the RC-bound 15-cis-spheroidene, which includes the rotational motion around the cis C15=C15' double bond.

*4.4.1 Dependence of the Triplet-Energy and the Photoprotective Function of Cars on the Length of the Conjugated Chain*

The $T_1$ energies of neurosporene, spheroidene, rhodopin + lycopene bound to the LH2 from *Rb. sphaeroides* G1C, *Rb. sphaeroides* 2.4.1 and *Rsp. molischianum* were determined with high-sensitivity emission spectroscopy [35]. Most importantly, the populations of $^3$BChl and $^3$Car attain a stationary state under the conditions of continuous (CW) excitation. As is shown in the bottom part of Figure 4, the $T_1$ energies were determined to be 7030, 6920 and 6870 cm$^{-1}$ for Cars with $n = 9$–11, respectively, whereas the $T_1$ energy of BChl is higher with a value of 7590 cm$^{-1}$. Assuming a Boltzmann distribution in thermal equilibrium, the population ratio of $^3$BChl/$^3$Car can be calculated to be 0.06, 0.04 and 0.03 for $n = 9$–11, respectively. Extrapolation of the linear relation between $T_1$ energy and $n$ leads to a $T_1$ energy of 6750 cm$^{-1}$ for a Car with $n = 13$ and, consequently, a population ratio of 0.02 for $^3$BChl/$^3$Car. These results support the idea that $^3$BChl can be efficiently quenched by Car, and that the quenching (triplet-energy transfer) efficiency should be higher in Cars having a longer conjugated chain.

The lifetimes of $^3$Car in the LH2 complexes from *Rb. sphaeroides* G1C, *Rb. sphaeroides* 2.4.1, *Rsp. molischianum* and *Rps. acidophila* containing neurosporene ($n = 9$), spheroidene ($n = 10$), rhodopin + lycopene (both $n = 11$) and rhodopin glucoside ($n = 11$) were determined, by submicrosecond time-resolved absorption spectroscopy, to be 9.6 ± 0.1, 6.2 ± 0.1, 4.5 ± 0.1, 4.2 ± 0.1 μs, respectively. The results indicate that the efficiency of triplet-energy dissipation increases with the length of the chain of conjugated double bonds.

It was shown by time-resolved Raman, absorption and EPR spectroscopies that a BChl radical cation (BChl$^{\cdot+}$) was generated from $^3$BChl in the carotenoidless LH1 and LH2 complexes from *Rb. sphaeroides* R26 and R26.1 [36]. In

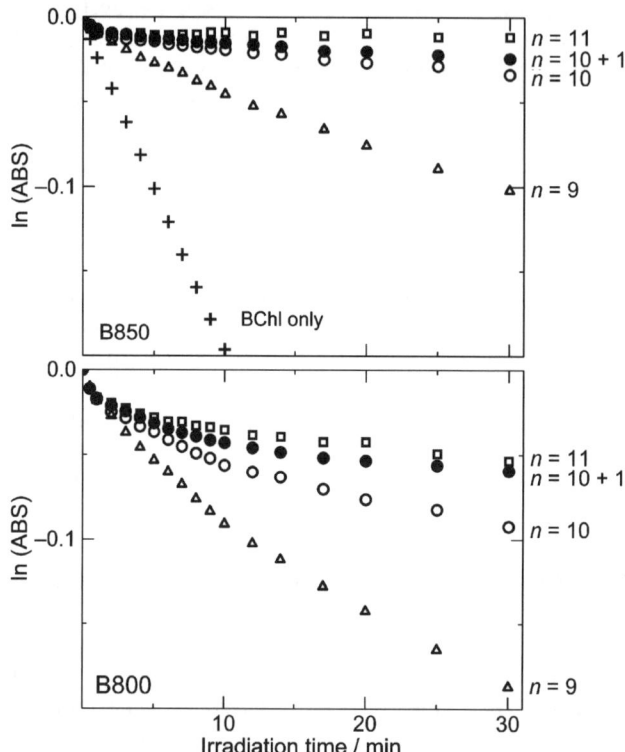

**Figure 18.** Bleaching of the $Q_y$ absorption of B850 (upper panel) and B800 (lower panel) BChls of different LH2 complexes as a function of irradiation with CW light of wavelength above 760 nm. The samples used were LH2 from the Car-free mutant *Rb. sphaeroides* R26.1 (crosses) and *Rb. sphaeroides* G1C (open triangles), *Rb. sphaeroides* 2.4.1 (open circles) and *Rps. acidophila* (open squares) grown anaerobically and containing neurosporene ($n=9$), spheroidene ($n=10$) and rhodopin glucoside ($n=11$), respectively. *Rb. sphaeroides* 2.4.1 was also grown semiaerobically to enrich spheroidenone ($n=10+1$) up to 75% (filled circles).

marked contrast, the generation of BChl$^{\cdot +}$ was totally prevented in the LH2 complex from *Rb. sphaeroides* 2.4.1 that contains spheroidene, because in this case $^3$BChl becomes quenched by the Car. This type of reaction appears to be a general mechanism of the photoprotective function by Cars against the photo-oxidation of BChl.

Figure 18 shows in the upper and the lower panels time-dependent bleaching curves of the $Q_y$ absorptions of B850 BChl and B800 BChl, respectively, that were obtained when suspensions of different LH2 complexes were irradiated with CW light of wavelengths above the 760 nm that excite the BChls. LH2 samples from the following organisms were used: *Rb. sphaeroides* R26.1 (a carotenoidless mutant), *Rb. sphaeroides* G1C, *Rb. sphaeroides* 2.4.1 and *Rps. acidophila*, containing neurosporene ($n=9$), spheroidene ($n=10$) and rhodopin glucoside ($n=11$), respectively. *Rb. sphaeroides* 2.4.1 was grown also under semiaerobic conditions to accumulate spheroidenone ($n = 10 + 1$), with an enrichment factor being about 75% [Limantara et al., unpublished]. The results in the upper panel reveal that Cars in the LH2 complexes reduce the rate of the $Q_y$ bleaching of B850 BChl. Furthermore, the efficiency of protection increases in the order, $n = 9$, 10, $10 + 1$ and 11, thus indicating that Cars with a longer chain of conjugated double bonds provide a better protection. A comparison with the lower panels shows that this efficiency order of protection is virtually the same for B800 BChl, and that B800 BChl is more sensitive to the photo-oxidation than B850 BChl. Since the macrocycles of B850 BChl and B800 BChl are aligned almost parallel and perpendicular, respectively, to the conjugated chain of Car, the higher efficiency of the photoprotection of B850 BChl by Car is understandable. A similar trend was also seen for the $Q_y$ absorption of accessory BChl in the RC.

This short description shows that Cars with a longer chain of conjugated double bonds are more efficient quenchers of $^3$BChl. This property can be rationalized the basis of their $T_1$ energies.

*4.4.2 Rapid 15-Cis to All-Trans Isomerization in Cars Upon Triplet Excitation: the Role of the Triplet-Excited Region*

One characteristic of Cars is the possibility of undergoing cis-to-trans isomerization. The configurational dependence of this process upon triplet excitation of the molecules by using a sensitizer (anthracene) has been examined for the 13′-cis, 9-cis, 13-cis and 15-cis isomers of spheroidene by applying submicrosecond time-resolved absorption spectroscopy and the determination of the quantum yields of triplet sensitized isomerization [37]. The SVD and global-fitting analysis of the spectral data matrix for each isomer, by the use of a double minimum potential in the $T_1$ state, showed that the lifetime of the decay of cis isomers ($\sim 0.83\,\mu s$) is much shorter than that of the all-trans isomer of spheroidene (4.76 μs), and that, with respect to the time constant of cis-to-trans isomerization, the molecules exhibit the following order: 13′-cis (0.91 μs) > 9-cis (0.83 μs) > 13-cis (0.77 μs) > 15-cis (0.56 μs). Interestingly, the time constants of isomerization are of the same order of magnitude as the triplet lifetimes of the cis isomers. This suggests that the rotational motion around the cis double bond causes $T_1 \rightarrow S_0$ intersystem crossing (relaxation). Table 4 lists the quantum yields of triplet-sensitized isomerization of spheroidene isomers. The values are in the order: 15-cis > 13-cis > 9-cis > 13′-cis.

With β-carotene, the 15-cis to all-trans isomerization in the $T_1$ state was so rapid that both the 15-cis and the all-trans isomers gave rise to the same transient-Raman [38] and transient-absorption [39] spectra. The quantum yields of triplet-sensitized isomerization in β-carotene isomers are also listed in Table 4 [40]. In this case, the quantum yields of the central-cis isomers are much higher than those in the peripheral-cis isomers, and the quantum yield of the 15-cis isomer is almost unity.

The fact that the 15-cis forms of spheroidene and β-carotene exhibit the fastest rate and the highest quantum yield of isomerization in the $T_1$ state among

Table 4. Quantum yields of cis-to-trans isomerization in the $T_1$ state ($\Phi_{iso}$), as defined by decrease in the starting isomer per triplet species produced [37,40]

| $T_1$ species | Spheroidene | β-Carotene |
|---|---|---|
| All-trans | – | – |
| 7-Cis | – | 0.12 |
| 13'-Cis | 0.48 | – |
| 9-Cis | 0.50 | 0.15 |
| 13-Cis | 0.52 | 0.87 |
| 15-Cis | 0.60 | 0.98 |

the different isomers of these species can be explained in terms of "the triplet-excited region" where large changes in bond order take place, *i.e.*, double bonds become more single bond-like, and, vice versa, single bonds become more double bond-like [41]. The triplet-excited region is localized in the central part of a long conjugated chain, it has a span of approximately six conjugated double bonds, and it triggers cis-to-trans isomerization by reducing the barrier of internal rotation around the central C=C bonds. This feature is illustrated in the upper panel of Figure 19. It shows for the triplet-excited region of all-trans-spheroidene in *n*-hexane the carbon–carbon stretching force constants that were determined by normal-coordinate analyses of the $S_0$ and $T_1$ Raman spectra of undeuterated and six different deuterated species [42]. The C=C and C–C stretching force constants in the $S_0$ state (open circles) systematically change into those of the $T_1$ state (close circles) in a way where in the central part of the conjugated chain double bonds become more single bond-like and single bonds become more double bond-like. The force constants shown in double circles on both peripherals were assumed, but could not be determined due to the limited number of deuterated species. Pariser–Parr–Pople type calculations of model polyenes also predicted the presence of triplet-excited region in linear polyenes (see Figure 6 of [40]). Thus, a decrease in the bond order, upon triplet excitation, in the cis C15=C15' bond must enhance the rotational motion toward all-trans, supported by the strong steric repulsion in the 15-cis isomer.

In summary, the most efficient $T_1$-state isomerization from 15-cis to all-trans has been proven for the pair of Cars and rationalized by the triplet-excited region. We suspect that this unique triplet-state property should be relevant to the natural selection of the 15-cis configuration by the RC-bound Cars.

*4.4.3 Structure of the RC-Bound 15-cis-Spheroidene in the $T_1$ State*

Now, we know that large changes in the bond order must take place in the central part of the chain of conjugated double bonds upon triplet excitation of 15-cis-spheroidene bound to the RC, and that the twisting of the conjugated chain may take place around the cis C15=C15' bond due to the rotational motion toward all-trans, although complete isomerization into the all-trans configuration is inhibited by the binding pocket of the apo-peptide (M). To

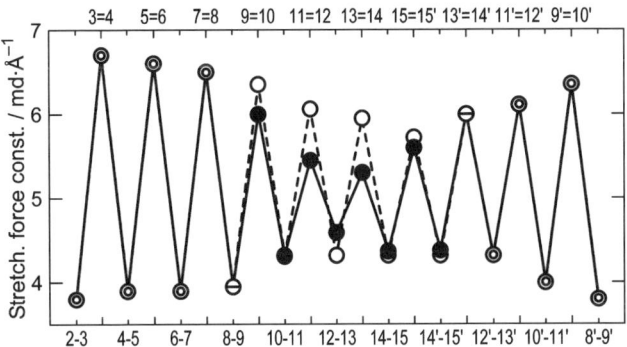

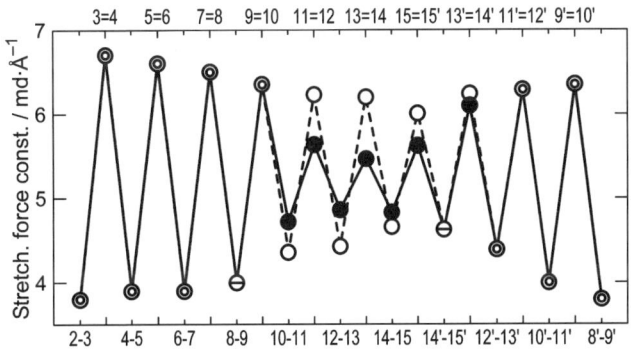

**Figure 19.** "Triplet-excited region" of all-trans-spheroidene in *n*-hexane (upper panel) and of 15-cis-spheroidene bound to the RC from *Rb. sphaeroides* 2.4.1 (lower panel). The triplet-excited region is shown by the use of the C=C and C–C stretching force constants in the ground state (open circles) and in the $T_1$ state (closed circles). The force constants were determined by normal-coordinate analyses of the $S_0$ and $T_1$ Raman spectra for undeuterated and seven different deuterated species [42]. Since corresponding deuterated species were lacking, the force constants of peripheral bonds remain to be determined. Circles with bar indicate the $S_0$ and $T_1$ force constants in agreement, and double circles indicate the assumed force constants in the $S_0$ state.

address this problem, resonance-Raman spectroscopy was used as a powerful probe for the structure in the $T_1$ state. Actually, an empirical spectral analysis of the $S_0$ and $T_1$ Raman spectra of the RC-bound 15-cis-spheroidene provided some information on structural changes upon triplet excitation [43]. However, to determine the changes both in the bond order and in the molecular structure (concerning the rotational degree of freedom) it was necessary to incorporate at first various deuterated spheroidenes into the carotenoidless RC and then to measure their $S_0$ and $T_1$ Raman spectra followed by a numerical data analyses to obtain normal vibrations [42].

Figure 20 shows the $S_0$ and $T_1$ Raman spectra of 15-cis-spheroidene bound to the native RC from *Rb. sphaeroides* 2.4.1 [42]. The $S_0$ Raman spectrum indicates

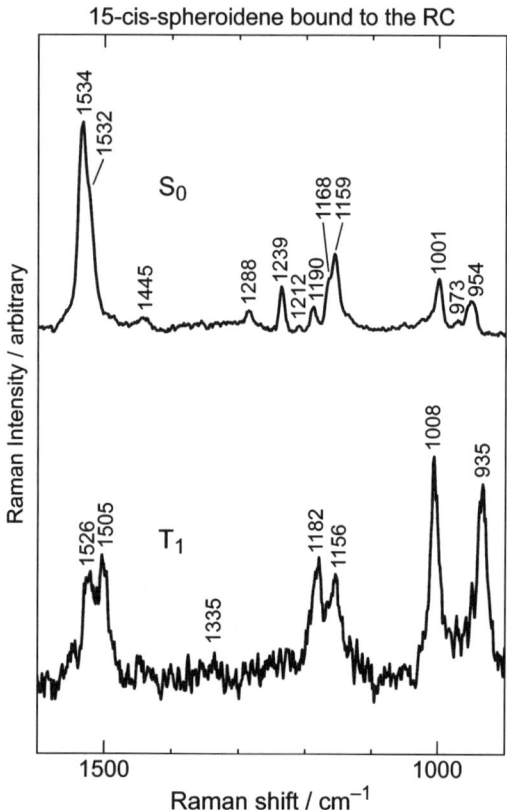

**Figure 20.** Resonance Raman spectra of 15-cis-spheroidene bound to the RC from *Rb. sphaeroides* 2.4.1 in the $S_0$ (ground) and $T_1$ states [42].

that the chain of conjugated double bonds attains a planar 15-cis configuration, in agreement with the structure gathered from X-ray crystallography [44; PDB (protein data bank): 1YST]: in the case of a planar configuration, each of the C=C and the C–C stretching vibrations couple with each other to form a pair of overall normal modes, thus giving rise to two strong Raman lines around 1530 and 1160 cm$^{-1}$. Furthermore, the methyl in-plane rockings couple with one another to give a medium Raman line around 1000 cm$^{-1}$ and the localized C–H out-of-plane waggings give rise to a weak Raman line around 950 cm$^{-1}$. As a reflection of the 15-cis configuration, the Raman spectrum exhibits a key line due to the coupled C–H in-plane vibrations around the cis-bend that is a "finger-print" of this isomer. This Raman line is located at 1239 cm$^{-1}$. In addition, Raman lines are observed for the slightly-split C=C stretching (1534 + 1532 cm$^{-1}$) and C–C stretching (1168 + 1159 cm$^{-1}$), reflecting the bent conjugated chain.

The $T_1$ Raman spectrum of the RC-bound 15-cis-spheroidene indicates that there is substantial twisting of the chain of conjugated double bonds. In this case, the overall coupling of the C=C and C–C stretching vibrations is prevented because this phenomenon is possible only in the planar configuration. As a consequence, more localized vibrations give rise to two clearly-split Raman lines of C=C stretching ($1526 + 1505$ cm$^{-1}$) and C–C stretching ($1182 + 1156$ cm$^{-1}$). The strong enhancement of the methyl in-plane rocking (1008 cm$^{-1}$) and the C–H out-of-plane wagging (935 cm$^{-1}$) Raman lines are clear indications of the in-plane distortion and substantial twisting of the conjugated chain.

The lower panel of Figure 19 shows a set of carbon–carbon stretching force constants that were determined for the RC-bound 15-cis-spheroidene of the $S_0$ and $T_1$ states. The changes in the bond order are similar to those of all-trans-spheroidene in $n$-hexane.

Concerning the conformation of the RC-bound spheroidene in the $T_1$ state, a pair of models, i.e., one in which the rotational angles around the cis C15=C15′, trans C13=C14 and trans C11=C12 bonds are (45°, −30°, 30°), and the other in which they are (45°, 30°, 30°), respectively, could explain the spectral data. However, the former model was proposed [42] because it fits much better to the Car binding pocket that had been determined by X-ray crystallography [44].

### 4.4.4 Conformational Changes in the RC-Bound $T_1$ Spheroidene: Evidence for the Hypothetical Mechanism of Triplet-Energy Dissipation

Based on (1) the intrinsic $T_1$-state property of 15-cis-spheroidene, i.e., rapid isomerization toward all-trans, and (2) the conformational change of the RC-bound spheroidene in the $T_1$ state, i.e., from the flat to the substantially-twisted conformation, we previously proposed the following hypothetical mechanism of triplet-energy dissipation by Cars.

The rotational motions around the central double bonds can cause a change in the orbital angular momentum (due to the re-arrangement of electrons following that of nuclei) and, as a result, a change in the spin angular momentum, through the spin–orbit coupling conserving the total angular momentum. The change in the spin angular momentum facilitates the $T_1 \rightarrow S_0$ intersystem crossing, which dissipates the triplet energy [42,43].

Time-resolved EPR spectroscopy of the RC-bound $T_1$ spheroidene at low temperatures [45] has provided additional supporting evidence for this mechanism: Figure 21 shows a schematic presentation (a summary) for the transformations of $^3$Car species, which include (i) the initial species, $^3$Car(I), generated by triplet-energy transfer from the special-pair BChls (P), (ii) the final $^3$Car species, $^3$Car(II), in the $T_1$ stationary state, and (iii) an intermediate species, $^3$Car(R), which facilitates a leaking channel of triplet population (energy). This scheme has been obtained by the four-component, SVD and global-fitting analysis of the spectral data matrix at 100 K. Figure 22 presents the results, including the species-associated spectra (SAS), i.e., the EPR signals (left-hand-side), and the populations of the $^3$Car forms, i.e., $^3$P, $^3$Car(I), $^3$Car(R) and $^3$Car(II), in two different time scales (right-hand-side). The lower panel also presents the decay time constant of each triplet species. $^3$Car(R),

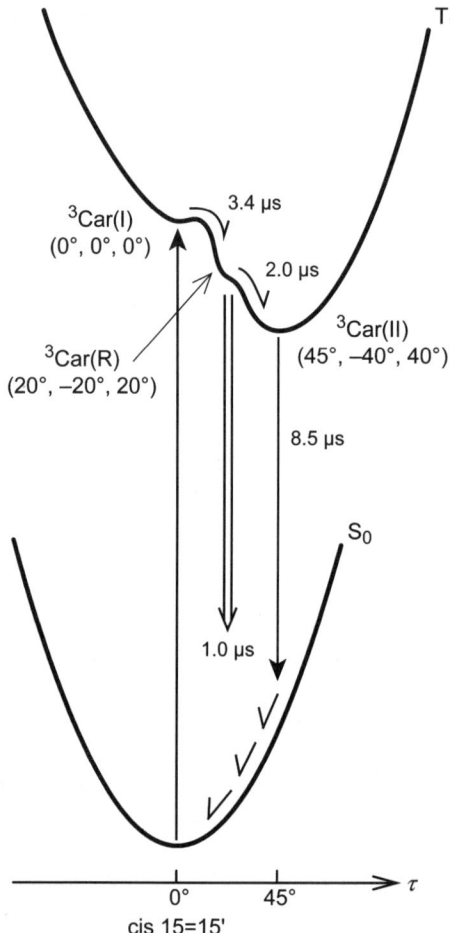

**Figure 21.** Scheme of potential curves of $^3$Car (T$_1$) and $^1$Car (S$_0$). The time constants for conformational transformations within the $^3$Car state and for the transitions into S$_0$ were obtained by the four-component, SVD and global-fitting analyses of data from measurements at 100 K.

providing the leaking channel of triplet population (with a time constant shorter than 1 μs), plays the key role in the triplet-energy dissipation.

Figure 23 (upper panels) illustrates the spectral patterns of $^3$Car(I), $^3$Car(R) and $^3$Car(II) in detail; the observed zero-field splitting parameters, *i.e.*, $|D|$ and $|E|$, listed in Table 5 (left-hand-side) were determined by the use of the $y$–$y'$ and $z$–$z'$ splittings shown in the figure (solid vertical lines); the $x$–$x'$ splitting, derived from those parameters, are also indicated (broken vertical line). The zero-field splitting parameters exhibit the following changes: compared with $^3$Car(I), in $^3$Car(R), both the $|D|$ and $|E|$ values decrease down to ~90%; while the $|D|$ and $|E|$ values decrease to ~75%, to ~50%, respectively, in $^3$Car(II).

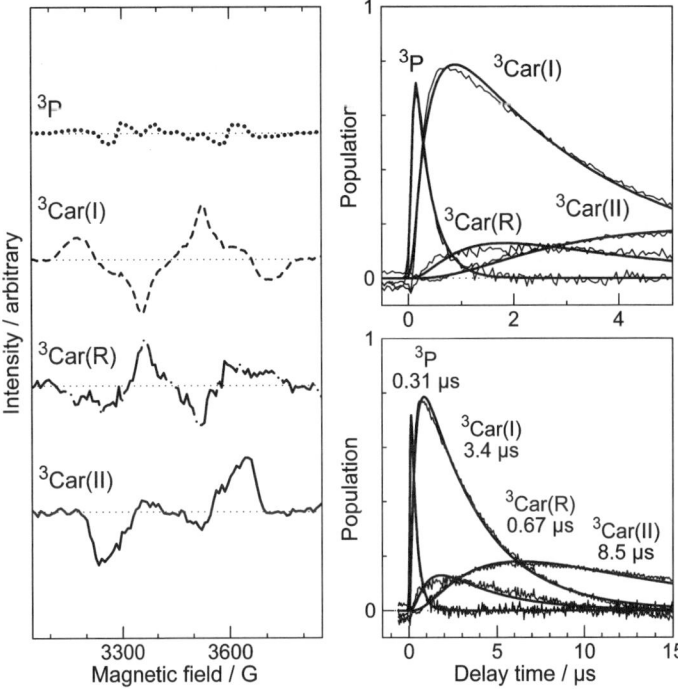

**Figure 22.** Results of four-component, SVD and global-fitting analyses of the time-resolved data matrix of the EPR measurement performed at 100 K [45]. Species-associated spectra (SAS) of $^3$P, $^3$Car(I), $^3$Car(R) and $^3$Car(II) are shown in left-hand-side panel and their transient populations in right-hand panels at different time scales.

To determine the conformations of the conjugated chain in $^3$Car(R) and $^3$Car(II), relative to $^3$Car(I) that apparently attains the flat (0°, 0°, 0°) conformation, we calculated on the basis of polyene models the zero-field splitting parameters as a function of the rotational angles (incremental changes by a 5° interval) around the cis C15=C15′, trans C13=C14 and trans C11=C12 bonds. Table 5 also lists the $|D|$ and $|E|$ values that were calculated for the most likely models. A shift from the (0°, 0°, 0°) to the (20°, –20°, 20°) conformation reduces the $|D|$ and $|E|$ values to 98 and 89%, respectively. Likewise, a transition from the (0°, 0°, 0°) to the (45°, –40°, 40°) conformation reduces the $|D|$ and $|E|$ values to 82 and 50%, respectively. (The model calculation tends to give larger $|D|$ values than experimentally observed.) The agreement between the observed and the calculated values led us to conclude that $^3$Car(R) and $^3$Car(II) are characterized by conformations (20°, –20°, 20°), and (45°, –40°, 40°), respectively. [The latter conformation slightly deviates from the one gathered from Raman spectroscopy and normal-coordinate analysis, i.e., (45°, –30°, 30°).] Figure 24 depicts the conformations of the conjugated chain (on the side of the longer chain of conjugated double bonds) proposed for $^3$Car(I), $^3$Car(R) and $^3$Car(II). The two steps of conformational changes, i.e., $^3$Car(I) → $^3$Car(R) and $^3$Car(R) → $^3$Car(II), are now explained in terms of concerted rotational

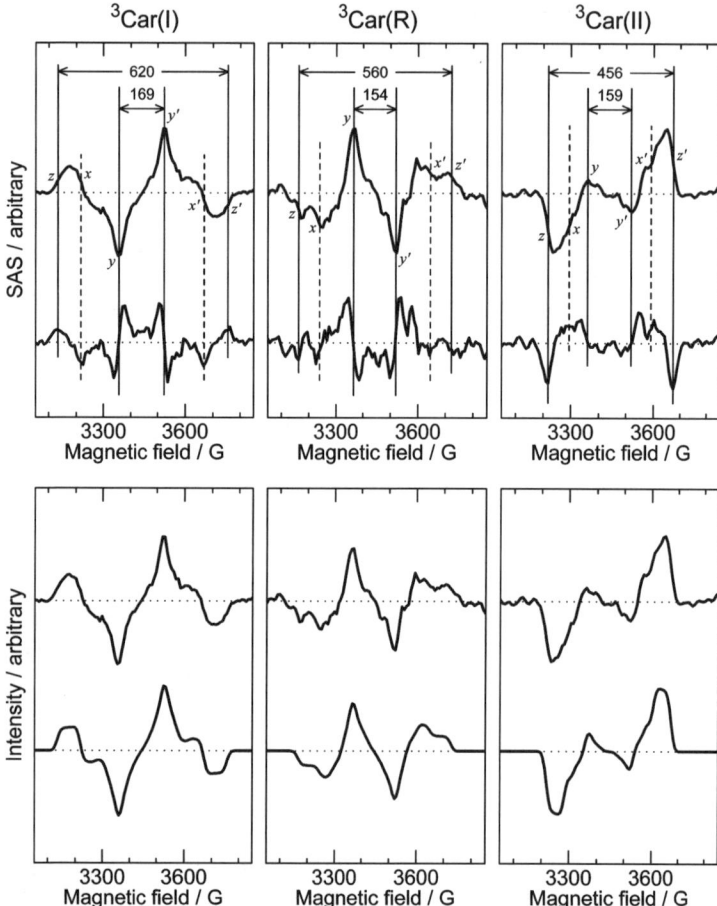

**Figure 23.** EPR spectral patterns of $^3$Car(I), $^3$Car(R) and $^3$Car(II) (upper panels) that are reproduced from the set of SAS in Figure 22. The $z$–$z'$ and the $y$–$y'$ splittings (solid vertical lines) were used to determine the zero-field splitting parameters, $|D|$ and $|E|$; the $x$–$x'$ splittings derived from those parameters are also indicated (vertical broken lines). The lower panels present the results of simulation of the set of SAS (the above) as a sum of the $x$–$x'$, $y$–$y'$ and $z$–$z'$ components (the bottom).

**Table 5.** Zero-field splitting parameters, $|D|$ and $|E|$, observed for the RC-bound spheroidene and calculated for polyene models [45]

|  | Observed ($10^{-4}$ cm$^{-1}$) | | | Calculated ($10^{-4}$ cm$^{-1}$) | | |
| --- | --- | --- | --- | --- | --- | --- |
|  | $^3$Car(I) | $^3$Car(R) | $^3$Car(II) | (0°, 0°, 0°) | (20°, −20°, 20°) | (45°, −40°, 40°) |
| $|D|$ | 290 (1) | 262 (0.90) | 213 (0.73) | 289 (1) | 283 (0.98) | 238 (0.82) |
| $|E|$ | 44 (1) | 39 (0.89) | 22 (0.50) | 62 (1) | 55 (0.89) | 31 (0.50) |

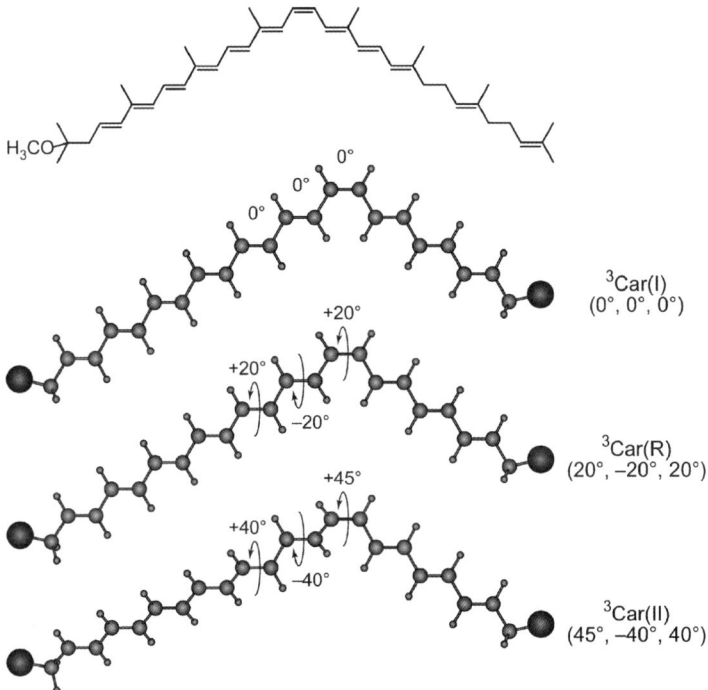

**Figure 24.** Chemical structure of 15-cis-spheroidene (top), and a set of polyene models for $^3$Car(I), $^3$Car(R) and $^3$Car(II) with rotational angles around (the cis-C15=C15′, trans-C13=C14, trans-C11=C12 bonds) equal to (0°, 0°, 0°), (20°, −20°, 20°) and (45°, −40°, 40°), respectively.

motions around the cis C15=C15′ bond and the trans C13=C14 and C11=C12 bonds.

The SAS of $^3$Car(I), $^3$Car(R) and $^3$Car(II) shown on the top in each of the upper and the lower panels of Figure 23 are isotropic powder spectra, and are determined mainly by their three principal components, $x$–$x'$, $y$–$y'$ and $z$–$z'$. We tried to decompose each SAS into these three components, and to determine the time-dependent changes in the spin polarization along the $X$, $Y$ and $Z$ axes. First, we simulated the spectral patterns of the $x$–$x'$, $y$–$y'$ and $z$–$z'$ components, taking a cone around the $X$, $Y$ and $Z$ principal axes whose opening angle was adjusted empirically. Here, we used the zero-field splitting parameters, $|D|$ and $|E|$, experimentally determined for the three triplet species (Table 5). Second, we multiplied those unit spectra by a set of scaling factors to obtain the SAS spectra when summing over the three components (see the results of fitting shown on the bottom of the lower panels in Figure 23). Finally, we calculated the time-dependent changes in the spin polarization for the three components by the use of those factors and the time-dependent changes in population shown in Figure 22 (right-hand-side).

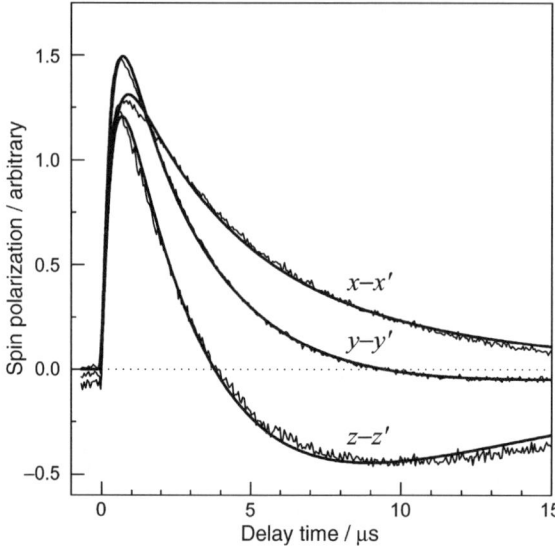

**Figure 25.** Time-dependent changes in the spin polarization for the $x$–$x'$, $y$–$y'$ and $z$–$z'$ components [45]. The ordinate scale presents the difference in the triplet population, $N_0$ minus $N_{+1} = N_{-1}$.

Figure 25 shows the time-dependent changes in the spin polarization (the difference in the spin sublevel population, i.e., $N_0$ minus $N_{+1} = N_{-1}$) for the $x$–$x'$, $y$–$y'$ and $z$–$z'$ components thus obtained. The time profiles clearly show that the decay of spin polarization varies, depending on the direction of the external magnetic field, i.e., along the $X$, $Y$ and $Z$ axes. A sudden increase in the spin polarization, reflecting the population of $N_0 > N_{+1} = N_{-1}$, takes place in all orientations immediately after excitation. This rising phase and its observed polarization pattern reflect the triplet-energy transfer from $^3$P that has been generated by the radical-pair mechanism [46]. The decay phase of each orientation can be characterized as follows: (i) the $x$–$x'$ component decays to zero keeping the same spin polarization; (ii) the $y$–$y'$ component slightly reverses its spin polarization before decaying to zero; and (iii) the $z$–$z'$ component exhibits rapid decay, strong inversion, followed by slow decay to zero of its spin polarization.

The decay of the spin polarization, in general, reflects two different processes, i.e., (i) the predominant decay of $N_0$ relative to $N_{+1} = N_{-1}$ and (ii) the total decay of the population on all sublevels, i.e., $N_0$, $N_{+1}$ and $N_{-1}$. The initial fast decay must be mainly due to the relative population, whereas the final convergence to zero comes with the loss of the over-all triplet population. The rapid decay and inversion of the spin polarization in the $z$–$z'$ component (along the $Z$ axis) must therefore be due to the changes in the relative population, in the order, $N_0 > 2N_{+1} \to N_0 = 2N_{+1} \to N_0 < 2N_{+1}$. The timing of the population inversion (3.8 µs) roughly agrees with that of the generation of the $^3$Car(R) leaking channel (3.4 µs) shown in Figure 21. This observation provides us with another piece of evidence for the leaking channel, and a deeper insight into the mechanism of triplet-energy dissipation: it strongly suggests that the most efficient $T_1 \rightarrow S_0$ intersystem crossing pathway (or in other words, a change in the spin angular momentum from $S=1$ to $S=0$) takes place through the depopulation of $N_0$ along the Z axis. This suggests that the change in the orbital angular momentum due to the conformational changes of $^3$Car must be responsible for the above change in the spin angular momentum. Further, it is to be noted that the Z axis of triplet 15-cis-spheroidene is approximately parallel to the C15=C15', C13=C14 and C11=C12 bonds (Figure 24), around which the rotational motion takes place in the triplet transformation of $^3$Car(I) → $^3$Car(R) → $^3$Car(II).

The two steps of rotation around the central double bonds can be nicely explained when the $^3$Car(I), $^3$Car(R) and $^3$Car(II) models (Figure 24) are located in the Car binding pocket that have been determined by X-ray crystallography [44]. The shorter-conjugated side of the cis double bond of 15-cis-spheroidene is tightly bound to the RC peptide, whereas the longer-conjugated side directs to "an open space". Therefore, we tried to change only the conformation on the longer-conjugated side. Figure 26 shows the results of fitting. The $^3$Car(I) model in the (0°, 0°, 0°) conformation can as comfortably fit to the binding pocket as for the Car in the $S_0$ state [panels (a) and (b)]. When the $^3$Car(R) model with the (20°, 0°, 0°) conformation is fit to the binding pocket, severe collision takes place with Phe M67, and, therefore, its side-chain needs to be rotated substantially around the $C^\alpha$–$CH_2$ bond (74°). A simultaneous change to (20°, −20°, 20°) has to take place in the conformation of the longer-conjugated side to completely release the collision [panels (c) and (d)]. The $^3$Car(II) model in the (45°, −40°, 40°) conformation can be fit to the binding pocket after slightly pushing also the Phe side-chain (86°) [panels (e) and (f)]. Obviously, large changes in the rotational angles around the trans C13=C14 and C11=C12 bonds with the opposite signs can shift the planer conjugated plane to avoid the severe contacts between the non-conjugated end group of the conjugated chain (shown by a ball) and the side-chains of quinone ($Q_B$) and bacteriopheophytin ($H_M$). Thus, (1) the initial rotation around the cis C15=C15' bond originating from the rapid isomerization toward all-trans and (2) the secondary rotations around the trans C13=C14 and C11=C12 bonds originating from the collision with the side-chain of Phe M67 with the side-chains of $Q_B$ and $H_M$ can give rise to the two steps of rotational motion of $^3$Car. During the time between these two steps, the leaking channel of the triplet population (energy) becomes activated.

## 4.5 Reasons for the Natural Selection of the Car Structures

### 4.5.1 Selection of A Shorter Conjugated Chain in the All-Trans Configuration by Cars in the Antenna Complexes

The approximate $C_{2h}$ symmetry of the stretched chain of all-trans conjugated double bonds gives rise to low-lying singlet states having different symmetries,

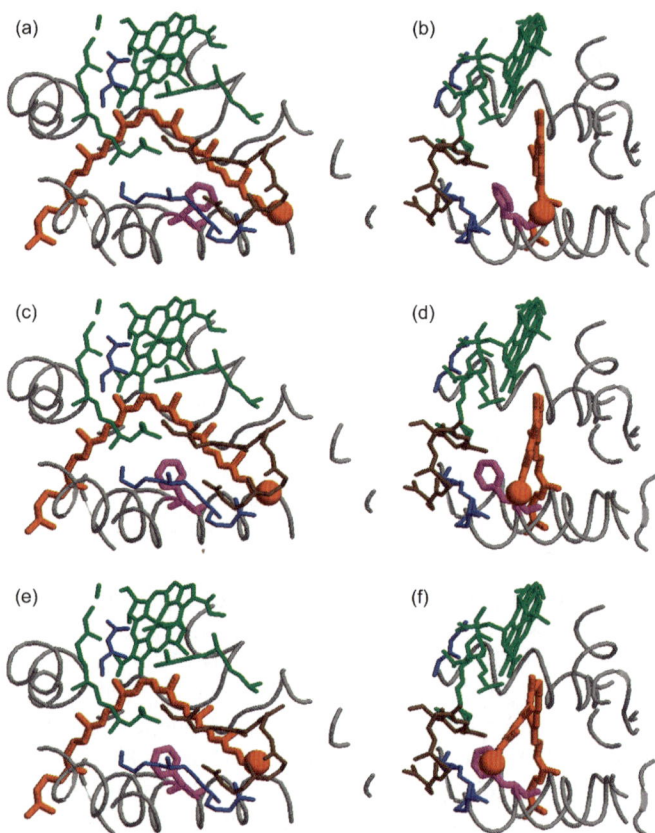

**Figure 26.** Modeling of conformational changes of the triplet states of 15-cis-spheroidone ($^3$Car) in the binding pocket determined by X-ray crystallography [44]. (a) and (b): $^3$Car(I) in the (0°, 0°, 0°) conformation, (c) and (d): $^3$Car(R) in the (20°, −20°, 20°) conformation, and (e) and (f): $^3$Car(II) in the (45°, −40°, 40°) conformation. $^3$Car (orange), Phe M67 (magenta), $B_M$ (light green), $H_M$ (sky blue), $Q_B$ (brown) and peptide (gray). The shorter-conjugated side of 15-cis-spheroidene [right-hand-side in Figure 24 and left-hand-side in (a), (c), (e) here] that is tightly bound by the peptide is assumed to keep the same conformation as in the $S_0$ state. The conformation in the longer-conjugated side [left-hand-side in Figure 24 and right-hand-side in (a), (c), (e) here] having the non-conjugated end group (an orange ball) is varied. The structures in panels (b), (d) and (f) are rotated by 60° compared with (a), (c) and (e), respectively.

including $1B_u^+$, $3A_g^-$, $1B_u^-$ and $2A_g^-$. According to the selection rule based on Pariser's signs the optical dipole transition from the ground state $1A_g^-$ to the electronically excited state $1B_u^+$ is allowed. Therefore, the Car molecule can be excited only to the $1B_u^+$ state by absorption of a single photon. Likewise, a sequence of electronic conversions, including $3A_g^- \to 1B_u^-$, $1B_u^- \to 2A_g^-$ and $2A_g^- \to 1A_g^-$, is allowed. According to the state ordering (Figure 4), a sequential electronic conversion of the type $1B_u^+ \to 1B_u^- \to 2A_g^- \to 1A_g^-$ can take place in Cars with $n=9$ and 10, whereas for Cars with $n=11$–13 the sequence

$1B_u^+ \to 3A_g^- \to 1B_u^- \to 2A_g^- \to 1A_g^-$ is expected. Both of the first steps should become possible due to the strong electronic mixing between the relevant close-by states. During these electronic conversion processes, Cars can transfer singlet energy to the $Q_x$ and $Q_y$ states of BChl, through multiple channels, as far as such energy transfer reactions are energetically feasible. Actually, the drastic drop in the Car-to-BChl singlet energy-transfer efficiency that occurs when $n$ increases from 10 to 11 can be explained in terms of the excited-state energies and dynamics of the Car and BChl molecules in the antenna complexes. When $n = 9$ or 10, all the singlet-energy transfer channels, including the states $1B_u^+$, $1B_u^-$ and $2A_g^-$, are open, whereas only the $1B_u^+$ channel is open for energy transfer in the presence of Cars with $n = 11$–13.

Although the optical transitions from states $1B_u^-$ and $2A_g^-$ to the state $1A_g^-$ are "forbidden" according to the selection rule, their transition dipole moments are nonzero due to the mixing with that of the optically strongly allowed $1B_u^+$ state. The extent of this mixing is inversely proportional to the energy gap between the relevant states. In particular, strong electronic mixing between the $1B_u^-$ and $1B_u^+$ states in Cars with a shorter chain of conjugated double bonds results in large transition-dipole moments of the $1B_u^-$ state, and an apparently long lifetime of the $1B_u^+$ fluorescence. Such effects may facilitate efficient singlet-energy transfer from the $1B_u^+$ and $1B_u^-$ states of Car to the $Q_x$ state of BChl.

The activated multiple channels for efficient singlet-energy transfer are most likely the reasons for the selection of a shorter conjugated chain in the all-trans configuration of Cars in the antenna complexes for the light-harvesting function.

### 4.5.2 Selection of A Longer Conjugated Chain in the 15-cis Configuration by Cars in the RC

The $T_1$ state decreases in energy as $n$ increases, and, therefore, $^3$BChl can be efficiently quenched by Cars having a longer chain of conjugated double bonds. This has been proven by the efficient protective function of such Cars against the photo-oxidation of $^3$BChls in the LH2. Thus, it can be concluded that a longer chain of conjugated double bonds is advantageous for quenching $^3$BChl by Car.

15-cis Cars have the potential for *rapid* isomerization toward the all-trans configuration upon triplet excitation. Rate and the quantum yield of isomerization are the highest for the 15-cis configuration. The spheroidene bound to the RC takes a flat 15-cis configuration in the $S_0$ state. In the $T_1$ state the Car molecule changes its structure into a substantially-twisted configuration around the central double bonds.

The long-standing hypothetical mechanism of triplet energy dissipation, including the rotational motion around the 15-cis double bond [3,6,43,47], is now being refined and clear evidence provided by Raman and EPR spectroscopies [42,45]. The mechanism is based on the following hypothesis: the *rotational motion* around the cis C15=C15' double bond causes a change in the orbital angular momentum. Conserving the total angular momentum, it causes a change in the spin angular momentum, and as a result, the $T_1 \to S_0$

intersystem crossing takes place accompanied by the dissipation of the triplet energy. The triplet-state property of the 15-cis configuration, *i.e.*, rapid isomerization toward all-trans, plays a crucial role for this hypothetical mechanism. In particular, an intermediate forming the channel of triplet-energy dissipation has been found during the process of conformational changes from the flat to the substantially twisted.

Thus, the efficient quenching of $^3$BChl and the efficient dissipation of the triplet energy are the reasons for the selection of a longer conjugated chain in the 15-cis configuration by Cars in the RC for the photoprotective function.

## 4.6 Concluding Remarks and Future Perspectives

In this chapter a general framework for the mechanisms of light-harvesting by all-trans Cars in the antenna complexes and of photoprotection by 15-cis Cars in the RC has been built. As a result, the reasons for the natural selection of configurations and conjugation lengths of Cars by the antenna and the RC complexes have been revealed. To completely elucidate these mechanisms, the dynamics, energetics and structures of Cars, in the excited states, need to be determined. For this purpose, time-resolved absorption, fluorescence and Raman spectroscopies have turned out to be the most useful analytical tools.

The key pieces of information to be obtained for a deeper understanding of the light-harvesting mechanism of Cars include internal conversion from one singlet state to the other, vibrational relaxation in each singlet state, and electronic mixing between the ionic $1B_u^+$ state and the covalent $3A_g^-$, $1B_u^-$ and $2A_g^-$ states. To solve these complicated issues, it is absolutely necessary to increase the *time resolution*. The situation can be easily understood by examining the present results: concerning the internal conversion, in spirilloxanthin, a comparison between the SADS of the states $1B_u^+$, $3A_g^-$, $1B_u^-$ and $2A_g^-$ obtained by the use of 5-fs pulses (Figure 9) with those gathered from measurements obtained by using 120-fs pulses (Figure 7) illustrates the importance of the time resolution. In the latter case, the contribution of the $3A_g^-$ state is covered with the strong stimulated emission from the $1B_u^+$ state and that of the $1B_u^-$ state by the transient absorption from the hot $2A_g^-$ state. Although a lifetime of 10 fs could correctly be determined by using the SVD and global-fitting analysis of data from measurements performed with 120-fs pulses when no spectral overlap was present (see Figure 6 and Table 1 for spirilloxanthin), the contribution of each electronic state needs to be clearly seen in the raw time-resolved spectra. Concerning electronic mixing and vibrational relaxation, examination of the results of fluorescence up-conversion spectroscopy depicted in Figure 10, and those of Kerr-gate fluorescence spectroscopy depicted in Figure 11, shows that the time-resolution (>200 fs) is still low, in comparison with the lifetimes indicated in the figures, when such severe spectral overlap is taken into account.

Notably, however, high time resolution results in *low spectral resolution* due to the uncertainty principle, *i.e.*, $\Delta \bar{\nu} \cdot \Delta t \simeq 10 \text{cm}^{-1}$ ps (a rough estimation), where $\Delta\bar{\nu}$ is the spectral width and $\Delta t$ is the pulse duration. At $\Delta t$ values of 10 fs and 100 fs, $\Delta\bar{\nu}$ values are 1000 and 100 cm$^{-1}$, respectively. Considering the state ordering in spirilloxanthin (Figure 4) and the vibrational progression with a spacing of $\sim 1400$ cm$^{-1}$ (Figure 13), we need a spectral width at least of this order to correctly determine the vibrational-relaxation processes. Then, $\Delta t$ turns out to be $\sim 70$ fs. One strategy is to use a rather long pulse duration (60–90 fs), to choose a region of little spectral overlap, and to apply the SVD and global-fitting analysis.

A three-pulse spectroscopy [48], i.e., a combination of pump–dump–probe and pump–repump–probe, applied after carefully tuning the wavelength of the second pulse to bleach the overlapping transition, may be useful to selectively probe a particular transition when severe spectral overlap is present.

Key pieces of information to be obtained for a deeper understanding of the photoprotective mechanism include the energetics and dynamics of the $T_1$ state. High-sensitivity emission spectroscopy [35] is most promising to simultaneously probe the energetics and dynamics of $T_1$ BChl and $T_1$ Car, the latter of which must be conjugation-length dependent (Section 4.4.1). The mechanism of triplet-energy dissipation that is proposed in this chapter, for the first time, needs to be proven by time-resolved absorption and Raman spectroscopies and, eventually, by time-resolved X-ray crystallography.

## 4.7 Other Proposals

As mentioned in the Introduction, this chapter is a condensed summary of our work. Some of the data have not yet been published. The authors thought that this consistent way of presentation makes the flow of ideas clear. However, it is fair and appropriate to introduce the proposals of other investigators in the field of "Carotenoids in Photosynthesis", and to discuss them in relation to ours. For this purpose, we chose two "hot topics" that are most relevant to the contents of this chapter: (a) newly-identified singlet states that can play key roles in the light-harvesting by all-trans carotenoids, and (b) the mechanism of photoprotection by 15-cis carotenoids in the reaction center of anoxygenic purple bacteria.

To introduce readers to the most important literature relevant to this chapter, which must lead to a more general perspective and more objective viewpoints on what is written here, a bibliography is given below, which may also highlight the uniqueness of our work.

### 4.7.1 Newly-Identified Singlet States

A new electronic state, named "$S^*$", other than the $1B_u^+$ and $2A_g^-$ states, has been proposed by van Grondelle and co-workers [49]. It is a singlet state that is a precursor of the triplet state, and the singlet-to-triplet conversion takes place in picoseconds. This rapid triplet formation, first identified in spirilloxanthin bound to the LH1 complex from *Rsp. rubrum*, was ascribed to a singlet fission reaction based on the theory of Tavan and Schulten [13,50]. It was inferred that the $S^*$ state may be the $1B_u^-$ state that had been identified by us (Section 4.3.1).

The $S^*$ state was also identified in spheroidene bound to the LH2 complex from *Rb. sphaeroides* [51]. Most importantly, the $S^*$ state was found to be actively involved in the Car-to-BChl singlet-energy transfer, competing with the singlet-to-triplet conversion within Car. Again, the authors assessed that the $S^*$ state very likely corresponds to the $1B_u^-$ state. Furthermore, the triplet yield was found to depend on the conformation of the chain of all-trans conjugated double bonds when the Car is integrated into the antenna complexes [52]. The triplet yield is 5–10% when spirilloxanthin is incorporated into the carotenoid-less B850 LH complex from *Rb. sphaeroides* R26.1 (a carotenoidless mutant) and attains a flat conformation. In contrast, in the native LH1 complex the spirilloxanthin with a twisted conformation exhibits a triplet yield of 25–30%. The results led the authors to the idea that the twisting of the conjugated chain enhances the triplet generation.

All the above results and interpretations are in complete agreement with our data, if we assume that the $S^*$ state is actually the $1B_u^-$ state. A controversial issue, to be solved before establishing this assignment, is the spectral pattern of the $S^*$ states. The SADS of the $S^*$ state presented in Figure 5 of [49] and Figure 5 of [51] resemble those of our triplet state rather than of our $1B_u^-$ state.

Based on results obtained by using 10–15 fs time-resolved absorption spectroscopy, Silvestri, Cogdell, Hashimoto and co-workers proposed that in β-carotene and lycopene a transient singlet state exists, named "$S_x$", which is located between the states $1B_u^+$ and $2A_g^-$ [53]. The lifetimes of the $1B_u^+$ state of β-carotene and lycopene were determined to be $10 \pm 2$ and $9 \pm 2$ fs, and those of the subsequent $S_x$ state, 150 and 90 fs, respectively. The authors seem to infer that the $S_x$ state could be the $1B_u^-$ state, but a comparison between the spectrum shown in Figure 1 of [53] with that of Figure 9 in this chapter suggests that the $S_x$ state could be the $3A_g^-$ state.

Another excited state, named "$S^{\ddagger}$", was identified for β-carotene in *n*-hexane by van Grondelle and co-workers using subpicosecond pump–dump–probe and pump–repump–probe spectroscopy [48]. This $S^{\ddagger}$ state that was produced by excitation of the $1B_u^+$ at the blue-edge of the absorption gave rise to an absorption in the 450–550 nm region (Figure 2 in [48]), and exhibited a longer lifetime than the $2A_g^-$ state. These observations suggest that the $S^{\ddagger}$ state is actually our $T_2$ state (Figures 7 and 8).

### 4.7.2 Mechanism of Photoprotection by 15-cis Carotenoids in the Reaction Center

On the basis of our identification of 15-cis-spirilloxanthin in the RC from *Rsp. rubrum* [9], and its isomerization into all-trans-spirilloxanthin [54], we proposed an early version of the hypothetical mechanism of triplet-energy dissipation that includes a rotational motion around the C15=C15′ double bond, as a consequence of rapid isomerization of triplet Cars in the $T_1$ state (Section 4.4.2).

This hypothesis was questioned by Frank and co-workers [55] on the basis of results obtained by the use of 15-cis-spheroidene where the C15=C15′ cis configuration was fixed by chemical bonds. The authors found that the spectroscopic properties and the excited-state dynamics were not very different between RCs from *Rb. sphaeroides* R26.1 containing incorporated locked-15-cis-spheroidene and those for native RC from *Rb. sphaeroides* 2.4.1 containing (unlocked) 15-cis-spheroidene. The rise and decay kinetics of the $T_n \leftarrow T_1$ absorption were earlier found to be characterized by lifetimes of $25 \pm 1$ ns and $7 \pm 1$ μs in the former and 10 ns and 4–5 μs [56], respectively, in the latter sample. The following arguments were presented: "If cis-to-trans isomerization at 15,15′ position were required to assist in triplet energy transfer, one would expect a change in either the dynamics of the rise and/or decay of the carotenoid triplet state." (Actually, we were proposing the mechanism of triplet-energy dissipation, instead.) "The natural selection of a cis-isomer of spheroidene for incorporation into native reaction centers of *Rb. sphaeroides* wild type strain 2.4.1 is more determined by the structure or assembly of the reaction center protein than by any special quality of the cis-isomer of the carotenoid that would affect its ability to participate in triplet energy transfer or carry out photoprotection."

However, the results of Section 4.4.4 offer a straightforward explanation. The key feature is the presence of a triplet intermediate, $^3$Car(R) forming a transiently open channel for triplet-energy dissipation (triplet depopulation) that is populated during the decay pathway from $^3$Car(I), immediately present after excitation, to the final stationary state, $^3$Car(II). The $^3$Car(R) state must have escaped detection even in the case of native RC due to the authors use of nanosecond time-resolved absorption spectroscopy at room temperature. We are grateful for the authors objection, which motivated us to look for the leaking channel of triplet population.

## Acknowledgements

This work has been supported by a grant from the Ministry of Education, Culture, Sports, Science and Technology (Open Research Center Project) and a grant from NEDO (New Energy and Industrial Technology Development Organization) International Joint Research Grant. The authors thank Professor Gernot Renger, the editor, for revising the manuscript and for correcting the English.

## Bibliography

Finally, we present a list of further reading, classified into different categories.

*I. Reviews on Carotenoids in Photosynthesis*

Cogdell et al. [57,58]; Hu et al. [59]; Christensen [60]; Sundström et al. [61]; Sundström and van Grondelle [62]; Frank and Christensen [63]; Koyama et al. [64] (see also [1,2,4,5]).

*II. The Light-Harvesting Function*

(a) Excited-state properties, electronic conversion and vibrational relaxation: Frank et al. [65]; Macpherson and Gillbro [66]; Andersson et al. [67]; Polívka et al. [68]; Akimoto et al. [69]; Yoshizawa et al. [70]; Billsten et al. [71].
(b) Car-to-BChl singlet-energy transfer: Papagiannakis et al. [72]; Polívka et al. [73]; Macpherson et al. [74]; Walla et al. [75]; Krueger et al. [76]; Desamero et al. [77].

*III. The Photoprotective Function*

(a) Triplet-energy transfer in the RC: Hartwich et al. [78]; Frank [79].
(b) EPR spectroscopy of the RC: Borovykh et al. [80].

## References

1. T. Polívka, V. Sundström, Ultrafast dynamics of carotenoid excited states – from solution to natural and artificial systems. *Chem. Rev.* **104** (2004) 2021–2071.
2. T. Ritz, A. Damjanović, K. Schulten, J.-P. Zhang, Y. Koyama, Efficient light harvesting through carotenoids. *Photosynth. Res.* **66** (2000) 125–144.
3. Y. Koyama, R. Fujii, Cis-trans carotenoids in photosynthesis: Configurations, excited-state properties and physiological functions, in: *The Photochemistry of Carotenoids* (1999) (H.A. Frank, A.J. Young, G. Britton, R.J. Cogdell, eds.), Kluwer Academic Publishers, Dordrecht, pp. 161–188.
4. Y. Koyama, M. Kuki, P.O. Andersson, T. Gillbro, Singlet excited states and the light-harvesting function of carotenoids in bacterial photosynthesis. *Photochem. Photobiol.* **63** (1996) 243–256.
5. H.A. Frank, R.J. Cogdell, The photochemistry and function of carotenoids in photosynthesis, in: *Carotenoids in Photosynthesis* (1993) (A. Young, G. Britton, eds.), Chapmen & Hall, London, pp. 252–326.
6. Y. Koyama, Structures and functions of carotenoids in photosynthetic systems. *J. Photochem. Photobiol. B: Biol.* **9** (1991) 265–280.
7. M. Lutz, W. Szponarski, G. Berger, B. Robert, J.-M. Neumann, The stereoisomerism of bacterial, reaction-center-bound carotenoids revisited: An electronic absorption, resonance Raman and $^1$H-NMR study. *Biochim. Biophys. Acta* **894** (1987) 423–433.
8. Y. Koyama, M. Kanaji, T. Shimamura, Configurations of neurosporene isomers isolated from the reaction center and the light-harvesting complex of *Rhodobacter sphaeroides* G1C. A resonance Raman, electronic absorption, and $^1$H-NMR study. *Photochem. Photobiol.* **48** (1988) 107–114.
9. Y. Koyama, I. Takatsuka, M. Kanaji, K. Tomimoto, M. Kito, T. Shimamura, J. Yamashita, K. Saiki, K. Tsukida, Configurations of carotenoids in the reaction center and the light-harvesting complex of *Rhodospirillum rubrum*. Natural selection of carotenoid configurations by pigment protein complexes. *Photochem. Photobiol.* **51** (1990) 119–128.
10. T. Sashima, H. Nagae, M. Kuki, Y. Koyama, A new singlet-excited state of all-trans-spheroidene as detected by resonance-Raman excitation profiles. *Chem. Phys. Lett.* **299** (1999) 187–194.

11. T. Sashima, Y. Koyama, T. Yamada, H. Hashimoto, The $1B_u^+$, $1B_u^-$, and $2A_g^-$ energies of crystalline lycopene, β-carotene, and mini-9-β-carotene as determined by resonance-Raman excitation profiles: Dependence of the $1B_u^-$ state energy on the conjugation length. *J. Phys. Chem. B* **104** (2000) 5011–5019.
12. K. Furuichi, T. Sashima, Y. Koyama, The first detection of the $3A_g^-$ state in carotenoids using resonance-Raman excitation profiles. *Chem. Phys. Lett.* **356** (2002) 547–555.
13. P. Tavan, K. Schulten, The low-lying electronic excitations in long polyenes: A PPP-MRD-CI study. *J. Chem. Phys.* **85** (1986) 6602–6609.
14. R. Fujii, T. Inaba, Y. Watanabe, Y. Koyama, J.-P. Zhang, Two different pathways of internal conversion in carotenoids depending on the length of the conjugated chain. *Chem. Phys. Lett.* **369** (2003) 165–172.
15. F.S. Rondonuwu, Y. Watanabe, R. Fujii, Y. Koyama, A first detection of singlet to triplet conversion from the $1^1B_u^-$ to the $1^3A_g$ state and triplet internal conversion from the $1^3A_g$ to the $1^3B_u$ state in carotenoids: Dependence on the conjugation length. *Chem. Phys. Lett.* **376** (2003) 292–301.
16. R. Englman, J. Jortner, The energy gap law for radiationless transitions in large molecules. *Mol. Phys.* **18** (1970) 145–164.
17. H. Nagae, M. Kuki, J.-P. Zhang, T. Sashima, Y. Mukai, Y. Koyama, Vibronic coupling through the in-phase, C=C stretching mode plays a major role in the $2A_g^-$ to $1A_g^-$ internal conversion of all-trans-β-carotene. *J. Phys. Chem. A* **104** (2000) 4155–4166.
18. K. Nishimura, F.S. Rondonuwu, R. Fujii, J. Akahane, Y. Koyama, T. Kobayashi, Sequential singlet internal conversion of $1B_u^+ \to 3A_g^- \to 1B_u^- \to 2A_g^- \to (1A_g^-$ ground) in all-trans-spirilloxanthin revealed by two-dimensional sub-5-fs spectroscopy. *Chem. Phys. Lett.* **392** (2004) 68–73.
19. R. Pariser, Theory of the electronic spectra and structure of the polyacenes and of alternant hydrocarbons. *J. Chem. Phys.* **24** (1956) 250–268.
20. P.R. Callis, T.W. Scott, A.C. Albrecht, Perturbation selection rules for multiphoton electronic spectroscopy of neutral alternant hydrocarbons. *J. Chem. Phys.* **78** (1983) 16–22.
21. R. Fujii, K. Onaka, M. Kuki, Y. Koyama, Y. Watanabe, The $2A_g^-$ energies of all-trans-neurosporene and spheroidene as determined by fluorescence spectroscopy. *Chem. Phys. Lett.* **288** (1998) 847–853.
22. R. Fujii, K. Onaka, H. Nagae, Y. Koyama, Y. Watanabe, Fluorescence spectroscopy of all-trans-lycopene: Comparison of the energy and the potential displacements of its $2A_g^-$ state with those of neurosporene and spheroidene. *J. Lumin.* **92** (2001) 213–222.
23. R. Fujii, T. Ishikawa, Y. Koyama, M. Taguchi, Y. Isobe, H. Nagae, Y. Watanabe, Fluorescence spectroscopy of all-trans-anhydrorhodovibrin and spirilloxanthin: Detection of the $1B_u^-$ fluorescence. *J. Phys. Chem. A* **105** (2001) 5348–5355.
24. R. Fujii, T. Fujino, T. Inaba, H. Nagae, Y. Koyama, Internal conversion of $1B_u^+ \to 1B_u^- \to 2A_g^-$ and fluorescence from the $1B_u^-$ state in all-trans-neurosporene as probed by up-conversion spectroscopy. *Chem. Phys. Lett.* **384** (2004) 9–15.
25. J.-P. Zhang R. Fujii P. Qian, T. Inaba, T. Mizoguchi, Y. Koyama, K. Onaka, Y. Watanabe, H. Nagae, Mechanism of the carotenoid-to-bacteriochlorophyll energy transfer via the $S_1$ state in the LH2 complexes from purple bacteria. *J. Phys. Chem. B* **104** (2000) 3683–3691.
26. J.-P. Zhang, C.-H. Chen, Y. Koyama, H. Nagae, Vibrational relaxation and redistribution in the $2A_g^-$ state of all-trans-lycopene as revealed by picosecond time-resolved absorption spectroscopy. *J. Phys. Chem. B* **102** (1998) 1632–1640.

27. J.T. Fourkas, H. Kawashima, K.A. Nelson, Theory of nonlinear optical experiments with harmonic oscillators. *J. Chem. Phys.* **103** (1995) 4393–4407.
28. R. Nakamura, R. Fujii, H. Nagae, Y. Koyama, Y. Kanematsu, Vibrational relaxation in the $1B_u^+$ state of carotenoids as determined by Kerr-gate fluorescence spectroscopy. *Chem. Phys. Lett.* **400** (2004) 7–14.
29. M. Yoshizawa, M. Kurosawa, Femtosecond time-resolved Raman spectroscopy using stimulated Raman scattering. *Phys. Rev. A* **61** (1999) 013808-1–6.
30. K. Iwata, S. Yamaguchi, H. Hamaguchi, Construction of a transform-limited picosecond time-resolved Raman spectrometer. *Rev. Sci. Instrum.* **64** (1993) 2140–2146.
31. F.S. Rondonuwu, Y. Watanabe, J.-P. Zhang, K. Furuichi, Y. Koyama, Internal-conversion and radiative-transition processes among the $1B_u^+$, $1B_u^-$ and $2A_g^-$ states of all-trans-neurosporene as revealed by subpicosecond time-resolved Raman spectroscopy. *Chem. Phys. Lett.* **357** (2002) 376–384.
32. F.S. Rondonuwu, K. Yokoyama, R. Fujii, Y. Koyama, R.J. Cogdell, Y. Watanabe, The role of the $1^1B_u^-$ state in carotenoid-to-bacteriochlorophyll singlet-energy transfer in the LH2 antenna complexes from *Rhodobacter sphaeroides* G1C, *Rhodobacter sphaeroides* 2.4.1, *Rhodospirillum molischianum* and *Rhodopseudomonas acidophila*. *Chem. Phys. Lett.* **390** (2004) 314–322.
33. J. Akahane, F.S. Rondonuwu, L. Fiedor, Y. Watanabe, Y. Koyama, Dependence of singlet-energy transfer on the conjugation length of carotenoids reconstituted into the LH1 complex from *Rhodospirillum rubrum* G9. *Chem. Phys. Lett.* **393** (2004) 184–191.
34. H.A. Frank, V. Chynwat, A. Posteraro, G. Hartwich, I. Simonin, H. Scheer, Triplet state energy transfer between the primary donor and the carotenoid in *Rhodobacter sphaeroides* R-26.1 reaction centers exchanged with modified bacteriochlorophyll pigments and reconstituted with spheroidene. *Photochem. Photobiol.* **64** (1996) 823–831.
35. F.S. Rondonuwu, T. Taguchi, R. Fujii, K. Yokoyama, Y. Koyama, Y. Watanabe, The energies and kinetics of triplet carotenoids in the LH2 antenna complexes as determined by phosphorescence spectroscopy. *Chem. Phys. Lett.* **384** (2004) 364–371.
36. L. Limantara, R. Fujii, J.-P. Zhang, T. Kakuno, H. Hara, A. Kawamori, T. Yagura, R.J. Cogdell, Y. Koyama, Generation of triplet and cation-radical bacteriochlorophyll *a* in carotenoidless LH1 and LH2 antenna complexes from *Rhodobacter sphaeroides*. *Biochemistry* **37** (1998) 17469–17486.
37. R. Fujii, K. Furuichi, J.-P. Zhang, H. Nagae, H. Hashimoto, Y. Koyama, Cis-to-trans isomerization of spheroidene in the triplet state as detected by time-resolved absorption spectroscopy. *J. Phys. Chem. A* **106** (2002) 2410–2421.
38. H. Hashimoto, Y. Koyama, Time-resolved resonance Raman spectroscopy of triplet β-carotene produced from all-trans, 7-cis, 9-cis, 13-cis, and 15-cis isomers and high-pressure liquid chromatography analyses of photoisomerization via the triplet state. *J. Phys. Chem.* **92** (1988) 2101–2108.
39. H. Hashimoto, Y. Koyama, K. Ichimura, T. Kobayashi, Time-resolved absorption spectroscopy of the triplet state produced from the all-trans, 7-cis, 9-cis, 13-cis, and 15-cis isomers of β-carotene. *Chem. Phys. Lett.* **162** (1989) 517–522.
40. M. Kuki, Y. Koyama, H. Nagae, Triplet-sensitized and thermal isomerization of all-trans, 7-cis, 9-cis, 13-cis, and 15-cis isomers of β-carotene: Configurational dependence of the quantum yield of isomerization via the $T_1$ state. *J. Phys. Chem.* **95** (1991) 7171–7180.

41. Y. Koyama, Y. Mukai, M. Kuki, Excited-state properties and physiological functions of biological polyenes: "The triplet-excited region" of retinoids and carotenoids, in: *Laser Spectroscopy of Biomolecules* (1993) (J.E. Korppi-Tommola, ed.), SPIE – The International Society for Optical Engineering, Bellingham, Vol. 1921, pp. 191–202.
42. Y. Mukai-Kuroda, R. Fujii, N. Ko-chi, T. Sashima, Y. Koyama, M. Abe, R. Gebhard, I. van der Hoef, J. Lugtenburg, Changes in molecular structure upon triplet excitation of all-trans-spheroidene in $n$-hexane solution and 15-cis-spheroidene bound to the photo-reaction center from *Rhodobacter sphaeroides* as revealed by resonance-Raman spectroscopy and normal-coordinate analysis. *J. Phys. Chem. A* **106** (2002) 3566–3579.
43. N. Ohashi, N. Ko-chi, M. Kuki, T. Shimamura, R.J. Cogdell, Y. Koyama, The structures of $S_0$ spheroidene in the light-harvesting (LH2) complex and $S_0$ and $T_1$ spheroidene in the reaction center of *Rhodobacter sphaeroides* 2.4.1 as revealed by Raman spectroscopy. *Biospectroscopy* **2** (1996) 59–69.
44. B. Arnoux, J.-F. Gaucher, A. Ducruix, F. Reiss-Husson, Structure of the photochemical reaction centre of a spheroidene-containing purple bacterium, *Rhodobacter sphaeroides* Y, at 3 Å resolution. *Acta Crystallogr., Sect. D: Biol. Crystallogr.* **51** (1995) 368–379.
45. Y. Kakitani, R. Fujii, Y. Koyama, H. Nagae, L. Walker, B. Salter, A. Angerhofer, Triplet-state conformational changes in 15-cis-spheroidene bound to the reaction center from *Rhodobacter sphaeroides* 2.4.1 as revealed by time-resolved EPR spectroscopy: Strengthened hypothetical mechanism of triplet-energy dissipation. *Biochemistry* **45** (2006) 2053–2062.
46. M.C. Thurnauer, J.J. Katz, J.R. Norris, The triplet state in bacterial photosynthesis: Possible mechanisms of the primary photo-act. *Proc. Natl. Acad. Sci. U.S.A.* **72** (1975) 3270–3274.
47. Y. Koyama, Natural selection of carotenoid configurations by the reaction center and the light-harvesting complex of photosynthetic bacteria, in: *Carotenoids: Chemistry and Biology* (1989) (N.I. Krinsky, M.M. Mathews-Roth, R.F. Taylor, eds.), Plenum Press, New York, pp. 207–222.
48. D.S. Larsen, E. Papagiannakis, I.H.M. van Stokkun, M. Vengris, J.T.M. Kennis, R. van Grondelle, Excited state dynamics of β-carotene explored with dispersed multi pulse transient absorption. *Chem. Phys. Lett.* **381** (2003) 733–742.
49. C.C. Gradinaru, J.T.M. Kennis, E. Papagiannakis, I.H.M. van Stokkum, R.J. Cogdell, G.R. Fleming, R.A. Niederman, R. van Grondelle, An usual pathway of excitation energy deactivation in carotenoids: Singlet-to-triplet conversion on an ultrafast timescale in a photosynthetic antenna. *Proc. Natl. Acad. Sci. U.S.A.* **98** (2001) 2364–2369.
50. P. Tavan, K. Schulten, Electronic excitations in finite and infinite polyenes. *Phys. Rev. B* **36** (1987) 4337–4358.
51. E. Papagiannakis, J.T.M. Kennis, I.H.M. van Stokkum, R.J. Cogdell, R. van Grondelle, An alternative carotenoid-to-bacteriochlorophyll energy transfer pathway in photosynthetic light harvesting. *Proc. Natl. Acad. Sci. U.S.A.* **99** (2002) 6017–6022.
52. E. Papagiannakis, S.K. Das, A. Gall, I.H.M. van Stokkum, B. Robert, R. van Grondelle, H.A. Frank, J.T.M. Kennis, Light harvesting by carotenoids incorporated into the B850 light-harvesting complex from *Rhodobacter sphaeroides* R-26.1: Excited-state relaxation, ultrafast triplet formation, and energy transfer to bacteriochlorophyll. *J. Phys. Chem. B* **107** (2003) 5642–5649.

53. G. Cerullo, D. Polli, G. Lanzani, S. de Silvestri, H. Hashimoto, R.J. Cogdell, Photosynthetic light harvesting by carotenoids: Detection of an intermediate excited state. *Science* **298** (2002) 2395–2398.
54. M. Kuki, M. Naruse, T. Kakuno, Y. Koyama, Resonance Raman evidence for 15-cis to all-trans photoisomerization of spirilloxanthin bound to a reduced form of the reaction center of *Rhodospirillum rubrum* S1. *Photochem. Photobiol.* **62** (1995) 502–508.
55. J.A. Bautista, V. Chynwat, A. Cua, F.J. Jansen, J. Lugtenburg, D. Gosztola, M.R. Wasielewski, H.A. Frank, The spectroscopic and photochemical properties of locked-15,15′-cis-spheroidene in solution and incorporated into the reaction center of *Rhodobacter sphaeroides* R-26.1. *Photosynth. Res.* **55** (1998) 49–65.
56. R.J. Cogdell, T.G. Monger, W.W. Parson, Carotenoid triplet states in reaction centers from *Rhodopseudomonas sphaeroides* and *Rhodospirillum rubrum*. *Biochim. Biophys. Acta* **408** (1975) 189–199.
57. R.J. Cogdell, N.W. Isaacs, A.A. Freer, T.D. Howard, A.T. Gardiner, S.M. Prince, M.Z. Papiz, The structural basis of light-harvesting in purple bacteria. *FEBS Lett.* **555** (2003) 35–39.
58. R.J. Cogdell, T.D. Howard, R. Bittl, E. Schlodder, I. Geisenheimer, W. Lubitz, How carotenoids protect bacterial photosynthesis. *Phil. Trans. R. Soc. Lond. B* **355** (2000) 1345–1349.
59. X. Hu, T. Rits, A. Damjanović, F. Autenrieth, K. Schulten, Photosynthetic apparatus of purple bacteria. *Q. Rev. Biophys.* **35** (2002) 1–62.
60. R.L. Christensen, The electronic states of carotenoids, in: *The Photochemistry of Carotenoids* (1999) (H.A. Frank, A.J. Young, G. Britton, R.J. Cogdell, eds.), Kluwer Academic Publishers, Dordrecht, pp. 137–159.
61. V. Sundström, T. Pullerits, R. van Grondelle, Photosynthetic light-harvesting: Reconciling dynamics and structure of purple bacterial LH2 reveals function of photosynthetic unit. *J. Phys. Chem. B* **103** (1999) 2327–2346.
62. V. Sundström, R. van Grondelle, Kinetics of excitation transfer and trapping in purple bacteria, in: *Anoxygenic Photosynthetic Bacteria* (1995) (R.E. Blankenship, M.T. Madigan, C.E. Bauer, eds.), Kluwer Academic Publishers, Dordrecht, pp. 349–372.
63. H.A. Frank, R.L. Christensen, Singlet energy transfer from carotenoids to bacteriochlorophylls, in: *Anoxygenic Photosynthetic Bacteria* (1995) (R.E. Blankenship, M.T. Madigan, C.E. Bauer, eds.), Kluwer Academic Publishers, Dordrecht, pp. 373–384.
64. Y. Koyama, F.S. Rondonuwu, R. Fujii, Y. Watanabe, Light-harvesting function of carotenoids in photo-synthesis: The roles of the newly found $1^1B_u^-$ state. *Biopolymers* **74** (2004) 2–18.
65. H.A. Frank, J.S. Josue, J.A. Bautista, I. van der Hoef, F.J. Jansen, J. Lugtenburg, G. Wiederrecht, R.L. Christensen, Spectroscopic and photochemical properties of open-chain carotenoids. *J. Phys. Chem. B* **106** (2002) 2083–2092.
66. A.N. Macpherson, T. Gillbro, Solvent dependence of the ultrafast $S_2$–$S_1$ internal conversion rate of β-carotene. *J. Phys. Chem. A* **102** (1998) 5049–5058.
67. P.O. Andersson, S. Takaichi, R.J. Cogdell, T. Gillbro, Photophysical characterization of natural cis-carotenoids. *Photochem. Photobiol.* **74** (2001) 549–557.
68. T. Polívka, J.L. Herek, D. Zigmantas, H.-E. Åkerlund, V. Sundström, Direct observation of the (forbidden) $S_1$ state in carotenoids. *Proc. Natl. Acad. Sci. U.S.A.* **96** (1999) 4914–4917.

69. S. Akimoto, I. Yamazaki, S. Takaichi, M. Mimuro, Excitation relaxation of carotenoids within the $S_2$ state probed by the femtosecond fluorescence up-conversion method. *Chem. Phys. Lett.* **313** (1999) 63–68.
70. M. Yoshizawa, H. Aoki, H. Hashimoto, Vibrational relaxation of the $2A_g^-$ excited state in all-trans-β-carotene obtained by femtosecond time-resolved Raman spectroscopy. *Phys. Rev. B* **63** (2001) 180301-1–4.
71. H.H. Billsten, D. Zigmantas, V. Sundström, T. Polívka, Dynamics of vibrational relaxation in the $S_1$ state of carotenoids having 11 conjugated C=C bonds. *Chem. Phys. Lett.* **355** (2002) 465–470.
72. E. Papagiannakis, I.H.M. van Stokkum, R. van Grondelle, R.A. Niederman, D. Zigmantas, V. Sundström, T. Polívka, A near-infrared transient absorption study of the excited-state dynamics of the carotenoid spirilloxanthin in solution and in the LH1 complex of *Rhodospirillum rubrum*. *J. Phys. Chem. B* **107** (2003) 11216–11223.
73. T. Polívka, D. Zigmantas, J.L. Herek, Z. He, T. Pascher, T. Pullerits, R.J. Cogdell, H.A. Frank, V. Sundström, The carotenoid $S_1$ state in LH2 complexes from purple bacteria *Rhodobacter sphaeroides* and *Rhodopseudomonas acidophila*: $S_1$ energies, dynamics, and carotenoid radical formation. *J. Phys. Chem. B* **106** (2002) 11016–11025.
74. A.N. Macpherson, J.B. Arellano, N.J. Fraser, R.J. Cogdell, T. Gillbro, Efficient energy transfer from the carotenoid $S_2$ state in a photosynthetic light-harvesting complex. *Biophys. J.* **80** (2001) 923–930.
75. P.J. Walla, P.A. Linden, C.-P. Hsu, G.D. Scholes, G.R. Fleming, Femtosecond dynamics of the forbidden carotenoid $S_1$ state in light-harvesting complexes of purple bacteria observed after two-photon excitation. *Proc. Natl. Acad. Sci. U.S.A.* **97** (2000) 10808–10813.
76. B.P. Krueger, G.D. Scholes, R. Jimenez, G.R. Fleming, Electronic excitation transfer from carotenoid to bacteriochlorophyll in the purple bacterium *Rhodopseudomonas acidophila*. *J. Phys. Chem. B* **102** (1998) 2284–2292.
77. R.Z.B. Desamero, V. Chynwat, I. van der Hoef, F.J. Jansen, J. Lugtenburg, D. Gosztola, M.R. Wasielewski, A. Cua, D.F. Bocian, H.A. Frank, Mechanism of energy transfer from carotenoids to bacteriochlorophyll: Light-harvesting by carotenoids having different extents of π-electron conjugation incorporated into the B850 antenna complex from the carotenoidless bacterium *Rhodobacter sphaeroides* R-26.1. *J. Phys. Chem. B* **102** (1998) 8151–8162.
78. G. Hartwich, H. Scheer, V. Aust, A. Angerhofer, Absorption and ADMR studies on bacterial photosynthetic reaction centres with modified pigments. *Biochim. Biophys. Acta* **1230** (1995) 97–113.
79. H.A. Frank, Carotenoids in photosynthetic bacterial reaction centers: Structure, spectroscopy, and photochemistry, in: *The Photosynthetic Reaction Center* (1993) (J. Deisenhofer, J.R. Norris, eds.), Academic Press, San Diego, Vol. II, pp. 221–237.
80. I.V. Borovykh, I.B. Klenina, I.I. Proskuryakov, P. Gast, A.J. Hoff, Magnetophotoselection study of the carotenoid triplet state in *Rhodobacter sphaeroides* reaction centers. *J. Phys. Chem. B* **106** (2002) 4305–4312.

# IV. Structure and Function of Antenna Systems

*Chapter 5*

# The Light-Harvesting System of Purple Anoxygenic Photosynthetic Bacteria

## Christopher J. Law and Richard J. Cogdell

**Table of Contents**

| | | |
|---|---|---|
| 5.1 | Introduction......................................................... | 207 |
| | 5.1.1   Intracytoplasmic Membrane ........................ | 207 |
| | 5.1.2   Photosynthetic Pigment–Protein Complexes ............. | 209 |
| | 5.1.3   Bacterial Photosynthetic Unit ........................ | 210 |
| | 5.1.4   Regulation of Photosynthetic Unit Expression ........... | 212 |
| 5.2 | Pre-Structural Studies on Antenna Complexes ................. | 215 |
| | 5.2.1   Amino Acid Sequencing ............................. | 215 |
| | 5.2.2   Limited Proteolysis of Antenna Complexes ............. | 218 |
| | 5.2.3   Modeling of Antenna Complexes...................... | 218 |
| 5.3 | Three-Dimensional Structure of the LH2 Complex from *Rps. acidophila*................................................... | 220 |
| | 5.3.1   The Protein Scaffold................................. | 221 |
| | 5.3.2   Binding and Arrangement of the Bchl a Molecules........ | 223 |
| | 5.3.3   Bacteriochlorophyll Phytyl Tails Play an Important Structural Role................................................... | 224 |
| | 5.3.4   Structure and Arrangement of Carotenoids in the *Rps. acidophila* LH2 Complex ........................... | 225 |
| 5.4 | Structure of the RC-LH1 Core Complex ...................... | 227 |
| | 5.4.1   Reconstitution Studies of LH1 Complexes ............... | 228 |
| | 5.4.2   Electron Microscopy Studies of RC-LH1 Core Complexes .. | 229 |
| |     5.4.2.1   The *Rhodopseudomonas viridis* Core Complex ..... | 229 |
| |     5.4.2.2   The *Rhodospirillum rubrum* Core Complex......... | 230 |
| | 5.4.3   Debate About the Size of the LH1 Ring ................ | 231 |
| | 5.4.4   Does the LH1 Complex Completely Encircle the RC?...... | 233 |
| | 5.4.5   The PufX Polypeptide................................ | 234 |
| | 5.4.6   Three-Dimensional Structure of the RC-LH1 Complex from *Rps. palustris* ................................... | 235 |

5.5 Arrangement of the Photosynthetic Apparatus in the ICM ....... 237
    5.5.1 Spectroscopic Investigations of PSU Organization ........ 237
    5.5.2 Molecular Modeling of the PSU ..................... 238
    5.5.3 Energy Transfer Within the PSU..................... 239
5.6 Conclusions................................................ 242
Acknowledgements .............................................. 242
References..................................................... 242

## Abstract

The anoxygenic purple photosynthetic bacteria synthesize a group of integral membrane pigment–protein complexes that function to absorb the solar energy that allows photosynthetic growth. These complexes, called light-harvesting complex 1 (LH1) and light-harvesting complex 2 (LH2), are circular structures that transfer the absorbed light to the photochemical reaction centre (RC), where charge separation across the membrane occurs. This ultimately results in creation of a proton gradient that is used to drive production of cellular fuel in the form of adenosine triphosphate (ATP). The LH complexes reside in an extensive membrane system, derived from the cytoplasmic membrane, that is synthesized *de novo* in response to light and low oxygen concentrations. Now is a rich time for researchers interested in the light reactions of the photosynthetic process in purple bacteria, as the 3D structures of all the components involved have been elucidated. This chapter focuses on the purple non-sulfur photosynthetic bacteria and the structure and function of their light-harvesting complexes.

## 5.1 Introduction

The anoxygenic photosynthetic bacteria are a diverse group of organisms that are defined by their ability to carry out photosynthesis in the absence of air and without evolving oxygen. The anoxygenic photosynthetic bacteria can be divided into the green and purple bacteria [1]. The latter are further subdivided into the sulfur and non-sulfur purple bacteria. The purple non-sulfur bacteria are the focus of this chapter. The metabolic capabilities of these purple bacteria are extremely diverse [1]. For example, they can grow photosynthetically under anaerobic conditions in the light, by respiration in the presence of oxygen, or by fermentation under anaerobic conditions in the dark. When grown aerobically, the cells are usually unpigmented and have smooth cell membranes. However, when the cells become anaerobic they switch to photosynthetic growth. During this mode of growth the cells become highly pigmented and the cell membranes invaginate to form an extensive system of intracytoplasmic membranes [2].

### 5.1.1 Intracytoplasmic Membrane

Intracytoplasmic membranes (ICM) (also known as photosynthetic membranes) were first detected by electron microscopy (EM) studies of purple non-sulfur bacteria. These studies allowed the formation of ICM by invagination of the cytoplasmic membrane to be observed for the first time [3]. The formation of ICM was subsequently also visualized using immunochemical techniques [4]. Although the ICM is contiguous with and derived from the cytoplasmic membrane [5–7], it possesses different chemical and structural components and has different physical properties [1,8,9]. The morphology of the ICMs varies depending upon the species of purple bacteria that contain them: in some they are vesicular, whereas in others they can be tubular or lamellar (Table 1) [2,10]. Indeed, ICM morphology has often been used as a tool for the taxonomic classification of purple bacteria. What regulates ICM shape is not understood, although one study suggested that the inherent asymmetry of proteins within the ICM can act as a determinant of membrane shape [11]. A recent EM study on semiaerobically-grown *Rhodobacter* (*Rb.*) *sphaeroides* LH2-minus mutants demonstrated that the presence of a protein component of the photosynthetic apparatus, PufX (which is discussed in detail in Section 5.4.5), has a profound effect on membrane architecture and leads to elongated cells containing extended tubular membranes. In the absence of PufX the ICMs consist of large, granular vesicles. Interestingly, fractionation of the membranes by density gradient centrifugation revealed both strains also contained small ICM vesicles [12].

Whether or not cells synthesize ICM is primarily governed by oxygen tension, and its extent is determined by light intensity [13–15]. When grown under aerobic conditions purple bacteria generally do not synthesize ICM. However, there are exceptions – notably *Rb. capsulatus*. This species can constitutively synthesize small amounts of tubular ICM even when grown aerobically [16,17]. Typically, when cells are switched to anaerobic light conditions, the rapid, *de novo* formation of ICM is induced. Freeze–fracture electron microscopy showed that aerobic cells contain small indentations within the cytoplasmic membrane that appear to be converted into discrete ICM invaginations within one hour of the imposition of anaerobiosis. Microscopic examination also revealed a series of morphological changes in the structure and organization of newly synthesized ICM during the adaptation to photosynthetic growth conditions [11]. It has been suggested that the size of ICM vesicles in some mutant strains of *Rb. sphaeroides* may be influenced by the protein composition of the membrane [12,18,19]. Although we know the switch that controls ICM formation, we do not yet know how it is actually translated into the *de novo* synthesis of new membrane.

Table 1. Intracytoplasmic membrane (ICM) morphologies and cell shapes of several different species of purple bacteria

| Species | Cell shape | ICM type |
|---|---|---|
| *Rhodospirillum rubrum* | Spiral | Vesicles |
| *Rhodospirillum molischianum* | Spiral | Stacks |
| *Rhodospirillum salexigens* | Spiral | Lamellae |
| *Rhodobacter capsulatus* | Rod | Vesicles |
| *Rhodobacter sphaeroides* | Ovoid-rod | Vesicles |
| *Rhodobacter sulfidophilus* | Rod | Vesicles |
| *Rhodopseudomonas palustris* | Rod | Lamellae |
| *Blastochloris* (formerly *Rhodopseudomonas*) *viridis* | Rod | Lamellae |
| *Rhodopseudomonas blastica* | Rod | Lamellae |
| *Rhodopseudomonas acidophila* | Rod | Lamellae |
| *Rhodobium marinum* | Rod | Lamellae |
| *Rhodocyclus tenuis* | Spiral | Tubules |
| *Rubrivivax gelatinosus* | Rod | Tubules |

## 5.1.2 Photosynthetic Pigment–Protein Complexes

Concomitant with the enlargement of the ICM in purple bacteria is an increase in the cellular photopigment content. These pigments, bacteriochlorophyll (Bchl) and carotenoids, are not free in the membrane, but non-covalently associated with largely hydrophobic polypeptides to form integral membrane pigment–protein complexes. The photosynthetic pigments are located in different chemical environments within the proteins that bind them. This endows them with different spectral characteristics. This spectral heterogeneity is revealed by the absorption spectrum of photosynthetic membranes of a representative species of the purple non-sulfur bacteria (Figure 1). The spectrum represents absorption by three spectrally distinct populations of Bchl $a$ and of the carotenoid molecules. Two strong near-infrared (NIR) absorption bands are located at about 800 and 858 nm, and these are due mainly to the $Q_y$ transitions of Bchl $a$ molecules that are located in two different binding sites within a particular type of pigment–protein complex. The shoulder at ~875 nm on the red edge of the major NIR peak results from the contribution by the $Q_y$ transition of Bchl $a$ molecules that are bound to a different type of LH protein [20]. In contrast to the situation observed in the NIR region of the spectrum, the positions of the $Q_x$ transition and Soret absorption bands of all three Bchl populations are not affected very much by the chemical environment of their binding sites. They all have their Soret absorbance located at ~390 nm and that of their $Q_x$ transition located at ~590 nm. The "three-fingered" absorptions between 450 and 550 nm arises from the carotenoids.

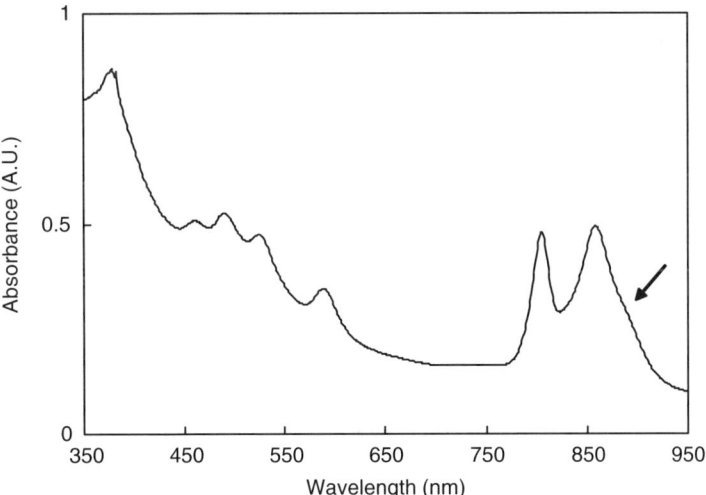

**Figure 1.** Absorption spectrum of photosynthetic membranes of *Rhodopseudomonas acidophila* strain 10050. The spectrum shows two major peaks in the near-infrared, located at about 800 and 858 nm, that are primarily due to absorption by LH2. The shoulder to the red of the 858 nm peak (arrowed) is due to absorption by the LH1 complex.

Pigment–protein complexes were first isolated from detergent-solubilized membranes [21–25] (see [26] for a lively personal account of this work). This showed that photosynthetic purple bacteria synthesize two fundamentally different types of pigment–protein complex – light-harvesting (LH) complexes and reaction centers (RCs). Most of the pigments are associated with the LH antenna complexes. These function to absorb light energy and then to efficiently and rapidly transfer that energy to specialized pigments (the Bchl "special pair") in the RC. When the excitation energy arrives at the RC it induces a charge separation across the membrane. These redox reactions in the RC then initiate cyclic electron transport that also involves cytochrome $b/c_1$ and cytochrome $c_2$, producing a proton gradient that is used to drive ATP synthesis via the ATP synthase.

Most purple bacteria possess two major types of light-harvesting complexes, termed LH1 and LH2. The LH2 complexes bind Bchl *a* molecules in two different binding sites. The differences in the chemical environments provided by these binding sites give rise to the two intense NIR absorption bands at ~800 and ~850 nm seen in the absorption spectrum of the isolated complex (Figure 2a). Hence, these complexes are also known as B800–850 complexes (where the "B" stands for "bulk" Bchl) [27]. In contrast, in the LH1 complex, the Bchl *a* molecules only have a single large NIR absorption band centered at ~880 nm (Figure 2b). LH1 complexes are also known as B875, B880 or B890 complexes, depending on the actual position of their NIR absorption maximum.

The LH1 complex is intimately associated in a fixed equimolar stoichiometry with the RC to form the so-called RC-LH1 "core" complex and all wild-type purple bacteria contain it. Most, but not all species, also contain the LH2 antenna complex. This complex is present in amounts that vary with growth conditions. When it is present, LH2, sometimes referred to as the peripheral or variable antenna complex, forms a network that surrounds and connects the core complexes. Such an arrangement of RCs surrounded by an antenna system ensures each RC is kept well supplied with excitation energy and increases the effective absorption cross section of the RC. It is a combination of a RC with its LH complexes that constitutes the bacterial photosynthetic unit (PSU).

*5.1.3 Bacterial Photosynthetic Unit*

The concept of the PSU was derived from the experiments of Emerson and Arnold, and it forms the basis of our current understanding of the primary events of photosynthesis [28]. In simple terms a PSU can be defined as the ratio of total Bchl to RC Bchl. In their now seminal work, Aagaard and Sistrōm [29] showed that the size of the purple bacterial PSU is variable and can range from about 30 to 300 Bchl molecules per RC. In species such as *Rhodospirillum* (*Rs.*) *rubrum*, which synthesize LH1 as their only antenna complex, the RC-LH1 core complex represents the maximal size of a PSU. In these species, decreases in light intensity are compensated for by increasing the number of PSUs per cell. However, in species such as *Rb. sphaeroides*, which can synthesize peripheral

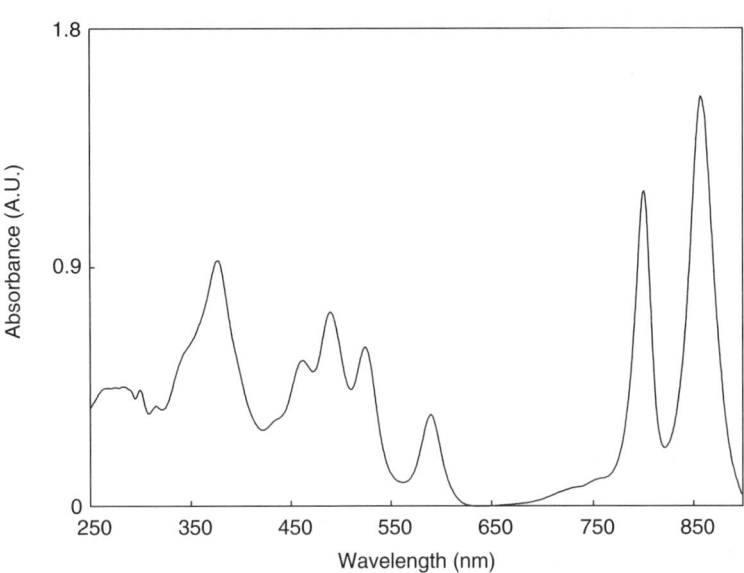

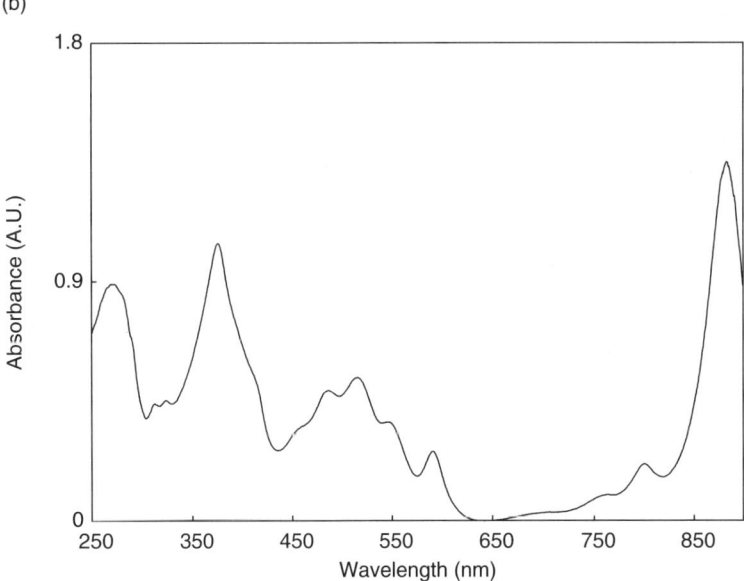

**Figure 2.** Absorption spectra of the *Rhodopseudomonas acidophila* LH2 (a) and RC-LH1 (b) complexes.

LH2 as well as core complexes, the RC-LH1 core represents the minimal size of the PSU. Downshifts in light intensity can be dealt with by increasing the size of the PSU. This is achieved by simply increasing the ratio of LH2 complexes to RC complexes. Under conditions of very low-light stress some species, including *Rhodopseudomonas* (*Rps.*) *cryptolactis* and *Rps. acidophila*, can even synthesize a different type of peripheral complex (sometimes referred to as LH3), thereby altering the absorbing range of their peripheral antennas [30,31]. These examples clearly demonstrate the inherent plasticity of the purple bacterial light-harvesting system. By employing a PSU to feed excitation energy to a RC, the purple bacteria can readily adapt to changes in light conditions while at the same time keeping energy expenditure on protein and pigment biosynthesis to a minimum.

*5.1.4 Regulation of Photosynthetic Unit Expression*

The major environmental stimuli that regulate the synthesis, development and size of the PSU are oxygen tension and light intensity. Of these, oxygen tension is the dominant determinant for PSU synthesis. Incident light intensity determines the cellular levels of ICM and amounts of the different LH complexes in the PSU. Fifty years ago Cohen-Bazire et al. measured the repressive effects of light and oxygen on the synthesis of the purple bacterial photosystem [32]. They demonstrated that cells grown anaerobically synthesized photosynthetic pigments but synthesis of these pigments halted immediately when the cells were shifted to aerobic conditions. Similar effects were observed when cells growing photosynthetically were subjected to an increase from low to high light intensity. What regulatory mechanisms are responsible for the observed effects? Although the multiple regulatory mechanisms that mediate PSU formation at the molecular level are incompletely understood they involve tight regulation with checkpoints at all levels of information flow from gene transcription initiation through to post-translational modification of enzyme activity (reviewed in [33–35]). Regulation also occurs at the level of assembly and insertion into the membrane of the pigment–protein complexes, and may involve assembly factors [36] and molecular chaperones [37,38].

Nearly all of the molecular genetics work aimed at elucidating the regulatory pathways of photosystem synthesis in the non-sulfur purple bacteria has been performed on two species, namely *Rb. sphaeroides* and *Rb. capsulatus*. Table 2 summarizes the *Rb. sphaeroides* genes (and their *Rb. capsulatus* homologues) that are either proposed or known to regulate the amounts of photosynthetic apparatus in response to oxygen levels or light intensity.

In purple bacteria the transcriptional regulation of photosystem genes involves several classical two-component bacterial regulatory systems (summarized schematically in Figure 3). These systems consist of a sensor kinase component and a phosphorylatable, DNA-binding protein component [33,39]. In *Rb. sphaeroides*, the transcriptional activation of most of the photosynthetic unit genes by low oxygen tension is mediated by the two-component PrrBA (photosynthetic response regulator) system [40]. This system acts in response to an altered signal originating from the oxygen-sensing $cbb_3$/RdxB pathway [41]. PrrB is a membrane-spanning sensor histidine kinase/phosphatase [42] that responds to a lowering of oxygen tension by undergoing autophosphorylation before transferring the phosphate moiety onto PrrA, a cytosolic response

**Table 2.** List of *Rhodobacter sphaeroides* genes (and their *Rb. capsulatus* homologues) known or proposed to play a role in regulation of PSU gene expression

| *Rb. sphaeroides* gene | *Rb. capsulatus* homologue | Known or proposed gene product function |
|---|---|---|
| *prrB* | *regB* | Sensor kinase |
| *prrA* | *regA* | Transcription regulator |
| *ppsR* | *crtJ* | Transcription regulator |
| *ppbC* | *hvrA* | Light-sensitive transcription regulator |
| *fnrL* | – | Oxygen/redox-sensitive transcription regulator |
| *himA* | *himD* | Subunits of IHF (DNA-binding protein) |
| *appA* | – | Unknown |
| *mgpS* | – | Unknown |
| *prrC* | *senC* | Transcription regulator |

regulator protein. Activated PrrA then initiates gene expression either by binding to DNA directly or by forming transcriptional complexes involving other protein factors [43]. The PrrBA system is homologous to the RegBA system of *Rb. capsulatus* [44–46].

Phototrophic growth of *Rb. sphaeroides* is also regulated by the *fnrL* gene that encodes the anaerobic regulator FnrL [47]. FnrL is a DNA-binding factor that binds to a recognition sequence that resembles the *Escherichia coli* Fnr (fumarate nitrate regulator) consensus sequence [48]. Several genes involved in Bchl and carotenoid synthesis as well as the *puc* operon (that encodes LH2 proteins) possess sequences that are similar or identical to the FNR consensus sequence [48,49]. Evidence suggests that under low oxygen tension FnrL binds to these consensus sequences and induces gene expression. FnrL also affects *puc* operon transcription indirectly by regulating genes that encode components of the $cbb_3$/RdxB signal pathway, thereby affecting the signal (either positively or negatively) that reaches the PrrBA system [33]. In contrast to FnrL, the PpsR (photopigment suppression) factor is involved in the repression of photosystem gene expression under aerobic growth conditions [50]. PpsR represses both the *puc* operon and Bchl and carotenoid biosynthesis pathway genes that contain a specific repressor-binding sequence [51,52]. The repressor activity of PpsR does not respond directly to oxygen levels, and other factors are required to signal to PpsR the state of oxygen availability in the environment. One of these factors may be the AppA (activation of photopigment and *puc* expression) protein [53,54]. Although repression by PpsR is relieved when oxygen tension is lowered, it is still responsive to light intensity under these conditions. In this way it can regulate the cellular abundance of LH2 complex.

The control of photosystem gene expression by light intensity is less well understood than that of oxygen control. However, at least two light-responsive factors have been identified in *Rb. sphaeroides*. The first of these, the Spb (*sphaeroides puf*-binding) protein is homologous with the light-responsive element, HʋrA, from *Rb. capsulatus* [33,55]. Both SpB and HʋrA control RC and LH1 protein expression in response to changes in light intensity by binding upstream of the *puf* operon. They do not effect expression of LH2 proteins or Bchl biosynthesis [56]. A 17-kDa outer membrane protein, TspO

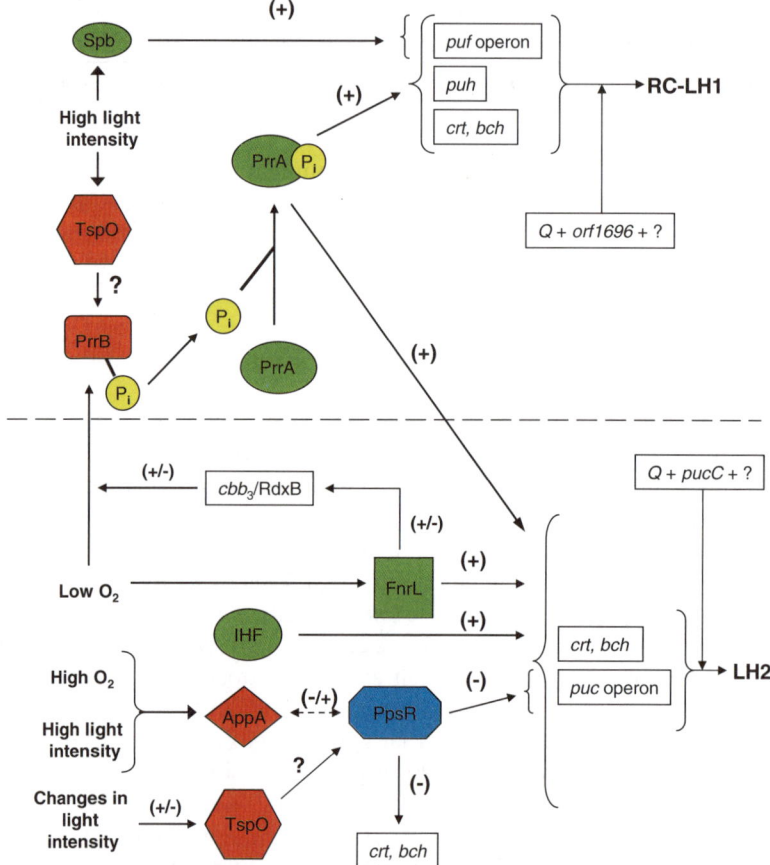

**Figure 3.** Schematic diagram of the major, known regulatory components of photosynthetic unit gene expression in *Rhodobacter sphaeroides* (see text for details). The components that act as effectors of gene expression are depicted in green, whereas the sensory components are colored red. The component in blue (PpsR) can act as both a sensor and effector. The genes they regulate are in boxes. Symbols: (+), enhances expression of target gene; (−), represses expression of target gene; ?, putative pathway of regulation; $P_i$, inorganic phosphate.

(tryptophan-rich sensory protein), has also been implicated as a light-responsive modulator of photosystem gene expression. However, the mechanism of signal transduction from the outer membrane-bound TspO to the cell interior is not known [57].

The picture of how photosystem gene expression is regulated becomes more complicated when one considers that some species possess more than one set of genes encoding the protein components of a particular LH complex. In *Rb. sphaeroides*, there appears to be a second set of *pucBA* genes that encode the LH2 proteins [58], and the purple sulfur bacterium *Chromatium* (*Chr.*)

*vinosum* contains genes that encode a second set of LH1 protein homologues [59]. *Rps. acidophila, Rps. palustris* and *Chr. vinosum* even contain a multi-gene family encoding for LH2 structural genes, some of which are "silent" [60–62]. It appears that the LH2 structural genes are transcribed differentially under different growth conditions. This may allow the bacteria to customize the LH2 antennas to suit small changes in their environment [63]. How the preferential expression of one particular set of genes over another in the multi-gene family is regulated is not understood at all.

## 5.2 Pre-Structural Studies on Antenna Complexes

### 5.2.1 Amino Acid Sequencing

Before the structural determination of the first purple bacterial light-harvesting complex in 1995 [64], these complexes were extensively studied by a range of biochemical, biophysical and molecular biological techniques (see [65] and references therein). These studies showed that purple bacterial antenna complexes are constructed from oligomers of small (4–7 kDa), very hydrophobic, membrane-spanning polypeptides that act as a scaffold for the non-covalent attachment of the photosynthetic pigments.

The primary amino acid sequences of the antenna polypeptides of both LH2 and LH1 complexes from a range of purple bacteria were also determined [66–69]. Analysis of these sequences revealed that all antenna complexes consist of $\alpha$ and $\beta$ polypeptides and that they have rather homologous amino acid sequences (Figure 4). The degree of homology between the antenna polypeptides of the LH2 and LH1 complexes from different species lies between 28 and 78% [70]. Probably the most important structural characteristic of all purple bacterial antenna polypeptides is their tripartite structure, which consists of a central, hydrophobic domain of 21–23 amino acid residues flanked by polar N and C-terminal domains [69,71,72]. The N-terminal domain of both LH2 and LH1 $\alpha$ polypeptides consists of 12–14 residues, whereas in the LH1 $\beta$ polypeptide it is 17–25 residues, and in the LH2 $\beta$ polypeptide it is 13–23 residues. The C-terminal domain of the $\alpha$ polypeptides of both types of antenna complex is 16–20 residues long, and in the $\beta$ polypeptides of both complexes it consists of five residues. Exceptions to the latter occur in *Rs. rubrum, Rps. viridis* and *Rps. acidophila*. In these species the C-terminal domain of the $\beta$ polypeptides consists of 11 or 12 residues. The greater length of the C-terminal domains of the LH1 complex $\beta$ polypeptide from *Rs. rubrum, Rps. viridis* and *Rps. acidophila*, and the presence of Trp and Tyr residues in the lengthened polypeptide, is correlated with the much stronger near-infrared (NIR) circular dichroism (CD) signal observed in these species compared with the weak NIR CD signals reported for the core complexes from *Rb. sphaeroides* and *Rb. capsulatus* [69].

The amino acid sequences of the antenna polypeptides are characterized by the presence of both conserved single amino acid residues and clusters of

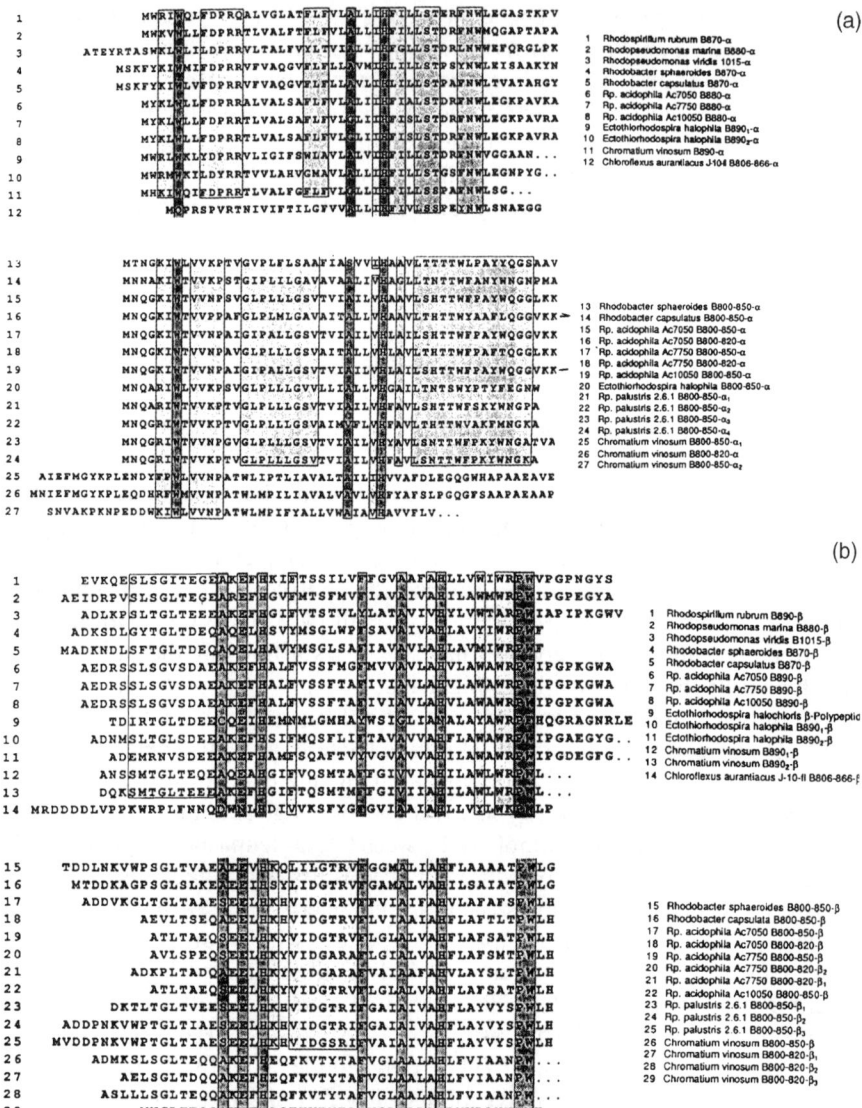

**Figure 4.** (a) Amino acid sequences of the α polypeptides of the LH1 (1–12) and LH2 (13–24) complexes of representative species of the purple bacteria. (b) Amino acid sequences of the β polypeptides of the LH1 (1–14) and LH2 (15–25) of several species and strains of purple bacteria. Sequence homologous amino acid residues or complex specific clusters of residues with pronounced homology are in bold typeface. An asterisk indicates amino acid residues that are totally conserved within the polypeptides of the species listed. [Figure adapted from Zuber and Cogdell [65].

conserved residues. These are characteristic both of the α and β polypeptides and of the LH2 and LH1 complexes, indicating an important structural and functional role for them. Primary sequence analysis also revealed the presence of a large number of basic amino acid residues (Arg, Lys) in the N-terminal region of the α polypeptide and acidic residues (Glu, Asp) in the N-terminal region of the β polypeptide. The most highly conserved amino acid in both the LH2 and LH1 α and β polypeptides is a His residue [73–75]. This residue is located either four residues (α polypeptide) or six residues (β polypeptide) from the boundary between the central, membrane-spanning domain and the polar C-terminal domain. The conserved His provides the binding site for the central Bchl molecules that absorb at 820 nm (LH3), 850 nm (LH2) or 880 nm (LH1). A second, typically conserved His is also present near the N-terminal domain of the β polypeptide. It was suggested that this residue provides a binding site for the Bchl molecules that absorb at 800 nm in LH2 and LH3 complexes [76]. However, this conserved His is also found in the β polypeptide of the LH1 antenna even though these complexes do not bind an additional Bchl. In the *Rc. gelatinosus* LH2 β polypeptide the His residue is replaced by Gln, which also has the ability to bind Bchl [69].

Other conserved amino acid residues are found at certain distances from the conserved central His in the primary sequence. It was thought that these might act as secondary binding sites for Bchl molecules as well as playing a role in controlling the specific orientation of the Bchl tetrapyrrole rings. Of special importance in the latter role are Ala residues located at His-4 in both the α and β polypeptides, and Leu at His+4 in the β polypeptide [77]. The presence of hydrophobic amino acid residues (Ala, Val, Ile, Leu and Phe) in the region of His±4, and conserved aromatic residues (Trp, Tyr) at a distance from the central His of His+4, +6 and +9 in the LH1 β polypeptide (or His+9 in the LH2 β polypeptide) and at His+11 in the LH1 α polypeptide (or His+9 and His+14 in the LH2 α polypeptide) influence the spectral characteristics of the Bchls bound to the central His residue [70,74]. It was postulated that substitution of Trp (His+14) by Leu or Thr in the LH2 complex of *Rps. acidophila* (strains 7050 and 7750) was responsible for the blue-shift of the Bchl absorbance, from 850 nm in LH2 to 820 nm in the LH3 complex [70]. The postulated functional role of the antenna complex aromatic amino acid residues was demonstrated by site-directed mutagenesis studies on the LH1 complex of *Rb. capsulatus* [78]. An 8–11 nm blue-shift was observed when Trp (His+11) was substituted by Ala, Leu or Tyr. In LH2 from *Rb. sphaeroides*, substitution of Trp (His+13) and (His+14) with Phe resulted in an 11 nm blue-shift of the Bchl absorbance. However, a double mutant, in which both His residues were substituted by Phe-Leu, produced a blue-shift of 24 nm [79]. Interestingly, there is a Trp residue in the α polypeptide of the RC-LH1 core complex of Bchl *b*-containing *Rps. viridis* at position His+12. It was suggested that the Trp residue may be the cause of the large redshift (to 1015 nm) observed in the core complex of this species [80].

## 5.2.2 Limited Proteolysis of Antenna Complexes

The important contributions of the aromatic Trp residue to the spectral characteristics of Bchl was demonstrated by performing limited proteolysis of the α and β polypeptides of purified antenna complexes [81]. Hydrolytic cleavage of the polypeptide chains of *Rps. acidophila* (strain 10050) LH2 by elastase and carboxypeptidase A and B, followed by analysis of any spectral changes associated with the proteolysis, showed that elastase-treated complexes had a strongly decreased 858 nm absorption band and a small (2 nm) blue-shift. The enzyme cleaved the α polypeptide at the C-terminus, removing the residues Lys-Ala-Ala. In the β polypeptide, Leu-His or Trp-Leu-His were removed. Carboxypeptidase A treatment resulted in a blue-shift of the NIR absorption maximum to 853 nm. This was connected with a strong decrease in both the absorption and NIR-CD signal. Carboxypeptidase A cleaved the C-terminal residues Lys-Ala-Ala in the α polypeptide, and Trp-Leu-His in the β polypeptide. Limited proteolysis using a combination of carboxypeptidase A and B caused a further blue-shift of the NIR absorption maximum to 837 nm. This spectral change was a result of a further cleavage of the α polypeptide chain up to the region of Trp (His + 14).

## 5.2.3 Modeling of Antenna Complexes

From the previously described studies, it was known that the antenna complex polypeptides were the basic building blocks of much larger polypeptide aggregates that bound Bchl to form the functional LH complexes. It was assumed that a combination of interactions between the α-helical, membrane-spanning regions of the α and β apoproteins, in addition to Bchl-Bchl and Bchl-polypeptide interactions, were the decisive factors in the formation of the functional antennas. Using these data several attempts were made to model the purple bacterial light-harvesting complexes [69,82–84] (reviewed in [65]). One of these models, the "four tilted helices" model, predicted a crucial role played by specific interactions between amino acid residues on the surface of the helices [69,76]. Such interactions permitted optimal packing of the tilted helices in the formation of both αβ subunits and aggregates of those subunits in the membrane environment (Figure 5). The smallest functional aggregate appeared to be a cyclical hexamer. This arrangement seemed to apply to both the peripheral and core antenna complexes.

A Fourier-transform analysis, using primary structural information from a range of both core and peripheral antenna complexes, was also utilized to predict the conformation and orientation of the membrane-spanning regions of the purple bacterial antenna complexes [83]. During the analysis, the direction of the hydrophobic face of the helix was calculated with reference to the helical wheel. The best fit to the data was arrived at when a four-helix bundle, consisting of an $\alpha_2\beta_2$ unit, was assumed. The Fourier analysis also indicated that each helix extended from the hydrophobic region of the membrane and reached out into the polar head group region, and even into the aqueous environment (Figure 6).

# THE LIGHT-HARVESTING SYSTEM

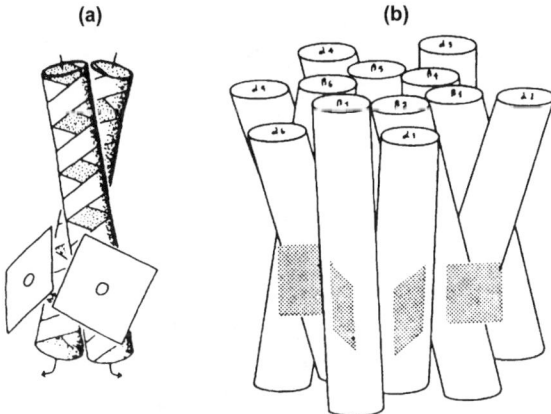

**Figure 5.** (a) An αβ heterodimer (helix pair) of the "four tilted helices" model. The polypeptides are represented as tubes and the Bchl pigment molecules as squares. The helices are tightly packed and twisted by about 30–35°. (b) Model of the cyclical hexamer ($\alpha_6\beta_6$) of α-helices that was considered to be the smallest functional unit of the LH complexes. [Figure reproduced from Zuber and Brunisholz [69].]

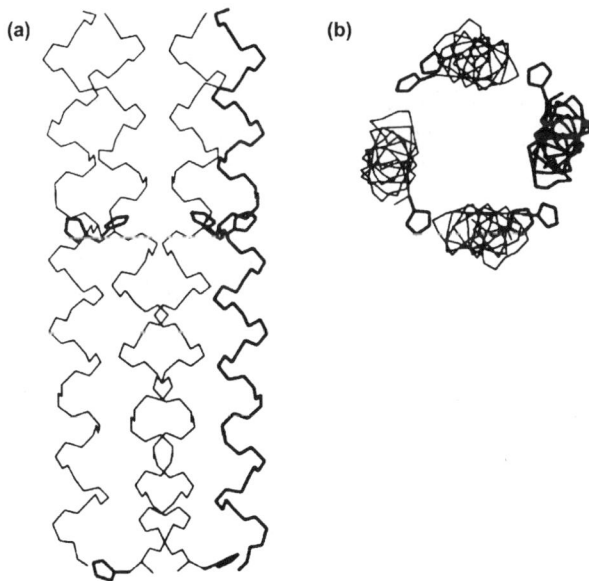

**Figure 6.** The Donnelly and Cogdell model of the proposed tetrameric ($\alpha_4\beta_4$) building block of a purple bacterial antenna complex [83]. (a) View from within, and (b) perpendicular to the plane of the membrane. One α subunit and the conserved histidine residues are depicted in bold.

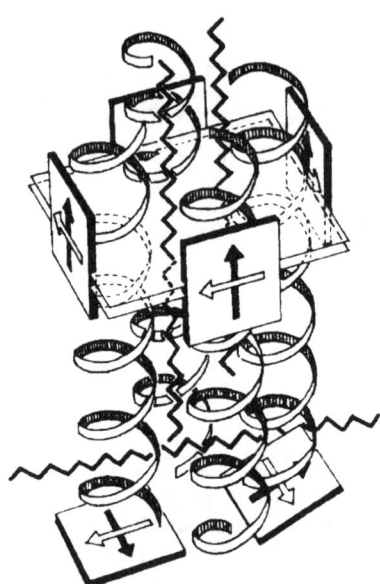

**Figure 7.** The Kramer model for the bacterial LH2 complex $\alpha_2\beta_2$. The protein component is represented as ribbons. The squares represent the bacteriochlorin rings of the Bchl $a$ molecules. The $Q_x$ and $Q_y$ dipole moments are represented as solid and open arrows, respectively. [Reproduced from Kramer et al. [82] with permission.]

Various other models of antenna complexes had also been proposed around this time [82,84]. Of particular significance was work that combined photophysical data from energy transfer studies with biochemical data to produce a model that, in retrospect, did a remarkably good job of describing the relative orientation and arrangement of the Bchl molecules in the antenna complex (Figure 7). Unfortunately, none of the aforementioned models managed to predict the beautiful ring-like structure of the purple bacterial light-harvesting complexes. However, an approach that compared calculated and experimental absorption spectra was particularly successful at predicting the circular arrangement of the Bchl molecules in the LH1 complex [85–87].

## 5.3 Three-Dimensional Structure of the LH2 Complex from *Rps. acidophila*

The past 15 years has been a boom time for researchers interested in the structural biology of photosynthetic light harvesting. In this time the 3D structures of the purple bacterial RC [88–91] and of three peripheral antenna complexes [64,92,93] have been determined. Recently, our laboratory has also published a 4.8 Å resolution structure of the RC-LH1 complex from *Rps. palustris* [94]. In the next few sections we describe in detail the structures of the LH2 and RC-LH1 complexes.

*5.3.1 The Protein Scaffold*

Our understanding of light-energy capture and transfer in the purple bacteria was hindered for many years by a lack of detailed structural information about the light-harvesting complexes. However, the picture changed dramatically with the elucidation, by X-ray crystallography, of high-resolution 3D structures of LH2 complexes from *Rps. acidophila* [64] and *Rs. molischianum* [92]. As can be seen in Figure 8, the LH2 complex from *Rps. acidophila* strain 10050 is a nonamer of two apoproteins (a 53 amino acid α subunit and a β subunit of 41 amino acids) and their associated Bchl *a* and carotenoid molecules. The apoprotein dimers are arranged in a ring-like structure. The membrane-spanning helices of the nine α and β apoproteins form two concentric rings with diameters of 36 and 68 Å, respectively, that surround a lipid-filled central region [95]. The α apoprotein helices lie perpendicular to the membrane plane whereas those of the β apoproteins are tilted by about 15° with respect to it. Although, within the transmembrane domain of the complex, there are strong helix–helix interactions between the α polypeptides, there are no helix–helix interactions between the α and β-apoproteins. In fact, the whole structure is dominated by extensive pigment–pigment interactions. This may explain the failure of detailed models of LH2 to predict the ring-like structure of the complex. The N and C-termini of both apoproteins fold over and interact with one another to enclose the cytoplasmic and periplasmic surfaces of the ring, respectively. Large aromatic residues located at the C-termini of both apoproteins interact, via hydrogen bonds to the Bchl *a* molecules, to interlock the whole structure [96,97]. It is this protein structure that acts as a scaffold for the attachment of the photosynthetic pigments. Interestingly, in *Rubrivivax* (*Rv.*) *gelatinosus*, the C-terminal of the α polypeptide is much longer than that of other species and contains several stretches of poly-Ala residues. Although it has been suggested this C-terminal may actually be another membrane-spanning domain, 2D electron cryomicroscopy (cryo-EM) has shown that it lies across the face of the periplasmic side of the complex and does not fold back into the membrane [98].

The structure of the LH2 complex from *Rs. molischianum* is very similar to that of *Rps. acidophila* but instead of a being nonameric it consists of an octamer of αβ apoproteins [92]. The α and β apoproteins of the *Rs. molischianum* complex are longer than those of the *Rps. acidophila* complex, consisting of 56 and 45 amino acid residues, respectively. The αβ dimers of the *Rs. molischianum* LH2 complex show the same basic protein folds as those of the *Rps. acidophila* complex even though there is only a 26% and 31% sequence similarity for the α and β apoproteins, respectively [96].

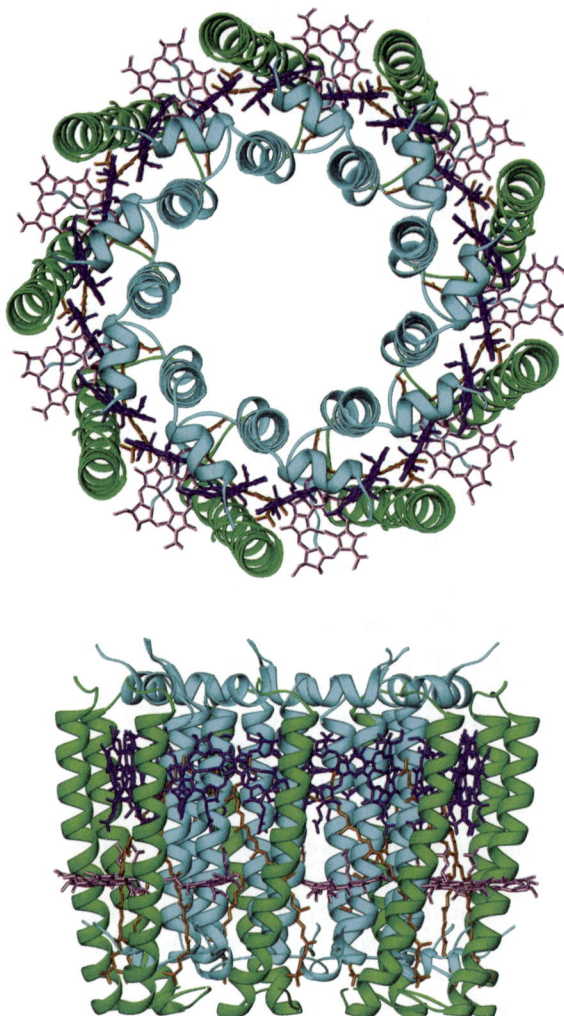

**Figure 8.** The 2.5 Å structure of LH2 from *Rhodopseudomonas acidophila* strain 10050 [64]. The upper figure represents a top view of the complex looking down from the periplasmic side of the membrane. The α and β apoproteins are drawn as ribbons and are colored turquoise and green, respectively. The pigments are all drawn as stick models. The B850 Bchl *a* molecules are colored blue and the B800 Bchls purple. The rhodopin glucoside carotenoids are orange. At this resolution only one carotenoid molecule was assigned per αβ heterodimer unit. The lower part of the figure shows the LH2 complex viewed parallel to the plane of the membrane with the periplasmic side on the top. The color coding of the polypeptides and pigments is the same as in the upper part.

The ubiquity of the ring-like structure of the purple bacterial peripheral antennas has been shown by electron microscopy and, more recently, by atomic force microscopy (AFM) studies. Electron diffraction of 2D crystals of the LH2 complexes from *Rhodovulum sulfidophilum* [99], *Rb. sphaeroides* [100],

## THE LIGHT-HARVESTING SYSTEM

*Rb. capsulatus* and an *Ectothiorhodospira* species [101] have shown that these complexes too are ring-like. The first three are nonameric in arrangement, the latter is octameric. Advances in AFM technology have allowed the LH2 complexes from *Rb. sphaeroides* [102,103], *Rps. acidophila* [104] and *Rv. gelatinosus* [105] to be visualized. Again these studies showed the complexes to be rings. It is not yet understood what controls the oligomeric size of the complexes but it may be a function of the exact primary sequence at the N-and C-termini where the $\alpha$ and $\beta$ apoproteins interact [106]. It has also been suggested that the size of the ring may vary in certain species [107].

*5.3.2 Binding and Arrangement of the Bchl a Molecules*

The Bchl *a* molecules of the LH2 complex from both *Rps. acidophila* and *Rs. molischianum* are arranged into two distinct populations. Each minimal $\alpha\beta$ subunit of the *Rps. acidophila* LH2 complex binds a total of 3 Bchl *a* and 1–2 carotenoids (in this case rhodopin glucoside) molecules [82,108,109], giving a total of 27 Bchl *a* and 9–18 rhodopin glucoside molecules in the holocomplex. In each heterodimeric unit, two of the three Bchl molecules are arranged, near the periplasmic surface of the complex, as a closely coupled dimer with the plane of their bacteriochlorin rings approximately perpendicular to the plane of the membrane. The centers of their bacteriochlorin rings are about 10 Å from the periplasmic surface of the membrane. The Bchl dimers form a ring of 18 overlapping pigments that are sandwiched, in a very hydrophobic environment, between the concentric rings formed by the transmembrane helices of the $\alpha$ and $\beta$ apoproteins [64] (Figure 8). A combination of excitonic and protein–pigment interactions cause the absorption maximum of these Bchls to redshift dramatically, from about 770 nm for monomeric Bchl *a* in organic solvents to about 850 nm in LH2 [110–112]. Hence, these pigments are known as B850 Bchls [27]. Each pair of B850 Bchls are coordinated, via their central $Mg^{2+}$, to two highly conserved His residues, one located on the $\alpha$ apoprotein ($\alpha$-His 31) and the other on the $\beta$ apoprotein ($\beta$-His 30). Resonance Raman spectroscopy suggested that Tyr and Trp residues at positions 44 and 45 of the $\alpha$ apoprotein are hydrogen bonded to the C-9 acetyl group of Bchl *a* and play an important role in determining the position of the B850 $Q_y$ absorption band [79,111,113] The crystallographic structure confirmed this. In the B800–820 LH2 complex (confusingly also termed LH3 in some of the literature) from *Rps. acidophila* strain 7050 the hydrogen bonding to the Bchl a C-9 acetyl group is absent [93,114]. This results in a reorientation of the C-9 acetyl group causing it to twist out of the plane of the bacteriochlorin ring and, in turn, blue-shifting the Bchl $Q_y$ absorption band [93].

The individual environments and conformations of the B850 Bchls are not all equivalent. The $Mg^{2+}$–$Mg^{2+}$ distance between the two B850 Bchls within each $\alpha\beta$ apoprotein dimer is 9.7 Å, whereas the $Mg^{2+}$–$Mg^{2+}$ distance between the nearest B850 Bchls of adjacent $\alpha\beta$ apoprotein dimers is only 8.7 Å [109,115]. The orientation of the Bchls alternates going around the ring. The face of the $\alpha$-B850 Bchl bacteriochlorin ring is presented to the inside of the complex whereas that of the β-B850 Bchl is presented to the outside. The configuration of each type of Bchl also differs. The bacteriochlorin ring of the α-B850 is almost planar while that of the β-B850 Bchl shows a significant "bowing" along the direction of the $Q_y$ transition [97].

The remaining nine Bchl $a$ molecules of the LH2 complex are located 16.5 Å further into the membrane than the B850 Bchls in a rather polar binding pocket between the α-helices of the β apoproteins. In contrast to the B850 Bchls, these essentially monomeric molecules absorb at 800 nm and are therefore termed B800 Bchls. The planes of the bacteriochlorin rings lie more or less parallel to the presumed plane of the membrane. The bacteriochlorins of these peripheral B800 Bchls take on a slightly "domed" conformation [97]. In contrast to the 18 tightly coupled Bchls, the central $Mg^{2+}$ ions of the nine monomeric Bchls are not liganded to a His residue. In the original 2.5 Å structure of LH2 it was thought that the central $Mg^{2+}$ was liganded to a formyl group on the α apoprotein N-terminal methionine residue (α–Met1)[64]. However, a subsequent 2.0 Å resolution structure revealed the B800 Bchls to be liganded to a carboxylate moiety on the α-Met1 residue [109]. The $Mg^{2+}$–$Mg^{2+}$ distance between each of the B800 Bchls is 21.2 Å. The whole B800 binding site is stabilized by hydrogen bonding between the O2 oxygen atom of the COO-α-Met1 residue and several surrounding residues (N-αAsn2, N-αGln3 and NE2-β-His12) [109] (Figure 9). The B800 is further held in place by hydrogen bonds formed between an acetyl group on the bacteriochlorin ring and the Arg20 residue of the β polypeptide. A combination of the polar environment of the binding pocket and the weak coupling between B800 Bchls account for the absorption characteristics of this particular Bchl $a$ population.

The central $Mg^{2+}$ ions of the *Rs. molischianum* B800 Bchls are liganded to the γ oxygen atom of the α-Asp6 residue [92]. This is a consequence of the greater length of the α apoprotein in the *Rs. molischianum* complex [96]. The result is that the plane of the bacteriochlorin ring dips into the membrane at an angle of about 20°. The orientation of the ring is also rotated by 90° relative to that of the B800 Bchls of *Rps. acidophila*.

*5.3.3 Bacteriochlorophyll Phytyl Tails Play an Important Structural Role*

The highly hydrophobic phytyl chains of the Bchl $a$ molecules are very important, and often overlooked, structural moieties of the LH2 antenna that play a crucial role in aligning the Bchl molecules correctly within the complex. The Bchl molecules need their optical transition dipole moments oriented in such a way as to optimize energy transfer between donor and acceptor molecules. The phytyl tail of each Bchl starts this alignment process by providing the protein scaffold with a "handle" to "grab" onto and use to hold the planes of the bacteriochlorin rings in the correct orientation with respect to each other. Once the Bchls are correctly aligned, they are locked into place by a combination of coordination of the central $Mg^{2+}$ ion to the protein and of H-bonding adjacent phytyl tails and pigments [115]. Closer inspection of the pigment molecules assembled as a unit reveals an obvious "hole" in the arrangement.

# THE LIGHT-HARVESTING SYSTEM 225

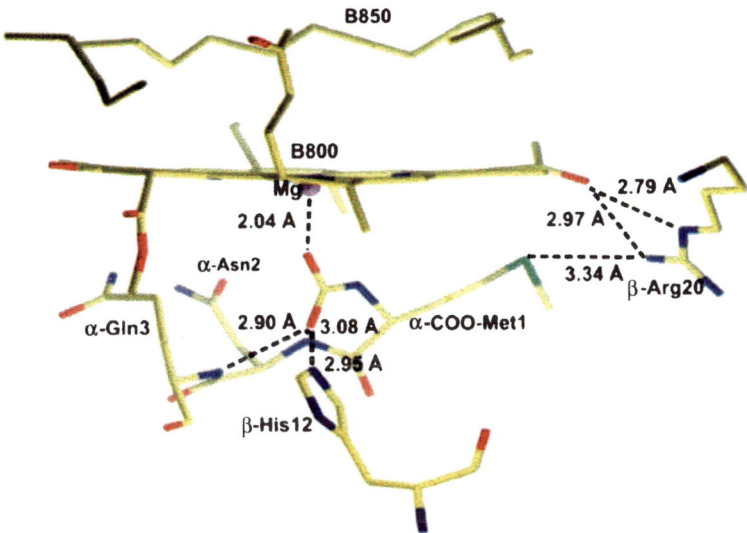

**Figure 9.** The hydrogen-bonding network (dashed lines) surrounding a B800 Bchl molecule of the *Rhodopseudomonas acidophila* strain 10050 LH2 complex. The O1 of the α-Met1 carboxyl group ligates the central $Mg^{2+}$ of the B800 molecule, forming a bond 2.04 Å long, while the O2 hydrogen bonds to α-Asn2-N (3.08 Å), α-Gln3-N (2.90 Å) and β-His12-NE2 (2.95 Å). β-Arg20-NE and $NH_2$ form hydrogen bonds with the C3′ acetyl OBB of B800 (2.79 and 2.97 Å, respectively). A possible weak H-bond of 3.34 Å could exist between the S atom of COO-α-Met1 and $NH_2$ of β-Arg20 to provide extra stability to the ligating amino acid [109].

The totally conserved β apoprotein Phe22 residue (which is present in all species of purple bacteria) protrudes into this "hole" and is cradled by a bed of oxygen atoms from nearby Bchl molecules and phytyl tail ester oxygens [115].

The phytyl tails also aid in maintaining the structural integrity of the LH2 complex [116]. The B800 phytyl chain traverses through the complex, wraps around the phytyl chain of the β-B850 Bchl then passes across the face of the β B850 Bchl macrocycle. In turn, the phytyl tail of the β-B850 Bchl passes across the face of the B800 Bchl. These "hand-shaking" interactions effectively hold the B800 Bchl molecules in place within the complex. In contrast to the β-B850 Bchls, the phytyl chain of the α-B850 Bchl is almost fully extended and does not pass across the face of any bacteriochlorin ring. Instead, it makes three close contacts (of 3.70, 3.68 and 4.13 Å) with the isoprenoid chain of a carotenoid molecule and probably functions to correctly orient the carotenoid within the complex [97].

### 5.3.4 Structure and Arrangement of Carotenoids in the Rps. acidophila LH2 Complex

Carotenoids play several important roles in light-harvesting complexes. These include accessory light-harvesting, photoprotection and structure stabilization

[117]. The original electron density map of LH2 at 2.5 Å resolved only a single molecule of the carotenoid rhodopin glucoside per αβ subunit [64]. This carotenoid possesses a typical all-trans conformation and traverses the whole membrane-spanning region of the complex. Viewed down its axis, the carotenoid is twisted and this gives rise to the strong circular dichroism signal observed in the visible region of the spectrum [118]. Its glucoside head group interacts with polar residues on the N-terminus of the α apoprotein, and its hydrocarbon, conjugated tail passes across the face of the β-B850 macrocycle of an adjacent αβ subunit. In doing so, this carotenoid acts as a cross-strut to lock adjacent αβ dimers in place within the LH2 structure. The stabilizing function played by mutual interactions between the carotenoids and Bchl molecules has been demonstrated in studies using carotenoid deletion mutants of purple bacteria [119,120]. These studies have shown that LH2 either fails to assemble or is rapidly turned over in the absence of colored carotenoids.

A higher resolution structure of LH2 at 2.0 Å has revealed the existence of a second rhodopin glucoside molecule per αβ dimer (Figure 10) [109]. Located on the periphery of the complex between the β polypeptides, this carotenoid is severely bent. To accommodate this bend, two cis bonds are required and these have been tentatively assigned to the C12 and C15 carbons of the carotenoid hydrocarbon tail. The severe distortion of this molecule may, however, not reflect its actual *in vivo* conformation. Its location on the periphery of the LH2 ring makes it vulnerable to attack by detergents. It is possible, therefore, that some loss of carotenoid has occurred during the detergent solubilization step of sample preparation. The partial occupancy that would result may offer an explanation for the severely distorted conformation of the second carotenoid observed in the 2.0 Å crystal structure. Hence, it is more probable that the actual *in vivo* conformation of the second carotenoid is more like that of the first.

The second carotenoid is oriented in the opposite direction to the first with its glucoside head group located in the periplasmic, rather than the cytoplasmic, surface of the complex. The glucoside ring is located in a pocket created by α-Trp40, Ala43-Tyr44 and β-Leu40-His41, with H-bonds to the glucoside hydroxyl groups facilitated through a network of eight water molecules. In contrast, the first carotenoid H-bonds directly to α-Lys5 and β-Glu10 residues. The isoprenoid chain of the second carotenoid travels over the outer surface of the B850 Bchl *a* molecule liganded to the α apoprotein while that of the first terminates at its inner surface. The presence of a second carotenoid surrounding the B850 pigments may offer the complex greater protection against photo-oxidative damage.

Both carotenoids are in van der Waal's contact with all three Bchl *a* molecules of each LH2 dimer unit. This allows them to fulfill their accessory light-harvesting role by transferring absorbed solar energy to the Bchl molecules. The efficiency of this energy transfer depends on both the type of carotenoid and type of LH complex. In *Rps. acidophila* LH2 this energy transfer is about 55% efficient [121]. In the *Rhodobacter* (*Rb.*) *sphaeroides* 2.4.1 LH2 complex it occurs with about 95% efficiency [122].

# THE LIGHT-HARVESTING SYSTEM

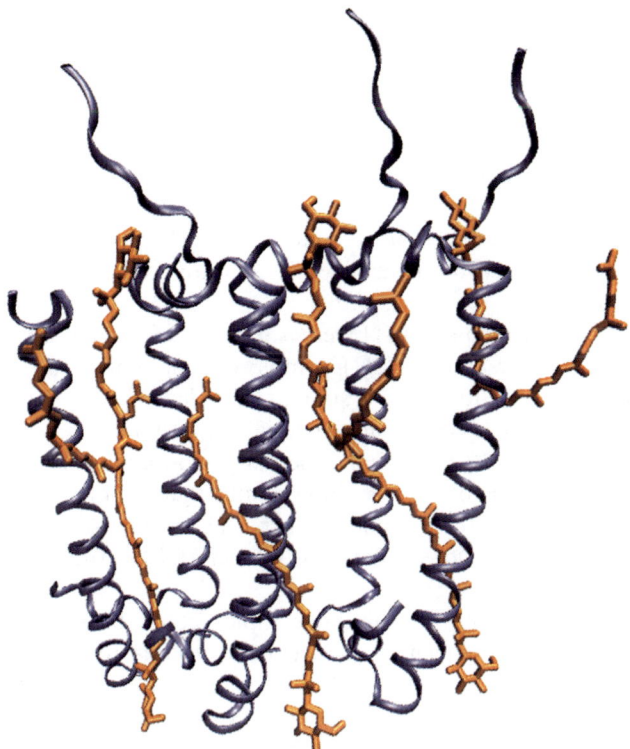

**Figure 10.** Crystallographic asymmetric unit of LH2 from *Rhodopseudomonas acidophila* strain 10050 at a resolution of 2.0 Å, showing the additional distorted carotenoid molecule per αβ heterodimer subunit [109]. Carotenoid molecules are shown in orange, and the apoproteins are shown as blue ribbons. For clarity, the Bchl *a* molecules have been omitted. Viewed from within the membrane with the periplasmic side on top. Figure drawn with VMD 1.81 [254] using PDB file 1NKZ.

## 5.4 Structure of the RC-LH1 Core Complex

The LH1 antenna is built using the same modular principle as the LH2 complex. The αβ dimer unit of LH1 binds two Bchl molecules and a single carotenoid [123]. Even though the sequence identity between the α and β polypeptides of heterodimer subunit of the two complexes is relatively low, the His residues that coordinate the B850 Bchls in LH2 are totally conserved in LH1 [69]. The latter, therefore, ligates a "ring" of Bchl molecules that are located at the same depth in the membrane as the LH2 B850s. This has important implications for energy transfer. Slight differences in the chemical environments of the LH2 and LH1 Bchl binding sites result in the absorption maximum of the LH1 Bchls being further redshifted to ∼875 nm. There is no equivalent to the LH2 B800 binding site in LH1.

*5.4.1 Reconstitution Studies of LH1 Complexes*

Much useful information about purple bacterial LH1 complex structure and formation has been gained from characterization of the structural subunit of LH1 and by reconstitution studies. In the 1980s Loach and co-workers developed an *in vitro* system that allowed them to prepare and characterize a dissociated intermediate of LH1 for each of five different species of purple bacteria and their mutants [124]. A similar approach was taken by Ghosh and co-workers who studied the reversible dissociation of the LH1 complex from *Rs. rubrum* [125,126].

The α and β apoproteins of LH1 were isolated, purified and mixed with Bchl *a* in detergent solution to form LH1 complexes very similar to those found *in vivo* [124,127,128]. Additionally, a subunit complex of LH1 was isolated for several species of Bchl *a*-containing bacteria (*Rs. rubrum*, *Rb. sphaeroides* and *Rb. capsulatus*) [126,127,129–136] and the Bchl *b*-containing species *Rps. viridis* [137–139]. The presence of carotenoid was not required for LH1 formation in these species. However, the presence of a specific carotenoid, hydroxyspheroidene, was required for successful reconstitution of LH1 from *Rv. gelatinosus* [140].

It was also found that the subunit complex could be reconstituted from isolated α and β apoproteins in a manner similar to that for LH1. On the basis of almost identical spectroscopic and biochemical properties, and the demonstration that in each case native LH1 complex was formed by association of the subunits, it was concluded that this subunit represented the basic structural moiety of LH1 [141]. The subunit was purported to consist of αβ · 2Bchl *a*, and has an absorption maximum located at 820 nm (hence it is termed the B820 subunit) [142,143]. It was further proposed that this B820 subunit was ubiquitous among LH1 complexes in the purple bacteria.

Interestingly, a subunit-like complex was reconstituted with Bchl and β apoproteins only – no α polypeptide was required [128,144]. Furthermore, hybrid reconstitution assays using α and β apoproteins from different species allowed many of the structural features required for subunit formation to be identified [144]. These experiments underlined the importance of a conserved region of amino acid residues for both subunit and LH1 complex formation, as well as the likelihood of specific interactions between residues of the N-terminal regions of the polypeptides [128]. The structural features required for LH1 formation were further defined by reconstitution studies that used chemically and enzymatically modified, and mutant α and β polypeptides [145–149]. The complete RC-LH1 core complex was also reconstituted from the B820 subunit and RC from *Rs. rubrum*. The reconstituted core complex exhibited absorption and CD spectra identical to the native complex and also showed efficient charge separation properties [150].

The use of structural analogues of Bchl in reconstitution experiments with the α and β polypeptides of *Rs. rubrum* and *Rb. sphaeroides* enabled the LH1 Bchl binding site to be probed. These experiments indicated that the central $Mg^{2+}$ ion, a carbonyl group at $C3^1$, and a carbomethoxy at $C13^2$ were the

## THE LIGHT-HARVESTING SYSTEM

structural requirements for Bchl binding [151–153]. All the above studies have proved a useful way of beginning to study the process of assembly of the purple bacteria antenna complexes *in vitro*.

### 5.4.2 Electron Microscopy Studies of RC-LH1 Core Complexes

Until very recently, the best visual structural information we had about the RC-LH1 core complex came from several low-resolution structures, based on single particle analyses of isolated LH1-RC cores [154,155] and electron microscopy (EM) of photosynthetic membranes and 2D crystals [100,156–165]. These studies suggested that the LH1 complex consists of a ring-like structure that encircles the photochemical reaction centre.

#### 5.4.2.1 The Rhodopseudomonas viridis Core Complex

LH1-RC core complexes were first visualized in electron microscopy studies of the photosynthetic membranes of the Bchl *b*-containing, "core only" bacterium, *Rps. viridis* [160,164,166,167]. This species is useful for electron microscopy studies because it possesses flat, lamellar photosynthetic membranes that contain extensive, quasi-crystalline 2D arrays of core complexes [168]. Fourier processing and averaging of the membrane images produced a map with a resolution of $\sim 20$ Å, which revealed the *Rps. viridis* core complex to be a roughly circular structure with hexagonal symmetry. This unit consists of a core of 45 Å diameter surrounded by a ring of about 20 Å wide (Figure 11) [164]. The whole structure is 100–120 Å in diameter. The central core, which extends through the PS membrane and protrudes $\sim 40$ Å above its surface on the periplasmic side, was postulated to be the photochemical RC. The surrounding ring, which consists of 12 and 6 subunits on the cytoplasmic and periplasmic sides, respectively, was proposed to be the LH1 antenna. Similar results were obtained from EM studies on the photosynthetic membrane of *Ectothiorhodospira halochloris* [168]. This led to the suggestion that this type of structure was a feature common to all Bchl *b*-containing photosynthetic membranes [164].

A later study of 2D crystals of the LH1-RC complex from *Rps. viridis* using cryo-EM produced a higher resolution (10 Å) projection map of the core complex structure [156]. This map also revealed three regions of density (an asymmetric central core and two concentric rings surrounding it), which were equated to a RC surrounded by an LH1 ring (Figure 12). Despite the improvement in resolution the projection map could not give unambiguous evidence as to the number of subunits in the LH1 ring. However, the density of the outer LH1 ring appeared to be significantly higher than that of the inner one. As each subunit of the LH1 complex from *Rps. viridis* consists of three polypeptides ($\alpha$, $\beta$ and $\gamma$) in a stoichiometric ratio of 1:1:1 [80,169], the higher density of the outer ring was interpreted as being due to the presence of two membrane-spanning helices per subunit. Accordingly, the inner, lower density ring was due to the third transmembrane helix of the subunit [156]. Analogous with the LH2

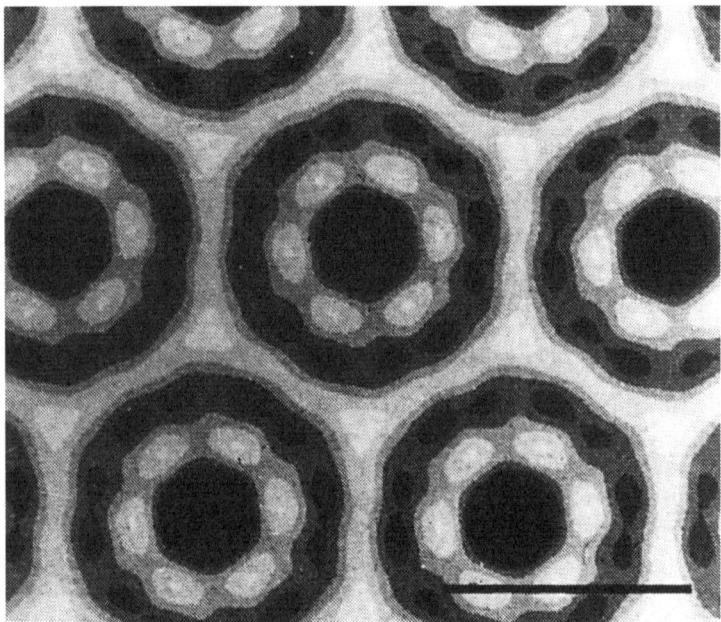

**Figure 11.** Fourier processed image of an electron micrograph of a tantalum/tungsten rotary shadowed, Triton X-100 treated, single sheet of photosynthetic membrane (with the plasmic face upwards) from *Rhodopseudomonas viridis*. [Reproduced with permission from Stark et al. [164].]

complex from *Rps. acidophila* [64], the Bchl *b* molecules of the *Rps. viridis* LH1 complex were assumed to be sandwiched between the membrane-spanning α-helices of the α and β apoproteins. This implied a total of 24 Bchl molecules per LH1 complex.

### 5.4.2.2 The Rhodospirillum rubrum Core Complex

Two-dimensional crystals of highly purified LH1 antenna from *Rs. rubrum* have been studied by cryo-EM techniques. These studies yielded an 8.5 Å resolution projection map of the LH1 complex [158]. The map showed the complex to consist of a closed ring of 16 αβ subunits. This ring had an overall diameter of 116 Å with a 68 Å diameter hole in the centre. Intriguingly, the hole in the centre of the structure was just large enough to house a RC *in vivo* (Figure 13). Three domains of density could be resolved within each subunit of the averaged projection map of the LH1 ring. The inner face of the ring showed 16 large peaks separated by $\sim 15$ Å. These peaks were proposed to be due to the α apoproteins of the complex. The outer face of the ring showed 16 less dense peaks, separated from each other by $\sim 20$ Å and from the inner peaks by $\sim 15$ Å, which were assigned to the β apoproteins of the complex. The lower density of the β apoproteins was thought to be due to their helices being more tilted than those of the α apoproteins. The density between the inner and outer peaks of the

# THE LIGHT-HARVESTING SYSTEM

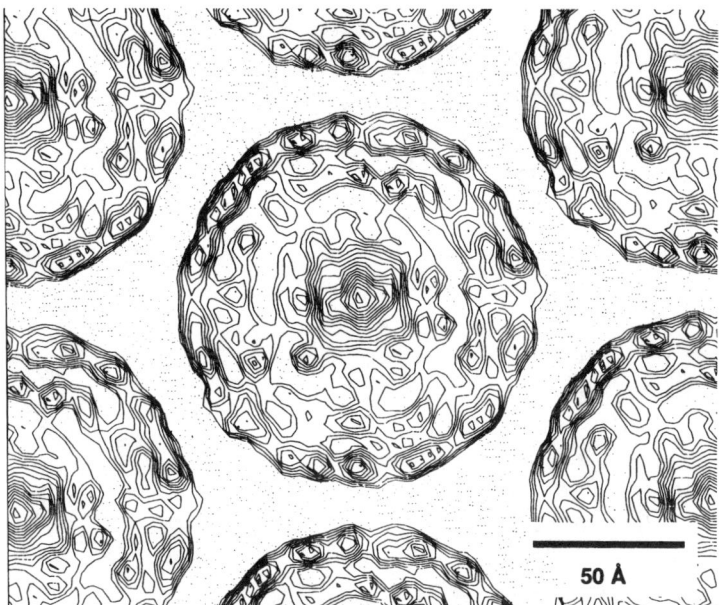

**Figure 12.** Unsymmetrized projection map of the RC-LH1 core complex from *Rhodopseudomonas viridis* calculated using the Fourier components from eight images to a resolution of 10 Å. [Reproduced from Ikeda-Yamasaki et al. [156], with permission.]

ring was attributed to the Bchl *a* and carotenoid molecules of the complex [158]. This model therefore implied a ratio of 32 Bchl *a* molecules per RC.

A criticism of the above work was that the LH1 complexes were reconstituted from their αβ subunits prior to crystallization and, therefore, the ring-like structure may not reflect the actual *in vivo* structure of the LH1 complex. However, this problem was addressed by Walz and Ghosh [165] who grew 2D crystals of the complete LH1-RC complex from a carotenoidless strain of *Rs. rubrum*. Image analysis of these crystals supported a model of the core complex in which the LH1 ring completely surrounded a RC that was probably free to assume various orientations within the ring.

Further cryo EM studies on 2D crystals of RC-LH1 from *Rs. rubrum* have shown this complex can produce two crystal forms [157]. The 8.5 Å projection maps of these crystals show a single RC surrounded by 16 LH1 αβ subunits. In one crystal form the subunits form a circular ring, whilst in the other the LH1 complex is clearly ellipsoidal. This suggested an inherent flexibility of the complex within the membrane. In contrast to the studies of Walz and Ghosh [165], it was observed that in both crystal forms the RC had a preferential orientation within the LH1 ring.

*5.4.3 Debate About the Size of the LH1 Ring*

The number of subunits that constitute the LH1 complex has long been a contentious matter. Although the 8.5 Å projection map of the LH1 complex

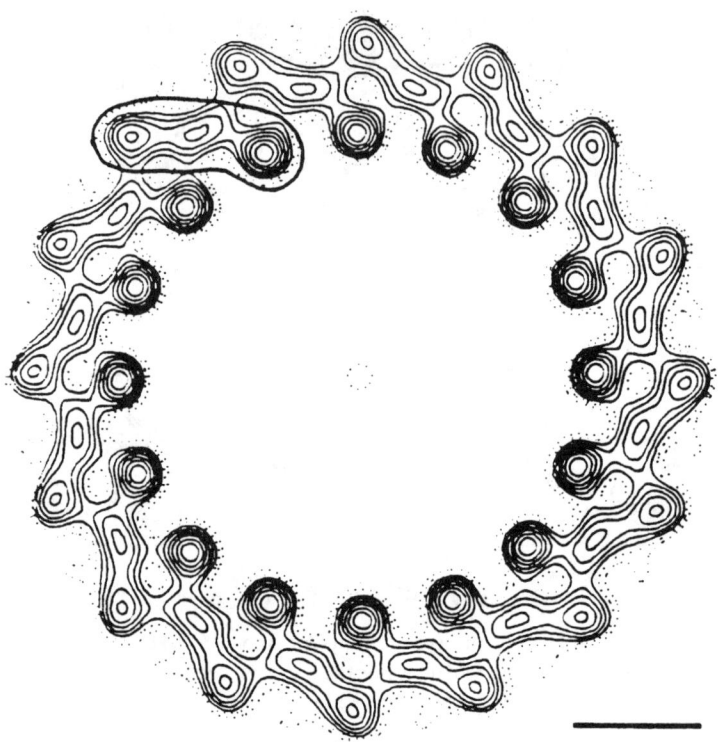

Figure 13. A 16-fold rotationally filtered image extracted from an 8.5 Å resolution projection map of a reconstituted LH1 complex from *Rhodospirillum rubrum*. The density corresponding to the α and β apoproteins can be clearly discerned. The hole in the centre of the structure is large enough to house a RC. The scale bar represents 20 Å. [Reproduced with permission from Karrasch et al. [158].]

from *Rs. rubrum* indicated it consisted of 16 αβ subunits, previous EM studies of the core complexes from the Bchl *a*-containing species *Rb. sphaeroides* [154], *Rs. molischianum* [155], and isolated LH1 from *Rhodobium* (*Rh.*) *marinum* [159] suggested the LH1 ring was, like that of *Rps. viridis*, composed of 12 αβ subunits. However, the resolution of these images was very low (40–50 Å) and analysis of them may have necessitated symmetrization according to a preconceived model [165].

Measurements of the ring size using biochemical methods have also given apparently conflicting results. Since there is a definite relationship between the size of an LH1 ring and its capacity to completely surround a RC, the stoichiometry of the LH1 antenna Bchls per RC provides a useful method of calculating the LH1 ring size (assuming each αβ subunit of the LH1 ring binds two Bchl molecules). Indeed, this method was used in several studies that encompassed a wide range of species [170–172]. Dawkins et al. [170] investigated the LH1 ring size of nine different species and strains of Bchl *a*-containing purple bacteria, and obtained Bchl *a*:RC ratios of between 21:1 and 41:1, with an average of ~30:1. The latter value was similar to that reported by Ueda et al. [173] for the Bchl *a*-containing species *Rb. sphaeroides*, *Chromatium* (*Chr.*) *vinosum* and *Rs. rubrum*. Due to the variability in the values it was difficult to assign a ring size for the LH1 complex, although the average value of ~30:1 would suggest an LH1 ring consisting of 16 αβ subunits. Careful measurements of the LH1 Bchl *a*:RC ratio for seven species of purple bacteria were made by Gall [171]. Although the data again showed some variability, an average value of $33 \pm 4$:1 was obtained. These data were consistent with the 16 αβ subunit model of the LH1 complex, assuming that each apoprotein dimer bound two Bchls. In contrast, measurements conducted by Francke and Amesz [172] on six Bchl *a*-containing and one Bchl *b*-containing species of purple bacteria yielded values that were more consistent with a ring composed of 12 αβ subunits. However, using molecular modeling techniques, Papiz et al. demonstrated that a ring consisting of 12 αβ subunits is not sufficient to completely enclose the RC [174].

There may be several reasons for the variability reported in the measurements of the size of the LH1 complex: (i) the ring size may vary between species; (ii) the instability of some of the isolated core complexes in detergent [170]; and (iii) there may be heterogeneity in the ring size within a given species [107]. Although no direct evidence exists for the latter in vivo, it was reported that LH1 forms 2D crystals of two different types [158]. One consisted of rings with a diameter of 116 Å and the other of rings with a diameter of 80 Å. The larger ring consisted of 16 αβ subunits, whereas the smaller rings probably consisted of ~9 αβ subunits. AFM studies of 2D crystals of *Rb. sphaeroides* LH1 complex also showed large complex-to-complex variations, not only in terms of size but also in shape [103]. It was suggested that the apparent flexibility of the LH1 ring allows passage of quinol from the RC $Q_B$ site to the membrane-bound quinone pool prior to reduction of the cytochrome $bc_1$ complex.

*5.4.4 Does the LH1 Complex Completely Encircle the RC?*

A structure of the core complex in which the LH1 ring encircles the RC is at odds with the hypothesis that electron transfer between the RC and cytochrome *bc*1 complex occurs via the diffusion of a membrane-bound quinone between them (reviewed in [175]). This fact, along with the differences reported for the size of the LH1 complex, have led some to question whether LH1 actually forms a complete ring in vivo. Electron microscopy analysis of tubular membranes from an LH2-null mutant of *Rb. sphaeroides* has shown that in this particular strain the LH1 rings are incomplete and form arcs around the RC [176]. However, another way to enable an LH1 antenna of less than 16 αβ subunits to completely encircle a RC would be to include an additional component in the ring. A strong body of evidence suggests that a protein, termed PufX, may be such a component in the LH1 antenna of *Rb. capsulatus* and *Rb. sphaeroides* [177–186]. In *Rs. rubrum* no gene (or gene product) homologous to *pufX* has been found [187]. However, a small 4 kDa polypeptide, termed the Ω-polypeptide, that copurifies with the LH1 αβ subunit may prove to be a candidate for this role [188,189].

### 5.4.5 The PufX Polypeptide

PufX is crucial for photosynthetic growth in *Rb. sphaeroides* and *Rb. capsulatus* strains that contain native LH1 antenna [177,181]. Its presence is also a requirement for both efficient ubiquinone/ubiquinol exchange between the RC and the cytochrome $bc_1$ complex as well as light driven electron-transfer and photophosphorylation [178,190,191]. Photosynthetic growth is not compromised by deletion of the *pufX* gene in RC-only mutants or those in which the LH1 antenna is reduced in size [182]. Additionally, suppressor mutants of *Rb. capsulatus* and *Rb. sphaeroides* that lacked the *pufX* gene apparently compensated for its loss by point mutations in the α and β LH1 apoproteins [177]. These observations, along with another that showed that the absence of PufX caused LH1 to increase in size by approximately two αβ subunits per RC support the suggestion that PufX plays an important role in the structural organization of the PSU [181,191].

The PufX protein from *Rb. capsulatus* and *Rb. sphaeroides* has been isolated and used in reconstitution experiments to examine its effect on LH1 antenna formation *in vitro* [186]. The isolated protein was shown to have a specific, high affinity for the LH1 α polypeptide and that it was inhibitory to LH1 formation at low concentrations. Further studies showed that the transmembrane region of PufX was responsible for this inhibition [183]. To explain these results it was suggested that PufX interrupts the molecular architecture of the LH1 ring (presumably at a position adjacent to the $Q_B$ site of the RC) by binding to the LH1 α apoprotein in the presence of Bchl *a*, thus preventing LH1 from impeding the free passage of ubiquinol from the RC to cytochrome $bc_1$. PufX not only has been implicated in organizing a specific orientation of the RC within the LH1 ring but, in LH2-minus mutants of *Rb. sphaeroides* that were grown under dark, partially aerobic conditions, it has also been shown to be responsible for the formation of long-range regular arrays of core complexes in the photosynthetic membrane [12,192]. Cryo-EM studies on 2D crystals of PufX-containing core complexes from *Rb. sphaeroides* suggest that the complexes form S-shaped dimers upon reconstitution into a lipid environment. In these studies PufX was purported to be the structural key for dimer formation rather than a quinone channel [193]. AFM studies of purified and reconstituted RC-LH1-PufX core complex from *Rb. sphaeroides* also implied that PufX was responsible for the formation of dimeric complexes [12]. However, in this case the RC was completely encircled by the LH1-PufX ring.

The exact structural and functional role of PufX, including how it interacts with the other components of the PSU, will most probably have to await the arrival of a high-resolution, 3D structure of a PufX-containing core complex. However, intriguingly, all AFM studies of LH1 have shown the complex to be closed, whereas EM studies have almost always shown the ring to be broken.

# THE LIGHT-HARVESTING SYSTEM 235

It is unclear why this difference is apparent but it may be inherent in the way the two techniques process the image data.

*5.4.6 Three-Dimensional Structure of the RC-LH1 Complex from Rps. palustris*

Although no high-resolution information of a core complex that contains PufX yet exists, a 4.8 Å resolution 3D structure of the RC-LH1 core complex from *Rps. palustris* has been published [94]. This structure shows a RC surrounded by an oval, rather than circular, LH1 complex that consists of 15 αβ subunits and their associated pigment molecules (Figure 14). The elliptical LH1 complex has approximate outer ellipsoid dimensions of 110 × 95 Å. The longest dimension of the inner LH1 ellipsoid is ca. 78 Å, allowing the RC (whose in-membrane longest dimension is about 70 Å) to be accommodated. The orientation of the long axis of the LH1 ellipse also coincides with the long "axis" of the RC so that LH1 appears to be wrapped tightly around the RC. The LH1 oval is prevented from completely encircling the RC by a single transmembrane helix (called protein W) that is out of register with the array of inner α apoproteins. The presence of protein W raises the question as to whether it is a 16th α apoprotein of the LH1 inner ring or a part of a PufX-like protein that acts to facilitate ubiquinone exchange. An equivalent gene for the PufX protein has not been found in the *Rps. palustris* genome. This is not entirely surprising because the PufX protein sequences, even for such two closely related species as *Rb. sphaeroides* and *Rb. capsulatus*, show only 23% identity and even for the α-helical membrane-spanning region of PufX the identity is only 38% [183]. To date the identity of the W gene is still unknown.

The structure reveals a second intriguing and important feature at the location of protein W. Inspection of Figure 14 reveals the elliptical LH1 structure to have a unique orientation with respect to the RC. Both the break of the outer ring of β apoprotein helices and helix W of the LH1 complex are positioned on the opposite side of RC with respect to the single transmembrane helix of the RC H subunit. The latter itself breaks the overall two-fold symmetry of the RC. The W helix is therefore located adjacent to the groove in the RC through which the tail of the secondary $UQ_B$ projects from. The hydrophobic tail of $UQ_B$ points towards the gap in the LH1 complex next to the W helix, strongly suggesting that it forms a "portal" through which fully reduced $UQ_B$ can communicate with the UQ pool located in the membrane lipid phase outside the LH1. It further suggests that the location of helix W imparts a significant role in the unique positioning of the RC within the RC-LH1 complex. Concomitantly, the location of the single transmembrane α-helix of the H subunit of the RC indicates that it could also play an important role in the orientation of the RC within the LH1 complex.

Although this structure could explain much of the biophysical and biochemical data obtained for RC-LH1 core complexes, it must be asked if it actually reflects the *in vivo* structure. The 10 Å resolution AFM images of core complexes in native membranes from *Rps. viridis* have shown that LH1 consists of a closed ellipsoid of 16 subunits [194]. However, the low resolution of the AFM

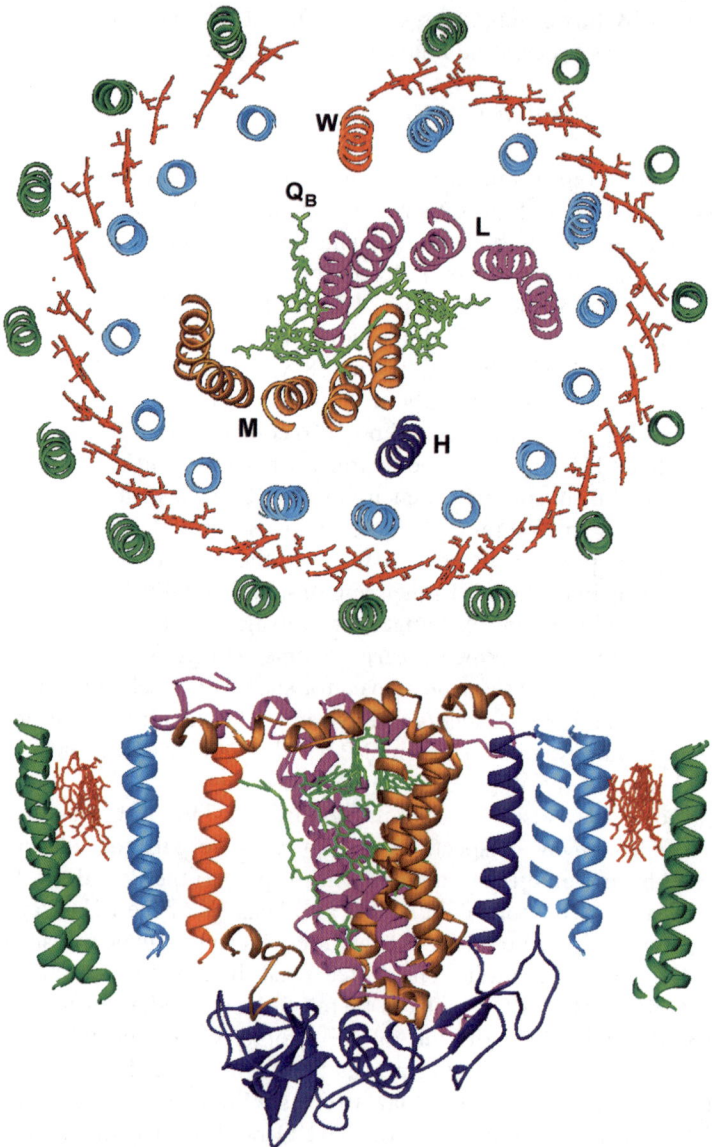

**Figure 14.** 4.8-Å Resolution structure of the RC-LH1 "core" complex from *Rhodopseudomonas palustris*. The upper diagram represents a view perpendicular to the plane of the membrane. The protein components of the complex are drawn as ribbons. The RC H, L and M subunits are colored blue, mauve and orange, respectively. The LH1 α and β polypeptides are shown in turquoise and green, respectively. Sandwiched between these polypeptides are the Bchl *a* molecules (red). Protein W is labeled and depicted in red. The RC pigments and ubiquinones are represented as stick models and shown in lime green. The lower diagram is a cross sectional view of the core complex viewed parallel to the plane of the membrane. The components are color coded as described for the upper diagram. [Adapted from Roszak et al. [94].]

images prevents visualization of the break in the LH1 structure. Interestingly, these experiments have also shown that the LH1 subunits rearrange into a circular ring structure after removal of the RC from the core complex. These AFM studies clearly show that the oval structure for the RC-LH1 complex from *Rps. palustris* observed in the crystalline state is indicative of its *in vivo* condition.

## 5.5 Arrangement of the Photosynthetic Apparatus in the ICM

*5.5.1 Spectroscopic Investigations of PSU Organization*

Although we have a relative wealth of information about the structures of the LH2 [64,92,93] and RC-LH1 complexes [165,94] reconstituted in various systems, there is a paucity of detail about the spatial relationships and interactions between the complexes in the photosynthetic membrane *in vivo*. Some early spectroscopic studies led to theoretical models of the arrangement of the photosynthetic apparatus, although at the time these had no structural basis [195,196]. Antenna organization in the photosynthetic membrane was first visualized in EM studies that were designed to investigate the membrane architecture of *Thiocapsa pfennigii* [197] and *Rps. viridis* cells. At the time the significance of what was recorded on the electron micrographs was not recognized. However, subsequent EM studies were designed to specifically address the question of how the components of the purple bacterial PSU were organized [160,164,168,198–200]. More recently, time-resolved picosecond absorption spectroscopy, fluorescence decay kinetics and fluorescence yield measurements have all been recruited to probe antenna organization in the natural photosynthetic membrane [201–205]. This work has enabled several models of antenna organization to be proposed (reviewed in [206]). At one extreme, it is purported that there is a static arrangement of a group of antenna pigments that are permanently associated with a single RC. In this "puddle" model a PSU has a totally independent existence and is not energetically connected to any other RCs. The other extreme envisages that RCs are embedded in a "lake" of LH pigments, and that they are all energetically connected [195,196,201]. In such an arrangement, if energy absorbed by an antenna was transferred to a RC that was in an inactive or "closed" state (*i.e.*, the RC was in the process of performing photochemistry) then that energy could migrate over the network of antennas until it arrived at an active or "open" RC before being lost. Although there is evidence to suggest the "lake" model is applicable to many of the purple bacteria [207], the actual organization of LH and RC complexes in the membrane may be represented by an intermediate case in which individual PSUs have a limited ability to transfer energy between each other [202,203,205]. A recent EM study on the photosynthetic membranes of a *Rb. sphaeroides* LH2-minus mutant has even suggested that the arrangement of PSUs may vary in different regions of the membrane [12].

### 5.5.2 Molecular Modeling of the PSU

A molecular modeling approach has also been employed to investigate PSU organization [174,208]. Using known 3D structural information about the individual components of the PSU, Papiz et al. [174] proposed an elegant model of the PSU of the LH2-containing purple bacterium, *Rps. acidophila*. In the model the structure of the *Rb. sphaeroides* RC [90] was built into an LH1 ring, the structure of which was based on a combination of the known structure of LH2 from *Rps. acidophila* [64] and the 8.5 Å projection map of the *Rs. rubrum* LH1 complex [158]. The model showed that eight LH2 complexes can surround each RC-LH1 core complex in a lattice with hexagonal symmetry and that this may represent the PSU (Figure 15). However, in reality the lattice can only be approximately regular as other membrane proteins, such as ATPases and cytochromes, must also be incorporated into the membrane.

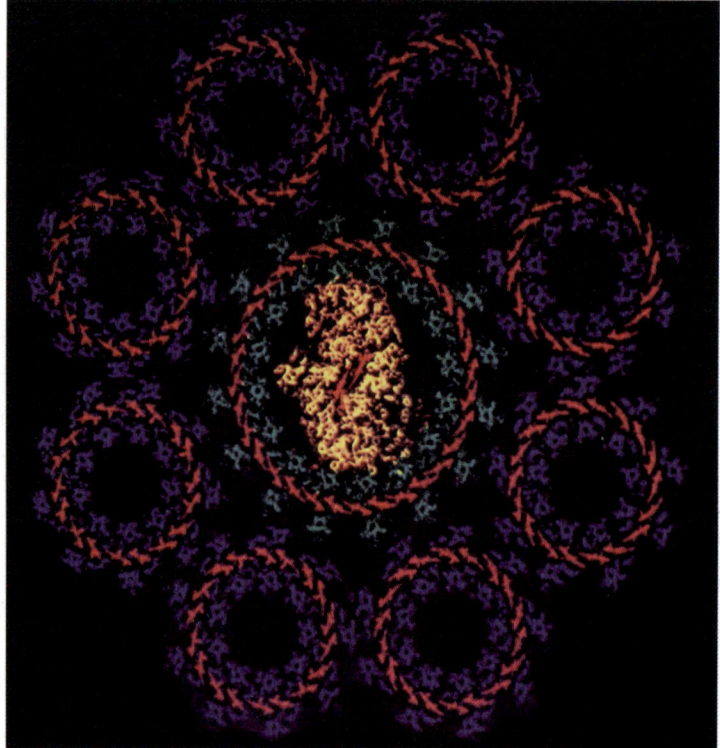

**Figure 15.** A model of the PSU, consisting of a core complex surrounded by eight LH2 complexes. The figure represents a section of a view perpendicular to the membrane plane at a height level with the B850 and B880 Bchls of the LH2 and LH1 complex, respectively, and the RC special pair. LH2 polypeptides are shown in blue, LH1 polypeptides in green, and RC polypeptides in yellow. The Bchl molecules are colored red. [Reproduced from Papiz et al. [174].]

Hu et al. took a similar approach [208], only in this case the known structure of LH2 from *Rs. molischianum* [92] was used to model the *Rb. sphaeroides* PSU. The model detailed the pigment organization of the PSU and enabled a quantum mechanical description of the entire light-harvesting process. To date, no direct evidence exists to either confirm or disprove such models and more detailed studies on intact photosynthetic membranes are required to test them. Nevertheless, they clearly illustrate the potential of modeling techniques provided that detailed structural information on the proteins of interest is available.

### 5.5.3 Energy Transfer Within the PSU

The relative wealth of detailed structural information available for the components of the bacterial PSU in combination with advances in very fast flash photolysis techniques (reviewed in [209,210]) has allowed dissection of the energy transfer events that occur upon absorption of a photon by LH2 and the subsequent separation of charge in the RC. Energy transfer within the PSU is a directed process that is "guided" by the energy gradient going from LH2 to LH1 and then to the RC (B800 → B850 → B875 → RC) [211,212]. In this way the photosynthetic light-harvesting system acts as a funnel to direct excitation energy to the RC. It is this directionality that is the key to its efficiency. The importance of this type of "energy funneling" is illustrated by large, artificial antenna systems that lack it. In these cases, once a critical size is exceeded, the absorbed light energy gets "lost" and is unable to perform useful work [213].

Energy transfer processes within the PSU can be described in terms of a combination of three distinct transfer mechanisms. Each of these mechanisms represents an extreme and the actual situation *in vivo* is probably represented by an intermediate process. The first type of energy transfer process is the Förster induced dipole–dipole resonance transfer mechanism [214]. This mechanism, which typically applies to weakly coupled pigments, separated by about 20–80 Å, occurs via a non-radiative resonance process that can be thought of equivalent to (but not actually occurring as) a donor molecule emitting absorbed photons as fluorescence and the acceptor molecule re-absorbing the emitted photons [215]. Energy transfer by this mechanism is governed by several factors: (i) the magnitude of the spectral overlap of the fluorescence of the donor and the absorbance of the acceptor; (ii) the distance, $R$, between the donor and acceptor; (iii) geometry of the donor and acceptor transition dipoles; and (iv) the refractive index of the medium between the donor and acceptor. There is a $1/R^6$ dependence of energy transfer by the Förster mechanism.

The strong Coulombic coupling of the transition dipoles of closely interacting pigments, such as those in the LH2 B850 ring, gives rise to the second type of energy transfer process [216]. A third possible mechanism of energy transfer can occur when pigments are in van der Waals contact. In this case energy transfer, via electron exchange, occurs in a Dexter-type process [217]. Such an exchange is of crucial importance for the deactivation of triplet state Bchls [218].

The physical mechanisms of energy transfer within the purple bacterial PSU depend upon which pigments are involved and whether they are strongly coupled or weakly interacting. Once a Bchl pigment has absorbed a photon it must transfer that energy to another pigment before the absorbed energy can be lost in a wasteful process such as fluorescence. Therefore, the organization of pigments in an antenna system is an important factor, *i.e.*, the time required for energy migration from pigment to pigment must be short compared with the time required for a non-productive process. As the lifetime of the first excited singlet state of a Bchl *a* molecule is of the order of a few nanoseconds, antenna pigments must transfer energy to the RC in less than $\sim 100$ ps [211,219].

Examination of the structure of LH2 from *Rps. acidophila* [64,115] reveals an organization that is beautifully adapted to optimize the orientation of the Bchls for a rapid and efficient energy transfer (refer to Figure 5). Kinetic studies using low energy pump–probe techniques have shown that energy transfer from B800 to B850 in this complex takes place with a rate constant of 0.9 ps at room temperature [220]. This energy transfer reaction is remarkably temperature insensitive and decreases to only 1.8 ps at 77 K and 2.4 ps at 1.4 K [221,222]. Measurements of the decay of the anisotropy of the excited B800 population at room temperature indicated a rapid, but limited, B800 to B800 energy transfer step [223]. The time constant for this decay was 0.3 ps, which translated into a B800 to B800 transfer time of about 0.5 ps [224]. The energy transfer kinetics in the LH2 complexes from *Rb. sphaeroides* and *Rps. palustris* have also been investigated [225]. These experiments also showed that energy transfer from B800 to B850 takes place with a rate constant of 0.7 ps at room temperature, and 1.8 ps at 77 K. Low temperature (1.2 and 4.2 K) spectral hole burning studies on mutated LH2 complexes from *Rb. sphaeroides* gave B800 to B850 transfer times of between 1.7 and 2.5 ps. This allowed the B800 to B850 energy transfer to be modeled in terms of a Förster process [226–229].

Upon arrival at the B850 ring, excitation energy can remain there for $>1$ ns, provided no other antenna complex is nearby [230]. The energy is rapidly mobile within the B850 ring and, since the B850 molecules are strongly interacting, the excited state is rapidly delocalized with transfers between Bchls occurring on the 50–150 fs timescale [231,232]. The rapid delocalization of excitation energy around the circumference of the LH2 ring has important implications for the function of the PSU. Within the excited state lifetime of LH2, every B850 molecule has the possibility of being visited by the excited state many times and so the rings of B850 molecules can be thought of as "storage rings". As a result of this, the probability of energy transfer out of the ring is equal from each and every B850 molecule. This means that energy is available for transfer from any part of the ring to any part of a neighboring ring, provided they are close enough. As such, a precise arrangement of LH2 and LH1 antenna complexes is not a prerequisite for the efficient function of the PSU. LH1 complexes simply need to lie close to excited LH2 complexes for energy transfer to occur with high efficiency [211]. The extent of the excitonic delocalization within the B850 ring is still debated (see review [212]) but one view is that it is probably delocalized over just a few Bchls of the ring [233–239].

## THE LIGHT-HARVESTING SYSTEM

However, single molecule spectroscopy studies of LH complexes, in which there is much less disorder in the system, have indicated the energy is much more delocalized over the ring [240–247]. Evidently, from this work, the exact number of Bchl $a$ molecules in the energy delocalization is contentious and much more experimentation is required to unambiguously resolve this issue.

The next energy transfer step, from B850 of LH2 to B880 of LH1, has a multiexponential rate with the major phase having a rate constant of 2–4 ps [224]. Once again, when the energy reaches the circular array of B880 molecules it is rapidly delocalized with B880 to B880 transfers occurring in about 80 fs [248]. The final and slowest energy transfer step, from B880 to the RC, occurs in about 20–40 ps [249–252]. The relatively slow rate of this transfer is a consequence of the distance between the RC special pair Bchls (P870) and the antenna Bchls [209]. Why this transfer rate is so slow, and why are the LH1 Bchl $a$ molecules not positioned nearer to the RC special pair Bchls? Oxidation of just a single Bchl $a$ molecule in LH1 results in a strong quenching of the fluorescence yield (which is equivalent to the singlet excited state lifetime), thereby preventing LH1 from acting as an effective antenna for the RC [253]. As oxidized P870 is strong enough to oxidize antenna Bchl $a$ molecules, it

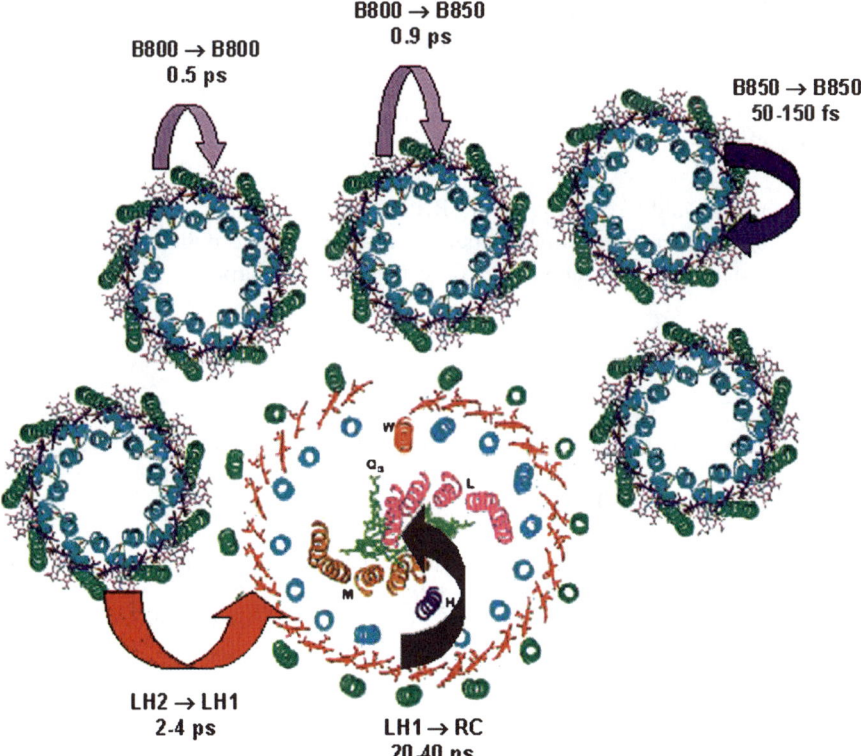

**Figure 16.** A schematic diagram summarizing the intra- and intermolecular energy transfer times within the purple bacterial PSU.

makes sense for the LH1 antenna Bchls to be located sufficiently far away to prevent this oxidation from occurring. Therefore, the actual positioning of the LH1 antenna Bchls relative to P870 is simply a compromise: they are sufficiently close enough to allow efficient energy transfer but not close enough to allow the possibility of electron transfer. Figure 16 summarizes the timescales for energy transfer within the purple bacterial PSU. Notably, all the energy transfer experiments performed on photosynthetic membranes are based on a very simplistic view of the organization of the antenna complexes. When a better picture of this organization becomes available the experiments will have to be revisited.

## 5.6 Conclusions

A great deal of progress has been made on understanding the structure and function of isolated, purified LH complexes. Though this will continue, the study of these complexes is entering a much more biological phase. The big questions are now how they are assembled and inserted into the photosynthetic membrane, and how they are arranged in that membrane. Indeed, how is this arrangement controlled and how do changes in their supramolecular organization effect function? We eagerly anticipate these questions being addressed.

## Acknowledgements

The authors would like to thank the BBSRC, the Wellcome Trust and NEDO for funding of their work, and numerous co-workers and colleagues who have contributed to many of the studies described in this chapter.

## References

1. J.M. Imhoff, U. Bias-Imhoff, Lipids, quinones and fatty acids of anoxygenic phototrophic bacteria, in: *Anoxygenic Photosynthetic Bacteria* (1995) (R.E. Blankenship, M. T. Madigan, C. E Bauer, eds.), Kluwer Academic Publishers, Dordrecht, pp. 179–205.
2. G. Drews, J.R. Golecki, Structure, molecular organization, and biosynthesis of membranes of purple bacteria, in: *Anoxygenic Photosynthetic Bacteria* (1995) (R.E. Blankenship, M.T. Madigan, C. E Bauer, eds.), Kluwer Academic Publishers, Dordrecht, pp. 231–257.
3. P.D. Giesbrecht, G. Drews, Elektronenmikroskopiische untersuschungen uber die entwicklung der chromatophoren von. *Rsp. molischianum. Arch. Mikrobiol.* **43** (1962) 152–161.
4. S.M. Crook, S.B. Treml, M.L.P. Collins, Immunochemical ultrastructural analysis of chromatophore membrane formation in. *Rhodospirillum rubrum. J. Bacteriol.* **167** (1986) 89–95.

5. G.K. Cohen-Bazire, R. Kunisawa, The fine structure of *Rhodospirillum rubrum*. *J. Cell Biol.* **16** (1963) 401–419.
6. E.S. Boatman, Observations on the fine structure of spheroplasts of *Rhodospirillum rubrum*. *J. Cell Biol.* **20** (1964) 297–311.
7. D.D.F. Hickman, A.W. Frenkel, Observations on the structure of *Rhodospirillum rubrum*. *J. Cell Biol.* **25** (1965) 279–291.
8. B. Wakim, G. Drews, J. Oelze, The unusual mode of altering the cellular membrane content by *Rhodosprillum tenue*. *FEMS Microbiol. Lett.* **4** (1978) 199–201.
9. J. Weckesser, G. Drews, H. Mayer, Lipopolysaccharides of photosynthetic prokaryotes. *Annu. Rev. Microbiol.* **33** (1979) 215–239.
10. J. Oelze, G. Drews, Membranes of photosynthetic bacteria. *Biochim. Biophys. Acta* **265** (1972) 209–239.
11. J. Chory, T. Donohue, A.R. Varga, L.A. Staehelin, S. Kaplan, Induction of the photosynthetic membranes of *Rhodopseudomonas sphaeroides:* Biochemical and morphological studies. *J. Bacteriol.* **159** (1984) 540–554.
12. C.A. Siebert, P. Qian, D. Fotiadis, A.C. Engel, C.N. Hunter, P.A. Bullough, Molecular architecture of photosynthetic membranes in *Rhodobacter sphaeroides:* The role of PufX. *EMBO J.* (2004) 1–11.
13. J. Lascelles, Adaptation to form bacteriochlorophyll in *Rhodobacter sphaeroides*: Changes in activity of enzymes concerned in pyrrole synthesis. *Biochem. J.* **72** (1959) 508–515.
14. S.C.M. Holt, A.G. Marr, Effect of light intensity on the formation of intracytoplasmic membrane in *Rhodospirillum rubrum*.. *J. Bacteriol.* **89** (1965) 1421–1429.
15. B.G. Marrs, H. Gest, Regulation of bacteriochlorophyll synthesis by oxygen in respiratory mutants of *Rhodopseudomonas capsulata*. *J. Bacteriol.* **114** (1973) 1052–1057.
16. H.H. Lampe, J. Oelze, G. Drews, Die fraktionierung des membransystems von *Rhodopseudomonas capsulata* und seine morphogenese. *Arch. Mikrobiol.* **83** (1972) 78–94.
17. M.T. Madigan, J.C. Cox, H. Gest, Photopigments in *Rhodopseudomonas capsulata* cells grown anaerobically in darkness. *J. Bacteriol.* **150** (1982) 1422–1429.
18. J.N. Sturgis, C.N. Hunter, R.A. Niederman, Assembly of intracytoplasmic membranes in *Rhodobacter sphaeroides* mutants lacking light-harvesting and reaction center complexes. *FEMS Symp.* **53** (1990) 219–226.
19. J.N. Sturgis, R.A. Niederman, The effect of different levels of the B800–850 light-harvesting complex on intracytoplasmic membrane development on *Rhodobacter sphaeroides*. *Arch. Microbiol.* **165** (1996) 235–242.
20. R.J. Cogdell, T.D. Howard, N.W. Isaacs, K. McLuskey, A.T. Gardiner, Structural factors which control the position of the $Q_y$ absorption band of bacteriochlorophyll *a* in purple bacterial antenna complexes. *Photosynth. Res.* **74** (2002) 135–141.
21. A. Garcia, L.P. Vernon, B. Ke, H.A. Mollenhauer, Structural and photochemical properties of *Rhodopseudomonas palustris* subchromatophore particles obtained by treatment with Triton X-100. *Biochemistry* **7** (1968) 319–325.
22. J.P. Thornber, J.M. Olsen, D.M. Williams, M.L. Clayton, Isolation of the reaction center of *Rhodopseudomonas viridis*. *Biochim. Biophys. Acta* **172** (1969) 351–354.
23. J.P. Thornber, M.K. Sokoloff, Photochemical reactions of purple bacteria as revealed by studies of three spectrally different carotenobacteriochlorophyll-protein complexes isolated from *Chromatium* strain D. *Biochemistry* **9** (1970) 2688–2698.

24. K.F. Nieth, G. Drews, Protein patterns of intracytoplasmic membranes and reaction center particles isolated from *Rhodopseudomonas capsulata*. *Arch. Microbiol.* **96** (1974) 161–174.
25. N.N. Firsov, G. Drews, Differentiation of the intracytoplasmic membrane of *Rhodopseudomonas palustris* induced by variations of oxygen partial pressure of light intensity. *Arch. Microbiol.* **115** (1977) 299–306.
26. J.P. Thornber, Thirty years of fun with antenna pigment–proteins and photochemical reaction centers: A tribute to the people who have influenced my career. *Photosynth. Res.* **44** (1995) 3–22.
27. R.J. Cogdell, H. Zuber, P.J. Thornber, G. Drews, G. Gingras, R.A. Niederman, W.W. Parson, G. Feher, Recommendations for the naming of photochemical reaction centers and light-harvesting pigment–protein complexes from purple photosynthetic bacteria. *Biochim. Biophys. Acta.* **806** (1985) 185–186.
28. R.A. Emerson, W.A. Arnold, The photochemical reaction in photosynthesis. *J. Gen. Physiol.* **16** (1932) 191–205.
29. J. Aagaard, W.R. Sistrom, Control of synthesis of reaction center bacteriochlorophyll in photosynthetic bacteria. *Photochem. Photobiol.* **15** (1972) 209–225.
30. A.T. Gardiner, R.J. Cogdell, S. Takaichi, The effect of growth conditions on the light-harvesting apparatus in *Rhodopseudomonas acidophila*. *Photosynth. Res.* **38** (1993) 159–167.
31. E. Halloren, G. McDermott, J.G. Lindsay, C. Miller, A.A. Freer, N.W. Isaacs, R.J. Cogdell, Studies on the light-harvesting complexes from the thermotolerant purple bacterium *Rhodopseudomonas cryptolactis*. *Photosynth. Res.* **44** (1995) 149–155.
32. G. Cohen-Bazire, W.R. Sistrom, R.Y. Stanier, Kinetic studies of pigment synthesis by purple non-sulphur bacteria. *J. Cell. Comp. Physiol.* **49** (1957) 25–68.
33. J. Zeilstra-Ryalls, M. Gomelsky, J.M. Eraso, A. Yeliseev, J. O'Gara, S. Kaplan, Control of photosystem formation in *Rhodobacter sphaeroides*. *J. Bacteriol.* **180** (1998) 2801–2809.
34. C.E. Bauer, Regulation of photosynthesis gene expression, in: *Anoxygenic Photosynthetic Bacteria* (1995) (R.E. Blankenship, M.T. Madigan, C.E. Bauer, eds.), Kluwer Academic Publishers, Dordrecht, pp. 1221–1234.
35. C.S.B. Young, J.T. Beatty, Regulation of purple bacterial LH complexes, in: *Light-Harvesting Antennas in Photosynthesis* (2003) (B.R.P. Green, W.W. Parson, eds.), Kluwer Academic Publishers, Dordrecht, pp. 449–470.
36. L. Gong, J.K. Lee, S. Kaplan, The *Q* gene of *Rhodobacter sphaeroides*: Its role in *puf* operon expression and spectral complex assembly. *J. Bacteriol.* **176** (1994) 2946–2961.
37. J.K. Lee, K.C. Terlesky, F.R. Tabita, Cloning and characterization of two groESL operons of *Rhodobacter sphaeroides*: Transcriptional regulation of the heat-induced groESL operon. *J. Bacteriol.* **179** (1997) 487–495.
38. A. Meryandini, G. Drews, Import and assembly of the. alpha. and .beta.-polypeptides of the light-harvesting complex I (B870) in the membrane system of *Rhodobacter capsulatus* investigated in an in vitro translation system. *Photosynth. Res.* **47** (1996) 21–31.
39. J.I. Oh, J.M. Eraso, S. Kaplan, Interacting regulatory circuits involved in orderly control of photosynthesis gene expression in *Rhodobacter sphaeroides* 2.4.1. *J. Bacteriol.* **182** (2000) 3081–3087.
40. J.M. Eraso, S. Kaplan, Complex regulatory activities associated with the histidine kinase PrrB in expression of photosynthesis genes in *Rhodobacter sphaeroides* 2.4.1. *J. Bacteriol.* **178** (1996) 7037–7046.

41. J.P. O'Gara, J.M. Eraso, S. Kaplan, A redox-responsive pathway for aerobic regulation of photosynthesis gene expression in *Rhodobacter sphaeroides* 2.4.1. *J. Bacteriol.* **180** (1998) 4044–4050.
42. J.I. Oh, I.J. Ko, S. Kaplan, The default state of the membrane-localized histidine kinase PrrB of *Rhodobacter sphaeroides* 2.4.1 is in the kinase-positive mode. *J. Bacteriol.* **183** (2001) 6807–6814.
43. J.M.K. Eraso, S. Kaplan, Oxygen-insensitive synthesis of the photosynthetic membranes of *Rhodobacter sphaeroides:* A mutant histidine kinase. *J. Bacteriol.* **177** (1995) 2695–2706.
44. K. Inoue, J.-L. Kouadio, C.S. Mosely, C.E. Bauer, Isolation and in vitro phosphorylation of sensory transduction components controlling anaerobic induction of light harvesting and reaction center gene expression in *Rhodobacter capsulatus*. *Biochemistry* **34** (1995) 391–396.
45. C.S. Mosley, J.Y. Suzuki, C.E. Bauer, Identification and molecular genetic characterization of a sensor kinase responsible for coordinately regulating light harvesting and reaction center gene expression in response to anaerobiosis. *J. Bacteriol.* **176** (1994) 7566–7573.
46. M.W. Sganga, C.E. Bauer, Regulatory factors controlling photosynthetic reaction center and light-harvesting gene expression in *Rhodobacter capsulatus*. *Cell* **68** (1992) 945–954.
47. J.H. Zeilstra-Ryalls, S. Kaplan, Role of the *fnrL* gene in photosystem gene expression and photosynthetic growth of *Rhodobacter sphaeroides* 2.4.1. *J. Bacteriol.* **180** (1998) 1496–1503.
48. J.H.K. Zeilstra-Ryalls, S. Kaplan, Aerobic and anaerobic regulation in *Rhodobacter sphaeroides* 2.4.1: the role of the *fnrL* gene. *J. Bacteriol.* **177** (1995) 6422–6431.
49. J.H. Zeilstra-Ryalls, K. Gabbert, R. Kranz, S. Kaplan, Analysis of the *fnrL* gene and its function in *Rhodobacter capsulatus*. *J. Bacteriol.* **179** (1997) 6422–6431.
50. M. Gomelsky, I.M. Horne, H.J. Lee, J.M. Pemberton, A.G. McEwan, S. Kaplan, Domain structure, oligomeric state, and mutational analysis of PpsR, the *Rhodobacter sphaeroides* repressor of photosystem gene expression. *J. Bacteriol.* **182** (2000) 2253–2261.
51. M.K. Gomelsky, S. Kaplan, Genetic evidence that PspR from *Rhodobacter sphaeroides* 2.4.1 functions as a repressor of *puc* and *bchF* expression. *J. Bacteriol.* **177** (1995) 1634–1637.
52. R.J.P. Penfold, J.M. Pemberton, Sequencing, chromosomal inactivation and functional expression of *ppsR*, a gene which represses carotenoid and bacteriochlorophyll synthesis in *Rhodobacter sphaeroides*. *J. Bacteriol.* **176** (1994) 2869–2876.
53. M.K. Gomelsky, S. Kaplan, Molecular genetic analysis suggesting interactions between AppA and PspR in regulation of photosynthesis gene expression in *Rhodobacter sphaeroides* 2.4.1. *J. Bacteriol.* **179** (1997) 128–134.
54. M. Gomelsky, S. Kaplan, AppA, a redox regulator of photosystem formation in *Rhodobacter sphaeroides* 2.4.1, is a flavoprotein-Identification of a novel FAD binding domain. *J. Biol. Chem.* **273** (1998) 35319–35325.
55. J.J. Buggy, M.W. Sganga, C.E. Bauer, Characterization of a light-responding trans-activator responsible for differentially controlling reaction center and light-harvesting-I gene expression in *Rhodobacter capsulatus*. *J. Bacteriol.* **176** (1994) 6936–6943.
56. H. Shimada, T. Wada, H. Handa, H. Ohta, H. Mizoguchi, K. Nishimura, T. Masada, Y. Shioi, K. Takamiya, A transcription factor with a leucine-zipper

motif involved in light-dependent inhibition of expression of the *puf* operon in the photosynthetic bacterium *Rhodobacter sphaeroides*. *Plant Cell Physiol.* **37** (1996) 515–522.
57. X.H. Zeng, S. Kaplan, TspO as a modulator of the repressor/antirepressor (PpsR/AppA) regulatory system in *Rhodobacter sphaeroides* 2.4.1. *J. Bacteriol.* **183** (2001) 6355–6364.
58. C. Mackenzie, M. Choudhary, F.W. Larimer, P.F. Predki, S. Stilwagen, J.P. Armitage, R.D. Barber, T.J. Donohue, J.P. Hosler, J.E. Newman, J.P. Shapleigh, R.E. Sockett, J. Zeilstra-Ryalls, S. Kaplan, The home stretch, a first analysis of the nearly completed genome of *Rhodobacter sphaeroides* 2.4.1. *Photosynth. Res.* **70** (2001) 19–41.
59. G.E. Corson, K.V.P. Nagashima, K. Matsuura, Y. Sakuragi, R. Wettasinge, H. Qin, R. Allen, D.B. Knaff, Genes encoding light-harvesting and reaction center proteins from *Chromatium vinosum*. *Photosynth. Res.* **59** (1999) 39–52.
60. A.T. Gardiner, R.C. MacKenzie, S.J. Barrett, K. Kaiser, R.J. Cogdell, The genes for the peripheral antenna complex apoproteins from *Rhodopseudomonas acidophila* 7050 form a multigene family, in: *Res. Photosynth. Proc. 9th Int. Congr. Photosynth.* (1992) (N. Murata, ed.), Kluwer Academic Publishers, Dordrecht, pp. 77–80.
61. M.H. Tadros, E. Katsiou, M.A. Hoon, N. Yurkova, D.P. Ramji, Cloning of a new antenna gene cluster and expression analysis of the antenna gene family of *Rhodopseudomonas palustris*. *Eur. J. Biochem.* **217** (1993) 867–875.
62. A.T. Gardiner, R.C. MacKenzie, S.J. Barrett, K. Kaiser, R.J. Cogdell, The purple photosynthetic bacterium *Rhodopseudomonas acidophila* contains multiple puc peripheral antenna complex (LH2) genes: Cloning and initial characterization of four $\alpha\beta$ pairs. *Photosynth. Res.* **49** (1996) 223–235.
63. A.T. Gardiner, S. Takaichi, R.J. Cogdell, The effect of changes in light intensity and temperature on the peripheral antenna of *Rhodopseudomonas acidophila*. *Biochem. Soc. Trans.* **21** (1993) 6S.
64. G. McDermott, S.M. Prince, A.A. Freer, A.M. Hawthornthwaite-Lawless, M.Z. Papiz, R.J. Cogdell, N.W. Isaacs, Crystal structure of an integral membrane light-harvesting complex from photosynthetic bacteria. *Nature* **374** (1995) 517–521.
65. H. Zuber, R.J. Cogdell, Structure and organization of purple bacterial antenna complexes, in: *Anoxygenic Photosynthetic Bacteria* (1995) (R.E. Blakenship, M.T. Madigan, C.E. Bauer, eds.), Kluwer Academic Publishers, Dordrecht, pp. 315–348.
66. J.A. Shiozawa, P.A. Cuendet, G. Drews, H. Zuber, Isolation and characterization of the polypeptide components from light-harvesting pigment–protein complex B800–850 of *Rhodopseudomonas capsulata*. *Eur. J. Biochem.* **111** (1980) 455–460.
67. T. Nozawa, M. Ohta, M. Hatano, H. Hayashi, K. Shimada, Sequence homology and structural similarity among B 870 (B 890) polypeptides of purple photosynthetic bacteria and the mode of bacteriochlorophyll binding. *Chem. Lett.* **3** (1985) 343–346.
68. M.H. Tadros, G. Drews, Pigment–proteins of antenna complexes from purple non-sulfur bacteria: Localization in the membrane, alignments of primary structure and structural predictions. *FEMS Symp.* **53** (1990) 181–192.
69. H. Zuber, R.A. Brunisholz, Structure and function of antenna polypeptides and chlorophyll-protein complexes: Principles and variability, in: *Chlorophylls* (1991) (H. Scheer, ed.), CRC, Boca Raton, FL, pp. 627–703.
70. R.A. Brunisholz, H. Zuber, Structure, function and organization of antenna polypeptides and antenna complexes from the three families of Rhodospirillaneae. *J. Photochem. Photobiol B.* **15** (1992) 113–140.

71. R.A. Brunisholz, V. Wiemken, F. Suter, R. Bachofen, H. Zuber, The light-harvesting polypeptides of *Rhodospirillum rubrum*. II. Localization of the amino-terminal regions of the light-harvesting polypeptides B 870-α and B 870-β and the reaction-center subunit L at the cytoplasmic side of the photosynthetic membrane of *Rhodospirillum rubrum* G-9. *Hoppe-Seyler's Z. Physiol. Chem.* **365** (1984) 689–701.
72. H. Zuber, Structure and function of light-harvesting complexes and their polypeptides. *Photochem. Photobiol.* **42** (1985) 821–844.
73. R.A. Brunisholz, P.A. Ceundet, R. Theiler, H. Zuber, The complete amino acid sequence of the single light harvesting protein from chromatophores of *Rhodospirillum rubrum* G-9+. *FEBS Lett.* **129** (1981) 150–154.
74. R.A. Brunisholz, F. Suter, H. Zuber, The light-harvesting polypeptides of *Rhodospirillum rubrum*. I. The amino acid sequence of the second light-harvesting polypeptide B 880-β (B 870-β) of *Rhodospirillum rubrum* S 1 and the carotenoidless mutant G-9. Aspects of the molecular structure of the two light-harvesting polypeptides B 880-α (B 870-α) and B 880-β (B 870-β) and of the antenna complex B 880 (B 870) from *Rhodospirillum rubrum*. *Hoppe-Seyler's Z. Physiol. Chem.* **365** (1984) 675–688.
75. R. Theiler, F. Suter, V. Wiemken, H. Zuber, The light-harvesting polypeptides of *Rhodopseudomonas sphaeroides* R-26.1. I. Isolation, purification and sequence analyses. *Hoppe-Seyler's Z. Physiol. Chem.* **365** (1984) 703–719.
76. H. Zuber, R. Brunisholz, W. Sidler, Structure and function of light-harvesting pigment–protein complexes. *New Compr. Biochem. (Photosynthesis)* **15** (1987) 233–271.
77. R. Theiler, H. Zuber, The light-harvesting polypeptides of *Rhodopseudomonas sphaeroides* R-26.1. II. Conformational analyses by attenuated total reflection infrared spectroscopy and the possible molecular structure of the hydrophobic domain of the B 850 complex. *Hoppe-Seyler's Z. Physiol. Chem.* **365** (1984) 721–729.
78. M. Babst, H. Albrecht, I. Wegmann, R.A. Brunisholz, H. Zuber, Single amino acid substitutions in the B870 α and β light-harvesting polypeptides of *Rhodobacter capsulatus*. Structural and spectral effects. *Eur. J. Biochem.* **202** (1991) 277–284.
79. G.J.S. Fowler, R.W. Visschers, G.G. Grief, R. van Grondelle, C.N. Hunter, Genetically modified photosynthetic antenna complexes with blueshifted absorbance bands. *Nature* **355** (1992) 848–850.
80. R.A. Brunisholz, F. Jay, F. Suter, H. Zuber, The light-harvesting polypeptides of *Rhodopseudomonas viridis*. The complete amino-acid sequences of B1015-α, B1015-β and B1015-γ. *Biol. Chem. Hoppe-Seyler* **366** (1985) 87–98.
81. R.A. Brunisholz, H. Zuber, Spectral modification of bacterial antenna complexes by limited proteolysis. *Photochem. Photobiol.* **57** (1993) 6–12.
82. H.J.M. Kramer, R. van Grondelle, C.N. Hunter, W.H.J. Westerhuis, J. Amesz, Pigment organization of the B800–850 antenna complex of *Rhodopseudomonas sphaeroides*. *Biochim. Biophys. Acta* **765** (1984) 156–165.
83. D. Donnelly, R.J. Cogdell, Predicting the point at which transmembrane helixes protrude from the bilayer: A model of the antenna complexes from photosynthetic bacteria. *Protein Eng.* **6** (1993) 629–635.
84. J.D. Olsen, C.N. Hunter, Protein structure modeling of the bacterial light-harvesting complex. *Photochem. Photobiol.* **60** (1994) 521–535.
85. V.I. Novoderezhkin, A.P. Razjivin, Excitonic interactions in the light-harvesting antenna of photosynthetic purple bacteria and their influence on picosecond absorbance difference spectra. *FEBS Lett.* **330** (1993) 5–7.

86. V.I. Novoderezhkin, A.P. Razjivin, Exciton interactions and their influence on picosecond absorbance difference spectra of light-harvesting antenna of purple bacteria. *Proc. SPIE-Int. Soc. Opt. Eng.* **1921** (1993) 102–106.
87. V.I. Novoderezhkin, A.P. Razjivin, Exciton states of the antenna and energy trapping by the reaction center. *Photosynth. Res.* **42** (1994) 9–15.
88. J. Deisenhofer, O. Epp, K. Miki, R. Huber, H. Michel, X-ray structure analysis of a membrane protein complex. Electron density map at 3Å resolution and a model of the chromophores of the photosynthetic reaction center from *Rhodopseudomonas viridis*. *J. Mol. Biol.* **180** (1984) 385–398.
89. J. Deisenhofer, H. Michel, The crystal structure of the photosynthetic reaction center from *Rhodopseudomonas viridis*. *NATO ASI Ser., Ser. A* **126** (1987) 421–423.
90. J.P. Allen, G. Feher, T.O. Yeates, D.C. Rees, Structure analysis of the reaction center from *Rhodopseudomonas sphaeroides:* Electron density map at 3.5 Å resolution, in: *Prog. Photosynth. Res., Proc. 7th Int. Congr. Photosynth.* (1987) (J. Biggins, ed.), Nijhoff, Dordrecht, pp. 375–378.
91. J.P. Allen, G. Feher, T.O. Yeates, H. Komiya, D.C. Rees Structure of the reaction center from *Rhodobacter sphaeroides* R-26 and 2.4.1. *NATO ASI Ser., Ser. A* **149** (1988) 5–11.
92. J. Koepke, X. Hu, C. Meunke, K. Schulten, H. Michel, The crystal structure of the light-harvesting complex II (B800–850) from *Rhodospirillum molischianum*. *Structure* **4** (1996) 581–597.
93. K. McLuskey, S.M. Prince, R.J. Cogdell, N.W. Isaacs, The crystallographic structure of the B800–820 LH3 light-harvesting complex from the purple bacteria *Rhodopseudomonas acidophila* strain 7050. *Biochemistry* **40** (2001) 8783–8789.
94. A.W. Roszak, T.D. Howard, J. Southall, A.T. Gardiner, C.J. Law, N.W. Isaacs, R.J. Cogdell, Crystal structure of RC-LH1 core complex from *Rhodopseudomonas palustris*. *Science* **203** (2003) 1969–1972.
95. S.M. Prince, T.D. Howard, D.A.A. Myles, C. Wilkinson, M.Z. Papiz, A.A. Freer, R.J. Cogdell, N.W. Isaacs, Detergent structure in crystals of the integral membrane light-harvesting complex LH2 from *Rhodopseudomonas acidophila* strain 10050. *J. Mol. Biol.* **326** (2003) 307–315.
96. R.J. Cogdell, N.W. Isaacs, A.A. Freer, J. Arrelano, T.D. Howard, M.Z. Papiz, A.M. Hawthornthwaite-Lawless, S.M. Prince, The structure and function of the LH2 (B800–850) complex from the purple photosynthetic bacterium *Rhodopseudomonas acidophila* strain 10050. *Prog. Biophys. Mol. Biol.* **68** (1997) 1–27.
97. S.M. Prince, M.Z. Papiz, A.A. Freer, G. McDermott, A.M. Hawthornthwaite-Lawless, R.J. Cogdell, N.W. Isaacs, Apoprotein structure in the LH2 complex from *Rhodopseudomonas acidophila* strain 10050: Modular assembly and protein pigment interactions. *J. Mol. Biol.* **268** (1997) 412–423.
98. J. Ranck, T. Ruiz, G. Pehau-Arnaudet, B. Arnoux, F. Reiss-Husson, Two-dimensional structure of the native light-harvesting complex LH2 from *Rubrivivax gelatinosus* and of a truncated form. *Biochim. Biophys. Acta* **1506** (2001) 67–78.
99. H. Savage, M. Cyrklaff, G. Montoya, W. Kuhlbrandt, I. Sinning, Two-dimensional structure of light-harvesting complex II (LHII) from purple bacterium *Rhodovulum sulfidophilum* and comparison with LHII from *Rhodopseudomonas acidophila*. *Structure* **4** (1996) 243–252.
100. T. Walz, S.J. Jamieson, C.M. Bowers, P.A. Bullough, C.N. Hunter, Projection structures of three photosynthetic complexes from *Rhodobacter sphaeroides:* LH2 at 6 Å, LH1 and RC-LH1 at 25 Å. *J. Mol. Biol.* **282** (1998) 833–845.

101. F. Oling, E.J. Boekema, I. Ortiz de Zarate, R. Visschers, R. van Grondelle, W. Keegstra, A. Brisson, R. Picorel, Two-dimensional crystals of LHII light-harvesting complexes from *Ectothiorhodospira* sp. and *Rhodobacter capsulatus* investigated by electron microscopy. *Biochim. Biophys. Acta* **1273** (1996) 44–50.
102. S. Scheuring, J. Seguin, S. Marco, D. Levy, C. Breyton, B. Robert, J.-L. Rigaud, AFM characterization of tilt and intrinsic flexibility of *Rhodobacter sphaeroides* light harvesting complex 2 (LH2). *J. Mol. Biol.* **325** (2003) 569–580.
103. S. Bahatyrova, R.N. Frese, K.O. van der Werf, C. Otto, C.N. Hunter, J.D. Olsen, Flexibility and size heterogeneity of the LH1 light harvesting complex revealed by atomic force microscopy: Functional significance for bacterial photosynthesis. *J. Biol. Chem.* **279** (2004) 21327–21333.
104. A. Stamouli, S. Kafi, D.C.G. Klein, T.H. Oosterkamp, J.W.M. Frenken, R.J. Cogdell, T.J. Aartsma, The ring structure and organization of light harvesting 2 complexes in a reconstituted lipid bilayer, resolved by atomic force microscopy. *Biophys. J.* **84** (2003) 2483–2491.
105. S. Scheuring, F. Reiss-Husson, A. Engel, J.-L. Rigaud, J.L. Ranck, High-resolution AFM topographs of *Rubrivivax gelatinosus* light- harvesting complex LH2. *EMBO J.* **20** (2001) 3029–3035.
106. R.J. Cogdell, P.K. Fyfe, S.J. Barrett, S.M. Prince, A.A. Freer, N.W. Isaacs, P. McGlynn, C.N. Hunter, The purple bacterial photosynthetic unit. *Photosynth. Res.* **48** (1996) 55–63.
107. W. Kühlbrandt, Structure and function of bacterial light-harvesting complexes. *Structure* **3** (1995) 521–525.
108. R.J. Cogdell, P.K. Fyfe, T.D. Howard, N. Fraser, N.W. Isaacs, A.A. Freer, K. McKluskey, S.M. Prince, The structure and function of the LH2 complex from *Rhodopseudomonas acidophila* strain 10050, with special reference to the bound carotenoid. *Adv. Photosynth.* **8** (1999) 71–80.
109. M.Z. Papiz, S.M. Prince, T.D. Howard, R.J. Cogdell, N.W. Isaacs, The structure and thermal motion of the B800–850 LH2 complex from *Rps.acidophila* at 2.0A resolution and 100K: New structural features and functionally relevant motions. *J. Mol. Biol.* **326** (2003) 1523–1538.
110. R.J. Cogdell, H. Scheer, Circular dichroism of light-harvesting complexes from purple photosynthetic bacteria. *Photochem. Photobiol.* **42** (1985) 669–678.
111. B. Robert, M. Lutz, Structure of antenna complexes of several *Rhodospirillales* from their resonance Raman spectra. *Biochim. Biophys. Acta* **807** (1985) 10–23.
112. R.J. Cogdell, N.W. Isaacs, A.A. Freer, T.D. Howard, A.T. Gardiner, S.M. Prince, M.Z. Papiz, The structural basis of light-harvesting in purple bacteria. *FEBS Lett.* **555** (2003) 35–39.
113. G.J.S. Fowler, G.D. Sockalingum, B. Robert, C.N. Hunter, Blue shifts in bacteriochlorophyll absorbance correlate with changed hydrogen bonding patterns in light-harvesting 2 mutants of *Rhodobacter sphaeroides* with alterations at α-Tyr-44 and α-Tyr-45. *Biochem. J.* **299** (1994) 695–700.
114. K. McLuskey, S.M. Prince, R.J. Cogdell, N.W. Isaacs, Crystallization and preliminary X-ray crystallographic analysis of the B800–820 light-harvesting complex from *Rhodopseudomonas acidophila* strain 7050. *Acta Crystallogr., Sect. D: Biol. Crystallogr.* **55** (1999) 885–887.
115. A.A. Freer, S. Prince, K. Sauer, M. Papiz, A. Hawthornthwaite-Lawless, G. McDermott, R. Cogdell, N.W. Isaacs, Pigment–pigment interactions and energy transfer in the antenna complex of the photosynthetic bacterium. *Rhodopseudomonas acidophila* **4** (1996) 449–462.

116. G. Klug, R. Liebetanz, G. Drews, The influence of bacteriochlorophyll biosynthesis on formation of pigment-binding proteins and assembly of pigmnet-protein complexes in *Rhodopseuodomonas capsulata*. *Arch. Microbiol.* **146** (1986) 284–291.
117. H.A. Frank, R.J. Cogdell, Carotenoids in photosynthesis. *Photochem. Photobiol.* **63** (1996) 257–264.
118. R.J. Cogdell, H.A. Frank, How carotenoids function in photosynthetic bacteria. *Biochim. Biophys. Acta* **895** (1987) 63–79.
119. J. Zurdo, C. Fernandez-Cabrera, J.M. Ramirez, A structural role of the carotenoid in the light-harvesting II protein of *Rhodobacter capsulatus*. *Biochem. J.* **290** (1993) 531–537.
120. H.P. Lang, C.N. Hunter, The relationship between carotenoid biosynthesis and the assembly of the light-harvesting LH2 complex in *Rhodobacter sphaeroides*. *Biochem. J.* **298** (1994) 197–205.
121. A. Angerhofer, R.J. Cogdell, M.F. Hipkins, A spectral characterization of the light-harvesting pigment–protein complexes from *Rhodopseudomonas acidophila*. *Biochim. Biophys. Acta* **848** (1986) 333–341.
122. R.J. Cogdell, M.F. Hipkins, W. McDonald, T.G. Truscott, Energy transfer between the carotenoid and the bacteriochlorophyll within the B-800–850 light harvesting pigment–protein complex of *Rhodopseudomonas sphaeroides*. *Biochim. Biophys. Acta* **634** (1981) 191–202.
123. R.J. Cogdell, J.G. Lindsay, J. Valentine, I. Durant, A further characterization of the B890 light-harvesting pigment–protein complex from *Rhodospirillum rubrum* strain S1. *FEBS Lett.* **150** (1982) 151–154.
124. P.A. Loach, P.S. Parkes-Loach, Structure–function relationships in core light-harvesting complexes (LHI) as determined by characterization of the structural subunit and by reconstitution experiments, in: *Anoxygenic Photosynthetic Bacteria* (1995) (R.E. Blankenship, M.T.Madigan, C.E. Bauer, eds.), Kluwer Academic Publishers, Dordrecht, pp. 437–471.
125. R. Bachofen, R. Ghosh, R. Schwerzmann. Topological studies on the light-harvesting-pigment–protein-complexes in the membrane of *Rhodospirillum rubrum*, in: *Prog. Photosynth. Res., Proc. 7th. Int. Congr. Photosynth.* (1987) (J. Biggins, ed.), Nijhoff, Dordrecht, pp. 21–24.
126. R. Ghosh, H. Hauser, R. Bachofen, Reversible dissociation of the B873 light-harvesting complex from *Rhodospirillum rubrum* G9+. *Biochemistry* **27** (1988) 1004–1014.
127. B.A. Heller, P.S. Parkes-Loach, M.C. Chang, P.A. Loach, Comparison of the structural subunit, B820, of core light-harvesting complexes of photosynthetic bacteria, in: *Curr. Res. Photosynth., Proc. 8th Int. Conf. Photosynth.* (1990) (M. Baltscheffsky, ed.), Kluwer, Dordrecht, pp. 65–68.
128. K.A. Meadows, J.W. Kehoe, P.A. Loach. Minimal structural requirements for formation of the subunit complex of LH1 of photosynthetic bacteria, in: *Photosynth.: Light Biosphere, Proc. 10th Int. Photosynth. Congr.* (1995) (P. Mathis, ed.), Kluwer, Dordrecht, pp. 159–162.
129. P.A. Loach, P.S. Parkes, J.F. Miller, S. Hinchigeri, P.M. Callahan, Structure–function relationships of the bacteriochlorophyll-protein light-harvesting complex of *Rhodospirillum rubrum*, in: *Mol. Biol. Photosynth. Appar.* (1985) (K.E. Steinbeck, ed.), Cold Spring Harbor Laboratory Press, Plainview, New York.
130. J.F. Miller, S.B. Hinchigeri, P.S. Parkes-Loach, P.M. Callahan, J.R. Sprinkle, J.R. Riccobono, P.A. Loach, Isolation and characterization of a subunit form of the light-harvesting complex of *Rhodospirillum rubrum*. *Biochemistry* **26** (1987) 5055–5062.

131. M.C. Chang, P.M. Callahan, P.S. Parkes-Loach, T.M. Cotton, P.A. Loach, Spectroscopic characterization of the light-harvesting complex of *Rhodospirillum rubrum* and its structural subunit. *Biochemistry* **29** (1990) 421–429.
132. M.C. Chang, L. Meyer, P.A. Loach, Isolation and characterization of a structural subunit from the core light-harvesting complex of *Rhodobacter sphaeroides* 2.4.1 and puc705-BA. *Photochem. Photobiol.* **52** (1990) 873–881.
133. C.M. Davis, P.L. Bustamante, P.A. Loach, Reconstitution of the bacterial core light-harvesting complexes of *Rhodobacter sphaeroides* and *Rhodospirillum rubrum* with isolated α- and β-polypeptides, bacteriochlorophyll *a*, and carotenoid. *J. Biol. Chem.* **270** (1995) 5793–5804.
134. B.A. Heller, P.A. Loach, Isolation and characterization of a subunit form of the B875 light-harvesting complex from *Rhodobacter capsulatus*. *Photochem. Photobiol.* **51** (1990) 621–627.
135. P. Parkes-Loach, J. Riccobono, P. Loach. Preparation of subunit forms of the light-harvesting complex of *Rhodospirillum rubrum*, in: *Prog. Photosynth. Res., Proc. 7th Int. Congr. Photosynth.* (1987) (J. Biggins, ed.), Nijhoff, Dordrecht, pp. 25–28.
136. P.S. Parkes-Loach, J.R. Sprinkle, P.A. Loach, Reconstitution of the B873 light-harvesting complex of *Rhodospirillum rubrum* from the separately isolated α- and β-polypeptides and bacteriochlorophyll *a*. *Biochemistry* **27** (1988) 2718–2727.
137. P.A. Loach, P.S. Parkes-Loach, M.C. Chang, B.A. Heller, P.L. Bustamante, T. Michalski, Comparison of structural subunits of the core light-harvesting complexes of photosynthetic bacteria. *FEMS Symp.* **53** (1990) 235–244.
138. P.S. Parkes-Loach, B.A. Heller, M.C. Chang, W.J. Bass, J.A. Chanatry, P.A. Loach, Reconstitution of the core light-harvesting complex of photosynthetic bacteria with selected polypeptides, in: *Curr. Res. Photosynth. Proc. 8th Int. Conf. Photosynth.* (1990) (M. Baltscheffsky, ed.), Kluwer Academic Publishers, Dordrecht, pp. 73–76.
139. P.S. Parkes-Loach, S.M. Jones, P.A. Loach, Probing the structure of the core light-harvesting complex (LH1) of *Rhodopseudomonas viridis* by dissociation and reconstitution methodology. *Photosynth. Res.* **40** (1994) 247–261.
140. V. Jirsakova, F. Reiss-Husson, A specific carotenoid is required for reconstitution of the *Rubrivivax gelatinosus* B875 light harvesting complex from its subunit form B820. *FEBS Lett.* **353** (1994) 151–154.
141. R.W. Visschers, M.C. Chang, F. van Mourik, P.A. Loach, R. van Grondelle, Spectroscopic characterization of a subunit form of light harvesting complex I from *Rhodospirillum rubrum* and *Rhodobacter sphaeroides*, in: *Curr. Res. Photosynth., Proc. 8th Int. Conf. Photosynth.* (1990) (M. Baltscheffsky, ed.), Kluwer Academic Publishers, Dordrecht, pp. 133–136.
142. R.W. Visschers, M.C. Chang, F. van Mourik, P.S. Parkes-Loach, B.A. Heller, P.A. Loach, R. van Grondelle, Fluorescence polarization and low-temperature absorption spectroscopy of a subunit form of light-harvesting complex I from purple photosynthetic bacteria. *Biochemistry* **30** (1991) 5734–5742.
143. Z.Y. Wang, Y. Muraoka, M. Nagao, M. Shibayama, M. Kobayashi, T. Nozawa, Determination of the B820 subunit size of a bacterial core light-harvesting complex by small-angle neutron scattering. *Biochemistry* **42** (2003) 11555–11560.
144. P.A. Loach, P.S. Parkes-Loach, C.M. Davis, B.A. Heller, Probing protein structural requirements for formation of the core light-harvesting complex of photosynthetic bacteria using hybrid reconstitution methodology. *Photosynth. Res.* **40** (1994) 231–245.

145. B.A. Heller, PhD Thesis (1992), Northwestern University, Illinois.
146. K.A. Meadows, K. Iida, K. Tsuda, P.A. Recchia, B.A. Heller, B. Antonio, M. Nango, P.A. Loach, Enzymic and chemical cleavage of the core light-harvesting polypeptides of photosynthetic bacteria: Determination of the minimal polypeptide size and structure required for subunit and light-harvesting complex formation. *Biochemistry* **34** (1995) 1559–1574.
147. C.M. Davis, P.L. Bustamante, J.B. Todd, P.S. Parkes-Loach, P. McGlynn, J.D. Olsen, L. McMaster, C.N. Hunter, P.A. Loach, Evaluation of structure–function relationships in the core light-harvesting complex of photosynthetic bacteria by reconstitution with mutant polypeptides. *Biochemistry* **36** (1997) 3671–3679.
148. K.A. Meadows, P.S. Parkes-Loach, J.W. Kehoe, P.A. Loach, Reconstitution of core light-harvesting complexes of photosynthetic bacteria using chemically synthesized polypeptides. 1. Minimal requirements for subunit formation. *Biochemistry* **37** (1998) 3411–3417.
149. J.W. Kehoe, K.A. Meadows, P.S. Parkes-Loach, P.A. Loach, Reconstitution of core light-harvesting complexes of photosynthetic bacteria using chemically synthesized polypeptides. 2. Determination of structural features that stabilize complex formation and their implications for the structure of the subunit complex. *Biochemistry* **37** (1998) 3418–3428.
150. P.L. Bustamante, P.A. Loach, Reconstitution of a functional photosynthetic receptor complex with isolated subunits of core light-harvesting complex and reaction centers. *Biochemistry* **33** (1994) 13329–13339.
151. P.A. Loach, T. Michalski, P.S. Parkes-Loach, Probing the bacteriochlorophyll binding site requirements of the core light-harvesting complex of photosynthetic bacteria using bacteriochlorophyll analogs, in: *Curr. Res. Photosynth., Proc. 8th Int. Conf. Photosynth.* (1990) (M. Baltscheffsky, ed.), Kluwer Academic Publishers, Dordrecht, pp. 69–72.
152. P.S. Parkes-Loach, T.J. Michalski, W.J. Bass, U. Smith, P.A. Loach, Probing the bacteriochlorophyll binding site by reconstitution of the light-harvesting complex of *Rhodospirillum rubrum* with bacteriochlorophyll *a* analogs. *Biochemistry* **29** (1990) 2951–2960.
153. C.M. Davis, P.S. Parkes-Loach, C.K. Cook, K.A. Meadows, M. Bandilla, H. Scheer, P.A. Loach, Comparison of the structural requirements for bacteriochlorophyll binding in the core light-harvesting complexes of *Rhodospirillum rubrum* and *Rhodobacter sphaeroides* using reconstitution methodology with bacteriochlorophyll analogs. *Biochemistry* **35** (1996) 3072–3084.
154. A.F. Boonstra, R.W. Visschers, F. Calkoen, R. van Grondelle, E.F.J. van Bruggen, E.J. Boekema, Structural characterization of the B800–850 and B875 light-harvesting antenna complexes from *Rhodobacter sphaeroides* by electron microscopy. *Biochim. Biophys. Acta* **1142** (1993) 181–188.
155. A.F. Boonstra, L. Germeroth, E.J. Boekma, Structure of the light-harvesting antenna from *Rhodospirillum molischianum* studied by electron microscopy. *Biochim. Biophys. Acta* **1184** (1994) 227–234.
156. I. Ikeda-Yamasaki, T. Odahara, K. Mitsuoka, Y. Fujiyoshi, K. Murata, Projection map of the reaction center-light harvesting 1 complex from *Rhodopseudomonas viridis* at 10Å resolution. *FEBS Lett.* **425** (1998) 505–508.
157. S.J. Jamieson, P. Wang, P. Qian, J.Y. Kirkland, M.J. Conroy, C.N. Hunter, P.A. Bullough, Projection structure of the photosynthetic reaction centre-antenna complex of *Rhodospirillum rubrum* at 8.5 Å resolution. *EMBO J.* **21** (2002) 3927–3935.

158. S. Karrasch, P.A. Bullough, R. Ghosh, The 8.5Å projection map of the light-harvesting complex I from *Rhodospirillum rubrum* reveals a ring composed of 16 subunits. *EMBO J.* **14** (1995) 631–638.
159. R.U. Meckenstock, K. Krusche, L.A. Staehelin, M. Cyrklaff, H. Zuber, The six fold symmetry of the B880 light-harvesting complex and the structure of the photosynthetic membranes of *Rhodopseudomonas marina*. *Biol. Chem. Hoppe Seyler* **375** (1994) 429–438.
160. K.R. Miller, Three-dimensional structure of a photosynthetic membrane. *Nature (London)* **300** (1982) 53–55.
161. K.R. Miller, J.S. Jacob, The *Rhodopseudomonas viridis* photosynthetic membrane: Arrangement *in situ*. *Arch. Microbiol.* **142** (1985) 333–339.
162. P. Qian, H.A. Addlesee, A.V. Ruban, P. Wang, P.A. Bullough, C.N. Hunter, A reaction center-light-harvesting 1 complex (RC-LH1) from a Rhodospirillum rubrum mutant with altered esterifying pigments: Characterization by optical spectroscopy and cryo-electron microscopy. *J. Biol. Chem.* **278** (2003) 23678–23685.
163. H. Stahlberg, J. Dubochet, H. Vogel, R. Ghosh, The reaction center of the photounit of *Rhodospirillum rubrum* is anchored to the light-harvesting complex with four-fold rotational disorder. *Photosynth. Res.* **55** (1998) 363–368.
164. W. Stark, W. Kuhlbrandt, I. Wildhaber, E. Wehrli, K. Muhlethaler, The structure of the photoreceptor unit of *Rhodopseudomonas viridis*. *EMBO J.* **3** (1984) 777–783.
165. T. Walz, R. Ghosh, Two-dimensional crystallization of the light-harvesting I-reaction center photounit from *Rhodospirillum rubrum*. *J. Mol. Biol.* **265** (1997) 107–111.
166. K.R. Miller, Structure of a bacterial photosynthetic membrane. *Proc. Natl. Acad. Sci. U.S.A.* **76** (1979) 6415–6419.
167. W. Welte, W. Kreutz, Formation structure and composition of a planar hexagonal lattice composed of specific protein-lipid complexes in the thylakoid membranes of *Rhodopseudomonas viridis*. *Biochim. Biophys. Acta* **692** (1982) 479–488.
168. H. Engelhardt, W. Baumeister, W.O. Saxton, Electron microscopy of photosynthetic membranes containing bacteriochlorophyll *b*. *Arch. Microbiol* **135** (1983) 169–175.
169. F. Jay, W. Stark, K. Muehlethaler, The preparation and characterization of native photoreceptor units from the thylakoids of *Rhodopseudomonas viridis*. *EMBO J.* **3** (1984) 773–776.
170. D. Dawkins, L.A. Ferguson, R.J. Cogdell, The structure of the purple bacteria photosynthetic unit, in: *Photosynthetic Light-Harvesting Systems* (1988) (H. Scheer, ed.), Walter de Gruyter, Berlin, pp. 115–127.
171. A. Gall, PhD Thesis (1994), Glasgow.
172. C. Francke, J. Amesz, The size of the photosynthetic unit in purple bacteria. *Photosynth. Res.* **46** (1995) 347–352.
173. T. Ueda, Y. Morimoto, M. Sato, T. Kakuno, J. Yamashita, T. Horio, Isolation, characterization, and comparison of a ubiquitous pigment–protein complex consisting of a reaction center and light-harvesting bacteriochlorophyll proteins present in purple photosynthetic bacteria. *J. Biochem. (Tokyo)* **98** (1985) 1487–1498.
174. M.Z. Papiz, S.M. Prince, A.M. Hawthornthwaite-Lawless, G. McDermott, A.A. Freer, N.W. Isaacs, R.J. Cogdell, A model for the photosynthetic apparatus of purple bacteria. *Trends Plant Sci.* **1** (1996) 198–206.

175. T.E. Meyer, T.J. Donohue, Cytochromes, iron-sulfur, and copper proteins mediating electron transfer from the Cyt bc1 complex to photosynthetic reaction center complexes, in: *Anoxygenic Photosynthetic Bacteria* (1995) (R.E. Blankenship, M.T.Madigan, C.E. Bauer, eds.), Kluwer Academic Publishers, Dordrecht, pp. 725–745.
176. C. Jungas, J.L. Ranck, J.L. Rigaud, P. Joliot, A. Vermeglio, Supramolecular organisation of the photosynthetic apparatus of *Rhodobacter sphaeroides*. *EMBO J.* **18** (1999) 534–542.
177. W.P. Barz, D. Oesterhelt, Photosynthetic deficiency of a pufX deletion mutant of *Rhodobacter sphaeroides* is suppressed by point mutations in the light-harvesting complex genes *pufB* or *pufA*. *Biochemistry* **33** (1994) 9741–9752.
178. W.P. Barz, G. Venturoli, F. Francia, B.A. Melandri, A. Vermeglio, D. Oesterhelt, The PufX protein of *Rhodobacter sphaeroides* is required for efficient ubiquinone/ubiquinol exchange between the reaction center and the cytochrome bc1 complex, in: *Photosynth.: Light Biosphere, Proc. 10th Int. Photosynth. Congr.* (1995) (P. Mathis, ed.), Kluwer Academic Publishers, Dordrecht, pp. 619–624.
179. J.W. Farchaus, D. Oesterhelt, A *Rhodobacter sphaeroides* pufL M, and X deletion mutant and its complementation in trans with a 5.3 kb puf operon shuttle fragment. *EMBO J.* **8** (1989) 47–54.
180. J.W. Farchaus, W.P. Barz, H. Gruenberg, D. Oesterhelt, Studies on the expression of the pufX polypeptide and its requirement for photoheterotrophic growth in *Rhodobacter sphaeroides*. *EMBO J.* **11** (1992) 2779–2788.
181. T.G. Lilburn, C.E. Haith, R.C. Prince, J.T. Beatty, Pleiotropic effects of *pufX* gene deletion on the structure and function of the photosynthetic apparatus of *Rhodobacter capsulatus*. *Biochim. Biophys. Acta* **1100** (1992) 160–170.
182. P. McGlynn, C.N. Hunter, M.R. Jones, The *Rhodobacter sphaeroides* PufX protein is not required for photosynthetic competence in the absence of a light harvesting system. *FEBS Lett.* **349** (1994) 349–353.
183. P.S. Parkes-Loach, C.J. Law, P.A. Recchia, J. Kehoe, S. Nehrlich, J. Chen, P.A. Loach, Role of the core region of the PufX protein in inhibition of reconstitution of the core light-harvesting complexes of *Rhodobacter sphaeroides* and *Rhodobacter capsulatus*. *Biochemistry* **40** (2001) 5593–5601.
184. R.J. Pugh, P. McGlynn, M.R. Jones, C.N. Hunter, The LH1-RC core complex of *Rhodobacter sphaeroides*: Interaction between components, time-dependent assembly, and topology of the PufX protein. *Biochim. Biophys. Acta* **1366** (1998) 301–316.
185. P.A. Recchia, PhD Thesis (1998) Northwestern University, Illinois.
186. P.A. Recchia, C.M. Davis, T.M. Lilburn, J.T. Beatty, P.S. Parkes-Loach, C.N. Hunter, P.A. Loach, Isolation of the PufX protein from *Rhodobacter capsulatus* and *Rhodobacter sphaeroides:* Evidence for its interaction with the α-polypeptide of the core light-harvesting complex. *Biochemistry* **37** (1998) 11055–11063.
187. G. Belanger, G. Gingras, Structure and expression of the *puf* operon messenger RNA in *Rhodospirillum rubrum*. *J. Biol. Chem.* **263** (1988) 7639–7645.
188. R. Ghosh, S. Ghosh-Eicher, M. DiBerardino, R. Bachofen, Protein phosphorylation in *Rhodospirillum rubrum:* Purification and characterization of a water-soluble B873 protein kinase and a new component of the B873 complex, $\Omega$, which can be phosphorylated. *Biochim. Biophys. Acta* **1184** (1994) 28–36.
189. R. Ghosh, P. Tschopp, S. Ghosh-Eicher, R. Bachofen, Protein phosphorylation in *Rhodospirillum rubrum:* Further characterization of the B873 kinase activity. *Biochim. Biophys. Acta* **1184** (1994) 37–44.

190. W.P. Barz, F. Francia, G. Venturoli, B.A. Melandri, A. Vermeglio, D. Oesterhelt, Role of PufX protein in photosynthetic growth of *Rhodobacter sphaeroides*. 1. PufX is required for efficient light-driven electron transfer and photophosphorylation under anaerobic conditions. *Biochemistry* **34** (1995) 15235–15247.
191. W.P. Barz, A. Vermeglio, F. Francia, G. Venturoli, B.A. Melandri, D. Oesterhelt, Role of the PufX protein in photosynthetic growth of *Rhodobacter sphaeroides*. 2. PufX is required for efficient ubiquinone/ubiquinol exchange between the reaction center $Q_B$ site and the cytochrome bc1 complex. *Biochemistry* **34** (1995) 15248–15258.
192. R.N. Frese, J.D. Olsen, R. Branvall, W.H.J. Westerhuis, C.N. Hunter, R. van Grondelle, The long-range supraorganization of the bacterial photosynthetic unit: A key role for PufX. *Proc. Natl. Acad. Sci. U.S.A.* **97** (2000) 5197–5202.
193. S. Scheuring, F. Francia, J. Busselez, B.A. Melandris, J.-L. Rigaud, D. Levy, Structural role of PufX in the dimerization of the photosynthetic core complex of *Rhodobacter sphaeroides*. *J. Biol. Chem.* **279** (2004) 3620–3626.
194. S. Scheuring, J. Seguin, S. Marco, D. Levy, B. Robert, J.-L. Rigaud, Nanodissection and high-resolution imaging of the *Rhodopseudomonas viridis* photosynthetic core complex in native membranes by AFM. *Proc. Natl. Acad. Sci. U.S.A.* **100** (2003) 1690–1693.
195. W.J.D. Vredenberg, L.N.M. Duysens, Transfer of energy from bacteriochlorophyll to a reaction center during bacteriochlorophyll photosynthesis. *Nature* **197** (1963) 355–357.
196. T.G. Monger, W.W. Parson, Singlet–triplet fusion in Rhodopseudomonas sphaeroides chromatophores. A probe of the organization of the photosynthetic apparatus. *Biochim. Biophys. Acta* **460** (1977) 393–407.
197. K.E. Eimhjellen, H. Steensland, J. Traetteberg, A *Thiococcus* sp. nov. gen., its pigments and internal membrane system. *Arch. Mikrobiol.* **59** (1967) 82.
198. L.A. Staehelin, J.R. Golecki, G. Drews, Supramolecular organization of chlorosomes (chlorobium vesicles) and of their membrane attachment sites in *Chlorobium limicola*. *Biochim. Biophys. Acta* **589** (1980) 30–45.
199. A.R. Varga, L.A. Staehelin, Membrane adhesion in photosynthetic bacterial membranes. Light harvesting complex I (LHI) appears to be the main adhesion factor. *Arch. Microbiol.* **141** (1985) 290–296.
200. W. Stark, F. Jay, K. Muehlethaler, Localization of reaction center and light harvesting complexes in the photosynthetic unit of *Rhodopseudomonas viridis*. *Arch. Microbiol.* **146** (1986) 130–133.
201. V.I. Novoderezhkin, A.P. Razjivin, The theory of Forster-type migration between clusters of strongly interacting molecules: Application to light-harvesting complexes of purple bacteria. *Chem. Phys.* **211** (1996) 203–214.
202. G. Deinum, S.C.M. Otte, A.T. Gardiner, T.J. Aartsma, R.J. Cogdell, J. Amesz, Antenna organization of *Rhodopseudomonas acidophila*: A study of the excitation migration. *Biochim. Biophys. Acta* **1060** (1991) 125–131.
203. H. Kramer, G. Deinum, A.T. Gardiner, R.J. Cogdell, C. Francke, T.J. Aartsma, J. Amesz, Energy transfer in the photosynthetic antenna system of the purple non-sulfur bacterium *Rhodopseudomonas cryptolactis*, in: *Photosynth.: Light Biosphere, Proc. 10th Int. Photosynth. Congr.* (1995) (P. Mathis, ed.), Kluwer Academic Publishers, Dordrecht, pp. 307–310.
204. H. Kramer, J. Amesz, Antenna organization in the purple sulfur bacteria. *Chromatium tepidum* and *Chromatium vinosum*. *Photosynth. Res.* **49** (1996) 237–244.

205. C.J. Law, R.J. Cogdell, H.-W. Trissl, Antenna organization in the purple bacterium *Rhodopseudomonas acidophila* studied by fluorescence induction. *Photosynth. Res.* **52** (1997) 157–165.
206. K.T. Bernhardt, H.-W. Trissl, Theories for kinetics and yields of fluorescence and photochemistry: How, if at all, can different models of antenna organization be distinguished experimentally? *Biochim. Biophys. Acta* **1409** (1999) 125–142.
207. R. van Grondelle, Excitation energy transfer, trapping and annihilation in photosynthetic systems. *Biochim. Biophys. Acta* **811** (1985) 147–195.
208. X. Hu, T. Ritz, A. Damjanovic, K. Schulten, Pigment organization and transfer of electronic excitation in the photosynthetic unit of purple bacteria. *J. Phys. Chem. B* **101** (1997) 3854–3871.
209. R. van Grondelle, R. Monshouwer, Excitation transfer and trapping in photosynthesis. *Springer Ser. Chem. Phys.* **62** (1996) 311–313.
210. B. Robert, R.J. Cogdell, R. van Grondelle, The light-harvesting system of purple bacteria, in: *Light-harvesting Antennas in Photosynthesis* (2003) (B.B. Green, W.W. Parson, eds.), Kluwer Academic Publishers, Dordrecht, pp. 169–194.
211. T. Pullerits, V. Sundström, Photosynthetic light-harvesting pigment–protein complexes: Toward understanding how and why. *Acc. Chem. Res.* **29** (1996) 381–389.
212. G.R. Fleming, R. van Grondelle, Femtosecond spectroscopy of photosynthetic light-harvesting systems. *Curr. Opin. Struct. Biol.* **7** (1997) 738–748.
213. S.F. Swallen, R. Kopelman, J.S. Moore, Excited rate dynamics in organic dendrimer supermolecules. *Electrochem. Soc. Proc.* **98** (1999) 85–92.
214. A.Y. Borisov, Energy-migration mechanisms in antenna chlorophylls, in: *The Photosynthetic Bacteria* (1978) Plenum Press, New York.
215. T. Förster, Intermolecular energy transfer and fluorescence. *Ann. Phys.* **2** (1948) 55–75.
216. A.S. Davydov, *Theory of Molecular Excitons* (1962), McGraw-Hill Book Co., New York.
217. D.L. Dexter, A theory of sensitized luminescence in solids. *J. Chem. Phys.* **21** (1953) 836–860.
218. R.J. Cogdell, T.D. Howard, R. Bittl, E. Scholodder, I. Geisenheimer, W. Lubitz, How carotenoids protect bacterial photosynthesis. *Philosophical Trans. Royal Soc. London, Ser. B: Biol. Sci.* **355** (2000) 1345–1349.
219. V. Sundström, R. van Grondelle, Kinetics of excitation transfer and trapping in purple bacteria, in: *Anoxygenic Photosynthetic Bacteria* (1995) (R.E. Blankenship, M.T. Madigan, C. E Bauer, eds.), Kluwer Academic Publishers, Dordrecht, pp. 349–372.
220. J.T.M. Kennis, A.M. Streltsov, S.I.E Vulto, T.J. Aartsma, J. Amesz, Excited state dynamics and exciton delocalization in photosynthetic light harvesting complexes at low temperature. *Springer Ser. Chem. Phys.* **62** (1996) 318–319.
221. N.R.S. Reddy, R.J. Cogdell, L. Zhao, G.J. Small, Nonphotochemical hole burning of the B800-B850 antenna complex of *Rhodopseudomonas acidophila*. *Photochem. Photobiol.* **57** (1993) 35–39.
222. S.I.E. Vulto, J.T.M. Kennis, A.M. Streltsov, J. Amesz, T.J. Aartsma, Energy relaxation within the B850 absorption band of the LH2 complex from *Rhodopseudomanas acidophila* at 77 K. *Photosynth. Mech.: Eff., Proc. 11th Int. Congr. Photosynth.* **1** (1998) 53–56.

223. J.M. Salverda, F. van Mourik, G. van der Zwan, R. van Grondelle, Energy transfer in the B800 ring of light harvesting antenna LH2 of purple bacteria *Rps. acidophila* and *Rs. molischianum* probed by three pulse echo peakshift. *Spectrosc. Biol. Mol.: New Dir., 8th Eur. Conf.* (1999), pp. 191-193
224. V. Sundström, T. Pullerits, R. van Grondelle, Photosynthetic light-harvesting: Reconciling dynamics and structure of purple bacterial LH2 reveals function of photosynthetic unit. *J. Phys. Chem. B* **103** (1999) 2327-2346.
225. S. Hess, E. Aakesson, R.J. Cogdell, T. Pullerits, V. Sundström, Energy transfer in spectrally inhomogeneous light-harvesting pigment–protein complexes of purple bacteria. *Biophys. J.* **69** (1995) 2211-2225.
226. H. van der Laan, C. De Caro, T. Schmidt, R.W. Visschers, R. van Grondelle, G.J.S. Fowler, C.N. Hunter, S. Voelker, Excited-state dynamics of mutated antenna complexes of purple bacteria studied by hole-burning. *Chem. Phys. Lett.* **212** (1993) 569-580.
227. R. Monshouwer, I. Ortiz de Zarate, F. van Mourik, R. van Grondelle, Low-intensity pump–probe spectroscopy on the B800 to B850 transfer in the light harvesting complex II of *Rhodobacter sphaeroides*. *Chem. Phys. Lett.* **246** (1995) 341-346.
228. S. Matsuzaki, V. Zazubovich, N.J. Fraser, R.J. Cogdell, G.J. Small, Energy transfer dynamics in LH2 complexes of *Rhodopseudomonas acidophila* containing only one B800 molecule. *J. Phys. Chem. B* **105** (2001) 7049-7056.
229. J. Linnanto, J.E.I. Korppi-Tommola, Theoretical study of excitation transfer from modified B800 rings of the LH II antenna complex of *Rps. acidophila*. *Phys. Chem. Chem. Phys.* **4** (2002) 3453-3460.
230. R. van Grondelle, R. Monshouwer, L. Valkunas, Photosynthetic light-harvesting. *Ber. Bunsen-Ges.* **100** (1996) 1950-1957.
231. C. De Caro, R.W. Visschers, R. van Grondelle, S. Voelker, Inter- and intraband energy transfer in LH2-antenna complexes of purple bacteria. A fluorescence line-narrowing and hole-burning study. *J. Phys. Chem.* **98** (1994) 10584-10590.
232. R. Jimenez, S. Dikshit, S.E. Bradforth, G.R. Fleming, Electronic excitation transfer in the LH2 complex from *Rhodobacter sphaeroides*. *J. Phys. Chem.* **100** (1996) 6825-6834.
233. R.G. Alden, E. Johnson, V. Nagarajan, W.W. Parson, C.J. Law, R.J. Cogdell, Calculations of the spectroscopic properties of the LH2 bacteriochlorophyll-protein antenna complex from *Rhodopseudomonas acidophila*. *J. Phys. Chem B* **101** (1996) 4667-4680.
234. M.H.C. Koolhaas, G. van der Zwan, R.N. Frese, R. van Grondelle, Structure-based calculations of absorption and CD spectra of the LH2 antenna system of *Rhodopseudomonas acidophila*. *J. Phys. Chem. B* **101** (1996) 7262-7270.
235. K. Sauer, R.J. Cogdell, S.M. Prince, A.A. Freer, N.W. Isaacs, H. Scheer, Structure-based calculations of the optical spectra of the LH2 bacteriochlorophyll-protein complex from *Rhodopseudomonas acidophila*. *Photochem. Photobiol.* **64** (1996) 564-576.
236. M.H.C. Koolhaas, G. van der Zwan, R.N. Frese, R. van Grondelle, Red shift of the zero crossing in the CD spectra of the LH2 antenna complex of *Rhodopseudomonas acidophila*: A structure-based study. *J. Phys. Chem. B* **101** (1997) 7262-7270.
237. G.R. Fleming, R. Jimenez, Ultrafast spectroscopy of excitation transfer dynamics in biological systems, in: *Femtochem. Femtobiol.: Ultrafast React. Dyn. At.-Scale*

Resolut., Nobel Symp. 101 (1997) (V. Sundström, ed.), Imperial College Press, London, pp. 701–723.
238. J.P. Zhang, H. Nagae, P. Qian, L. Limantara, R. Fujii, Y. Watanabe, Y. Koyama, Localized excitations on the B850α and B850β bacteriochlorophylls in the LH2 antenna complex from *Rhodospirillum molischianum* as probed by the shifts of the carotenoid absorption. *J. Phys. Chem. B* **105** (2001) 7312–7322.
239. T. Kakitani, A. Kimura, Empirical formula of exciton coherent domain in oligomers and application to LH2. *J. Phys. Chem. A* **106** (2002) 2173–2179.
240. M.A. Bopp, Y. Jia, L. Li, R.J. Cogdell, R.M. Hochstrasser, Fluorescence and photobleaching dynamics of single light-harvesting complexes. *Proc. Natl. Acad. Sci. U.S.A.* **94** (1997) 10630–10635.
241. A.M. van Oijen, M. Ketelaars, J. Koehler, T.J. Aartsma, J. Schmidt, Spectroscopy of single light-harvesting complexes from purple photosynthetic bacteria at 1.2 K. *J. Phys. Chem. B* **102** (1998) 9363–9366.
242. M.A. Bopp, A. Sytnik, T.D. Howard, R.J. Cogdell, R.M. Hochstrasser, The dynamics of structural deformations of immobilized single light-harvesting complexes. *Proc. Natl. Acad. Sci. U.S.A.* **96** (1999) 11271–11276.
243. Y. Zhao, T. Meier, W.M. Zhang, V. Chernyak, S. Mukamel, Superradiance coherence sizes in single-molecule spectroscopy of LH2 antenna complexes. *J. Phys. Chem. B* **103** (1999) 3954–3962.
244. A.M. van Oijen, M. Ketelaars, J. Kohler, T.J. Aartsma, J. Schmidt, Spectroscopy of individual light-harvesting 2 complexes of *Rhodopseudomonas acidophila:* Diagonal disorder, intercomplex heterogeneity, spectral diffusion, and energy transfer in the B800 band. *Biophys. J.* **78** (2000) 1570–1577.
245. J. Kohler, A.M. van Oijen, M. Ketelaars, C. Hofmann, M. Matsushita, T.J. Aartsma, J. Schmidt, Optical spectroscopy of individual photosynthetic pigment protein complexes. *Int. J. Modern Phys. B* **15** (2001) 3633–3636.
246. M. Ketelaars, C. Hofmann, J. Kohler, T.D. Howard, R.J. Cogdell, J. Schmidt, T.J. Aartsma, Spectroscopy on individual light-harvesting 1 complexes of *Rhodopseudomonas acidophila. Biophys. J.* **83** (2002) 1701–1715.
247. M. Ketelaars, W.P.F. de Rujiter, C. Hofmann, J. Kohler, T.D. Howard, R.J. Cogdell, J. Schmidt, T.J. Aartsma, Single molecule spectroscopy of LH1 at low temperature. *Biophys. J.* **82** (2002) 232.
248. H.M. Visser, O.J.G. Somsen, F. van Mourik, R. van Grondelle, Sub-picosecond energy equilibration via energy transfer in the light harvesting antenna of LH-1 only mutants of *Rb. sphaeroides,* at RT and 4K; experiments and modeling, in: *Photosynth.: Light Biosphere Proc. 10th Int. Photosynth. Congr.* (1995) (P. Mathis, ed.), Kluwer Academic Publishers, Dordrecht, pp. 343–346.
249. K.J. Visscher, H. Bergström, V. Sundström, C.N. Hunter, R. van Grondelle, Temperature dependence of energy transfer from the long wavelength antenna BChl-869 to the reaction center in *Rhodospirillum rubrum, Rhodobacter sphaeroides* (w.t. and M 21 mutant) from 77 to 177 K studied by picosecond absorption spectroscopy. *Photosynth. Res.* **22** (1989) 211–217.
250. H. Bergström, R. van Grondelle, V. Sundström, Characterisation of excitation energy trapping in photosynthetic purple bacteria at 77K. *FEBS Lett.* **250** (1989) 503–508.
251. S.C.M. Otte, F.A.M. Kleinherenbrink, J. Amesz, Energy transfer between the reaction center and the antenna in purple bacteria. *Biochim. Biophys. Acta* **1143** (1993) 84–90.

252. J.T.M. Kennis, T.J. Aartsma, J. Amesz, Energy trapping in the purple sulfur bacteria *Chromatium vinosum* and *Chromatium tepidum*. *Biochim. Biophys. Acta* **1188** (1994) 278–286.
253. C.J. Law, R.J. Cogdell, The effect of chemical oxidation on the fluorescence of the LH1 (B880) complex from the purple bacterium *Rhodobium marinum*. *FEBS Lett.* **432** (1998) 27–30.
254. W. Humphrey, A. Dalke, K. Schulten, VMD-visual molecular dynamics. *J. Mol. Graphics* **14** (1996) 33–38.

## Chapter 6

# Oxygen-Evolving Cyanobacteria

### Mamoru Mimuro, Masami Kobayashi, Akio Murakami, Tohru Tsuchiya and Hideaki Miyashita

**Table of Contents**

| | | |
|---|---|---|
| 6.1 | Introduction | 263 |
| 6.2 | Photosynthetic Pigments | 265 |
| | 6.2.1 Chlorophylls and Related Pigments | 265 |
| |     6.2.1.1 Diversity of Chlorophylls | 265 |
| |     6.2.1.2 Functions of Minor Pigments | 266 |
| |     6.2.1.3 Chl $d$ | 266 |
| | 6.2.2 Carotenoids | 268 |
| | 6.2.3 Phycobiliproteins | 269 |
| | 6.2.4 Molecular Species of Phycobiliproteins | 270 |
| 6.3 | Phycobilisomes | 271 |
| | 6.3.1 Molecular Structure of Hemi-Discoidal Phycobilisomes | 272 |
| | 6.3.2 Crystal Structures of Components | 273 |
| | 6.3.3 Phycobilisome-Lacking Cyanobacteria | 273 |
| 6.4 | Membrane-Bound Antenna Complexes | 273 |
| | 6.4.1 Photosystem I | 275 |
| | 6.4.2 Photosystem II | 276 |
| | 6.4.3 CP43′ and Iron-Stress-Induced (Isi) Protein Family | 277 |
| | 6.4.4 Molecular Assembly of Photosystems in Thylakoid Membranes | 277 |
| 6.5 | Excitation Energy Transfer (EET) | 278 |
| | 6.5.1 Phycobilisomes as Transient Excitation Energy Reservoir | 278 |
| | 6.5.2 Energy Transfer from Phycobilisomes to Membrane Proteins | 279 |
| | 6.5.3 Energy Transfer in Photosystems and Trapping in Reaction Centers | 280 |
| | 6.5.4 State Transition | 282 |
| | 6.5.5 Energy Dissipation by Carotenoids | 283 |

6.6 Antenna Systems Induced under Iron-Depleted Conditions....... 283
    6.6.1 Physiology and Activity under Iron-Stress Conditions...... 284
    6.6.2 Structures of the IsiA–Photosystem I Complex........... 284
    6.6.3 Origin and Phylogeny of Light-Harvesting Complex (LHC) Superfamily...................................... 284
6.7 Regulation of Photosystem Stoichiometry and Accompanying Changes in Antenna Architecture ......................... 285
6.8 Chlorophyll Biosynthesis – Characteristics in Cyanobacteria...... 286
    6.8.1 Protochlorophyllide a Reductase..................... 287
    6.8.2 *In Vivo* Reconstitution of Pigments .................. 287
6.9 Future Prospects ...................................... 288
Acknowledgements ......................................... 288
References................................................ 288

## Abstract

This chapter describes photosynthetic antenna systems of cyanobacteria, with special emphasis on two points: (i) diversity of pigments and associated changes in proteins of antenna and reaction centers and (ii) stress-induced changes in antenna systems. The basic concepts of the constitution of pigment-protein complexes and energy transfer processes are very important for a general understanding of the systems. Furthermore, analyses of perturbed systems will also provide important information. After a short introduction, three kinds of photosynthetic pigments, chlorophylls, carotenoids, and phycobiliproteins, are briefly discussed with respect to their functions and diversity, including minor pigments. Secondly, we focus on the molecular architecture of the complexes and their functional relationships. A third point of the description is stress-induced changes in antenna, i.e., the iron-depleted condition, followed by considerations on changes in the stoichiometric ratio between photosystem I and photosystem II and their relevance for the antenna systems. Throughout this chapter, the evolution of cyanobacteria from anoxygenic photosynthetic bacteria is always considered as a cryptic topic, like figured bass.

## 6.1 Introduction

Cyanobacteria are the first prokaryotes in the evolution of photosynthetic organisms that are able to evolve molecular oxygen. Owing to the presence of molecular oxygen, organisms can perform oxygenic respiration as a bioenergetic prerequisite for their evolution through enlargement of cell sizes and multi-cellular systems. In this sense, the appearance of cyanobacteria can be considered the "big bang" of all higher forms of life on earth.

The main free energy source of cyanobacteria is photosynthetic transformation of solar radiation, while the contribution of respiration to the total metabolism under illumination is comparatively small [1]. The photosynthetic electron-transfer chain of cyanobacteria is a hybrid of two types of photosynthetic bacteria, i.e., purple bacteria and green sulfur bacteria (or heliobacteria) ([2], see also Chapter 12). ATP, a "high-energy" compound common in all organisms, is synthesized by an ATP synthase, with a difference in electrochemical potential of protons across the thylakoid membrane acting as the driving force (for details see Chapter 21). This mechanism of ATP synthesis is essentially similar to that of the oxygenic respiration, thus leading to the idea that the photosynthetic system was created after oxygenic respiration. The main difference in the electron-transfer chain between oxygenic photosynthesis and respiration is the presence of the photochemical reaction centers (RCs) that drive photo-induced charge separation and antenna systems that absorb the light and transfer the electronic excitation energy to the RCs. These two systems are the largest innovation in the photosynthetic systems (Figure 1).

Two kinds of materials are used for building RCs and antenna, proteins and pigments or cofactors. Pigments carry out the photophysical and/or

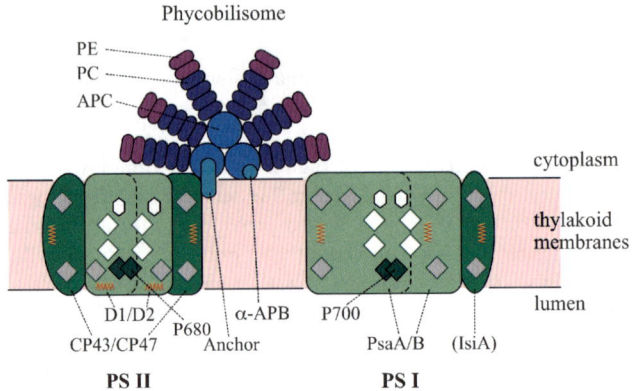

**Figure 1.** Schematic model of the antenna system of cyanobacteria. In phycobilisomes, hatched components represent phycoerythrin (PE) when present. If PE is not present, it is replaced with phycocyanin (PC). Two subunits [anchor (ApcE) and α-APB (ApcD)] function as outputs of excitation energy from phycobilisomes. In thylakoid membranes, diamonds symbolize Chl or related molecules with hatched symbols for antenna Chl molecules and open symbols for electron-transfer cofactors (Chl, Phe, and PQ). Hexagons represent quinone molecules. Wavy lines represent carotenoid molecules. The connecting site of phycobilisome with PS II is uncertain.

photochemical reactions, while proteins not only supply loci for proper binding of pigments/cofactors but also modulate their reactivity via coupling to vibrational mode(s). Recognition of pigments by proteins and interaction between pigments and proteins are fundamental and important issues for the primary processes of photosynthesis. Therefore, to fully understand the functional mechanisms of RCs and antenna systems it is very important to know the molecular structures at atomic resolution. Since the diversity of pigments and protein structures are equivalent to perturbations, a suitable modification of the respective systems is an alternative approach for analyses.

The diversity of photosynthetic pigments is remarkable in cyanobacteria; there are eight species of chlorophyll (Chl) and one species of pheophytin (Phe). Some of them are involved in the photochemical charge separation, while the vast majority of the Chl molecules are constituents of the antenna system. Interactions between pigments and proteins are different in these two systems. Therefore, it is important to analyze these two kinds of pigment-proteins and find characteristics that are common and/or specific to individual systems.

This chapter focuses on a description of the antenna systems of cyanobacteria. Accordingly, mainly two topics are outlined: (a) the diversity of pigments and associated changes in antenna proteins and (b) stress-induced changes in antenna systems. Furthermore, the Chl metabolism is also briefly discussed in relation to the development of antenna systems. For complementary reading several recent reviews on the antenna system of cyanobacteria are recommended [3–7].

## 6.2 Photosynthetic Pigments

There are three kinds of photosynthetic pigments in cyanobacteria: chlorophylls, carotenoids and phycobilins. Among these, Chls and carotenoids are ubiquitous in photosynthetic organisms while phycobilins are limited to Cyanophytes, Glaucophytes, Rhodophytes and Crytpophytes. The general properties of Chls and carotenoids are described in Chapters 4 and 5. Therefore, in this chapter, only some properties of Chls and carotenoids specific to cyanobacteria and general properties of phycobiliproteins are briefly discussed.

### 6.2.1 Chlorophylls and Related Pigments

#### 6.2.1.1 Diversity of Chlorophylls

Cyanobacteria exhibit diversity in Chls and related pigments. There are six species of Chl molecules, Chl $a$, divinyl-Chl $a$ (or Chl $a_2$), Chl $b$, divinyl-Chl $b$ (or Chl $b_2$), Chl $c$-type pigment (Mg-DVP), Chl $d$, and two stereoisomeric Chl molecules, Chl $a'$ and Chl $d'$, and in addition the Mg-free molecule, Phe $a$. Among these, Chl $a$, Chl $a'$, and Phe $a$ are present in almost all cyanobacterial species. Other pigments are found in specific clade(s) of cyanobacteria. For example, Chl $b$ is present in addition to Chl $a$ in *Prochlorothrix* [8] and *Prochloron* [9], divinyl-Chl $a$ and divinyl-Chl $b$ instead of Chl $a$ and Chl $b$ in *Prochlorococcus* [10]. To date, Chl $d$ has been found only in the clade of *Acaryochloris* [11]. The Chl $c$-type pigment, i.e., Mg-3,8-divinyl pheoporphyrin $a_5$ monomethyl ester (Mg-DVP), is associated with *Prochloron* [9] in significant amounts, and with *Prochlorothrix* [8,12], *Prochlorococcus* [13], and *Acaryochloris* [14] in trace amounts. This pigment is considered as an intermediate of Chl biosynthesis; however, in *Prochloron*, Mg-DVP is present in a fraction of 4–15% (w/w) of the total chlorophyll [9]. It is localized in a light-harvesting chlorophyll pigment complex (LHC) and is functional. Mg-DVP is not found in other cyanophytes.

The reason for this Chl diversity is not yet resolved. Chl $a$ is common to oxygenic photosynthesis. Chl $b$ might be present in a progenitor common to current cyanobacteria and the cyanobacterium that is associated with a eukaryotic cell [15], leading to the primary symbiosis. On the other hand, divinyl-Chl $a$ and $b$ [10] and Chl $d$ [11] may be acquired during evolution to specific clade(s), because their presence is limited to these organisms. Mg-DVP is an intermediate of metabolites [16], so it is rather easy to adopt it to the antenna system.

Diversity in pigments is always associated with a complementary diversity of proteins that accommodate those pigments. Recognition of pigments by protein moieties is one of the basic principles for functions in antenna and reaction center. Therefore, specific interactions between these pigments and the corresponding proteins are very important to understand the mechanisms of RCs and antenna systems. This point will be discussed for antenna systems afterwards (for reaction centers, see Chapters 13 and 15 of this volume).

### 6.2.1.2 Functions of Minor Pigments

In the electron-transfer system of cyanobacteria, two kinds of minor pigments act as functional cofactors: the Chl epimer, Chl $a'$ in PS I and Phe $a$ in PS II. The $13^2$-epimer of Chl $a$ was first reported by Strain and Manning in 1942 [17], and its presence was enigmatic until 1985 [18]. Precise HPLC analyses revealed that Chl $a'$ is present as one molecule per P700, widely referred to the photoactive pigment complex of PS I [19]. Its presence was confirmed by the crystal structure of PS I of the thermophilic cyanobacterium *Thermosynechococcus elongatus* ([20]; for further details, see Chapter 13). [P700 is a heterodimer consisting of a Chl $a$ and a Chl $a'$ molecule. P700 forms a stable radical pair with the primary electron acceptor ($A_0$ or Chl $a$) and further with the secondary electron acceptor ($A_1$ or phylloquinone).]

Absorption and fluorescence spectra of Chl $a'$ in organic solvents are almost identical to those of Chl $a$ (Figure 2A) while the circular dichroism spectrum is very different due to reflection of twisting of the macrocycle structure by epimerization [21,22]. Electrochemical properties, such as oxidation and reduction potentials, seem to be identical to those of Chl $a$, even though accurate measurements have not yet been performed. Chl $a'$ is easily incorporated into the PS I apoprotein [23].

Phe $a$, a demetallized Chl $a$, was first identified as the primary electron acceptor of PS II by Klimov et al. [24] (also see [25]), following a suggestion by van Gorkom [26]. Phe $a$ was found in PS II RC complexes isolated from spinach chloroplasts [27–29], and it was proved by Nanba and Satoh [28] to be the electron acceptor of light induced charge separation in PS II preparations of the minimum polypeptide composition. Phe $a$ exhibits spectroscopic properties that are different from those of Chl $a$ (Figure 2A). The absorption maximum of the $Q_Y$ band in organic solvents is shifted to the red by several nanometers, and the extinction coefficient of the red maximum decreased to approximately 60% of Chl $a$ (Table 1). Oxidation and reduction potentials are shifted to positive values (Table 1). Phe $a$ was found even in *Acaryochloris marina*, whose major Chl is Chl $d$ [30–32]. Minor pigments in *Prochlorococcus* sp. are not yet identified.

### 6.2.1.3 Chl d

Chl $d$ is a major pigment in a specific clade of cyanobacteria, the genus *Acaryochloris* [11,33]. It was first found in macrophytic red algae over 60 years ago [34]. However, Chl $d$ in red algae was ascribed to *Acaryochloris* sp. that is attached to the surface of red algal thalli [11]. Therefore, to date, Chl $d$ is known to be present only in one clade of cyanobacteria. According to a phylogenetic tree based on the small subunit (SSU) rRNA sequence, *Acaryochloris* is rather independent of other cyanobacterial clades. This is in marked contrast to *Synechococcus* sp. PCC 7001 (or *Synechococcus* sp. PCC 6307) and *Prochlorococcus* sp. [35], which are closely related species, although the latter contains divinyl-Chl $a$ and divinyl-Chl $b$. *Acaryochloris* evolved independently from other clades. Accordingly, acquisition of Chl $d$ and accompanying

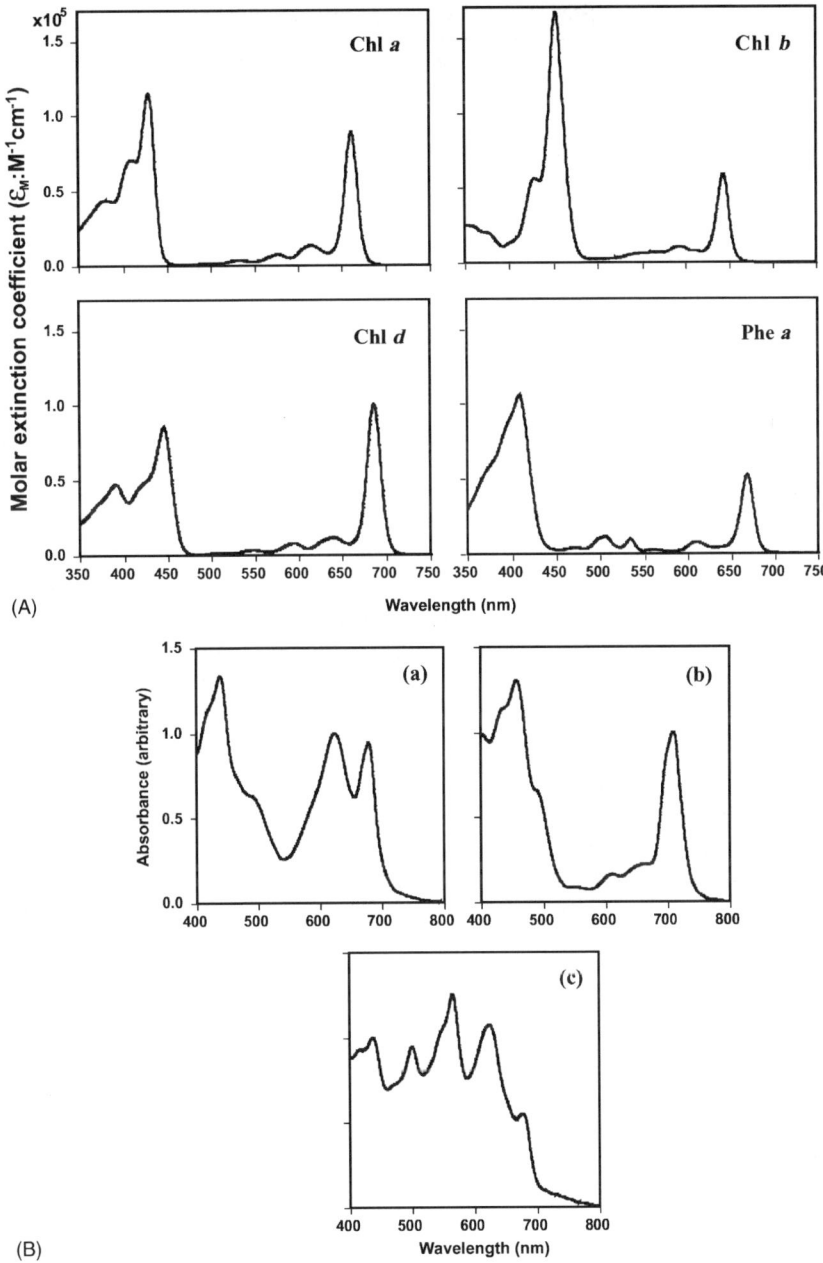

Figure 2. Absorption spectra of a few Chl and related molecules in diethyl ether (A) and intact cells of three species of cyanobacteria (B). (A) Individual spectra are normalized by their extinction coefficients. Spectra of Chl $a'$ and Chl $d'$ are identical to those of Chl $a$ and Chl $d$, respectively. For an absorption spectrum of DV-Chl $a$ and DV-Chl $b$, see Jeffrey et al. (1997) [144]. (B) Absorption spectra of *Synechocystis* sp. PCC 6803 (a), *Acaryochloris marina* (b) and *Gloeobacter violaceus* PCC 7421 (c) at room temperature.

Table 1. Spectral and chemical properties of chlorophylls

| Chlorophyll | $Q_Y$ (nm) | $10^{-4}\varepsilon$ ($M^{-1}$ $cm^{-1}$) | $E^a_{red}$ (V vs. SHE) | $E^a_{ox}$ (V vs. SHE) |
|---|---|---|---|---|
| Chl $a$ | 661 | 8.98 | −1.12 | +0.81 |
| Chl $a'$ | 661 | n.d. | n.d. | n.d. |
| Phe $a$ | 667 | 5.26 | −0.75 | +1.14 |
| Chl $b$ | 643 | 5.67 | −1.02 | +0.94 |
| Chl $c_1$ | 625 | 2.39 | n.d. | n.d. |
| Chl $c_2$ | 628 | 2.27 | n.d. | n.d. |
| Chl $c_3$ | 626 | –[b] | n.d. | n.d. |
| Mg-DVP | 625 | –[c] | n.d. | n.d. |
| Chl $d$ | 686 | 9.9 | n.d. | n.d. |
| Chl $d'$ | 686 | n.d. | n.d. | n.d. |

$Q_Y$ transition in diethyl ether. n.d.: not determined.
[a] Redox potential in acetonitrile.
[b] Unknown, however, Jeffery et al. [144] recommended $2.2 \times 10^5$ at 453 nm in acetone containing 1% pyridine.
[c] Unknown, however, Jeffery et al. [144] recommended $3.6 \times 10^4$ at 623 nm in methanol.

changes in protein moieties for accommodation of a new type of pigment provide a good example to study modification of photosynthetic systems.

Chl $d'$ has been found in *A. marina* [30,31], but Chl $a'$ was not detected. The photoactive pigment complex of PS I in this organism is P740, consisting of Chl $d$ and Chl $d'$ [36] in analogy to the Chl $a/a'$ heterodimer of P700. Phe $d$ was not detected in *A. marina* [30–32].

### 6.2.2 Carotenoids

In cyanobacteria, β-carotene is common to almost all species. In some species, β-carotene is replaced by α-carotene; however, this is rare. Interestingly, α-carotene is dominant in *Prochlorococcus* [10] and *Acaryochloris* [14], where Chl $a$ is not the major pigment. At present it is not clear as to what extent a correlation exists between the presence of these two features. As for xanthophylls, zeaxanthin is common in cyanobacteria and other xanthophylls, i.e., echinenone and canthaxanthin, are frequently found. Many species contain xanthophylls with a sugar-compound, such as myxoxanthophyll or oscillaxanthin [37]. Oscillaxanthin is a unique xanthophyll that does not have a ring structure(s) at the end of the molecules. This structure is commonly found in photosynthetic bacteria but is very rare in oxygen-evolving photosynthetic organisms. Carotenoids with a sugar chain are not found in the other groups of photosynthetic organisms, thus they are unique in cyanobacteria.

The molecular structures of carotenoids in cyanobacteria are simple; a modification of side chains, such as oxidation and hydroxylation, is limited. An allene group or an acetylene group is not introduced; this is closely related to the presence of an enzyme(s) that is responsible for the biosynthesis. Biosynthesis of carotenoids in cyanobacteria is rather simple, and this might be a reflection of undeveloped biosynthetic pathways [38].

As carotenoids are hydrophobic, their presence is limited in membranes or proteins. In the photosynthetic system, their presence is mainly restricted to PS I and PS II complexes (a prominent exception is the Cyt $b_6/f$ complex; see [39] and Chapter 20). Other carotenoids are postulated to be present in the membranes without binding to proteins. However, this idea has not yet been clearly analyzed. Under strong-light conditions, carotenoids are synthesized and accumulated in cells, and are postulated to be localized in the membranes. In some cyanobacteria, carotenoid-proteins are outside of the cells [40]. Their function(s) is (are) not yet clarified.

### 6.2.3 Phycobiliproteins

Phycobiliproteins are characteristic pigment-protein complexes in cyanobacteria. These units are also common to Glaucophyte and red algae. In cyanobacteria, phycobiliproteins exhibit a marked diversity, especially in oceanic small-sized cyanobacteria, so-called picoplanktons [41]. This divergence might be related to the evolution into the specific clade of cyanobacteria, thus resembling the divergence of Chl molecules between *Prochlorococcus* and marine *Synechococcus* [35].

There are four major types of phycobiliproteins: allophycocyanin (APC), phycocyanin (PC), phycoerythrocyanin (PEC) and phycoerythrin (PE) (Table 2). Each pigment-protein consists of a hetero-dimeric protein matrix of the α- and β-subunits and the chromophores. This complex is the basic structural unit for higher-order architecture. In each subunit, characteristic phycobilin chromophores attach covalently to polypeptides [42]. The number and chemical nature of the phycobilin are strictly determined by individual phycobiliproteins. Variations in the number and type of chromophore molecules give rise to variations in the optical characteristics of individual phycobiliproteins [6].

All phycobiliproteins belong to one family, as illustrated by the similarity in their three-dimensional structures even though the primary structures are not well conserved (Table 2). At the beginning of evolution, α- and β-subunits were separated by gene duplication, and thereafter individual subunits evolved to the currently existing phycobilins. According to Apt et al. [43], an anchor polypeptide with two domains is located at the root of the phycobiliprotein family, one for the chromophore attachment and the other for the interaction site with other subunits. The order of branching, APC, PC and PE, follows the energy levels for light absorption. APC is at first branched off and has the lowest energy level, while PE with the highest energy level is the last species to branch off. APC is integrated in the core part of phycobilisomes (see next section). Therefore, APC is inevitable for functional excitation energy transfer (EET) in cyanobacteria. In contrast, PE is located at the periphery of phycobilisomes. Therefore, it is not an indispensable constituent of the phycobilisomes as is the case in some cyanobacteria. In the APC branch, two new subunits emerged: α-APB (ApcD) and $\beta^{18}$ (ApcF) (or $\beta^{16}$ depending on species). These subunits are necessary for building up the core part of phycobilisomes, and for

Table 2. Components of phycobilisomes in cyanobacteria

| Component | *Synechocystis* sp. PCC 6803 | *Gloeobacter violaceus* PCC 7421 | Identity (%) |
|---|---|---|---|
| **APC core** | | | |
| α-Subunit | *apcA* (161) | *apcA* (161) | 75 |
| β-Subunit | *apcB* (161) | *apcB* (161) | 78 |
| Linker | *apcC* (67) | *apcC* (69) | 64 |
| α-APB | *apcD* (161) | *apcD* (161) | 48 |
| Anchor | *apcE* (896) | *apcE* (1155) | 51 |
| β$^{18}$ | *apcF* (169) | *apcF* (161) | 41 |
| **PC rod** | | | |
| α-Subunit | *cpcA* (162) | *cpcA* (162), 2 copies | 60 |
| β-Subunit | *cpcB* (172) | *cpcB* (172), 2 copies | 65 |
| Linker | *cpcC1* (291) | *cpcC* (219) | 56 |
| | *cpcC1* (291) | *cpcC* (219) | 52 |
| | *cpcD* (83) | *cpcD* (76) | 42 |
| | *cpcD* (83) | *cpcD* (70) | 28 |
| Rod–core linker | *cpcG1* (249) | absent | |
| Ligase | *cpcE* (272) | *cpcE* (247) | 43 |
| | *cpcF* (214) | *cpcF* (193) | 35 |
| | *Fremyella diplosiphon* UTEX 481 | *Gloeobacter violaceus* PCC 7421 | Identity (%) |
| **PE rod** | | | |
| α-Subunit | *cpeA* (164) | *cpeA* (164) | 59 |
| β-Subunit | *cpeB* (184) | *cpeB* (177) | 62 |
| Linker | *cpeC* (286) | *cpeC* (285) | 50 |
| | *cpeD* (249) | *cpeD* (255) | 59 |
| | *cpeE* (252) | *cpeE* (254) | 61 |
| Ligase | *cpeY* (429) | *cpeY* (428) | 53 |
| | *cpeZ* (205) | *cpeZ* (204) | 50 |
| γ-Subunit | – | – | |

The numbers of amino acid residues of the individual polypeptides are presented in parentheses. Since *Synechocystis* sp. PCC 6803 does not contain phycoerythrin and the encoding genes, the corresponding amino acid sequences of *G. violaceus* PCC 7421 were compared with those of PE of *F. diplosiphon* UTEX481. Genes for the γ-subunit of PE were not detected in both species.

establishing functional EET to the membrane-integral antenna complexes. An anchor protein (ApcE) is the key component of phycobilisomes.

*6.2.4 Molecular Species of Phycobiliproteins*

The three major phycobiliproteins, APC, PC, and PE (Table 2), are classified into subgroups. PC is separated into two subgroups, C-PC (Cyanophyte PC) and R-PC (Rhodophyte PC), and PE into four major subgroups (C-PE, b-PE, B-PE and R-PE). In APC, qualitatively different subunits are known, i.e., α-APB, β$^{18}$, and L$_{CM}$. This leads to variations in the molecular species of APC (see below). PEC, however, is a single molecular species. The basic structural unit of APC, PC, PEC, C-PE and b-PE is a trimer and that of B-PE and R-PE, a hexamer. In the latter two PEs, an additional γ-subunit is associated with one hexamer unit. Polypeptide compositions and chromophore contents are different in individual phycobiliproteins [6]. Even in the same trimer or hexamer unit the binding of specific linker polypeptides induces differences in optical and biochemical properties [44], thus leading to discrimination of phycobiliproteins.

In the four major subgroups of PE, the α- and β-subunits bind two and three chromophores, respectively. The γ-subunit has four chromophore-binding sites. Accordingly, in total 34 chromophores are associated with one hexamer of PE. In contrast, in the marine *Synechococcus* sp., two different types of PE species are found, i.e., PE-I and PE-II; PE-I contains five chromophore-binding sites per monomer, and PE-II has six sites [45]. Phycourobilin and phycoerythrobilin are bound to those binding sites with different molar ratio, thus leading to variation of their optical properties. This variation might be related to the adaptation to the light environment of their habitats.

As a result of differences in pigment species and contents, variations in absorption spectra are evident among cyanobacterial cells (Figure 2B). *Synechocystis* sp. PCC 6803 exhibits the typical pattern of cyanobacteria; however, the other two are very unique among cyanobacteria.

## 6.3 Phycobilisomes

The first type of phycobilisomes, a supramolecular assembly of phycobiliproteins, was discovered in a red alga *Porphyridium cruentum* by Gantt and Conti [46]. A round cluster was found on thylakoid membranes, which disappeared when phycobiliproteins were washed out. A second type of phycobilisomes was observed in cyanobacteria, where these antennas are attached to thylakoid membranes through a core. From the core, several rods radially protruded to the outside [47] (Figure 1). The two typical shapes are called hemi-spherical and hemi-discoidal for the former and the latter phycobilisomes, respectively. A hemi-spherical type is frequently found in R-PE or B-PE rich cells. In cyanobacteria, the phycobilisomes commonly exhibit a hemi-discoidal shape. Phycobilisomes are present in almost all cyanobacteria that contain phycobiliproteins [44,48], but there are a few exceptions in some species, as will be shown in Section 6.3.3.

The size and shape of hemi-discoidal phycobilisomes depend markedly on the light conditions. In general, when growing under low light intensities, the antenna size is enlarged by expanding the rod elements, whereas under high light intensities the antenna is reduced by diminishing the rod elements. In extreme cases, the rod disappears and only the APC core remains. This is one way to adapt to variations of light intensity. Another type is called "complementary chromatic adaptation" that is induced by the spectral properties of light for growth [3,7]. Under green light the content of individual phycobiliproteins is changed so that more green light is absorbed by replacement of C-PC by C-PE. In contrast, when illuminated with red light the C-PC content increases, thus leading to enhanced absorption of red light. These adaptation processes are regulated by light sensors. Recently, the nature of the sensor and molecular mechanism(s) of this phenomenon were resolved by extensive studies [49].

### 6.3.1 Molecular Structure of Hemi-Discoidal Phycobilisomes

Hemi-discoidal phycobilisomes consist of two parts, the APC core and rod elements (Figure 1). PC is always included in the rod and localized in proximity to the APC core. When cyanobacteria contain either PEC or PE, these two units are localized on the rod elements that are distal to the core. The APC core has the specific function of direct EET connection from phycobiliproteins to the antenna Chl $a$ in thylakoid membranes. Therefore, in addition to the α-β subunits of APC, special components are present that fulfill this function: an anchor polypeptide ($L_{CM}$) [50] and the $α^{APB}$ subunit [51]. In addition, the $β^{18}$ subunit was acquired to adjust for replacement of the α-subunit by the anchor protein (Table 2).

The constitution of the APC core is not uniform in all species. An essential unit is the dodecamer. Depending on the species, the number of dodecamers varies. Three dodecamer units are observed in many cyanobacteria, but in *Anabaena* sp. PCC 7021 it increases to five, while *Synechococcus* sp. PCC 6301 contains only two [4]. In contrast to the varying number of dodecamers, the constitution within one dodecamer is uniform; i.e., four different trimer units are properly arranged. Those are $(αβαβαβ)$, $(αβαβαβ)L_C$, $(αβαβL_{CM}β^{18})$, and $(αβαβα^{APB}β)L_C$, where $L_C$ is a core linker and $L_{CM}$, an anchor protein, that was originally assigned to a linker between the phycobilisome core and the thylakoid membrane. The order of arrangement of these four trimer units in the APC core is postulated to be $(αβαβαβ)$, $(αβαβL_{CM}β^{18})$, $(αβαβα^{APB}β)L_C$, and $(αβαβαβ)L_C$ [44].

In rods, a trimer of phycobiliproteins is the basic structural unit. These trimers are spontaneously built up from α-β monomers due to interaction among these monomers. For a higher order structure, such as hexamer or stacking of hexamers, additional polypeptides are necessary. These are designated as linker polypeptides. The components that form phycobilisomes and their genes for PC-containing *Synechocystis* sp. PCC 6803 [52], PE-containing *Gloeobacter violaceus* PCC 7421 [53], and *Fremyella diplosiphon* UTEX 481 (*Calothrix* PCC 7601) are compiled in Table 2. Table 2 also presents the genes encoding the polypeptides of these phycobilisomes and shows that the sequence similarities of amino acids are not necessarily high.

*G. violaceus* is a cyanobacterium that branched off at the earliest time in the phylogenetic tree based on the SSU rRNA sequence. This species contains R-PE as a major phycobiliprotein. However, the morphology of *G. violaceus* phycobilisome [54] is very different from that of *P. cruentum*, where B-PE is the dominant species. *G. violaceus* contains large rod-like phycobilisomes that are attached to cell membranes from the cytoplasm [55]. At present the reason for different phycobilisome morphology is not clear. Recent analysis of the complete genome sequence of this species provides a first indication for a possible reason [53]. *G. violaceus* was found to lack one specific gene for a rod-core linker polypeptide (*cpcG*) that might be responsible for the formation of a rod element from the core part. Instead, two new linkers are found to be associated with PBS that support formation of the PE/PC pile with three tandem sequences of linker motif in one polypeptide [164].

### 6.3.2 Crystal Structures of Components

In 1985 the first crystal structure of a phycobiliprotein (C-PC) was reported [56]. Since then, there are many reports on crystal structures of phycobiliproteins (APC, PC, PEC, R-PE, b-PE and C-PE, see Table 3). Many but not all of those data were deposited in the Protein Data Bank. Most of these structures are without a linker polypeptide(s), but a crystal structure with a linker polypeptide was presented (APC with a linker [57]). The over-all structures are very similar, i.e., trimers that exhibit a ring structure with a hole of 4 nm in diameter in the central part of the trimer unit. A linker polypeptide is associated with this hole [57]. The chromophore binding sites are well conserved, and with increasing number of chromophores a new one will attach from the outside of the ring so that the over-all structure of phycobiliproteins is not disturbed [6]. This common geometrical array is a fundamental requirement for building high order phycobilisomes.

### 6.3.3 Phycobilisome-Lacking Cyanobacteria

Only a few cyanobacterial species do not form phycobilisomes, even though they contain phycobiliproteins. One example is the Chl *d*-dominated *A. marina* [58]. A small amount of APC and PC is found in the cells; however, only phycobiliprotein aggregates but no phycobilisomes are detected by electron microscopy. This finding suggests that phycobilisomes are not formed despite the presence of an anchor polypeptide that connects phycobilisomes and thylakoid membranes. The reason for the absence of phycobilisomes is not clear [59]. This problem is expected to be resolved when the complete genome sequence of *A. marina* is disclosed. EET to Chl *a* in thylakoid membranes seems a possible occurrence even without a tight binding of APC to membranes, because spectral overlap and the distance between the chromophores should allow this process, although the efficiency will not necessarily be high [6].

Another example of PBS-less species is *Prochlorococcus marinus*. This divinyl-Chl *a/b*-containing cyanobacterium has only a trace amount of PE [60,61]. Recent genome analyses for three strains of *P. marinus* revealed that most of phycobiliprotein genes were deleted, except those for the α- and β-subunits of PE [62].

## 6.4 Membrane-Bound Antenna Complexes

The excitation energy of the antenna pigments is eventually transformed into chemical Gibbs energy via the process of photosynthesis or dissipated via fluorescence or heat. In all oxygen-evolving organisms the key steps of solar radiation trapping take place in the thylakoid membranes. These membranes

Table 3. Compilation of reports on crystal structures of phycobiliproteins

| Phycobiliprotein | PDB ID[a] | Resolution (Å) | Source species | Molecular composition | Reference |
|---|---|---|---|---|---|
| APC | 1ALL | 2.30 | *Spirulina platensis* | [α(1PCB) β(1PCB)]$_3$ | [145] |
|  | 1B33 | 2.30 | *Mastigocladus laminosus* | [α(1PCB) β(1PCB)]$_3$Lc$^{7,8}$ | [66] |
|  | 1KN1 | 2.20 | *Porphyra yezoensis* (R) | [α(1PCB) β(1PCB)]$_3$ | [146] |
|  | 1CPC | 1.66 | *Fremyella diplosiphon* | [α(1PCB) β(2PCB)]$_3$ | [147] |
|  | 1GH0 | 2.20 | *Spirulina platensis* | [α(1PCB) β(2PCB)]$_3$ | [148] |
|  | 1HA7 | 2.20 | *Spirulina platensis* | [α(1PCB) β(2PCB)]$_3$ | [149] |
| C-PC | 1I7Y | 2.50 | *Synechococcus vulcanus* | [α(1PCB) β(2PCB)]$_3$ | [150] |
|  | 1KTP | 1.60 | *Synechococcus vulcanus* | [α(1PCB) β(2PCB)]$_3$ | [151] |
|  | 1JBO | 1.45 | *Synechococcus elongatus* | [α(1PCB) β(2PCB)]$_3$ | [152] |
|  | 1ON7 | 2.70 | *Thermosynechococcus vulcanus* | [α(1PCB) β(2PCB)]$_3$ "unmethylated form" | [153] |
|  | 1PHN | 1.65 | *Cyanidium caldarium* (R) | [α(1PCB) β(2PCB)]$_3$ | [154] |
| R-PC | 1F99 | 2.40 | *Polysiphonia urceolata* (R) | [α(1PCB) β(1PCB, 1PEB)]$_3$ | [155] |
| PEC |  | 2.70 | *Mastigocladus laminosus* | [α(1PXB) β(2PCB)]$_3$ | [156] |
|  | 1LIA | 2.80 | *Polysiphonia urceolata* (R) | [α(2PEB) β(2PEB, 1PUB)$_6$ γ(3PEB, 2PUB) | [157] |
|  | 1B8D | 1.90 | *Griffithsia monilis* (R) | [α(2PEB) β(2PEB, 1PUB)]$_6$ γ(3PEB, 2PUB) | [158] |
| R-PE | 1EYX | 2.25 | *Gracilaria chilensis* (R) | [α(2PEB) β1PUB)]$_6$ γ(3PEB, 2PUB) | [159] |
|  |  | 1.90 | *Polysiphonia urceolata* (R) | [α(2PEB) β(2PUB, 1PUB)]$_6$ γ(3PEB, 2PUB) | [160] |
| B-PE |  | 2.20 | *Porphyridium sordidum* (R) | [α(2PEB) β(3PEB)$_6$ γ(2PEB, 2PUB) | [161] |
| b-PE |  | 2.30 | *Porphyridium cruentum* (R) | [α(2PEB) β(3PEB)]$_6$ | [162] |
| Cr-PE545 | 1QGW | 1.63 | *Rhodomonas* sp. "CS24" (Cr) | α$_1$(DBV) α$_2$(DBV) β(3PEB β(3PEB) | [163] |

[a]Crystal data without PDB ID were not deposited.
R and Cr stand for the origin of phycobiliproteins, R; red algal origin and Cr: cryptomonad origin.
PCB, PEB, PUB, PXB and DBV stand for chromophore species attached to phycobiliproteins; PCB, phycocyanobilin; PEB, phycoerythrobilin; PUB, phycourobilin, PXB, phycoviolobilin, and DBV, dihydrobiliverdin, respectively.

contain the four major complexes that are necessary for oxygenic photosynthetic electron transport and ATP formation: PS I, PS II, cytochrome $b_6/f$, and ATP synthase. Furthermore, the membranes of cyanobacteria also include components of the respiratory chain. Photosynthetic and respiratory electron flows are interrelated by sharing the common electron-transfer component, plastoquinone (for a review, see [1]). Under usual conditions the respiratory activity is low in cyanobacteria compared with photosynthesis. The driving force for photosynthetic electron transfer is provided by the light-induced charge separation within PS I and PS II that not only contain the cofactors for the photochemical reactions but also the pigments of the core antenna. The crystal structures of both photosystems of thermophilic cyanobacteria have been recently resolved by X-ray crystallography [20,63–66] and are described in details in Chapters 13 and 15. Here we concentrate only on the antenna system of the two photosystems in cyanobacteria. Notably, in marked contrast to the great variety of the pigment-protein complexes of peripheral and proximal antenna systems, the structure of the core antennas remained largely invariant to evolutionary development from cyanobacteria to higher plants.

*6.4.1 Photosystem I*

The PS I complex of the thermophilic cyanobacterium *Thermosynechococcus elongatus* consists of eleven polypeptides, with PsaA and PsaB being the major components. Some 96 Chl *a* molecules and 22 β-carotene molecules are bound to this complex ([20] and Chapter 13). Except for five Chl *a* molecules and one Chl *a'* that function as electron-transfer components of photochemical charge separation, the other 90 Chl *a* molecules form the antenna in PS I. Since under normal conditions there is no additional antenna complex for PS I in cyanobacteria, these 90 Chl *a* molecules are the basic unit for structure and function of the PS I antenna. Ligands for Chl *a* molecules were supplied by PsaA, PsaB, PsaI, PsaJ, PsaX and also by one lipid molecule. As an exception in the general molecular organization of PS I, *G. violaceus* lacks four genes of PS I subunits, *psaI*, *psaJ*, *psaK*, and *psaX* [53,67], but contains a new subunit, PsaZ [67].

The molecular arrangement of the Chl *a* molecules in the PS I complex exhibits several characteristic features. The cofactors for the photochemical charge separation are localized in the central part of the PsaA/PsaB heterodimer. There is a space between these components and the Chl *a* molecules that are constituents of the antenna. This space might have some functional role that is not yet resolved. Two layers of Chl *a* molecules parallel to the membrane surface are resolved in PS I ([20] and Chapter 13). This mode of arrangement is similar to that found in the antenna complexes LH 2 [68] and LH 1 with the RC bound to the central part [69] of anoxygenic purple bacteria. In PS I several Chl *a* molecules are located in the center of the two layers (for details on LH1 and LH2, see Chapter 5), suggesting that they function in the whole antenna system as bridging molecules to the photoactive pigment, P700 (Chapter 13).

Energy levels of individual Chl molecules in PS I were theoretically calculated based on the crystal structure [70], and an energy distribution was obtained. Furthermore, earlier experimental observations revealed that a certain number of Chl a molecules in PS I have excited singlet states in the $Q_Y$ region that are energetically below that of $^1$P700*. Accordingly, these pigments were called "Red" Chls [71]. On the basis of an ordered dimer or trimer structure of strongly coupled Chl a molecules, Byrdin et al. [70] proposed an assignment of the "Red" Chls within PS I. The energy levels of individual Chl a molecules are changed by trimer formation, so that the number of "Red" Chl increases [72]. This phenomenon indicates that aggregation affects the electronic state through modification of protein structure. Importantly, in contrast to cyanobacteria the PS I antenna of plants contains, in addition to the core, also chlorophyll-protein complexes (LHC I) as integral parts of the membrane. Interestingly, LHC I contains also "Red" Chls [73]. Chapter 7 gives further details of the PS I antenna in plants.

*6.4.2 Photosystem II*

Compared with PS I the currently available structure of PS II is of lower resolution (see Chapters 13 and 15). PS II is characterized by an unusually large number of small polypeptides ($\leq 10$ kDa) that remained almost invariant to evolutionary development (for a recent review, see [74]). Chapter 15 presents a detailed description of the structure, and Chapters 16 and 17 describe the functional pattern. Therefore, only a few points are briefly outlined. Over 13 polypeptides were resolved in *Thermosynechococcus vulcanus* by Kamiya and Shen [64] and 19 subunits in *T. elongatus* by Ferreira et al. [65]. Apart from the drastically different redox properties of P680 and P700 (see Chapter 16 for details) another marked difference between PS I and PS II is the much smaller heterodimeric protein matrix that houses the cofactors of light-induced charge separation of the latter system. It consists of polypeptides D1 and D2, each characterized by five transmembrane helices (in contrast to the eleven transmembrane helices of each PsaA and PsaB). This structure resembles that of anoxygenic purple bacteria. The arrangement of the cofactor ensemble (Chl $a)_4$, (Phe $a)_2$, $Q_A$, and $Q_B$ in PS II is also similar to that of the corresponding molecules in the reaction centers of the purple bacteria. Apart from the water-oxidizing complex another marked difference is the presence of two additional Chl a molecules at the periphery of the D1/D2 heterodimer. The pigments of the core antenna of PS II are bound to polypeptides PsbB and PsbC, each forming six transmembrane helices. The pigment protein complexes designated as CP47 and CP43 contain 16 and 14 Chl a molecules, respectively. Interestingly, the Chl a binding core complex polypeptides of PS II (D1, D2, CP43, and CP47) are characterized by the same total number of 22 transmembrane helices and a similar array as in the heterodimer PsaA/PsaB of PS I. However, the density of Chl binding is much lower in PS II with 36 Chl a, compared with 96 Chl a molecules in PS I. In addition to Chl a the PS II core complex contains nine β-carotene, two of them located in the D1/D2 heterodimer. Sound information on the structural arrangement of β-carotene is lacking; some provisional assignments have been reported recently [64–66]. Based on this data and for functional reasons (Chapter 16), β-carotene is inferred to be rather far from P680 so that it does not quench the triplet state of P680 [75]. The arrangement of the antenna Chl $a$ molecules within the PS II core complex was used to analyze their energy levels. This analysis led to the conclusion that two bridging Chl $a$ molecules exist between the core antenna pigments and the photochemically active (Chl $a)_4$ (Phe $a)_2$ components [76]. Compared with bulk antenna pigments, the bridging Chl $a$ molecules are optimized in orientation and distances for EET from the core antenna to P680. Interestingly, the two Chl $a$ molecules at the periphery of the D1/D2 heterodimer play only a marginal role at most for this process [76]. In contrast to PS I, the presence of "Red" Chls in PS II is not clearly shown, although the low temperature fluorescence spectra exhibit a pronounced emission at 695 nm. The Chl emitting at 695 nm is located in CP47 [77]. Therefore, the D1/D2/Cyt $b_{559}$ complex did not show this long-wavelength emission [78]. Apart from the phycobilisomes and the core complexes of PS I and PS II, in some cyanobacteria and under stress conditions additional pigment-proteins are found. These complexes will be briefly described in the following section and in more detail in Section 6.6.

*6.4.3 CP43' and Iron-Stress-Induced (Isi) Protein Family*

In cyanobacteria containing Chl $a/b$, i.e., *Prochloron* and *Prochlorothrix*, an additional antenna complex is present that is specifically associated with Chl $b$, symbolized by CP43' [79]. The polypeptide of CP43' (PcbA) and its amino acid sequence are similar to the CP43 polypeptide of the PS II core except for a short loop between helix regions E and F. This type of polypeptide is different from that of the LHC superfamily on the basis of sequence data, but forms a distinct group in the antenna complex. CP43' binds Chl $a$ and Chl $b$, at a Chl $a/b$ ratio higher than 1, indicating that Chl $a$ is preferentially bound. This might originate from the nature of this protein, i.e., the CP43' is originally designed for binding of Chl $a$, and Chl $b$ is able to bind through the flexibility of the polypeptide matrix.

*6.4.4 Molecular Assembly of Photosystems in Thylakoid Membranes*

It is very rare to find a complex in an intermediary step of assembly. In PS II under strong-light conditions, the well-known D1 turnover occurs [80]. In this case it is possible to find a premature complex; however, there is almost no report on the presence of an intermediate. In general, information on the molecular assembly of pigment-protein complexes in thylakoid membranes is rather limited. This point, together with the genesis of thylakoid membranes, will be an important issue for future work. In *G. violaceus*, thylakoid membranes are absent [81]. The formation of this intracytoplasmic membrane system is another topic on the photosynthetic systems of cyanobacteria.

It is postulated that, in cyanobacteria, PS I and PS II form a trimer and a dimer in membranes, respectively. The PS I trimer was confirmed by biochemical isolation from the thermophilic cyanobacterium *T. elongatus* and crystal structure analysis ([20] and Chapter 13). Likewise the PS II dimer structure of PS II core preparations has been resolved by crystal structures on *T. elongatus* [65,66] and *T. vulcanus* [64] (for further details, see Chapter 15). The actual aggregation form of PS II in thylakoid membranes is not yet resolved. This point, however, is very important when we consider the energy distribution or the state transitions of the antenna system as described below. In the former two sections the apparatus for light harvesting and transformation in cyanobacteria has been described. Now we will briefly discuss the EET processes (for a detailed description of the underlying principles of EET, see Chapter 2).

## 6.5 Excitation Energy Transfer (EET)

EET in cyanobacteria is considered from two aspects, i.e., processes and mechanism. The main excitation energy flow takes place from phycobiliproteins and carotenoids to Chl *a*, and after transfer to the Chl *a* pool, equilibration among Chl *a* molecules occurs in the same way as in other oxygenic photosynthetic organisms. Energy migration and equilibrium in the core of one phycobilisome is very critical in cyanobacteria, and the mode of this process is involved in EET between the two photosystems, i.e., spill over and state transitions. In cyanobacteria, β-carotene is confined to the pigment-protein complexes. Measurements of fluorescence excitation spectra clearly indicates that β-carotene is a sensitizer for PS I, but not for PS II [82].

In most antenna complexes the EET mechanisms can be satisfactorily described within the framework of Förster type incoherent hopping processes [83] (see also Chapter 2). This is applicable also to carotenoids, because the allowed excited state (so-called $S_2$ state, for details on the photophysics of carotenoids, see Chapter 4) of carotenoids is responsible for the main energy transfer [84]. In this sense, there is no other special mechanism to describe the energy transfer processes in cyanobacteria, except for the case of a specific interaction in PS I due to a close proximity among pigments.

### 6.5.1 Phycobilisomes as Transient Excitation Energy Reservoir

EET triggered by light absorption of phycobiliproteins is unidirectionally transferred to reaction center complex(es) through sequential EET in the order PE or PEC → PC → APC and finally to Chl *a* of the core complexes within the thylakoid membranes (Figure 3). These processes were nicely illustrated by measurements of time-resolved fluorescence spectra in the pico-second time range (see [85] and references therein). EET between individual chromophores of phycobiliproteins are also resolved by determining the energy levels of individual chromophores [86,87]. Kinetic analyses revealed the sequence of these processes [88].

On the other hand, energy migration within one phycobilisome is also observed. Since degeneracy of the energy levels of chromophores in phycobiliproteins exists, the excitation energy migrates within a pool of isoenergetic

# OXYGEN-EVOLVING CYANOBACTERIA

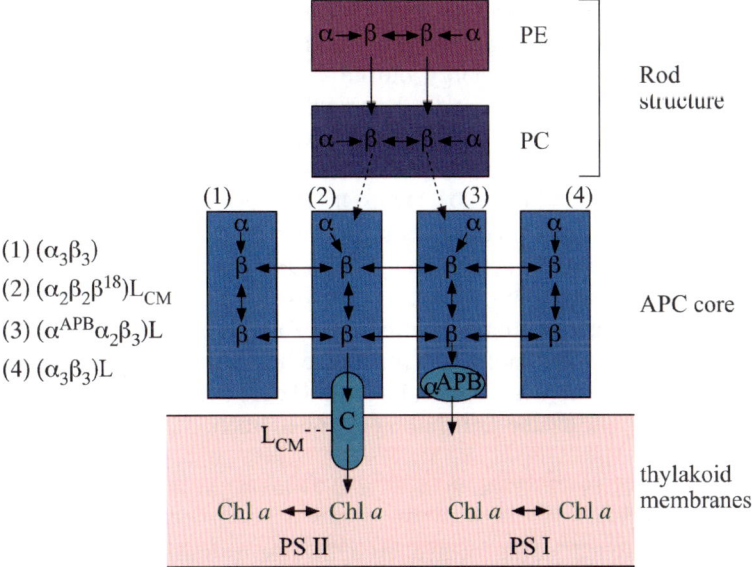

**Figure 3.** Excitation energy transfer (EET) pathway in phycobilisomes. EET pathways are symbolized by arrows. Double-headed arrows indicate the equilibration of EET. The EET pathways from PC β-chromophore to the APC β-chromophore at the connecting site between core and rods is not yet fully confirmed.

excited states (Figure 3). This migration process can be considered as a transient excitation energy reservoir. When the reaction center is open, unidirectional flow to the PS II core is the main route, but when the RC is closed, excitation energy can be transiently kept in phycobiliproteins. This process has long been known; however, its physiological function is not yet clearly stated. This is in contrast to the Chl $a$ molecules in membrane-bound complexes. Since the average distance of chromophores in phycobilisomes is long (>2 nm), the probability of annihilation processes is low.

### 6.5.2 Energy Transfer from Phycobilisomes to Membrane Proteins

In phycobilisomes, two terminal components function as an output of excitation energy to Chl $a$ bound to integral pigment-protein complexes within the thylakoid membranes: (i) the anchor proteins $L_{CM}$ or ApcE [50] and (ii) the protein $\alpha^{APB}$ (ApcD), sometimes called APC-B [51]. The energy levels of the two components are close to each other. The fluorescence maximum of the former is at approximately 685 nm and that of the latter at approximately 682 nm at low temperature [89]. Fluorescence polarization data indicate that the anchor protein is an excitation energy donor to Chl $a$ in PS II [89], whereas this is not the case for $\alpha^{APB}$. Instead, $\alpha^{APB}$ may be an output to other component(s), i.e., PS I [90]. According to the model of phycobilisomes, these two terminal pigments are localized in separate trimer units but two trimer units are located side-by-side [44]. This indicates that, at physiological temperature, both pigments are energetically equilibrated (Figure 3). As a consequence, the switch of the energy output is a suitable way to regulate the excitation energy distribution to PS I and PS II.

The acceptor Chl *a* molecule(s) for the excitation energy from the anchor protein is not yet resolved. It could be either located in the major core antenna polypeptides CP43/CP47 or in D1/D2 itself. The crystal structure of PS II does not provide any information on the interaction between phycobilisomes and PS II. If the dimer structure is kept in membranes, there is a wide space at the CP43 side for a possible association of phycobilisomes with the core complex. To solve this problem, a structure analysis is required for samples that keep phycobilisomes and PS II core complexes bound together. The excitation energy flow from phycobilisomes to Chl *a* molecules in PS II core complexes is critical for the overall EET in cyanobacteria, including the phenomenon of "state transitions".

*6.5.3 Energy Transfer in Photosystems and Trapping in Reaction Centers*

Electronically excited states formed by light absorption of phycobiliproteins, carotenoids and Chl *a* molecules are transferred to the primary electron donors P700 and P680 of PS I and PS II, respectively, and finally trapped via photochemical reactions. The overall EET process in individual photosystems has been analyzed by steady-state and time-resolved spectroscopy. However, due to the presence of many pigments in both systems, the actual pathways are not clearly resolved. Progress in our understanding can be expected by a combination of specific perturbations of the system (e.g., introducing the lack of a specific Chl *a* molecule by genetic engineering) with modern techniques of ultrafast spectroscopy.

The presence of the "Red" Chl is known in PS I. In the case of *Synechocystis* sp. PCC 6803 PS I, 9–11 molecules out of the 90 Chl *a* antenna form the "Red" Chls. This number strongly depends on the species [91]. EET among Chl *a* molecules has been resolved by kinetic analyses [91,92]. Several kinetic components were resolved; however, it is very hard to assign individual kinetic components to the actual EET steps between a specific donor and acceptor pair, simply because many possible pathways are expected from the crystal structures [70,91,92]. The kinetics are strongly affected by the presence of the "Red" Chls [70,72]. Compartmentation of pigment pools and EET among them is currently an acceptable model for the PS I antenna of cyanobacteria. An inherent problem of the EET mechanism is the inability to excite selectively a specific Chl *a* molecule in the antenna. Even in the case of excitation of pigments with a very narrow-bandwidth laser, several Chl *a* molecules are excited simultaneously. This difficulty can be partly circumvented by a complementary method, e.g., polarized spectroscopy.

Although there are significantly fewer Chl *a* in PS II, analysis of the EET pathway resembles that of PS I. In the CP43/D1/D2/CP47 complex there are 36 Chl *a* molecules (Chapter 15). Analysis of data gathered from transient absorption and fluorescence spectroscopy resulted in the resolution of several kinetic components [93]. However, to date, there has been no firm consensus on the energy transfer and charge-separation pathways in PS II (for a review, see [94]).

The energy trapping time in individual photosystems is reported to be rather low, several tenths of a picosecond. This time is closely related to a rather long distance from the final excitation energy donor to the electron transfer components that are localized in the central part of photosystems. Energy transferred to the RC is sometimes not used because the RC itself is not ready for a photochemical reaction, i.e., the RC is closed. In this case, the excitation energy is transferred back to the antenna. It is known that the energy difference between the excitation energy donor and the primary electron donor of RC is not large, so that thermal energy will fill the energy gap for back transfer, and thermal equilibration among antenna pigments is established.

An alternative to formation of an electronically excited state in the RC by EET from the antenna or direct light absorption is the reversal of charge separation that gives rise to delayed fluorescence (DF) or delayed light emission (DLE). Based on measurement and analysis of DLE, the primary electron donor of PS II in *A. marina* was reported to be Chl *a*, even though Chl *d* is the major Chl species in this cyanobacterium [32]. However, recently we identified the primary electron donor and acceptor to be Chl *d* homodimer and Phe *a*, respectively, and assigned Chl *a* to accessory Chl in the active branch [165] (Figure 4). In marked contrast to the well-described phenomena of DLE from PS II (for a review see Vass and Inoue [95]), in the case of PS I delayed fluorescence is not observed, because the electron transfer from the primary electron acceptor ($A_0$ or Chl *a*) to the secondary acceptor ($A_1$ or vitamin $K_1$) is very fast [96] and the quantum yield of $^1P700^*$ formation via charge recombination is very small, together with the low fluorescence yield in PS I at room temperature.

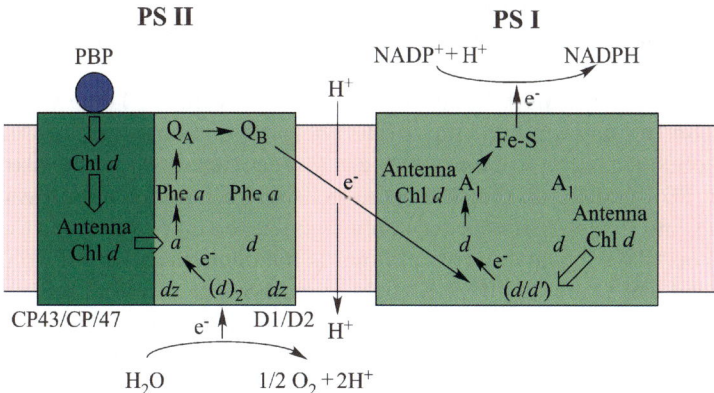

**Figure 4.** A tentative model for the two photosystems in *Acaryochloris marina*. In PS I, all Chl molecules are Chl *d*, except for Chl *d'* of the primary electron donor, and in PS II the primary electron donor (P713) is a Chl *d* homodimer and the primary electron acceptor Phe *a* [165]. Chl *a* is assigned to accessory Chl in the active branch. This architecture is regarded as a hybrid of the conserved PS II and the modified PS I. Open arrows symbolize the excitation energy flow and closed arrows the electron transfer flow.

"Red" Chls exhibit absorption maxima at wavelengths longer than 700 nm. Accordingly, for energetic reasons the fluorescence maxima are expected to be located at even longer wavelengths at lower temperatures. This gives rise to the typical PS I fluorescence band in the wavelength region 720–735 nm at liquid nitrogen temperature. Notably, this is not a general feature in all species with oxygenic photosynthesis. At low temperatures PS I fluorescence was not observed in the cyanobacterium *Gloeobacter violaceus* [97,98], the diatom *Skeletonema costatum* [99], and the Prasinophyceae *Mantoniella squamata* [100]. In these species, the "Red" Chl form(s) is (are) most probably not present. Interestingly, the photochemical activity or overall photosynthetic efficiency was not lower than of those species that contain "Red" Chls. Based on these observations the functional role of "Red" Chls appears to be an unresolved problem.

*6.5.4 State Transition*

Excitation energy distribution to individual photosystems is controlled by light conditions. When cells absorb light that preferentially excites PS I, ("PS I light") a large fraction of the electronically excited states is delivered to PS II by modification of the supply process of EET. In contrast, when the light predominantly excites PS II ("PS II light"), the direction of EET is reversed, and the supply to PS I becomes enhanced. This phenomenon, called "state transitions", is recognized as one of regulatory mechanisms for light energy distribution [101,102].

State transitions have been extensively studied on green algae or chloroplasts of higher plants. With cyanobacteria the phenomena are rather complicated due to the presence of phycobilisomes. Because phycobilisomes act as distributors of excitation energy between PS I and PS II, the state transitions are dependent on the behavior of phycobilisomes. In the mid-1990s it was proposed that phycobilisomes can migrate between PS I and PS II on the membranes, depending on illumination conditions [103,104], and this lateral movement is postulated to be the main reason for the state transitions. There were serious debates on the movement of phycobilisomes. An unambiguous answer is still not yet obtained. If phycobilisomes are acting in excitation energy distribution between PS I and PS II, they are connected via EET to both photosystems at any time, and the transfer efficiency is changed depending on the light "quality" ("PS I" or "PS II" light). A critical point is the connection between phycobilisomes and PS II under "PS II" light condition. If phycobilisomes always transfer excitation energy to PS II, the detachment of phycobilisomes from PS II is hardly compatible with the above model of state transitions in cyanobacteria. In 2002, McConnell et al. [105] proposed an alternative hypothesis on the mechanism of this phenomenon. It is assumed that phycobilisomes are always attached to PS II, but that there exist two excitation energy output pathways from phycobilisomes; one is provided by the anchor protein ($L_{CM}$ or ApcE) directly linking PBS to PS II core and the other unit, $\alpha^{APB}$ (ApcD), funnels excitation energy to PS I. The regulation of excitation energy supply is controlled by the relative EET fluxes via the anchor protein and $\alpha^{APB}$. Although the actual mechanism underlying the state transitions in cyanobacteria is not yet clearly resolved, the latter model is attractive and worth further investigation.

*6.5.5 Energy Dissipation by Carotenoids*

One of the important functions of antenna systems is the dissipation of superfluous excitation energy at high light intensities to protect against light-induced damage of the photosynthetic apparatus. Under illumination conditions that saturate the photosynthetic electron flow capacity, the probability of triplet formation increases for both the photoactive pigment P680 as a result of charge recombination and Chl molecules in the antenna due to intersystem crossing. Chl triplets sensitize the formation of singlet oxygen, which is a very reactive, harmful poison. Therefore, cells have developed strategies of protection. One most powerful way is the dissipation of Chl triplets and singlet oxygen via the "carotenoid valve" (see [106] for a review). A complementary mechanism is the decrease of the excited singlet state population via radiationless dissipation as heat. In the case of Chl *a/b* organisms, such as green algae and plants, the well-known xanthophyll cycle operates for this purpose [107,108]. It consists of the enzymatic interconversion of carotenoid molecules between violaxanthin and zeaxanthin [109]. Details of this quenching of excited singlet states of Chl have not yet been clarified (for further details, see Chapter 9). In cyanobacteria, however, a comparable mechanism is not known. In *Arabidopsis thaliana*, zeaxanthin can be a quencher [110]; this might be applicable to cyanobacteria, if zeaxanthin is confined in a pigment-protein complex.

The major carotenoid species in cyanobacteria are β-carotene and zeaxanthin. The former is bound to PS I and II core complexes not only in cyanobacteria but also in plants. β-Carotene is an antenna pigment for PS I Chl *a* but not for PS II [82] in cyanobacteria; this is understood by the energy levels of β-carotene and Chl *a*. In PS II complexes from plants, β-carotene does not quench the triplet state of P680 because the distance between both species has to be large to prevent β-carotene oxidation by P680$^{+\cdot}$ (for further details, see [94]). Therefore, the major role of β-carotene in PS II RC is assumed to be in quenching singlet oxygen that is formed at $^3$P680 (Chapter 16) [75]. The mode of zeaxanthin binding and its protein matrix are not known. Therefore, at present, there is no direct evidence for a quenching of excited singlet excited states of Chl *a* by zeaxanthin in cyanobacteria. It seems likely that cyanobacteria do not have a protection mechanism that is equivalent to the xanthophyll-cycle in organisms that contain Chl *a/b* LHCs. An alternate mechanism for photoprotection in cyanobacteria, however, is not yet known. This important problem remains to be solved in future studies.

## 6.6 Antenna Systems Induced under Iron-Depleted Conditions

In the early biosphere $Fe^{2+}$ was an abundant species in aqueous solutions of the oceans on earth. The situation drastically changed when $Fe^{2+}$ was oxidized to

$Fe^{3+}$, which is insoluble at physiological pH, thus forming precipitates. As a consequence, with the evolutionary development of oxygen evolving organisms in the form of cyanobacteria the vast majority of $Fe^{2+}$ became oxidized by atmospheric oxygen and currently Fe is known to be one of the limiting nutrients for biomass production, especially in the oceans. Accordingly, a supply of Fe induces a bloom of phytoplankton in the ocean [111]. To cope with the shortage of iron sources cyanobacteria developed a specific mechanism to adapt to this limiting condition, which was caused by their own existence owing to production of molecular oxygen via photosynthesis [112].

*6.6.1 Physiology and Activity under Iron-Stress Conditions*

When cyanobacteria cells are exposed to iron-depleted conditions, several kinds of changes occur. The quantities of thylakoid membranes, phycobilisomes and carboxysomes become reduced and the cell growth decreased to levels of one-half to three-third of the control [113]. Suppression of $O_2$ evolution was also observed due to a lower electron-transfer activity. Concomitant with these features the fluorescence spectra change with a blue-shift of a few nm of the PS II emission. This shift was assigned to the synthesis of a new type of antenna, IsiA. Gene analyses revealed that the iron-depleted condition induces the expression of genes *isiA* and *isiB* [114]. The former encodes for a new type of antenna, and the latter induces synthesis of flavodoxin that replaces the iron-containing ferredoxin as a redox component.

*6.6.2 Structures of the IsiA–Photosystem I Complex*

The overall structures of IsiA-PS I complexes have been resolved in several species of cyanobacteria. The PS I trimer was found to be surrounded by a ring with a certain number of IsiA. It consists of 18 units in *Synechococcus* sp. PCC 7942 [115] and *Synechocystis* sp. PCC 6803 [116]. Each IsiA monomer carries approximately ten Chl *a* molecules, i.e., the total number of Chl *a* molecules of the IsiA ring is about 180. The electronically excited states formed by light absorption of IsiA are efficiently transferred to the PS I core with a rate constant of 1.7 $ps^{-1}$ at the fastest [117]. Accordingly, the antenna size of PS I markedly increases. This might enhance ATP synthesis through stimulated cyclic electron flow around PS I. However, at present the physiological role of this ring is not yet clear. *G. violaceus* does not contain a gene that is comparable with *isiA* [53].

*6.6.3 Origin and Phylogeny of Light-Harvesting Complex (LHC) Superfamily*

The antenna systems of both PS I and in particular of PS II in plants are characterized by the presence of the superfamily of Chl *a/b* binding proteins (referred to as LHC) that are integral parts of the thylakoid membrane. In marked contrast, cyanobacteria do not contain LHCs. However, a precursor of LHC is present: the high-light inducible protein (HLIP) that has one membrane-spanning α-helix. This protein is found in all oxygen-evolving organisms from cyanobacteria to higher plants and has a similar motif for LHC family proteins [118,119]. In this sense, the HLIP is postulated to be an ancestor of all LHC family proteins. Green has described in detail the phylogeny of the LHC family [119].

Cyanobacteria, on the other hand, developed CP43' (or Prochlorophyte Chl $a/b$ protein, Pcb) and IsiA as extra antenna complexes that are similar to CP43. These two are core-like proteins forming six membrane-spanning α-helices. Therefore, both PSs in cyanobacteria have an affinity to the core-type complex. CP43' or Pcb can bind to the PS II core without phycobilisomes, and IsiA attaches to PS I that does not interact with phycobilisomes. This suggests that the binding site of phycobilisomes to the PS II core competes with the CP43'-type complex.

## 6.7 Regulation of Photosystem Stoichiometry and Accompanying Changes in Antenna Architecture

In cyanobacteria, the stoichiometry between PS I and PS II complexes varies, depending on light quality, light quantity (photon flux and spectral distribution), and some other growth condition such as nutrients [120,121]. The antenna size thus accompanies changes in PS stoichiometry and consequently the fraction of Chl $a$ molecules belonging to individual photosystems is also variable. Since 96 and 36 Chl $a$ molecules belong to a monomer unit of the PS I and PS II core, respectively [63–66], and in cyanobacteria grown under low light the PS I/PS II ratio is close to 2, the fraction of total Chl $a$ bound to PS II is expected to decrease down to approximately 15%, in agreement with an earlier observation [122]. This variation is closely related to the excitation energy flux distribution between PS I and PS II. Accordingly, a preferential excitation of Chl $a$ induces an imbalance of energy supply to the two photosystems (red drop, [123]), and the light absorption by phycobiliproteins is critical for survival of cyanobacterial cells.

When cells are grown under PS II light, i.e., green or orange light that preferentially excites phycobilisomes, the PS I content increases. On the contrary, PS I light, i.e., red light absorbed by Chl $a$, induces a decrease of the PS I content [124]. These are compensations to escape from lopsided excitation to, and imbalanced excitation of, the two photosystems. Apart from the spectral properties the photon flux density also gives rise to changes of the PS I/PS II ratio, i.e., strong light induces a low PS I/PS II ratio. After exposure of cyanobacteria to such an illumination the PS I content per cells decreases and this process is completed within 24 hours [125]. The PS I/PS II ratio covers a wide range of values, from less than 1 up to 3, and in an extreme case it was reported to be nearly 10 [126].

The molecular mechanism for changes in the PS I/PS II stoichiometry is not yet understood in detail. Recently, a gene was discovered and shown to be up-regulated by a shift of light intensity [127,128], but its role in regulation of the PS I/PS II ratio remains to be clarified. It is clear that changes in PS I/PS II stoichiometry are closely related to redox-responsive gene expression under physiological condition(s) [129], but more investigations are required to resolve the underlying mechanism(s).

Spectroscopic analyses of P700 and P680 are expected to provide a direct quantification of PS I and PS II. However, these measurements are complicated by several overlapping signals that prevent a straightforward evaluation of this subject. As for PS I, P700 can be monitored by redox-induced absorption changes as a relatively easy method [130]. A spectrophotometer with high sensitivity permits an accurate estimation. Other methods, e.g., photoinhibition of respiration [131] or HPLC analysis of prime-type Chl (Chl $a'$ or Chl $d'$) [19,36], are also appropriate for determination of PS I RC. However, as for PS II, estimation of P680 is almost impossible by steady-state measurements because P680 has a short lifetime, and also chemical oxidation in the dark is impossible due to the very high oxidation potential of P680. Thus, an alternative method(s) is required. Measurement of flash-induced oxygen evolution is a classical but accurate method [125] for functional PS II complexes with a fully competent oxygen-evolving complex. Alternative approaches for quantification of the PS II content are measurements of the light-induced absorption change of $Q_A$ [132], the amount of radio-labeled atrazine binding to the $Q_B$ site [133,134] and the content of cytochrome $b_{559}$ [135]. In the latter case, knowledge of the Cyt $b_{559}$:PSII stoichiometry is required. This ratio is 1:1 for cyanobacteria [63–66] and most likely also for plants (for a recent discussion, see [136]). Determination of the Phe $a$ amount is also a useful method that is based on the existence of two Phe $a$ molecules per one PS II RC [29,63–66].

Estimation of a prime-type Chl and Phe $a$, a pioneering work of Watanabe and Kobayashi, is useful, because HPLC analysis is widely adopted in many laboratories. However, their sophisticated method was not necessarily reproducible in other laboratories, because careful treatments, i.e., extraction, condensation, and elution conditions, are required to obtain reproducible data. A conventional method for estimating the PS I/PS II ratio is measurement of integrated fluorescence intensities at $-196\,°C$ of PS I and PS II under Chl $a$ excitation [137]. However, this approach needs a standard curve for the estimation, which makes this method difficult to adopt.

## 6.8 Chlorophyll Biosynthesis – Characteristics in Cyanobacteria

The biosynthesis of Chl is closely related to the steady-state stability of the antenna system and the electron-transfer chain. However, in most cases a linkage between pigment biosynthesis and integration into polypeptides is not considered as an interrelated phenomenon, but rather discussed as mostly independent events. There is only a limited amount of data available for a thorough description of the biosynthesis of pigment-protein complexes. Free Chl molecules are harmful to cells because they sensitize singlet oxygen formation via triplet state population of Chl. To suppress photo-induced damages, the biosynthetic pathways of complexes must be synchronized with respect to pigment and protein biosynthesis. At present detailed knowledge on this important process is lacking. However, it can be anticipated that information on the whole genome of different cyanobacteria will provide a sound basis for further analyses.

*6.8.1 Protochlorophyllide* a *Reductase*

The biosynthetic pathway of Chl is basically the same as that of bacteriochlorophyll. The pathway has branched from the heme biosynthesis pathway at the step of Mg-insertion into protoporphyrin IX by Mg-chelatase [16,138]. Although both photosynthetic bacteria and cyanobacteria utilize the same metabolic intermediates, several enzymes involved do not seem to be conserved between both types of organisms. The reduction of ring IV of protochlorophyllide is the key step in considering the evolution of cyanobacterial Chl biosynthesis. In photosynthetic bacteria, this step is catalyzed by three gene products (BchL, BchN, and BchB) that were referred to as dark-operative protochlorophyllide oxidoreductase (DPOR), because their reaction is independent of light. The subunits of DPOR exhibit sequence homology with those of nitrogenase. The DPOR activity is sensitively inhibited by oxygen, a characteristic property common to nitrogenase [139]. In addition to the orthologous genes (*chlL*, *chlN*, *chlB*), cyanobacteria have the light-dependent protochlorophyllide oxidoreductase (LPOR) that is not sensitive to oxygen. This enzyme remained conserved during the evolution from cyanobacteria to higher plants. LPOR is found in the cyanobacterium *G. violaceus* PCC 7421 and all other cyanobacteria whose genome sequence has been determined. Since *G. violaceus* is assigned to a primitive organism on the basis of the SSU rDNA sequence, this is the first organism that has LPOR. Therefore, this enzyme might be related to evolution from anoxygenic photosynthetic bacteria to oxygenic cyanobacteria. Its presence might be closely associated with the regulation of the biosynthesis of Chl proteins, such as CP43/CP47 and reaction center proteins.

*6.8.2* In Vivo *Reconstitution of Pigments*

Since almost all enzymes engaged in Chl biosynthesis have been cloned, it is now possible to manipulate genes and resultant enzymes. This opened the road for selective changes in pigment composition and content in cyanobacteria. This method has been applied to many cyanobacterial species. By this way new interesting findings were obtained. Satoh et al. [140] introduced the Chl *b* biosynthesis gene (chlorophyllide *a* oxygenase, *CAO* [141]) into *Synechocystis* sp. PCC 6803 and found that Chl *b* was accumulated up to approximately 10% of the total Chl, and that the newly synthesized Chl *b* was functional mainly in the PS I antenna. Similarly, a PS I-deficient mutant of *Synechocystis* sp. PCC 6803 carrying both *CAO* and *lhcb*, which encodes for LHC II from pea, accumulated Chl $b$ at an extent of over 50%, and this Chl $b$ was bound to PS II [142]. This method, which can be applied to manipulate core antenna and reaction center complexes, is advantageous compared with in vitro reconstitution. Therefore, in future investigations it might be more frequently used to analyze the synthesis and assembly of Chl-binding proteins [143].

## 6.9 Future Prospects

Phycobilisomes with their characteristic architecture are essential constituents of the antenna systems of cyanobacteria and the main light-energy absorber. Details of EET from phycobilisomes to the Chl $a$ molecules of PS I and PS II in the thylakoid membranes are still not satisfactorily clarified and are an important subject of further studies. The X-ray structure of co-crystallized phycobilisome-PS II core complexes will provide deeper insight into this problem. EET steps among individual pigments have to be kinetically resolved even though the energy levels of individual pigments are close to each other. Excitation energy migration among the same kinds of phycobilin chromophores will be described by a short time domain energy reservoir.

The regulation of antenna systems will also be an important topic of future research, in particular the synchronized synthesis of pigments and protein moieties, and their assembly into the thylakoid membranes. At the next level of structural hierarchy, the formation and development of thylakoid membranes have to be harmonized with cell division. As this very important point has not been seriously discussed so far in relation to the antenna system, it will also be a highly relevant subject of future studies. In terms of evolution of antenna systems, the diversity of pigments and associated proteins that are abundant in cyanobacteria remains to be resolved in terms of the biochemical reactions and genomics.

## Acknowledgements

The authors thank Dr S. Takaichi, Nippon Medical School, for discussions on the carotenoid biosynthesis, and Professor G. Renger for his help in improving the manuscript. Financial support from the Ministry of Education, Culture, Sports, Science, and Technology, Japan to M.M. (Grant No. 17GS0314) is gratefully acknowledged.

## References

1. G.A. Peschek, C. Obinger, M. Paumann, The respiration chain of blue green algae (cyanobacteria). *Physiol. Plant.* **120** (2004) 358–369.

2. R.E. Blankenship, *Molecular Mechanisms of Photosynthesis* (2002), Blackwell Science, Malden, MA.
3. A.R. Grossman, M.R. Schaefer, G.G. Chiang, J.L. Collier, The phycobilisome, a light-harvesting complex responsive to environmental conditions. *Microbiol. Rev.* **57** (1993) 725–749.
4. W. Sidler, (1994) Phycobilisomes and phycobiliprotein structures, in: *The Molecular Biology of Cyanobacteria* (1994) (D.A. Bryant, ed.), Kluwer Academic Publishers, Dordrecht, pp. 139–216.
5. M. Mimuro, H. Kikuchi, A. Murakami, Structure and function of phycobilisomes, in: *Concepts in Photobiology: Photosynthesis and Photomorphogenesis* (1999) (G.S. Singhal, G. Renger, S.K. Sopory, K.D. Irrgang, Govindjee, eds.), Narosa Publishers House, New Delhi, pp. 104–135.
6. M. Mimuro, H. Kikuchi, Antenna systems and energy transfer in cyanophyta and rhodophyta, in: *Light-harvesting Antennae* (2003) (B.R. Green, W.W. Parson, eds.), Kluwer Academic Publishers, Dordrecht, pp. 281–306.
7. A.R. Grossman, L.G. van Waasbergen, D. Kehoe, Environmental regulation of phycobilisome biosynthesis, in: *Light-harvesting Antennae* (2003) (B.R. Green, W.W. Parson, eds.), Kluwer Academic Publishers, Dordrecht, pp. 471–493.
8. R. Goericke, D.J. Repeta, The pigments of *Prochlorococcus marinus:* The presence of divinyl chlorophyll *a* and *b* in a marine prokaryote. *Limnol. Oceanogr.* **37** (1992) 425–433.
9. A.W.D. Larkum, C. Scaramuzzi, C. Cox, R.G. Hiller, A.G. Turner, Light-harvesting chlorophyll *c*-like pigment in *Prochloron*. *Proc. Natl. Acad. Sci. U.S.A* **91** (1994) 679–683.
10. S.W. Chisholm, S.L. Frankel, R. Goericke, R.J. Olson, B. Palenik, J.B. Waterbury, L. West-Johnsrud, E.R. Zettler, *Prochlorococcus marinus nov. gen. nov.* sp.: An oxyphototrophic marine prokaryote containing divinyl chlorophyll *a* and *b*. *Arch. Microbiol.* **157** (1992) 297–300.
11. A. Murakami, H. Miyashita, M. Iseki, K. Adachi, M. Mimuro, Chlorophyll *d* in an epiphytic cyanobacterium of red algae. *Science* **303** (2004) 1633.
12. T. Burger-Wiersma, M. Veenhuis, H.J. Korhals, C.C.M. van de Wiel, L.R. Mur, A new prokaryote containing Chls *a* and *b*. *Nature* **320** (1986) 262–264.
13. S.W. Chisholm, R.J. Olson, E.R. Zetter, R. Goericke, J.B. Waterbury, N.A. Welschmeyer, A novel free-living prochlorophyte abundant in oceanic euphotic zone. *Nature* **334** (1988) 340–343.
14. H. Miyashita, K. Adachi, N. Kurano, H. Ikemoto, M. Chihara, M. Miyachi, Pigment composition of a novel oxygenic photosynthetic prokaryote containing chlorophyll *d* as the major chlorophyll. *Plant Cell Physiol.* **38** (1997) 274–281.
15. A. Tomitani, K. Okada, H. Miyashita, H.C.P. Matthijs, T. Ohno, A. Tanaka, Chlorophyll *b* and phycobilins in the common ancestor of cyanobacteria and chloroplasts. *Nature* **400** (1999) 159–162.
16. S.I. Beale, Enzymes of chlorophyll biosynthesis. *Photosynth. Res.* **60** (1999) 43–73.
17. H.H. Strain, W.M. Manning, Isomerization of chlorophylls *a* and *b*. *J. Biol. Chem.* **146** (1942) 275–276.
18. T. Watanabe, M. Nakazato, H. Mazaki, A. Hongu, M. Konno, S. Saitoh, K. Honda, Chlorophyll *a* epimer and pheophytin *a* in green leaves. *Biochim. Biophys. Acta* **807** (1985) 110–117.
19. M. Kobayashi, T. Watanabe, M. Nakazato, I. Ikegami, T. Hiyama, T. Matsunaga, N. Murata, Chlorophyll $a'$/P700 and pheophytin $a$/P680 stoichiometries in higher

plants and cyanobacteria determined by HPLC analysis. *Biochim. Biophys. Acta* **936** (1988) 81–89.
20. P. Jordan, P. Fromme, H.T. Witt, O. Klukas, W. Saenger, N. Krauß, Three-dimensional structure of cyanobacterial Photosystem I at 2.5 Å resolution. *Nature* **411** (2001) 909–917.
21. T. Watanabe, A. Hongu, K. Honda, M. Nakazato, M. Konno, S. Saitoh, Preparation of chlorophylls and pheophytins by isocratic liquid chromatography. *Anal. Chem.* **56** (1984) 251–256.
22. T. Oba, M. Mimuro, Z.Y. Wang, T. Nozawa, S. Yoshida, T. Watanabe, Spectral characteristics and colloidal properties of chlorophyll $a'$ in aqueous methanol. *J. Phys. Chem. B* **101** (1997) 3261–3268.
23. T. Hiyama, T. Watanabe, M. Kobayashi, M. Nakazato, Interaction of chlorophyll $a'$ with the 65 kDa subunit protein of photosystem I reaction center. *FEBS Lett.* **214** (1987) 97–100.
24. V.V. Klimov, A.V. Klevanik, V.A. Shuvalov, A.A. Krasnovsky, Reduction of pheophytin in the primary light reaction of photosystem II. *FEBS Lett.* **82** (1977) 183–186.
25. V.V. Klimov, Discovery of pheophytin function in the photosynthetic energy conversion as the primary electron acceptor of photosystem II. *Photosynth. Res.* **76** (2003) 247–253.
26. H.J. van Gorkom, Identification of the reduced primary electron acceptor of photosystem II as a bound semiquinone anion. *Biochim. Biophys. Acta* **347** (1974) 439–442.
27. N. Murata, S. Araki, Y. Fujita, K. Suzuki, T. Kuwabara, P. Mathis, Stoichiometric determination of pheophytin in photosystem II of oxygenic photosynthesis. *Photosynth. Res.* **9** (1986) 63–70.
28. O. Nanba, K. Satoh, Isolation of a photosystem II reaction center consisting of D-1 and D-2 polypeptides and cytochrome b-559. *Proc. Natl. Acad. Sci. U.S.A.* **84** (1987) 109–112.
29. M. Kobayashi, H. Maeda, T. Watanabe, H. Nakane, K. Satoh, Chlorophyll *a* and β-carotene content in the D1/D2/cytochrome *b*-559 reaction center complex from spinach. *FEBS Lett.* **260** (1990) 138–140.
30. M. Akiyama, H. Miyashita, H. Kise, T. Watanabe, S. Miyachi, M. Kobayashi, Detection of chlorophyll $d'$ and pheophytin *a* in a chlorophyll *d*-dominating oxygenic photosynthetic prokaryote *Acaryochloris marina*. *Anal. Sci.* **17** (2001) 205–208.
31. M. Akiyama, H. Miyashita, H. Kise, T. Watanabe, M. Mimuro, S. Miyachi, M. Kobayashi, Quest for minor but key chlorophyll molecules in photosynthetic reaction centers. Unusual pigment composition in the reaction centers of the chlorophyll *d*-dominated cyanobacterium *Acaryochloris marina*. *Photosynth. Res.* **74** (2002) 109–120.
32. M. Mimuro, S. Akimoto, T. Gotoh, M. Yokono, M. Akiyama, T. Tsuchiya, H. Miyashita, M. Kobayashi, I. Yamazaki, Identification of the primary electron donor in PS II of the Chl *d*-dominated cyanobacterium *Acaryochloris marina*. *FEBS Lett.* **556** (2004) 95–98.
33. H. Miyashita, H. Ikemoto, N. Kurano, K. Adachi, M. Chihara, S. Miyachi, Chlorophyll *d* as major pigment. *Nature* **383** (1996) 402.
34. M.M. Manning, H.H. Strain, Chlorophyll *d*, a green pigment of red algae. *J. Biol. Chem.* **151** (1943) 1–19.
35. E. Urbach, D.J. Scanlan, D.L. Distel, J.B. Waterbury, S.W. Chisholm, Rapid diversification of marine picoplankton with dissimilar light-harvesting structures

inferred from sequence of *Prochlorococcus* and *Synechococcus* (cyanobacteria). *J. Mol. Evol.* **46** (1988) 188–210.

36. M. Akiyama, T. Gotoh, H. Kise, H. Miyashita, M. Mimuro, M. Kobayashi, Stoichiometries of chlorophyll $d'$/PSI and chlorophyll $a$/PSII in a chlorophyll $d$-dominated cyanobacterium *Acaryochloris marina*. *Jpn. J. Phycol.* **52** (2004) 67–72.
37. H. Scheer, The pigments, in: *Light-harvesting Antennae* (2003) (B.R. Green, W.W. Parson, eds.), Kluwer Academic Publishers, Dordrecht, pp. 29–81.
38. F.X. Cunningham Jr., Regulation of carotenoid synthesis and accumulation in plants. *Pure Appl. Chem.* **74** (2002) 1409–1417.
39. G. Kurisu, H. Zhang, J.L. Smith, W.A. Cramer, Structure of the cytochrome $b_6f$ complex of oxygenic photosynthesis: Tuning the cavity. *Science* **302** (2003) 1009–1014.
40. K.J. Reddy, G.S. Bullerjahn, L.A. Sherman, Characteristics of membrane-associated carotenoid-binding proteins in cyanobacteria and prochlorophytes. *Methods Enzymol.* **214** (1993) 390–401.
41. L.J. Ong, A.N. Glazer, J.B. Waterbury, An unusual phycoerythrin from a marine cyanobacteria. *Science* **224** (1984) 80–83.
42. H. Scheer, Biliprotein. *Angew. Chem.* **93** (1981) 230–250.
43. K.E. Apt, J.L. Collier, A.R. Grossman, Evolution of the phycobiliproteins. *J. Mol. Biol.* **248** (1995) 79–96.
44. A.N. Glazer, Light-harvesting by phycobilisomes. *Annu. Rev. Biophys. Biophys. Chem.* **14** (1985) 47–77.
45. L.J. Ong, A.N. Glazer, Phycoerythrin of marine unicellular cyanobacteria. I. Bilin types and locations and energy transfer pathways in *Synechococcus* species. *J. Biol. Chem.* **266** (1991) 9515–9527.
46. E. Gantt, S.F. Conti, Granules associated with the chloroplast lamellae of *Porphyridium cruentum*. *J. Cell Biol.* **29** (1966) 423–434.
47. E. Gantt, M.R. Edwards, S.F. Conti, Ultrastructure of *Porphyridium aerugineum*, a blue-green colored Rhodophyta. *J. Phycol.* **4** (1968) 65–71.
48. E. Gantt, Structure and function of phycobilisomes: Light harvesting pigment complexes in red and blue-green algae. *Int. Rev. Cytol.* **66** (1980) 45–80.
49. K. Terauchi, B.L. Montgomery, A.R. Grossman, J.C. Lagarias, D.M. Kehoe, RcaE is a complementary chromatic adaptation photoreceptor required for green and red light responsiveness. *Mol. Microbiol.* **51** (2004) 567–577.
50. T. Redlinger, E. Gantt, A $M_r$ 95,000 polypeptide in *Porphyridium cruentum* phycobilisomes and thylakoids: Possible function in linkage of phycobilisomes to thylakoids and in energy transfer. *Proc. Natl. Acad. Sci. U.S.A.* **79** (1982) 5542–5546.
51. A.N. Glazer, D.A. Bryant, Allophycocyanin B ($\lambda$max 671, 681 nm). A new cyanobacterial phycobiliprotein. *Arch. Microbiol.* **104** (1975) 15–22.
52. T. Kaneko, S. Sato, H. Kotani, A. Tanaka, E. Asamizu, Y. Nakamura, N. Miyajima, M. Hirosawa, M. Sugiura, S. Sasamoto, T. Kimura, T. Hosouchi, A. Matsuno, A. Muraki, N. Nakazaki, K. Naruo, S. Okumura, S. Shimpo, C. Takeuchi, T. Wada, A. Watanabe, M. Yamada, M. Yasuda, S. Tabata, Sequence analysis of the genome of the unicellular cyanobacterium *Synechocystis* sp. strain PCC6803. II. Sequence determination of the entire genome and assignment of potential protein-coding regions. *DNA Res.* **3** (1996) 109–136.
53. Y. Nakamura, T. Kaneko, S. Sato, M. Mimuro, H. Miyashita, T. Tsuchiya, S. Sasamoto, A. Watanabe, K. Kawashima, Y. Kishida, C. Kiyokawa, M. Kohara,

M. Matsumoto, A. Matsuno, N. Nakazaki, S. Shimpo, C. Takeuchi, M. Yamada, S. Tabata, Complete genome structure of *Gloeobacter violaceus* PCC 7421, a cyanobacterium that lacks thylakoids. *DNA Res.* **10** (2003) 137–145.

54. D.A. Bryant, G. Cohen-Bazire, A.N. Glazer, Characterization of the biliproteins of *Gloeobacter violaceus*. Chromophore content of a cyanobacterial phycoerythrin carrying phycourobilin chromophore. *Arch. Microbiol.* **129** (1981) 190–198.
55. G. Guglielmi, G. Cohen-Bazire, D.A. Bryant, The structure of *Gloeobacter violaceus* and its phycobilisomes. *Arch. Microbiol.* **129** (1981) 181–189.
56. T. Schirmer, W. Bode, R. Huber, W. Sidler, H. Zuber, X-ray crystallographic structure of the light-harvesting biliprotein C-phycocyanin from the thermophilic cyanobacterium *Mastigocladus laminosus* and its resemblance to globin structures. *J. Mol. Biol.* **184** (1985) 257–277.
57. W. Reuter, G. Wiegand, R. Huber, M.E. Than, Structural analysis at 2.2 Å of orthorhombic crystals presents the asymmetry of the allophycocyanin-linker complex, $AP.L_C^{7.8}$, from phycobilisomes of *Mastigocladus laminosus*. *Proc. Natl. Acad. Sci. U.S.A.* **96** (1999) 1363–1368.
58. J. Marquardt, H. Senger, H. Miyashita, S. Miyachi, E. Mörschel, Isolation and characterization of biliprotein aggregates from *Acaryochloris marina*, a *Prochloron*-like prokaryote containing mainly chlorophyll *d*. *FEBS Lett.* **410** (1997) 428–432.
59. M. Chen, R.G. Quinnell, A.W.D. Larkum, The major light-harvesting pigment protein of *Acaryochloris marina*. *FEBS Lett.* **514** (2002) 149–152.
60. W.R. Hess, F. Partensky, G.W.M. van der Staay, J.M. Garcia-Fernandez, T. Borner, D. Vaulot, Coexistence of phycoerythrin and a chlorophyll *a/b* antenna in a marine prokaryote. *Proc. Natl. Acad. Sci. U.S.A.* **93** (1996) 11126–11130.
61. W.R. Hess, C. Steglich, C. Lichtle, F. Partensky, Phycoerythrins of oxyphotobacterium *Prochlorococcus marinus* are associated to the thylakoid membrane and are encoded by a single large gene cluster. *Plant Mol. Biol.* **40** (1999) 507–521.
62. G. Rocap, F.W. Larimer, J. Lamerdin, S. Malfatti, P. Chain, N.A. Ahlgren, A. Arellano, M. Coleman, L. Hauser, W.R. Hess, Z.I. Johnson, M. Land, D. Lindell, A.F. Post, W. Regala, M. Shah, S.L. Shaw, C. Steglich, M.B. Sullivan, C.S. Ting, A. Tolonen, E.A. Webb, E.R. Zinser, S.W. Chisholm, Genome divergence in two *Prochlorococcus* ecotypes reflects oceanic niche differentiation. *Nature* **424** (2003) 1042–1047.
63. A. Zouni, H.T. Witt, J. Kern, P. Fromme, N. Krauß, W. Saenger, P. Orth, Crystal structure of photosystem II from *Synechococcus elongatus* at 3.8 Å resolution. *Nature* **409** (2001) 739–743.
64. N. Kamiya, J.R. Shen, Crystal structure of oxygen-evolving photosystem II from *Thermosynechococcus vulcanus* at 3.7-angstrom resolution. *Proc. Natl. Acad. Sci. U.S.A.* **100** (2003) 98–103.
65. K.N. Ferreira, T.M. Iverson, K. Maghlaoui, J. Barber, S. Iwata, Architecture of the photosynthetic oxygen-evolving center. *Science* **303** (2004) 1831–1838.
66. B. Loll, J. Kern, W. Saenger, A. Zouni, J. Biesiadka, Towards complete cofactor arrangement in the 3.0 Å resolution structure of photosystem II. *Nature* **438** (2005) 1040–1044.
67. H. Inoue, T. Tsuchiya, S. Satoh, H. Miyashita, T. Kaneko, S. Tabata, A. Tanaka, M. Mimuro, Unique constitution of photosystem I with a novel subunit in a cyanobacterium *Gloeobacter violaceus* PCC 7421. *FEBS Lett.* **578** (2004) 275–279.

68. G. McDermott, S.M. Prince, A.A. Freer, A.M. Hawthornthwaite-Lawless, M.Z. Papiz, R.J. Cogdell, N.W. Isaacs, Crystal structure of an integral membrane light-harvesting complex from photosynthetic bacteria. *Nature* **374** (1995) 517–521.
69. A.W. Roszak, T.D. Howard, J. Southall, A.T. Gardiner, C.J. Law, N.W. Isaacs, R.J. Cogdell, Crystal structure of the RC-LH1 core complex from *Rhodopseudomonas palustris*. *Science* **302** (2003) 1969–1972.
70. M. Byrdin, P. Jordan, N. Krauss, P. Fromme, D. Stehlik, E. Schlodder, Light-harvesting in photosystem I: Modeling based on the 2.5 angstrom structure of photosystem I from *Synechococcus elongatus*. *Biophys. J.* **83** (2002) 433–457.
71. R. van Grondelle, J.P. Dekker, T. Gillbro, V. Sundstrom, Energy transfer and trapping in photosynthesis. *Biochim. Biophys. Acta* **1994** (1187) 1–65.
72. L.-O. Palsson, C. Flemming, B. Gobets, R. van Grondelle, J.P. Dekker, E. Schlodder, Energy transfer and charge separation in photosystem I: P700 oxidation upon selective excitation of the long-wavelength chlorophylls of *Synechococcus elongatus*. *Biophys. J.* **74** (1998) 2611–2622.
73. A.N. Melkozernov, R.E. Blankenship, Structural modeling of the Lhca4 subunit of LHCI-730 peripheral antenna in photosystem I based on similarity with LHCII. *J. Biol. Chem.* **278** (2003) 44542–44551.
74. L.-X. Shi, W.P. Schröder, The low molecular mass subunits of the photosynthetic supracomplex, photosystem II. *Biochim. Biophys. Acta* **1608** (2004) 75–96.
75. A. Telfer, What is beta-carotene doing in the photosystem II reaction centre? *Philos. Trans. Royal Soc. London Ser B-Biol. Sci.* **357** (2002) 1431–1439.
76. S. Vasil'ev, J.R. Shen, N. Kamiya, D. Bruce, The orientations of core antenna chlorophylls in photosystem II are optimized to maximize the quantum yield of photosynthesis. *FEBS Lett.* **561** (2004) 111–116.
77. M.L. Groot, J. Breton, L.J.G.W. van Wilderen, J.P. Dekker, R. van Grondelle, Femtosecond visible/visible and visible/mid-IR pump–probe study of the photosystem II core antenna complex CP47. *J. Phys. Chem. B* **108** (2004) 8001–8006.
78. M. Mimuro, I. Yamazaki, S. Itoh, N. Tamai, K. Satoh, Dynamic fluorescence properties of D1-D2-cytochrome *b*-559 complex isolated from spinach chloroplasts: Analysis by means of the time-resolved fluorescence spectra in picosecond time range. *Biochim. Biophys. Acta* **933** (1988) 478–486.
79. H.C.P. Matthijs, G.W.M. van der Staay, L.R. Mur, Prochlorophytes: The 'other cyanobacteria?', in: *The Molecular Biology of Cyanobacteria* (1995) (D.A. Bryant, ed.), Kluwer Academic Publishers, Dordrecht, pp. 49–64.
80. B.A. Diner, F. Rappaport, Structure, dynamics, and energetics of the primary photochemistry of photosystem II of oxygenic photosynthesis. *Annu. Rev. Plant Biol.* **53** (2002) 551–580.
81. R. Rippka, J.B. Waterbury, G. Cohen-Bazire, A cyanobacterium which lacks thylakoids. *Arch. Microbiol.* **100** (1974) 419–436.
82. J.C. Goedheer, On the low temperature fluorescence spectra of blue-green and red algae. *Biochim. Biophys. Acta* **153** (1968) 903–906.
83. T. Förster, Zwischen molekulare energiewanderung und fluoreszenz. *Ann. Phys. Leipzig* **2** (1948) 55–75.
84. M. Mimuro, S. Akimoto, Energy transfer processes from fucoxanthin and peridinin to chlorophyll, in: *Photosynthesis in Algae* (2003) (A.W.D. Larkum, S. Douglas, J.A. Raven, eds.), Kluwer Academic Publishers, Dordrecht, pp. 335–349.

85. M. Mimuro, Visualization of excitation energy transfer processes in plants and algae. *Photosynth. Res.* **73** (2002) 133–138.
86. M. Mimuro, P. Füglistaller, R. Rümbeli, H. Zuber, Functional assignment of chromophores and energy transfer in C-phycocyanin isolated from the thermophilic cyanobacterium *Mastigocladus laminosus*. *Biochim. Biophys. Acta* **848** (1986) 155–166.
87. K. Sauer, H. Scheer, Excitation transfer in C-phycocyanin Förster transfer rate and exciton calculation based on new crystal structure form *Agmenellum quadruplicatum* and *Mastigocladus laminosus*. *Biochim. Biophys. Acta* **936** (1988) 157–170.
88. M. Mimuro, I. Yamazaki, N. Tamai, T. Katoh, Excitation energy transfer in phycobilisomes at $-196\,°C$ isolated from the cyanobacterium *Anabaena variabilis* (M-3): Evidence for the plural transfer pathways to the terminal emitters. *Biochim. Biophys. Acta* **973** (1989) 153–162.
89. M. Mimuro, C.A. Lipschultz, E. Gantt, Energy flow in the phycobilisome core of *Nostoc* sp (MAC): Two independent terminal pigments. *Biochim. Biophys. Acta* **852** (1986) 126–132.
90. Y.M. Gindt, J. Zhou, D.A. Bryant, K. Sauer, Core mutation of *Synechococcus* sp. PCC 7002 phycobilisomes: A spectroscopic study. *J. Photochem. Photobiol. B* **15** (1992) 75–89.
91. B. Gobets, I.H.M. van Stokkum, M. Rögner, J. Krulp, E. Schlodder, N.V. Karapetyan, J.P. Dekker, R. van Grondelle, Time-resolved fluorescence emission measurements of photosystem I particles of various cyanobacteria: A unified compartmental model. *Biophys. J.* **81** (2001) 407–424.
92. M.K. Sener, D. Lu, T. Ritz, S. Park, P. Fromme, K. Schulten, Robustness and optimality of light harvesting in cyanobacterial photosystem I. *J. Phys. Chem. B* **106** (2002) 7948–7960.
93. M. Seibert, M.R. Wasielewski, The isolated photosystem II reaction center: The first attempt to directly measure the kinetics of primary charge separation. *Photosynth. Res.* **76** (2003) 263–268.
94. G. Renger, A.R. Holzwarth, Primary electron transfer. in: Photosystem II, *The Light-Driven Water:Plastoquinone OxidoReductase* (2005) (T. Wydrzynski, K. Satoh, eds.), Kluwer Academic Publishers, Dordrecht, pp. 139–175.
95. I. Vass, Y. Inoue, The photosystems: Structure, function and molecular biology, in: *Topics in Photosynthesis* (1992) (J. Barber, ed.), Elsevier, Amsterdam, pp. 259–294.
96. S. Kumazaki, I. Ikegami, H. Furusawa, S. Yasuda, K. Yoshihara, Observation of the excited state of the primary electron donor chlorophyll (P700) and the ultrafast charge separation in the spinach photosystem I reaction center. *J. Phys. Chem. B* **105** (2001) 1093–1099.
97. F. Koenig, M. Schmidt, *Gloeobacter violaceus*–investigation of an unusual photosynthetic apparatus. Absence of the long wavelength emissions of photosystem I in 77K fluorescence spectra. *Physiol. Plant.* **94** (1995) 621–628.
98. M. Mimuro, T. Ookubo, D. Takahashi, T. Sakawa, S. Akimoto, I. Yamazaki, H. Miyashita, Unique fluorescence properties of a cyanobacterium *Gloeobacter violaceus* PCC 7421: Reasons for absence of the long-wavelength PS I Chl *a* fluorescence at $-196\,°C$. *Plant Cell Physiol.* **43** (2002) 587–594.
99. S. Shimura, Y. Fujita, Some properties of the chlorophyll fluorescence of the diatom *Phaeodactylum tricornutum*. *Plant Cell Physiol.* **14** (1973) 341–352.
100. C.W. Wilhelm, P. Kramer, I. Lenartz-Weiler, The energy distribution between the photosystems and light-induced changes in the stoichiometry of system I and II

reaction center in the chlorophyll *b*-containing alga *Mantoniella squamata* (*Prasinophyceae*). *Photosynth. Res.* **20** (1993) 221–233.
101. C. Bonaventura, J. Myers, Fluorescence and oxygen evolution from *Chlorella pyrenoidosa*. *Biochim. Biophys. Acta* **189** (1969) 366–383.
102. N. Murata, Control of excitation transfer in photosynthesis. I. Light-induced change of chlorophyll *a* fluorescence in *Porphyridium cruentum*. *Biochim. Biophys. Acta* **172** (1969) 242–251.
103. C.W. Mullineaux, Excitation energy transfer from phycobilisomes to photosystem I in a cyanobacterial mutant lacking photosystem II. *Biochim. Biophys. Acta* **1184** (1994) 71–77.
104. C.W. Mullineaux, M.J. Tobin, G.R. Jones, Mobility of photosynthetic complexes in thylakoid membranes. *Nature* **390** (1997) 421–424.
105. M.D. McConnell, R. Koop, S. Vasil'ev, D. Bruce, Regulation of the distribution of chlorophyll and phycobilin-absorbed excitation energy in cyanobacteria. A structure-based model for the light state transition. *Plant Physiol.* **130** (2002) 1201–1212.
106. D. Siefermann-Harms, The light harvesting and protective function of carotenoids in photsynthesic membranes. *Physiol. Plant.* **69** (1987) 561–568.
107. H.Y. Yamamoto, T.O.M. Nakayama, C.O. Chichester, Studies on the light and dark interconversions of leaf xanthophylls. *Arch. Biochem. Biophys.* **97** (1962) 168–173.
108. H.Y. Yamamoto, J.L. Chang, M.S. Aihara, Light-induced interconversions of violaxanthin and zeaxanthin in New Zealand spinach-leaf segments. *Biochim. Biophys. Acta* **141** (1967) 342–347.
109. H.Y. Yamamoto, Biochemistry of violaxanthin cycle in higher plants. *Pure Appl. Chem.* **51** (1979) 639–648.
110. Y.Z. Ma, N.E. Holt, X.P. Li, K.K. Niyogi, G.R. Fleming, Evidence for direct carotenoid involving in the regulation of photosynthetic light harvesting. *Proc. Natl. Acad. Sci. U.S.A.* **100** (2003) 4377–4382.
111. A. Tsuda, S. Takeda, H. Saito, J. Nishioka, Y. Nojiri, I. Kudo, H. Kiyosawa, A. Shiomoto, K. Imai, T. Ono, A. Shimamoto, D. Tsumune, T. Yoshimura, T. Aono, A. Hinuma, M. Kinugasa, K. Suzuki, Y. Sohrin, Y. Noiri, H. Tani, Y. Deguchi, N. Tsurushima, H. Ogawa, K. Fukami, K. Kuma, T. Saino, A mesoscale iron enrichment in the western subarctic pacific induces a large centric diatom bloom. *Science* **300** (2003) 958–961.
112. N.A. Straus, Iron deprivation: Physiology and gene regulation, in: *The Molecular Biology of Cyanobacteria* (1994) (D.A. Bryant, ed.), Kluwer Academic Publishers, Dordrecht, pp. 731–750.
113. D.M. Sherman, L.A. Sherman, Effect of iron deficiency and iron restoration on ultrastructure of *Anacystis nidulans*. *J. Bacteriol.* **156** (1983) 393–401.
114. R.L. Burnap, T. Troyan, L.A. Sherman, The highly abundant chlorophyll-protein complex of iron-deficient *Synechococcus* sp. PCC7942 (CD43) is encoded by the isiA gene. *Plant Physiol.* **103** (1993) 893–902.
115. E.J. Boekema, A. Hifney, A.E. Yakushevska, M. Piotrowski, W. Keegstra, S. Berry, K.P. Michel, E.K. Pistorius, J. Kruip, A giant chlorophyll-protein complex induced by iron deficiency in cyanobacteria. *Nature* **412** (2001) 745–748.
116. T.S. Bibby, J. Nield, J. Barber, Iron deficiency induces the formation of an antenna ring around trimeric photosystem I in cyanobacteria. *Nature* **412** (2001) 743–745.

117. A.N. Melkozernov, T.S. Bibby, S. Lin, J. Barber, R.E. Blankenship, Time-resolved absorption and emission show that the CP43' antenna ring of iron-stressed *Synechocystis* sp PCC6803 is efficiently coupled to the photosystem I reaction center core. *Biochemistry* **42** (2003) 3893–3903.
118. J. La Roche, G.W.M. van der Staay, F. Partensky, A. Ducret, R. Aebersold, R. Li, S.S. Golden, R.G. Hiller, P.M. Wrench, A.W.D. Larkum, B.R. Green, Independent evolution of the Prochlorophyte and green plant chlorophyll a/b light harvesting proteins. *Proc. Natl. Acad. Sci. U.S.A.* **93** (1996) 15244–15248.
119. B. Green, The evolution of light-harvesting antenna, in: *Light-harvesting Antennae* (2003) (B.R. Green, W.W. Parson, eds.), Kluwer Academic Publishers, Dordrecht, pp. 129–168.
120. Y. Fujita, A. Murakami, K. Aizawa, K. Ohki, Short-term and long-term adaptation of the photosynthetic apparatus: Homeostatic properties of thylakoids, in: *The Molecular Biology of Cyanobacteria*, (1994) (D.A. Bryant, ed.), Kluwer Academic Publishers, Dordrecht, pp. 677–692.
121. Y. Fujita, K. Ohki, A. Murakami, Acclimation of photosynthetic light energy conversion to the light environments, in: *Algal Adaptation to Environmental Stresses* (2001) (L.C. Rai, J.P. Gaur, eds.), Springer-Verlag, Berlin, pp. 135–171.
122. M. Mimuro, Y. Fujita, Estimation of chlorophyll *a* distribution in the photosynthetic pigments systems I and II of the blue-green alga *Anabaena variabilis*. *Biochim. Biophys. Acta* **459** (1977) 376–389.
123. R. Emerson, C.M. Lewis, The dependence of the quantum yield of *Chlorella* photosynthesis on wavelength of light. *Am. J. Bot.* **30** (1943) 165–178.
124. J. Myers, J.R. Graham, R.T. Wang, Light harvesting in *Anacystis nidulans* studied in pigment mutants. *Plant Physiol.* **66** (1980) 1144–1149.
125. M. Kawamura, M. Mimuro, Y. Fujita, Quantitative relationship between two reaction centers in the photosynthetic system of blue-green algae. *Plant Cell Physiol.* **20** (1979) 697–705.
126. Y. Fujita, K. Ohki, A. Murakami, Chromatic regulation of photosystem composition in the photosynthetic system of red and blue-green algae. *Plant Cell Physiol.* **26** (1985) 1541–1548.
127. Y. Hihara, K. Sonoike, M. Ikeuchi, A novel gene, pmgA, specifically regulates photosystem stoichiometry in the cyanobacterium *Synechocystis* species PCC 6803 in response to high light. *Plant Physiol.* **117** (1998) 1205–1216.
128. K. Sonoike, Y. Hihara, M. Ikeuchi, Physiological significance of the regulation of photosystem stoichiometry upon high light acclimation of *Synechocystis* sp PCC 6803. *Plant Cell Physiol.* **42** (2001) 379–384.
129. A. Murakami, Y. Fujita, Regulation of stoichiometry between PS I and PS II in response to light regime for photosynthesis observed with *Synechocystis* PCC6714: Relationship between redox state of Cyt $b_6$-$f$ complex and regulation of PS I. *Plant Cell Physiol.* **34** (1993) 1175–1180.
130. T. Hiyama, B. Ke, Difference spectra and extinction coefficients of P700*. *Biochem. Biophys. Acta* **267** (1972) 160–171.
131. V.A. Boichenko, V.V. Klimov, H. Miyashita, S. Miyachi, Functional characteristics of chlorophyll *d*-predominating photosynthetic apparatus in intact cells of *Acaryochloris marina*. *Photosynth. Res.* **65** (2000) 269–277.
132. A. Melis, J.S. Brown, Stoichiometry of system I and system II reaction centers and of plastoquinone in different photosynthetic membranes. *Proc. Natl. Acad. Sci. U.S.A.* **77** (1980) 4712–4716.

133. W.S. Chow, A. Melis, J.M. Anderson, Adjustments of photosystem stoichiometry in chloroplasts improve the quantum efficiency of photosynthesis. *Proc. Natl. Acad. Sci. U.S.A.* **87** (1990) 7502–7506.
134. E. Haag, J. Eaton-Rye, G. Renger, W.F.J. Vermaas, Functionally important domains of the large hydrophilic loop of CP 47 as probed by oligonucleotide-directed mutagenesis in *Synechocystis* sp. PCC 6803. *Biochemistry* **32** (1993) 4444–4454.
135. Y. Fujita, A. Murakami, Regulation of electron transport composition in cyanobacterial photosynthetic system: Stoichiometry among photosystem I and II complexes and their light-harvesting antennae and cytochrome $b_6$-$f$ complex. *Plant Cell Physiol.* **28** (1987) 1547–1553.
136. O. Kaminskaya, J. Kern, V.A. Shuvalov, G. Renger, Extinction coefficents of cytochromes b559 and c550 of *Thermosynechococcus elongates* and Cyt b559/PS II stoichiometry of higher plants, *Biochim. Biophys. Acta* **1708** (2005) 333–341.
137. A. Murakami, Quantitative analysis of 77K fluorescence emission spectra in *Synechocystis* sp. PCC 6714 and *Chlamydomonas reinhardtii* with variable PS I/PS II stoichiometries. *Photosynth. Res.* **53** (1997) 141–148.
138. A.B. Cahoon, M.P. Timko, Biochemistry and regulation of chlorophyll biosynthesis, in: *Photosynthesis in Algae* (2003) (A.W. Larkum, S.E. Douglas, J.A. Ravan, eds.), Kluwer Academic Publishers, Dordrecht, pp. 95–131.
139. Y. Fujita, C.E. Bauer, Reconstitution of light-independent protochlorophyllide reductase from purified BchL and BchN-BchB subunits. *In vitro* confirmation of nitrogenase-like features of a bacteriochlorophyll biosynthesis enzyme. *J. Biol. Chem.* **275** (2000) 23583–23588.
140. S. Satoh, M. Ikeuchi, M. Mimuro, A. Tanaka, Chlorophyll *b* expressed in cyanobacteria functions as a light-harvesting antenna in photosystem I through flexibility of the proteins. *J. Biol. Chem.* **276** (2001) 4293–4297.
141. A. Tanaka, H. Ito, R. Tanaka, N.K. Tanaka, K. Yoshida, K. Okada, Chlorophyll *a* oxygenase (*CAO*) is involved in chlorophyll *b* formation from chlorophyll *a*. *Proc. Natl. Acad. Sci. U.S.A.* **95** (1998) 12719–12723.
142. H. Xu, D. Vavilin, W. Vermass, Chlorophyll *b* can serve as the major pigment in functional photosystem II complexes of cyanobacteria. *Proc. Natl. Acad. Sci. U.S.A.* **98** (2001) 14168–14173.
143. M. Mimuro, A. Tanaka, The in vivo and in vitro reconstitution of pigment-protein complexes, and its implication in acquiring a new system. *Photosynth. Res.* **81** (2004) 129–137.
144. S.W. Jeffrey, R.F.C. Mantoura, S.W. Wright, *Phytoplankton Pigments In Oceanography: Guidelines to Modern Methods*, (1997), UNESCO Publishing, Paris.
145. K. Brejc, R. Ficner, R. Huber, S. Steinbacher, Isolation, crystallization, crystal structure analysis and refinement of allophycocyanin from the cyanobacterium *Spirulina platensis* at 2.3 Å resolution. *J. Mol. Biol.* **249** (1995) 424–440.
146. J.Y. Liu, T. Jiang, J.P. Zhang, D.C. Liang, Crystal structure of allophycocyanin from red algae *Porphyra yezoensis* at 2.2 Å resolution. *J. Biol. Chem.* **274** (1999) 16945–16952.
147. M. Dürring, G.B. Schmidt, R. Huber, Isolation, crystallization, crystal structure analysis and refinement of constitutive C-phycocyanin from the chromatically adapting cyanobacterium *Fremyella diplosiphon* at 1.66 Å resolution. *J. Mol. Biol.* **217** (1991) 577–592.
148. X.Q. Wang, L.N. Li, W.R. Chang, J.P. Zhang, L.L. Gui, B.J. Guo, D.C. Liang, Structure of C-phycocyanin from *Spirulina platensis* at 2.2 Å resolution: A novel

monoclinic crystal form for phycobiliproteins in phycobilisomes. *Acta Crystallogr., D* **57** (2001) 784–792.

149. A.K. Padyana, V.B. Bhat, K.M. Madyastha, K.R. Rajashankar, S. Ramakumar, Crystal structure of a light-harvesting protein C-phycocyanin from *Spirulina platensis*. *Biochem. Biophys. Res. Commun.* **282** (2001) 893–898.

150. N. Adir, Y. Dobrovetsky, N. Lerner, Structure of C-phycocyanin from the thermophilic cyanobacterium *Synechococcus vulcanus* at 2.5 Å: Structural implications for thermal stability in phycobilisome assembly. *J. Mol. Biol.* **313** (2001) 71–81.

151. N. Adir, R. Vainer, N. Lerner, Refined structure of C-phycocyanin from the cyanobacterium *Synechococcus vulcanus* at 1.6 angstroms: The insight into the role of solvent molecules in thermal stability and co-factor structure. *Biochim. Biophys. Acta* **1556** (2002) 168–174.

152. J. Nield, P.J. Rizkallah, J. Barber, N.E. Chayen, The 1.45 Å three-dimensional structure of C-phycocyanin from the thermophilic cyanobacterium *Synechococcus elongates*. *J. Struct. Biol.* **141** (2003) 149–155.

153. N. Adir, N. Lerner, The crystal structure of a novel unmethylated form of C-phycocyanin, a possible connector between cores and rods in phycobilisomes. *J. Biol. Chem.* **278** (2003) 25926–25932.

154. B. Stec, R.F. Troxler, M.M. Teeter, Crystal structure of C-phycocyanin from *Cyanidium caldarium* provides a new perspective on phycobilisome assembly. *Biophys. J.* **76** (1999) 2912–2921.

155. T. Jiang, J.P. Zhang, W.R. Chang, D.C. Liang, Crystal structure of R-phycocyanin and possible energy transfer pathways in the phycobilisome. *Biophys. J.* **81** (2001) 1171–1179.

156. M. Dürring, R. Huber, W. Bode, R. Rumbeli, H. Zuber, Refined three-dimensional structure of phycoerythrocyanin from the cyanobacterium *Mastigocladus laminosus* at 2.7 Å. *J. Mol. Biol.* **211** (1990) 633–644.

157. W.R. Chang, T. Jiang, Z.L. Wan, J.P. Zhang, Z.X. Yang, D.C. Liang, Crystal structure of R-phycoerythrin from *Polysiphonia urceolata* at 2.8 Å resolution. *J. Mol. Biol.* **262** (1996) 721–731.

158. S. Ritter, R.G. Hiller, P.M. Wrench, W. Welte, K. Diederichs, Crystal structure of a phycourobilin-containing phycoerythrin at 1.90-Å resolution. *J. Struct. Biol.* **126** (1999) 86–97.

159. C. Contreras-Martel, J. Martinez-Oyanedel, M. Bunster, P. Legrand, C. Piras, X. Vernede, J.C. Fontecilla-Camps, Crystallization and 2.2 Å resolution structure of R-phycoerythrin from *Gracilaria chilensis:* A case of perfect hemihedral twinning. *Acta Crystallogr. D.* **57** (2001) 52–60.

160. T. Jiang, J.P. Zhang, D.C. Liang, Structure and function of chromophores in R-phycoerythrin at 1.9 Å resolution. *Proteins: Struct. Funct. Genet.* **34** (1999) 224–231.

161. R. Ficner, K. Lobeck, G. Schmidt, R. Huber, Isolation, crystallization, crystal structure analysis and refinement of B-phycoerythrin from the red alga *Porphyridium sordidum* at 2.2 Å resolution. *J. Mol. Biol.* **228** (1992) 935–950.

162. R. Ficner, R. Huber, Refined crystal structure of phycoerythrin from *Porphyridium cruentum* at 0.23-nm resolution and localization of the α-subunit. *Eur. J. Biochem.* **218** (1993) 103–106.

163. E. Wilk, S.J. Harrop, L. Jankova, D. Edler, G. Keenan, F. Sharples, R.G. Hiller, M.G. Curmi, Evolution of a light-harvesting protein by addition of new subunits and rearrangement of conserved elements: Crystal structure of a cryptophyte phycoerythrin at 1.63-Å resolution. *Proc. Natl. Acad. Sci. U.S.A.* **96** (1999) 8901–8906.

164. K. Koyama, T. Tsuchiya, S. Akimoto, M. Yokono, H. Miyashita, M. Mimuro, New linker proteins in phycobilisomes isolated from the cyanobacterium *Gloeobacter violaceus* PCC 7421. *FEBS Lett.* **580** (2006) 3457–3461.
165. T. Tomo, T. Okubo, S. Akimoto, M. Yokono, H. Miyashita, T. Tsuchiya, T. Noguchi, M. Mimuro, Identification of the special pair of photosystem II in the chlorophyll *d*–dominated cyanobacterium. *Proc. Natl. Acad. Sci. U.S.A* **104** (2007) 7283–7288.

Chapter 7

# Antenna System of Higher Plants' Photosystem I and Its Interaction with the Core Complex

## Tomas Morosinotto and Roberto Bassi

**Table of Contents**

7.1 Introduction........................................... 303
7.2 Supramolecular Organization of PSI Antenna System in Vascular Plants............................................... 304
    7.2.1 Antenna Polypeptides Stoichiometry and Gap Pigments.... 304
    7.2.2 Organization and Assembly of the PSI Antenna System.... 307
    7.2.3 Regulation and Acclimation of PSI Antenna Size......... 309
7.3 Biochemical and Spectroscopic Properties of the PSI Antenna System 311
    7.3.1 Isolation of the Antenna System from PSI-LHCI......... 311
    7.3.2 Alternative Approaches Used in PSI Antenna Characterization: Reverse Genetics and Recombinant Proteins......... 313
7.4 A Spectroscopic Peculiarity of LHCI: Red Forms............... 315
    7.4.1 Which Polypeptides are Responsible for Red Forms?...... 315
    7.4.2 Properties of Red Forms............................ 316
    7.4.3 Which Chromophores are Responsible for Red Forms?.... 317
    7.4.4 What About Lhca5 (and Lhca6)?...................... 319
    7.4.5 Physiological Role of Red Forms: Increasing Light Absorption or Photoprotection?............................. 320
7.5 Concluding Remarks and Future Perspectives.................. 321
References................................................ 322

## Abstract

This chapter reviews our knowledge on the antenna system of higher plants' Photosystem I (PSI). Four polypeptides, denoted Lhca1, Lhca2, Lhca3 and Lhca4, are the major components of this antenna system (LHCI).

In the first part the association of the antenna with the core and the supramolecular organization of the PSI core with its Lhca-subunits are discussed. The three-dimensional (3D) structure of a PSI-LHCI supercomplex is now available and it shows that one copy of each Lhca1 to Lhca4 is bound asymmetrically to one side of the PSI core. Complementary biochemical and mutational studies have revealed that strong inter-subunit interactions maintain the association between core and antenna and lead to a very stable PSI supercomplex.

The second part describes the biochemical and spectroscopic properties of the antenna system. Under native conditions the isolation of individual antenna subunits from the PSI core is very difficult due to the stability of the PSI supercomplex. For this reason alternative approaches, such as in vitro reconstitution and reverse genetics, have furnished important contributions to the characterization of the individual polypeptides that compose the PSI antenna system.

The third part focuses on a unique spectroscopic property of Photosystem I, i.e., the presence of Chl $a$ molecules with $Q_y$ transitions at unusual long wavelengths. These special Chls denoted "red forms" represent the most striking example of the ability of the protein scaffold to modulate the physicochemical properties of pigments. In higher plants, the "red forms" have been localized in the antenna system, in particular in Lhca4 and Lhca3. Mutational studies, moreover, allowed the identification of two specific chlorophylls, establishing excitonic interactions as responsible for the red absorption.

## 7.1 Introduction

Photosystem I (PSI) is a light-dependent plastocyanin/ferredoxin oxidoreductase, which, in higher plants and green algae, is located in the stroma-exposed fraction of the thylakoid membranes. In vascular plants 18 protein subunits belonging to this supramolecular complex have been identified up to now and 16 of them have been localized in the X-ray structure recently resolved [1]. The functional antenna system of PSI is composed of around 175 chlorophylls and 35 carotenoid pigments that are bound to several subunits of the complex. Two pigment binding moieties can be distinguished in PSI: (i) the core complex and (ii) the antenna system. As well as Chls with antenna function, the core complex contains the primary donor P700 and it is responsible for the charge separation and the first steps of electron transport. In vascular plants 14 core subunits have been identified, encoded by either chloroplast and nuclear genomes [2]. In the plants PSI structure, 101 Chl molecules are coordinated by the core, with PsaA and PsaB binding the largest number of pigments, while other smaller subunits such as PsaH and PsaG or K can coordinate a few Chls each [1,3]. Although some small subunits are unique to either eukaryotes or prokaryotes, the PSI core complex is well conserved through organisms, from the polypeptide sequence, to the structure and the number and position of bound chlorophylls [1,2]. This suggests that core complex of plants should bind approx 20 β-carotene molecules, as determined in *Synechococcus elongatus* by high-resolution X-ray crystallography [4].

Besides these core-complex subunits, a substantial amount of pigments is also bound by the Chl *a/b* antenna system of PSI in eukaryotes [5,6]. Chromophores of this extended pigment–protein system are organized in two different ways: either directly bound within individual subunits or at the interface between different antenna and/or PSI core subunits [7]. The latter kind of pigment organization is unusual since in most photosynthetic systems, including Photosystem II of higher plants (Chapter 8), pigments are usually only coordinated within protein subunits.

This chapter focuses on the organization of PSI antenna system (LHCI) and on the pigments it organizes. LHCI in vascular plants is composed of four major polypeptides, called Lhca1–4, encoded by the nuclear genome and belonging to the multigenic family of *Light harvesting complexes* [5,8]. Two other gene sequences, *Lhca5* and *Lhca6*, have been identified as additional PSI antenna subunits based on homology. However, they are transcribed at far lower levels than *Lhca1–4* [9] and only the Lhca5 polypeptide has been detected in PSI, although in very low amounts [10,11]. The physiological relevance of Lhca5 and Lhca6, thus, is still unproven, although it can not be excluded that they may be more expressed and play a role in peculiar environmental or developmental conditions.

Four Lhca polypeptides, encoded by single genes, have been found in most vascular plants analyzed so far; yet, multiple copies of the same gene were found in some species [8]. In other organisms, however, there are some significant peculiarities: in an eukaryotic algae, *Chlamydomonas reinhardtii*, nine different PSI antenna proteins (Lhca1–9; note that the nomenclature is not consistent with the one for higher plants and in the work of the different authors) have been detected both at the sequence and the polypeptides level [12,13]. Moreover, although here the stoichiometry of antenna polypeptides per PSI core has not been clarified yet, the number of antenna polypeptides per PSI core should be higher in *Chlamydomonas* than in vascular plants, as shown by electron microscopy [14,15].

## 7.2 Supramolecular Organization of PSI Antenna System in Vascular Plants

*7.2.1 Antenna Polypeptides Stoichiometry and Gap Pigments*

The topology of the PSI antenna was first described by single particle electron microscopy analysis, which assigned an asymmetric mass bound to one side of the monomeric PSI core complex to LHCI subunits [16]. The 3D structure of PSI-LHCI supercomplex from *Pisum sativum*, recently resolved with 4.4 Å resolution, confirmed that Lhca1–4 polypeptides are bound to one side of the core complex and form a crescent-like structure (Figure 1A) [1].

# ANTENNA SYSTEM OF HIGHER PLANTS' PHOTOSYSTEM I

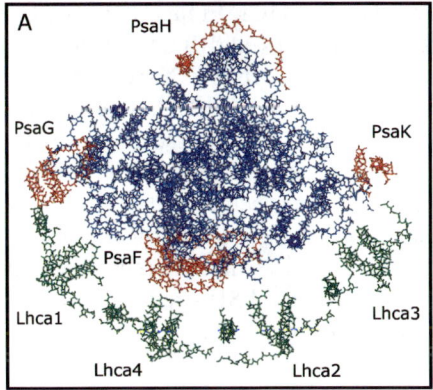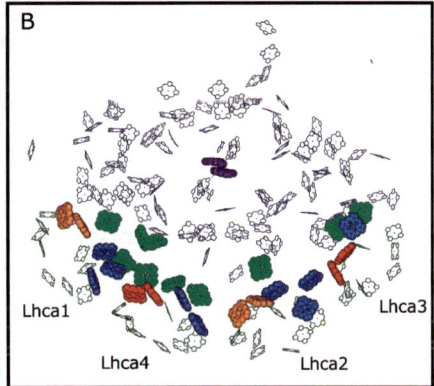

**Figure 1.** Three-dimensional structure of PSI-LHCI complex, top (stromal) view. (A) Polypeptide organization of the complex: the four Lhca subunits (in green) are aligned into a crescent-like structure on the lower part of the figure. Subunits exclusive of eukaryotic PSI complex (G, H) or relevant in the interaction with the antenna moiety (F, K) are shown in red, while all other core complex subunits are in cyan. [The coordinates of the polyA structure of PSI-LHCI were kindly provided by A. Ben Shem and N. Nelson from The George S. Wise Faculty of Life Sciences, Tel Aviv University, Tel Aviv 69978, Israel.] (B) Chlorophyll organization of PSI-LHCI. Chl molecules bound to antenna and core are, respectively, in dark green and blue. Gap and linker chlorophylls are shown (green and cyan, respectively). Chls bound to sites A5 and B5 of Lhca3 and Lhca4 or Lhca1 and Lhca2 are also shown (red and orange, respectively). The special pair P700 is shown in purple.

In addition to the antenna topology, the 3D structure gave new insights into Photosystem I of higher plants and showed some unexpected features of its antenna system. In fact, it shows the presence of only one copy of each Lhca1–4 polypeptide bound to the core complex (Figure 1A), while all previous estimations of antenna stoichiometry, based on pigment content and composition, suggested the presence of about eight Lhca per PSI core [16,17]. This discrepancy can, possibly, be due to a pool of loosely bound antenna subunits and, if this is true, the mildness of the purification method used would determine the number of Lhca polypeptides retained. This hypothesis was later tested by evaluating antenna stoichiometry in a PSI-LHCI purified so that no release of Lhca occurred. By determining the content of each polypeptide, rather than the pigment amount, it was demonstrated that one copy of each Lhca1–4 subunit is indeed found in PSI-LHCI within the thylakoids membranes [18]. This result implies that PSI does not have a loosely bound antenna pool, unlike with PSII where various supercomplexes with a diverse number of antenna polypeptides have been observed [19].

An additional unexpected feature of the PSI-LHCI structure is the presence of Chl molecules at the interface between the core complex and the LHCI crescent or between the Lhca polypeptides, defined, respectively, as "gap" and "linker" chlorophylls [1] (Figure 1). It was later shown that these pigments are not directly coordinated neither to the Core nor to LHCI. In fact, their binding depends on the interaction between the two moieties and they are liberated when the antenna is dissociated from the core [18]. In the X-ray structure, carotenoid molecules are not detectable, due to the relatively low resolution. However, analysis of the pigment fraction released upon dissociation of the PSI antenna from the core complex demonstrated that Chl $a$, Chl $b$ and also carotenoid (β-carotene, lutein and violaxanthin) molecules are also components of the "gap" pigments [18,20]. Recently, the contribution of the gap pigment to the absorption spectrum was determined as the difference between the spectra of PSI-LHCI *minus* the sum of the isolated PSI core and LHCI [7]. This result is shown in Figure 2(A). In the Soret region, the difference spectra

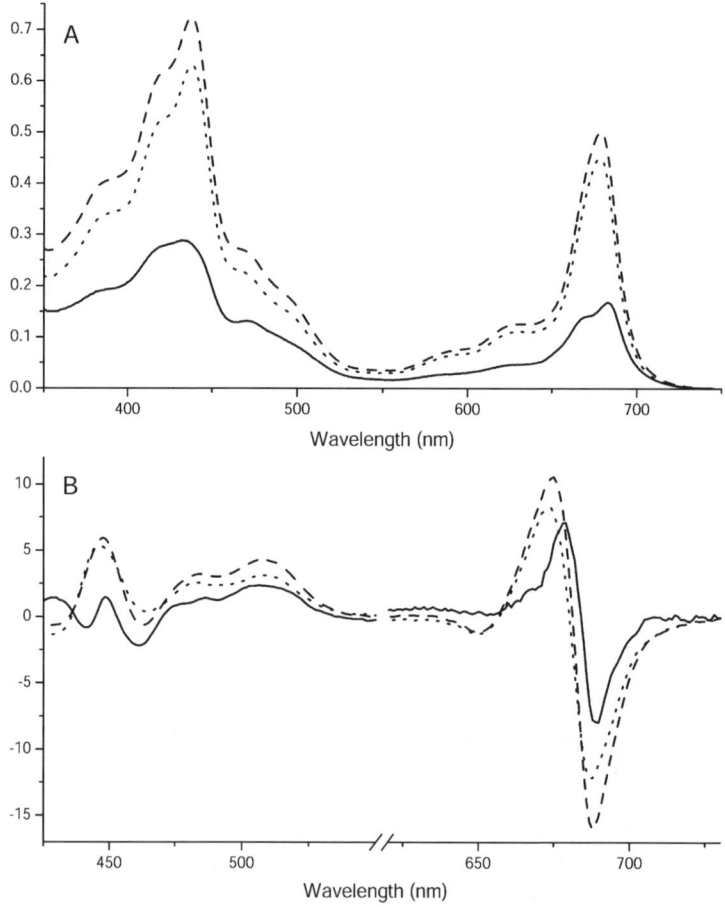

**Figure 2.** Absorption and CD spectra of gap pigments. (A) Absorption spectrum of gap pigments (solid line, ×3) is shown, calculated as the difference between PSI-LHCI complex (– – –) and PSI core+LHCI (- - - -). (B) CD spectrum of gap pigments (solid line, ×2), calculated as the difference between PSI-LHCI complex (– – –) and PSI core+LHCI (- - - -). [Both spectra are from [7]].

showed contributions at 434, 470 and around 500 nm. These wavelengths corresponding to Chl $a$, $b$ and carotenoids, thus confirming the presence of all three pigment species among gap pigments. CD spectra of gap pigments obtained by the same difference method (reported in Figure 2B) showed signal contributions at 670–678 nm (+) and 690–705 nm (−), 470–475 nm (+), 505–510 nm (+), wavelengths, corresponding, respectively, to Chl $a$, Chl $b$ and carotenoids. Since CD spectroscopy in the visible range detects the interactions involving pigments (see [21] and citations therein), the presence of CD signals originated from "gap" pigments suggests that they are involved in interactions with the polypeptide chains and with neighboring chromophores [7].

Are the gap pigments found only in PSI or are they are a common property of both higher plant photosystems? To answer this question a comparative determination of pigments released upon dissociation of the antenna moiety was performed: supercomplexes of both photosystems were first dissociated into their core and antenna components by detergent treatment. By this procedure, it was shown that a significant amount of pigment was released in the case of PSI, while this was negligible in the case of PSII. Thus, gap pigments appear to be a peculiar feature of PSI [18].

### 7.2.2 Organization and Assembly of the PSI Antenna System

In addition to the structure of PSI-LHCI complex, information on the organization and assembly of its antenna has been provided by the characterization of plants depleted in individual Lhca polypeptides [7,20,22]. This analysis demonstrated that the association between the antenna and the core complex is strongly cooperative. In fact, when a single polypeptide is not available for assembling, the whole antenna system is de-stabilized, suggesting that a network of interactions, contributed to by each Lhca subunit, maintains the binding of the whole LHCI system to the reaction center. Figure 3(A) compiles antenna complex stoichiometries determined in PSI particles purified from plants that were depleted in individual Lhca subunits (data from [7]). Inspection of these data reveals that the lack of a single Lhca gene product induces loss of the other components as well. The only exception is that of ΔLhca5 plants, in which the LHCI content is indistinguishable from WT. From data reported in Figure 3(A) it can be also inferred that Lhca1/4 and Lhca2/3 are mutually dependent: when one is depleted its "partner" is reduced to the same extent. In fact, in all genotypes, Lhca1/4 and Lhca2/3 are always found in equal amounts. This suggests that monomers cannot individually bind to the PSI core to a significant extent and that a heterodimer is the minimal unit of the PSI antenna system, which is consistent with previous data [17,23]. Thus, the detected protein–protein interactions within the PSI antenna are stronger between Lhca1/4 and Lhca2/3.

Analysis of the PSI-LHCI structure, looking for a structural basis of these interactions, is fruitful in the case of the dimers: in fact, evidence for interactions between monomeric polypeptides is found, at least between the membrane-exposed regions [1,24]. As an example, Helix D of Lhca1 is close to the lumen

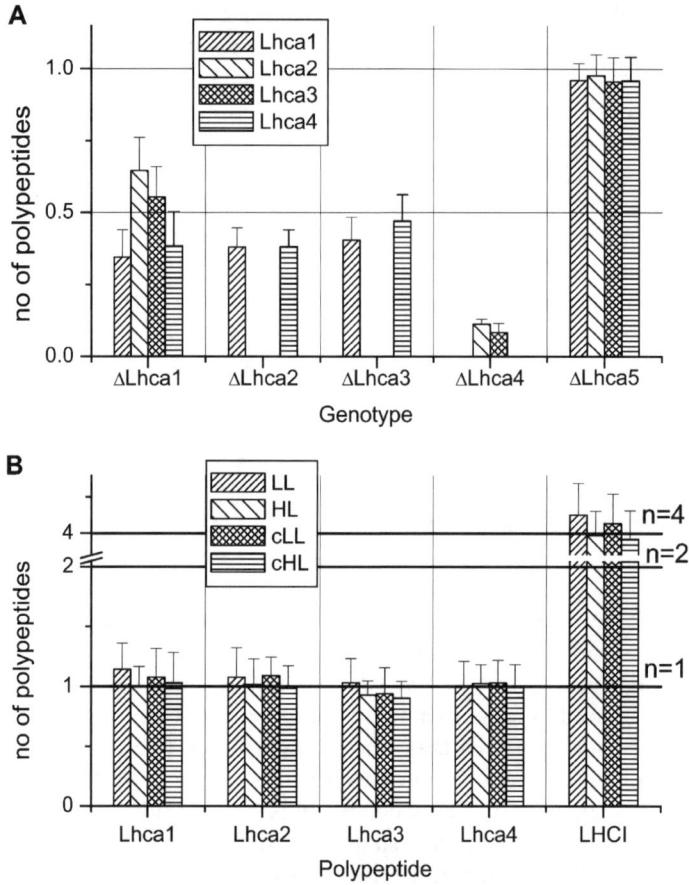

**Figure 3.** Lhca stoichiometry in PSI particles from antenna mutants and plants grown in different environmental conditions. (A) Quantitative evaluation of Lhca1–4 polypeptides per PSI core in PSI particles from plants depleted in individual Lhca. The stoichiometry was obtained by evaluation of Coomassie bound to each Lhca and normalization to PsaD and PsaF content. Data from [7]. (B) Stoichiometric determination of Lhca polypeptides in PSI from plants grown in different light intensities and temperatures. Antenna size was normalized to 100% in the case of the control (CTR) sample. [Data are from [28]]. Plants were adapted for three weeks under the following conditions: Control: 21 °C, 100 µE m$^{-2}$ s$^{-1}$; low light (LL): 21 °C, 25 µE m$^{-2}$ s$^{-1}$; high light (HL): 21 °C, 1600 µE m$^{-2}$ s$^{-1}$; cold low light (cLL): 5 °C, 25 µE m$^{-2}$ s$^{-1}$; cold high light (cHL): 5 °C, 600 µE m$^{-2}$ s$^{-1}$.

exposed extension of helix C from Lhca4 [1,24]. These structural data are consistent with the evaluation of dimerization capacity of recombinant Lhca1 with Lhca4 after deletion at their N and C terminal domains. Deletion at both C and N termini of Lhca1 prevents dimerization, which is consistent with their interaction with Lhca4. Conversely, similar deletions on Lhca4 were ineffective in abolishing dimerization unless the deletion affected the protein folding, according with the terminal domains of Lhca4 being directed away from the partner subunit Lhca1 [25]. On the other hand, in the X-ray structure no evidence was revealed for interactions between polypeptides in the transmembrane regions. Nevertheless, some chlorophylls molecules (linker Chls) were found to be bound at the interface between antenna subunits, and they probably play a role in the stabilization of dimers [1,24].

As for the association between LHCI and core complex subunits, instead, only Lhca1 shows a structural basis for a tight association, since a transmembrane helix and the stromal exposed domain interact with PsaG and PsaB [1,24]. Weaker interactions can be detected between the extramembrane domains of Lhca3 with both PsaA and PsaK. The putative interactions of Lhca2 and Lhca4 backbone with the core complex polypeptides are instead very reduced [1,24]. Based on structural organization, thus, Lhca1, followed by Lhca3, appear to be the key polypeptides that stabilize the interaction of the LHCI half-moon to the core complex, while Lhca2 and Lhca4 should be less relevant. Analysis of PSI in Lhca deletion mutants, instead, yielded contrasting results; in fact, the most severe antenna destabilization was observed in plants lacking Lhca4 [7,20] and there was no evidence of a prominent stabilization role played by Lhca1 or Lhca3. An explanation for such apparent discrepancy is offered by the hypothesis, not directly deducible from the structure, that gap pigments may stabilize the PSI-LHCI supercomplex [7]. In fact, notably, six out of ten gap Chls identified in the structure are close to Lhca4 (Figure 1B). The instability of PSI-LHCI in Lhca4 mutants is consistent with a role of these Chls in stabilizing LHCI by mediating Lhca4 interactions with surrounding protein subunits. In addition, gap pigments are stably bound only when core and the antenna moieties are assembled [18], implying they are non-covalently bound to polypeptides of both moieties and may act in bridging them.

*7.2.3 Regulation and Acclimation of PSI Antenna Size*

The modification of the antenna size is a well-known mechanism for adaptation of the photosynthetic machinery to environmental conditions [26]. This phenomenon, however, has been more thoroughly studied in PSII than in PSI. A first specific study suggested that the Lhca content respond to illumination regimes with Lhca2 and Lhca3 being accumulated at high irradiance more than Lhca1 and Lhca4, yielding a doubling of the LHCI content per PSI core with respect to low light [27]. This has been challenged by the finding that a single copy of each Lhca subunit is present per PSI core complex [1] and that the Lhca/PSI core stoichiometry remains unchanged upon adaptation to different light and temperature conditions (Figure 3B, data from [28]). These contrasting results cannot be explained by differences in the plant growth conditions, as judged from the fact that PSII antenna size is consistently reported to undergo important changes in both studies. A more likely explanation is the different response in the methods used to quantify the polypeptides: Bailey et al. [27] used Western blotting, while Ballottari et al. [28] used Coomassie staining quantification. The first method, in fact, is more sensitive, but the latter ensures a wider linearity range than immuno-detection [29].

Based on the structural analysis of the interactions between subunits in the PSI-LHCI supercomplex, Ben-Shem and co-workers concluded that LHCI assembly should be very flexible, since a low level of protein–protein interaction was detected both between LHCI subunits and between them and the core complex proteins [24]. Just the opposite emerges from the experimental analysis of antenna size, depending on growth conditions the carotenoid composition to PSI-LHCI ratio is a rigid system with unchanging number of Lhca subunits during acclimation [28]. The discrepancy between the experimental data and expectations from protein structure can be reconciled by attributing a stronger relevance to gap pigments in mediating interactions between protein subunits and acting as a "green glue" in the stabilization of the PSI- LHCI complex. In fact, as mentioned above, they play a fundamental role in the association of the antenna, but this is not evident from the structure analysis alone. Further support to a "rigid" model from PSI-LHCI comes from the analysis of Lhca deletion mutants, which shows that the lack of a subunit cannot be compensated by overaccumulation of the remaining ones [7]. This is in striking contrast with PSII where, in the absence of Lhcb1 and Lhcb2, Lhcb3 and Lhcb5 are overexpressed and form trimers that replace the missing polypeptides in the PSII supercomplexes [30]. This lack of exchangeability in PSI implies a specific binding site for each *Lhca* gene product, thus excluding the possibility of exchangeability of different antenna subunits in response to variable environmental conditions. Thus, while PSII modifies its antenna system in response to environmental conditions (Chapters 6, 8 and 9) [27–28,31], PSI cannot. This difference is consistent with the presence of gap pigments in PSI but not in PSII [18]. The presence of such an interfacial pigment pool is, in fact, incompatible with an antenna system that is changing extensively in size through association/dissociation of the component subunits: in a "gap" pigment-containing system, the dissociation of a subunit would release Chls molecules which would become loosely bound or, even worse, free in the membrane. These pigments would be poorly photoprotected due to lack of stable interactions with carotenoid molecules and thus very prone to the formation of reactive oxygen species.

It is worth asking if the stability of PSI antenna size implies that PSI is not involved in any kind of regulation of light harvesting. This is clearly not the case, since well-known mechanisms for the regulation of PSI light harvesting function have been described. One is the so-called "state 1-state 2 transition", which consists in the migration of LHCII subunits from PSII to PSI, equilibrating the excitation energy distribution between the two photosystems [32,33]. This phenomenon was recently shown to be relevant also in vivo for adaptation to different light regimes [34]. On a longer time domain, equilibrium between photosystems is maintained by the regulation of the PSI/PSII ratio in the thylakoids membranes. Interestingly, both these mechanisms control the balance of the electron transport activity between PSI and PSII. Consistently, several studies on PSI photoinhibition have suggested a major photoprotection role for the maintaining of plastoquinone reduction state rather than the regulation of the absolute amount of excitation energy reaching PSI [35].

A further mechanism for the regulation of PSI light-harvesting rate could be the modulation of the antenna properties without modifying the number of chromophores. This kind of effect is well known in PSII where it is catalyzed by several kinds of non-photochemical quenching mechanisms that modulate the chlorophyll fluorescence quantum yield and lifetime through activation of a PsbS-dependent de-excitation pathway [36] (for further details, see Chapter 9) or accumulation of zeaxanthin within Lhcb proteins [37]. Similar to the case of PSII, under light stress the PSI antenna binds relevant amount of zeaxanthin [38,39] that change the Lhca fluorescence yield, similarly to the case of Lhcb. However, owing to the faster charge separation rate in PSI vs. PSII, it is not clear if zeaxanthin accumulation in LHCI actually acts in avoiding PSI-RC overexcitation. Beside fluorescence quenching, zeaxanthin accumulation in PSII antenna system decreases LHCII stability, thus inducing degradation and reduction of antenna size [40]. This long-term acclimation mechanism seems not be at work in the case of zeaxanthin binding LHCI, whose stability is unaffected by carotenoid content [40]. A recent report of post translational modifications of Lhca proteins [10] may be related to further regulation mechanisms still to be unraveled.

## 7.3 Biochemical and Spectroscopic Properties of the PSI Antenna System

### 7.3.1 Isolation of the Antenna System from PSI-LHCI

Early work on PSI antenna proteins led to the isolation and characterization of LHCI preparations by several laboratories. The different methods employed, however, resulted in variable outcomes with respect to pigment composition (Table 1), spectral properties and pigment to protein ratio. The diverging results can be understood from an analysis of the PSI-LHCI complex structure [1]: gap pigments stabilize the LHCI-PSI core interactions and, thus, their dissociation requires relatively harsh detergent treatments, which easily induce denaturation of the pigment–protein complexes. These difficulties were not encountered in the isolation of Lhcb proteins, whose weaker antenna–core binding facilitates a gentle dissociation and isolation under native conditions.

The first evidence for the presence of a Chl $a/b$ antenna in higher plants PSI came from the work of Mullet et al. [41]. These authors purified PSI complexes for differing antenna size and for the presence of four polypeptides with molecular mass of between 20 and 24 kDa, thereafter identified as the antenna polypeptides of PSI. Afterwards, LHCI was isolated in two different fractions: one, monomeric, was enriched in Lhca2 and Lhca3, and the other, dimeric, contained Lhca1 and Lhca4 [42]. Based on their emission peaks at low temperature, these populations were named, respectively, LHCI-680 and LHCI-730 [43]. This nomenclature was largely employed in papers published in the 1980s and 1990s, although the polypeptide composition varied slightly in different preparations [44–46]. In some cases, however, it was possible to purify LHCI fractions containing all four Lhca polypeptides [5,47]. LHCI isolated with the latter method exhibited a fully dimeric aggregation state and emission forms at 702 and 730 nm [17,48]. The lack of any emission at shorter wavelengths indicates that this purification method conserved better the LHCI native properties and that no 680 nm emission is present in the native LHCI. The previously described LHCI-680 preparations were actually a partially denatured state of an originally dimeric complex with a longer fluorescence emission. This hypothesis is also supported by the observation of disconnected Chls in LHCI-680 [49]. Therefore, the nomenclature LHCI-680 and LHCI-730 appears to be outdated. LHCI is in fact composed of two heterodimers, Lhca1/4 and Lhca2/3, both containing Chls emitting around 730 nm, as shown by the PSI structure and reconstitution in vitro experiments [1,50].

Owing to the above-mentioned problems with purification, the alleged pigment binding characteristics of LHCI were also somehow uncertain. Nevertheless, some properties were conserved in the different preparations: Chl $a/b$ ratio varied between 3 and 4 [5,42], but some difference was also attributable to the plant species analyzed [17] (Table 1). As for the carotenoid composition, LHCI was shown to bind violaxanthin and lutein with minor amounts of β-carotene, while no neoxanthin was detected [17,51,52] (Table 1). Notably, however, these data from purified proteins are the average between the two dimeric populations present in the LHCI preparation. Purification to homogeneity of one heterodimeric population from the other has not yet been achieved.

**Table 1.** Pigment composition of LHCI. Data shown were obtained with different purification methods and from different plant species

| Plant Material | Fraction | Chl $a/b$ | Chl tot | Violaxanthin | Lutein | β-Carotene | Reference |
|---|---|---|---|---|---|---|---|
| Pea | LHCI | 3.7 | | | | | [41] |
| Spinach | 680/730 | 3.5 | 92 | 7 | 12 | 8 | [42] |
| | 680 | 3.0 | | | | | [42][a] |
| | 730 | 3.1 | | | | | [49] |
| | | 3.2 | | | | | [49] |
| Barley | 680[b] | 2.0 | | | | | [6] |
| | 730 | 2.2 | | | | | [6] |
| Tomato | 680 | 2.5 | 8.99 | 0.43 | 0.92 | 0.4 | [55] |
| | 730 | 2.57 | 7.17; | 0.39 | 0.84 | 0.18 | [52] |
| | | 2.48 | 11.41 | 0.54 | 0.99 | 0.42 | [55] |
| Maize | 680 | 4–5 | | | | | [58] |
| | 730 | 2–2.5 | 10 | 0.55 | 1.2 | 0.4 | [58] |
| | LHCI | 3.8 | 10 | 0.5–0.6 | 1.1–1.2 | 0.5–.65 | [58] |
| | Lhca2/Lhca3 | 3.8 | 10 | 0.6–0.7 | 1.3–1.4 | 0.36–0.4 | [58] |
| | Lhca1/Lhca4 | 3.6–3.8 | | | | | [58] |
| Arabidopsis | LHCI | 3.3 | 10 | 0.6 | 1.1 | 0.45 | [17] |

[a]Data were obtained by difference between the pigment composition of PSI-200 and PSI-core.
[b]This preparation contained only Lhca2.

### 7.3.2 Alternative Approaches Used in PSI Antenna Characterization: Reverse Genetics and Recombinant Proteins

Owing to the difficulty in isolating and characterizing LHCI, alternative approaches have been used to add to our present knowledge on the PSI antenna. One such method was the analysis of plants lacking one or more *Lhca* gene products, obtained by mutagenesis or antisense inhibition of protein accumulation. This work was useful, in particular, for the identification of the gene products responsible for PSI fluorescence emission, as reported in more details in the following section [22,53,54].

A further widely used approach is in vitro reconstitution of recombinant proteins with purified pigments, which allows biochemical and spectroscopic characterization of the individual Lhca proteins [17,50,52,55]. This method exploits the ability of Lhc proteins, either purified from chloroplasts or overexpressed in bacteria, to refold in vitro in the presence of chlorophylls and carotenoids [56], yielding pigment–proteins that are indistinguishable from native holoproteins [57].

The individual properties of Lhca1/4 from *Arabidopsis thaliana* reconstituted in vitro are summarized in Figure 4 (data from [17,50]). An inspection of this data shows that Lhca complexes can be divided into two groups, with respect to their pigment binding characteristics: Lhca1 and Lhca3, in fact, have high affinity for Chl *a*, as reflected by their Chl *a/b* ratios of 4.0 and 5.9. Consistently, Chl *b* is not essential for their refolding in vitro [55]. Both Lhca1 and Lhca3 bind three carotenoid molecules per polypeptide, mainly lutein and violaxanthin. On the other hand, Lhca2 and Lhca4, instead, have markedly lower Chl *a/b* ratios of 1.9 and 2.4, and cannot fold without both Chl *a* and Chl *b* [55]. They only bind two carotenoid molecules per polypeptide, again lutein and violaxanthin. Interestingly, pairing of Lhca is consistent with sequence homology: in fact, Lhca2 and 4 are more similar to each other than to Lhca1 or 3 [9]. Consistent with the findings with purified LHCI, recombinant Lhca1/4 bind preferentially lutein and violaxanthin, while neoxanthin was excluded. The situation is more complex for β-carotene: only Lhca3 binds significant amounts of this carotenoid as monomeric protein. However, the Lhca1/4 heterodimer was found to bind this pigment, suggesting the presence of a β-carotene binding site at the interface between the two monomers [17].

As mentioned above, LHCI is organized as heterodimers. To date, only the Lhca1/4 dimers have been reconstituted in vitro, while the Lhca2/3 heterodimer has never been obtained [52,55]. Thus, the dimers have not been compared directly. However, Lhca1/4 has been partially purified from Lhca2/3 by isoelectro-focusing [17] and by purification of LHCI from mutants depleted in individual Lhca proteins [7]. Both these analyses suggested that the biochemical and spectroscopic properties of Lhca1/4 are very similar to those of Lhca2/3, since no major differences were observed in different populations. Thus, although the properties of the individual polypeptides are different, the two heterodimers that comprise LHCI are very similar.

| Sample | Chl a/b | Chl /Car | Viola | Lutein | β-car |
|---|---|---|---|---|---|
| Lhca1 | 4.0 ± 0.1 | 3.5 ± 0.1 | 1.1 | 1.8 | - |
| Lhca2 | 1.9± 0.2 | 5.0 ± 0.1 | 0.5 | 1.5 | - |
| Lhca3 | 5.9± 0.3 | 3.6 ± 0.1 | 0.7 | 1.6 | 0.5 |
| Lhca4 | 2.4 ± 0.2 | 4.9 ± 0.1 | 0.5 | 1.5 | - |

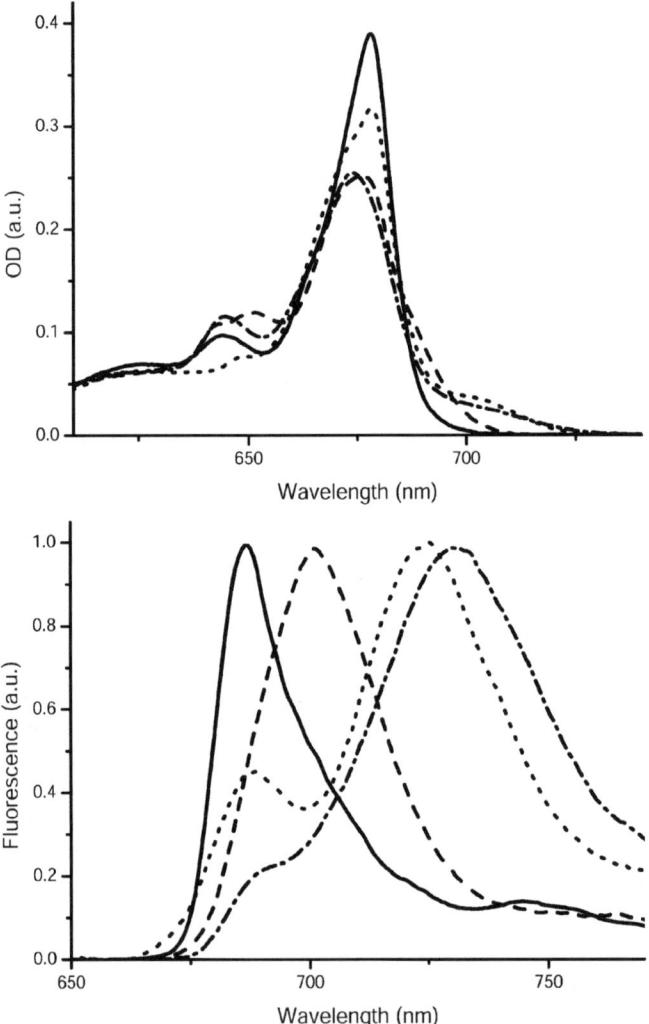

**Figure 4.** Biochemical and spectroscopic properties of Lhca1-4 from *Arabidopsis thaliana* reconstituted in vitro. (Top) Pigment binding properties. Data are from [17,50]. (Middle) Absorption spectra in the $Q_y$ region of Lhca1 (solid line), Lhca2 (–––), Lhca3 (----), Lhca4 (–---). Spectra are normalized to the Chl content. (Bottom) Fluorescence emission at 77 K of Lhca1 (solid), Lhca2 (–––), Lhca3 (----), Lhca4 (–---). Spectra are normalized to the emission maxima.

In analyzing data from recombinant proteins, it should be considered that recent structure of the PSI-LHCI complex showed that more chlorophylls are associated to each Lhca protein than estimated from isolated LHCI and recombinant proteins [1,17,58]. In fact, only 10–11 tightly bound pigments are present in the complexes refolded in vitro, while an additional 1–2 chromophores are not found. Moreover, linker chlorophylls bound between individual Lhca subunits are not expected to be stable in monomeric isolated Lhca complexes. Data on recombinant proteins need to be integrated with in vivo analyses to obtain information on the additional pigment binding sites [20].

## 7.4 A Spectroscopic Peculiarity of LHCI: Red Forms

The fluorescence emission spectra of thylakoids at 77 K show two main emission peaks, at 685 and 735 nm. The first is associated with grana membrane domains and, in particular, with the PSII-LHCII complex, while the latter originates from PSI-LHCI located in stroma lamellae. The peculiar PSI emission originates from Chl *a* molecules that absorb at wavelengths over 700 nm. The energy of these transitions, thus, is lower than that of the reaction center pigments, P700. Owing to their peculiar absorption wavelength with respect to P700 these Chls are often named "red Chls" or "red forms". The "red forms" are found in the PSI core in all organisms studied so far [59]. Nevertheless, in vascular plants the red-most Chls, emitting at 735 nm, are located in the antenna moiety rather than in the core complex, whose red-most emission is at 720 nm [5,41].

### 7.4.1 Which Polypeptides are Responsible for Red Forms?

Among all Chl *a* molecules bound to the photosynthetic apparatus, the "red forms" exhibit by far the strongest spectral shift with respect to monomeric Chl *a* in organic solvents. For this reason they have been thoroughly analyzed. Studies of plants depleted in individual Lhca polypeptides, obtained with both mutagenesis and antisense approaches, have been useful in determining the polypeptides binding the Chls with the red-most emission. Lhca4 was the first Lhca gene product shown to contain "red forms" [53,54]. This assignment was later confirmed by the in vitro reconstitution of the protein [52]. Subsequently, a redshifted emission was found to be associated with Lhca3 as well, although its fluorescence emission, at 725 nm, is slightly less redshifted than that in Lhca4 [22,50,55]. Redshifted Chls have since been identified in all Lhca subunits by analyzing Lhca1–4 proteins reconstituted in vitro. However, notably, each Lhca has different energy levels of the red-most transition, with Lhca1 and 2 emitting at 701–702 nm. The relative contribution of red forms to the absorption and fluorescence emission spectra are illustrated in the bottom two panels of Figure 4.

The red emission forms in PSI-LHCI can be detected in isolated antenna proteins reconstituted in vitro. This finding implies that monomeric complexes can induce the same energy shift in the Chls. Nevertheless, the total amplitude of "red absorption" of all monomeric Lhca is lower than that of the intact PSI-LHCI. This feature can be attributed to the effect of multiple interactions of Lhca subunits with neighbor protein and pigment molecules. The influence of protein–protein interactions on the "red forms" was first observed in dimeric Lhca1/4, which was shown to exhibit an increased "red absorption" with respect to the sum of the two monomeric components, i.e., Lhca1 and Lhca4 [17]. A further enhancement was detected when the sum of isolated LHCI and PSI core were compared with PSI-LHCI. Figure 2 shows that the contributions at wavelengths >700 nm in the absorption and CD spectra are larger in PSI-LHCI than in the sum of the isolated PSI and LHCI [7]. Consistently, in both isolated and reconstituted Lhca proteins, emission forms from bulk Chls are readily detectable, while only red ones are present in PSI-LHCI spectra. Based on these findings, it can be hypothesized that Lhca proteins can attain conformations with and without redshifted spectral forms, while interactions with gap pigments and core subunits stabilizes the red-most conformation in the PSI-LHCI complex [7].

*7.4.2 Properties of Red Forms*

While the fluorescence from "red Chls" is easily detected, especially at low temperature, the elucidation of their absorption characteristics is not straightforward, since they represent about the 5% of the total absorption in the Qy region [48]. Although these "red forms" are expected to be energetically distant from the bulk Chls, a clear band could not be detected even at 4 K, owing to lack of structure in the spectra. However, this finding is significant because it indicates that these spectral forms are strongly inhomogeneously broadened.

Site-selected fluorescence measurements of PSI-LHCI pointed to 716 nm as the upper limit for the maximum of the band responsible for the long wavelength emission [60]. A similar study on purified dimeric LHCI fraction led to an estimation of 711 nm [48]. The bandwidth of the 711 nm absorption was suggested to be 356 cm$^{-1}$ by using Gaussian deconvolution of the red tail of LHCI absorption spectra while site-selected fluorescence analysis showed that the contributions of the homogeneous and inhomogeneous broadening to the bandwidth are, respectively, 210 and 290 cm$^{-1}$ [61]. Consistently, a Huang Rhys factor value of 2.7 was derived from fluorescence line narrowing experiments [61], representing the strongest electron–phonon coupling found in photosynthetic antenna complexes. From these values a FWHM of 30 nm and a Stokes shift of 35 nm could be calculated for the red band in LHCI.

Analysis of reconstituted Lhca complexes at 77 K by Gaussian deconvolution of difference absorption spectra with mutants depleted in red forms (see below) suggested that the absorption is located between 700 and 705 nm for both monomeric Lhca3 and Lhca4 [62]. The band responsible for the 701 nm emission of Lhca1 and Lhca2 complexes, instead, was located at 686–690 nm, again by comparison of the spectra of WT and site selected mutant proteins [63,64]. Thus, the red-most absorptions of Lhca1 and Lhca2 are not over 700 nm and, in a strict sense, they should not be denoted as "red forms". However, they could still be considered as "red forms" as well since they are still redshifted compared with all other Chls in plant photosynthetic complexes and they also share a common origin with "red forms" (see next section).

*7.4.3 Which Chromophores are Responsible for Red Forms?*

The in vitro reconstitution of Lhca complexes offered a powerful tool in establishing the presence of redshifted Chls in all LHCI components. The same method was also exploited to analyze the origin of these peculiar spectral forms by mutational analyses of the Lhca gene products. All conserved Chl binding residues in the sequences of Lhca1–4 have been identified by comparison with Lhcb1, whose structure is known at high resolution [65,66]. These residues have been mutagenized into non-polar ones, which are not able to coordinate the central $Mg^{2+}$ of the Chls, thus obtaining mutated complexes depleted in specific pigments. This approach has been previously proven effective in the characterization of Lhcb proteins [68–70]. The analysis has been very recently completed for all Lhca1–4 proteins from *Arabidopsis thaliana* [63–64,71–72]. Interestingly, despite the different energies of the $Q_y$ transitions, the emission of "red forms" originates from Chls that are bound at the same binding sites in all different proteins: sites A5 and B5[†]. Other pigments may affect either the amplitude or the energy of red forms, but their role appears to be indirect, such as Chl B6 in Lhca1, 3 and 4 and Chl A4 in Lhca4. These Chls are not directly the responsible of the red emission, but they are probably important in maintaining the structure in the protein domain binding Chls A5-B5. In their absence the protein is perturbed and the "red forms" are somehow affected. Interestingly, when the binding of the carotenoid molecule in site L2 is perturbed, the "red forms" of Chls are also affected. An interpretation of the results of the mutational analysis in the framework of the Lhc protein structure led to the proposal that the "red forms" originate from an excitonic interaction between two Chl *a* molecules that are bound to the above-mentioned sites A5 and B5. The presence of this interaction has also been supported by the detection of a specific CD signal associated with the "red forms" [62,63]. However, it is, possibly, not the only contribution to the large energy shift observed in the "red Chls", although no evidence for the presence and the nature of additional components has emerged yet [71].

As mentioned in the previous section, Lhca1 and Lhca4 can be classified in pairs according to their biochemical properties and sequence homology. Two distinct pairs are distinguishable also with respect to their fluorescence emission

---

[†] The Chl binding sites nomenclature used here is from the LHCII structure of [67] and it does not have strict correlation with the sites occupancy by Chl *a* or *b*. The correspondence to nomenclature of the PSI-LHCI structure is reported in [71].

peaks (Figure 4B), but the pairing differs from those indicated above: Lhca3 and Lhca4, in fact, emit at 725–735 nm while Lhca1 and Lhca2 emit at 701–702 nm. The crucial sequence feature responsible for this difference was identified in the nature of the coordinating residue of Chl A5 – the ligand of this binding site, in fact, is Asn in Lhca3 and Lhca4, while it is an His in Lhca1 and Lhca2. Interestingly, His is the ligand for Chl A5 in all Lhcb complexes, none of which exhibit any red emission. The relevance of this difference was tested by building mutants where the Asn was exchanged with His in Lhca3 and Lhca4. The mutation was shown to have no effect on the number of pigments bound to each protein, demonstrating that His was able to coordinate Chl A5 as well as the Asn. Conversely, the fluorescence properties were drastically affected: the redshifted emission peak was depleted in mutant proteins (Figure 5A) [62]. A corresponding depletion was also induced in the signal over 700 nm of the absorption spectra. The difference absorption spectra between the WT and mutants allow the calculation of the contribution of "red Chls" to the absorption spectra, which peaks at 700 and 705 nm in Lhca3 and Lhca4 respectively (the latter is shown in Figure 5B, data from [62]). Difference spectra analysis also allowed the detection of the contribution of monomeric Chls to the absorption spectra upon disruption of the Chl–Chl interaction. Both Chl partners are characterized by peaks at 675 nm. Since modifications in both chromophore orientation and distance could affect the A5–B5 interaction, chromophore orientation was analyzed by linear dichroism: the LD signal of "red forms" was shifted in wavelength but its amplitude was conserved, thus suggesting that the mutation did not affect the orientations of the chromophores. It was, therefore, concluded that the depletion of red emission was due to an increased distance between Chls A5 and B5 in the mutated complexes [62].

This hypothesis was later supported by an analysis of the PSI-LHCI structure: Chls A5–B5 are 8 Å apart in Lhca4 while they are 10 Å apart in Lhca2 [1]. This 2 Å difference is fully consistent with the observed difference in interaction energy between the two complexes [64]. Based on these results and interpretations, it can be inferred that the replacement of His by Asn in the position of the A5 ligand of Lhca1 and Lhca2 gives rise to a redshifted emission in these subunits. This effect was indeed observed in the Lhca1NH mutant, although the increase was incomplete due to substoichiometric binding of the Chl at site A5 [62]. Possibly, steric hindrance prevents complete site occupancy in these subunits and thus "red forms" are missing. This result, however, clearly shows that an Asn as Chl ligand is not sufficient per se for the generation of the redshift. This is also supported by the analysis of the Lhca sequences from *Chlamydomonas reinhardtii:* here three Lhca sequences out of nine have an Asn ligand for Chl A5, but only one of them seems to be expressed to high levels [12]. Despite these Asn-containing sequences, the LHCI red-most emission is at around 705 nm; thus the redshift is not as pronounced as it is in vascular plants [73]. Further confirmation of this interpretation is the finding that Asn is the ligand of Chl in site A2 of all Lhc proteins from higher plants, except Lhcb4 and Lhcb6, and that the "red emission" is present in any of them [9]. Since Asn per se is not sufficient to induce the redshift the residue properties are probably

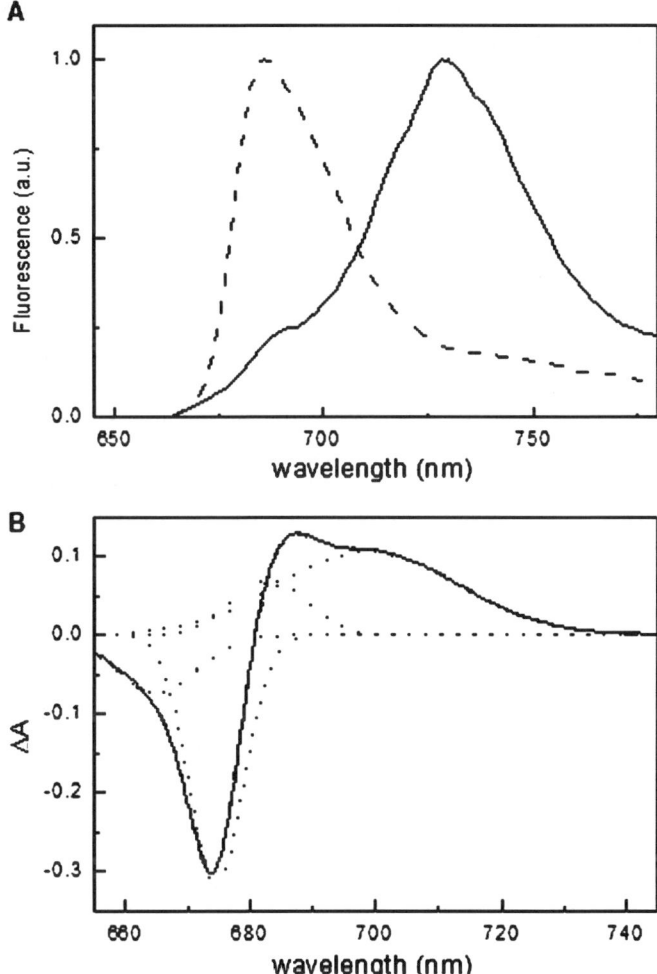

**Figure 5.** Absorption and fluorescence properties of mutants affecting red forms. (A) Fluorescence emission spectra at 77 K of WT (solid line) and NH mutant (---) of Lhca4. Spectra are normalized to the maximum. (B) Gaussian description of the difference absorption spectra of Lhca4-WT and Lhca4-N47H (solid line). Gaussians are dotted points and their sum is the dashed line. [Data of both parts are from [62]].

not the key factors for the redshift forms. On the other hand, it is more likely that the ligand influences the three-dimensional arrangement of the pigments within the protein.

### 7.4.4 What About Lhca5 (and Lhca6)?

So far, discussion has focused on Lhca1 to Lhca4, the major components of PSI antenna. However, two additional gene sequences for PSI antenna proteins have been identified in the genome, and the product of one (Lhca5) is found in thylakoids in low amounts [10,11]. Lhca5 was not found in the X-ray structure and it is a minor component of PSI, at least in plants grown in normal conditions [11]. As shown in Figure 3(A), plants depleted in Lhca5 did not show any relevant modification in the content of other Lhca polypeptides. Still, they exhibit some peculiarities and a small fraction of PSI particles (<5%) appears to be affected by the lack of this gene product [7]. Up to now, no data are available on the function of this protein. Since it is present only in very low amounts, it is unlikely that it has a significant role in the regulation of PSI antenna size [11]. The Lhca5 recombinant protein has been characterized and shown to have a low Chl $a/b$ ratio (2.6) and three xanthophyll binding sites [74]. Finally, it showed no "red forms", neither at 730 nor at 701 nm. It can form dimers in vitro with Lhca1 [74].

As for Lhca6, no data are available on this putative protein, apart from the deduced polypeptide sequence. Its analysis showed that it has a high homology with Lhca2 [9], thus suggesting it might have similar biochemical and spectroscopic properties. This similarity also supports the possibility that it could be a pseudogene.

### 7.4.5 Physiological Role of Red Forms: Increasing Light Absorption or Photoprotection?

Even though the presence of "red forms" in higher plants antenna systems has long been known, their physiological role is still poorly understood. One proposal is that "red forms" have a function in increasing light absorption beyond 700 nm. This ability is especially relevant in leaves under a canopy. In fact, solar light transmitted by a leaf is enriched in the far-red wavelength region and, therefore, under such illumination conditions the "red forms" could be responsible for up to 40% of the photon capture [75]. However, the function in light harvesting alone is probably not sufficient alone to explain why "red forms" have been found in all organisms [59]. In fact, several plant species never experience shaded light and, since they have an adapted morphology and physiology to grow in full light conditions, one could expect the "red forms" to be lost or at least reduced during their evolution. Moreover, if far-red light absorption is the crucial reason for the existence of "red-forms" in LHCI, questions arise as to why Lhca 3 and 4 only exhibit this feature rather than all four LHCI polypeptides.

An additional proposed function for "red forms" is a role in the photoprotection of PSI [76]. In fact, "red forms" have energy levels lower than the P700 and, therefore, most of the excitation energy populates these states even at room temperature [77]. As a consequence of this peculiar energy distribution, it is possible that excess energy could be dissipated in the antenna before being transferred to the reaction center.

Several different studies showed that isolated LHCI proteins have a high capacity for excitation energy dissipation. First, LHCI subunits are very efficient in non-radiative dissipation of excited singlet states of Chl, since they are characterized by a very low fluorescence yield, far below that of LHCII [78,79]. Secondly, they also are very efficient in quenching carotenoid triplets. In fact, the Chl and carotenoid triplet formation in recombinant Lhca4 has been analyzed recently by optically detected magnetic resonance (ODMR). This work showed that red chlorophylls are quenched by carotenoids with a 100% efficiency [78]. In fact, no chlorophyll triplet originating from red chlorophylls has been detected, even at very low temperatures (1.8 K), where excitation energy is localized on pigments with the lowest energy levels. In addition, it was shown that one peculiar carotenoid molecule, bound to site L2, has a major role in quenching chlorophylls triplets. This result is in good agreement with the mutational analyses of Lhca complexes, where a strong interaction between "red Chls" and the carotenoid in site L2 was shown [63]. The Lhca4 HN mutant, which is very similar to the WT but has a diminished level of "red forms", lacks this superior triplet quenching capacity. Therefore, it can be hypothesized that focusing excitation energy in a site (A5) having a special kind of connection with the carotenoid molecule in site L2 would allow better photoprotection in the whole LHCI complex and, thus, of the whole PSI.

Further, although indirect, evidence that antenna proteins with "red forms" can play a role in photoprotection came from the observation that, under light stress, LHCI exchanges violaxanthin with zeaxanthin [38]. Zeaxanthin is synthesized under excess light conditions, providing photoprotection in PSII [80–82]. Xanthophyll exchange in Lhc proteins could possibly be an evolutionary remainder, but this hypothesis seems unlikely, since Lhc proteins have evolved a high variability in the carotenoid exchange rate [39]. In conclusion, although evidence for a role in photoprotection is available from the study of isolated LHCI, a photoprotection function in vivo is still to be proven. In fact, PSI trapping is very efficient [83,84], thus making a decrease in lifetime of singlet Chl excited states far less efficient in decreasing the excitation of RC with respect to the case of PSII [85]. However, in vivo studies have shown that plants depleted in Lhca4 exhibit a strongly reduced fitness (calculated as the number of seeds produced from plants in natural environments), thus indicating a specific physiological role of LHCI [86]. Current knowledge on LHCI antenna proteins is still more limited than that for LHCII. However, recent work has been quite effective in filling the gap in the structure–function relation in this protein sub-family, suggesting that forthcoming work will be even more interesting and enlightening.

## 7.5 Concluding Remarks and Future Perspectives

Our current knowledge on the antenna system of Photosystem I is less advanced than that on Photosystem II. Recent years, however, have seen significant progress due to several studies using different approaches such as X-ray crystallography, biochemistry and molecular biology. Based on a 3D structure of the PSI-LHCI complex of higher plants, the association of PSI antenna to the core could be resolved. Some differences between PSI and PSII antenna organization emerged. The most striking features are (i) in PSI the antenna is bound asymmetrically to the core, in contrast with the more symmetric arrangement of PSII supercomplexes; (ii) the presence of peculiar "gap pigments" is unique for the PSI supercomplex; and (iii) PSI supercomplexes are stable and rigid, while PSII is more flexible.

Interesting phenomena have also been unraveled by the characterization of individual components of the antenna system (Lhca1–4), in particular by the discovery of the "red forms" of Chl *a* molecules in the PSI antenna of higher plants. These species exhibit a unique redshifted absorption. It is now clear that higher plants "red Chls" are located in the antenna and, in particular, in Lhca3 and Lhca4. Moreover, by mutational analyses, a Chl–Chl interaction was shown to be the responsible for the unique energy shift of these "red form" pigments.

The major challenge in future research on PSI-LHCI is to obtain a structure of the supercomplex with an atomic resolution. A successful achievement of this goal would allow the identification of all individual pigments bound to the system and the clarification of the nature of interactions between polypeptides. The availability of such a structure would also pave the way to a deeper understanding of the "red forms" since it would allow thorough applications of theoretical analyses (combination of quantum mechanical and molecular dynamics methods). These approaches are important in elucidating details of how the protein scaffold can modulate the chlorophyll energy levels so extensively. A further important task is to decipher the physiological role of the "red forms", which are found in PSI of all photosynthetic organisms. The reason for their high conservation in evolution is an enigma that needs to be unraveled.

# References

1. A. Ben Shem, F. Frolow, N. Nelson, Crystal structure of plant photosystem I. *Nature* **426** (2003) 630–635.
2. H.V. Scheller, P.E. Jensen, A. Haldrup, C. Lunde, J. Knoetzel, Role of subunits in eukaryotic Photosystem I. *Biochim. Biophys. Acta* **1507** (2001) 41–60.
3. J.A. Ihalainen, P.E. Jensen, A. Haldrup, I.H. van Stokkum, R. van Grondelle, H.V. Scheller, J.P. Dekker, Pigment organization and energy transfer dynamics in isolated photosystem I (PSI) complexes from Arabidopsis thaliana depleted of the PSI-G, PSI-K, PSI-L, or PSI-N subunit. *Biophys. J.* **83** (2002) 2190–2201.
4. P. Jordan, P. Fromme, H.T. Witt, O. Klukas, W. Saenger, N. Krauss, Three-dimensional structure of cyanobacterial photosystem I at 2.5 A resolution. *Nature* **411** (2001) 909–917.
5. P. Haworth, J.L. Watson, C.J. Arntzen, The detection, isolation and characterisation of a ligth-harvesting complex which is specifically associated with Photosystem I. *Biochim. Biophys. Acta* **724** (1983) 151–158.
6. R. Bassi, D. Simpson, Chlorophyll-protein complexes of barley photosystem I. *Eur. J. Biochem.* **163** (1987) 221–230.
7. T. Morosinotto, M. Ballottari, F. Klimmek, S. Jansson, R. Bassi, The association of the antenna system to photosystem I in higher plants. Cooperative interactions stabilize the supramolecular complex and enhance red-shifted spectral forms. *J. Biol. Chem.* **280** (2005) 31050–31058.

8. S. Jansson, The light-harvesting chlorophyll a/b-binding proteins. *Biochim. Biophys. Acta* **1184** (1994) 1–19.
9. S. Jansson, A guide to the Lhc genes and their relatives in Arabidopsis. *Trends Plant Sci.* **4** (1999) 236–240.
10. S. Storf, E.J. Stauber, M. Hippler, V.H. Schmid, Proteomic analysis of the photosystem I light-harvesting antenna in tomato (Lycopersicon esculentum). *Biochemistry* **43** (2004) 9214–9224.
11. U. Ganeteg, F. Klimmek, S. Jansson, Lhca5 - an LHC-Type Protein Associated with Photosystem I. *Plant Mol. Biol.* **54** (2004) 641–651.
12. E.J. Stauber, A. Fink, C. Markert, O. Kruse, U. Johanningmeier, M. Hippler, Proteomics of Chlamydomonas reinhardtii light-harvesting proteins. *Eukaryotic Cell* **2** (2003) 978–994.
13. D. Elrad, A.R. Grossman, A genome's-eye view of the light-harvesting polypeptides of Chlamydomonas reinhardtii. *Curr. Genet.* **45** (2004) 61–75.
14. M. Germano, A.E. Yakushevska, W. Keegstra, H.J. van Gorkom, J.P. Dekker, E.J. Boekema, Supramolecular organization of photosystem I and light-harvesting complex I in Chlamydomonas reinhardtii. *FEBS Letters* **525** (2002) 121–125.
15. J. Kargul, J. Nield, J. Barber, Three-dimensional reconstruction of a lightharvesting complex I-photosystem I (LHCI-PSI) supercomplex from the green alga Chlamydomonas reinhardtii - Insights into light harvesting for PSI. *Journal of Biological Chemistry* **278** (2003) 16135–16141.
16. E.J. Boekema, P.E. Jensen, E. Schlodder, J.F. van Breemen, H. van Roon, H.V. Scheller, J.P. Dekker, Green plant photosystem I binds light-harvesting complex I on one side of the complex. *Biochemistry* **40** (2001) 1029–1036.
17. R. Croce, T. Morosinotto, S. Castelletti, J. Breton, R. Bassi, The Lhca antenna complexes of higher plants photosystem I. *Biochimica et Biophysica Acta-Bioenergetics* **1556** (2002) 29–40.
18. M. Ballottari, C. Govoni, S. Caffarri, T. Morosinotto, Stoichiometry of LHCI antenna polypeptides and characterisation of gap and linker pigments in higher plants Photosystem I. *Eur. J. Biochem.* **271** (2004) 4659–4665.
19. E.J. Boekema, H. van Roon, F. Calkoen, R. Bassi, J.P. Dekker, Multiple types of association of photosystem II and its light- harvesting antenna in partially solubilized photosystem II membranes. *Biochemistry* **38** (1999) 2233–2239.
20. F. Klimmek, U. Ganeteg, J.A. Ihalainen, H. van Roon, P.E. Jensen, H.V. Scheller, J.P. Dekker, S. Jansson, Structure of the higher plant light harvesting complex I: in vivo characterization and structural interdependence of the Lhca proteins. *Biochemistry* **44** (2005) 3065–3073.
21. H. Van Amerongen, L. Valkunas, R. van Grondelle, *Photosyntheric excitons*. World Scientific Publishing Co. Pte. Ldt. (2000).
22. U. Ganeteg, A. Strand, P. Gustafsson, S. Jansson, The Properties of the Chlorophyll a/b-Binding Proteins Lhca2 and Lhca3 Studied in Vivo Using Antisense Inhibition. *Plant Physiol* **127** (2001) 150–158.
23. S. Jansson, B. Andersen, H.V. Scheller, Nearest-neighbor analysis of higher-plant photosystem I holocomplex. *Plant Physiol* **112** (1996) 409–420.
24. A. Ben Shem, F. Frolow, N. Nelson, Light-harvesting features revealed by the structure of plant Photosystem I. *Photosynthesis Research* **81** (2004) 239–250.
25. V.H.R. Schmid, H. Paulsen, J. Rupprecht, Identification of N- and C-terminal Amino Acids of Lhca1 and Lhca4 Required for Formation of the Heterodimeric Peripheral Photosystem I Antenna LHCI-730. *Biochemistry* **41** (2002) 9126–9131.

26. H.K. Lichtenthaler, G. Kuhn, U. Prenzel, D. Meier, Chlorophyll-protein levels and degree of thylakoid stacking in radish chloroplasts from high-light, low-light and bentazon- treated plants. *Physiol. Plant.* **56** (1982) 183–188.
27. S. Bailey, R.G. Walters, S. Jansson, P. Horton, Acclimation of Arabidopsis thaliana to the light environment: the existence of separate low light and high light responses. *Planta* **213** (2001) 794–801.
28. M. Ballottari, L. Dall'Osto, T. Morosinotto, R. Bassi, Contrasting behaviour of higher plant photosystem I and II antenna systems during acclimation. *J. Biol. Chem.* (2007).
29. E.H. Ball, Quantitation of proteins by eluition of Coomassie Brilliant Blue R from Stained bands after dodecyl sulfate polyacrilamide gel electrophoresis. *Anal. Biochem.* **155** (1986) 23–27.
30. A.V. Ruban, M. Wentworth, A.E. Yakushevska, J. Andersson, P.J. Lee, W. Keegstra, J.P. Dekker, E.J. Boekema, S. Jansson, P. Horton, Plants lacking the main light-harvesting complex retain photosystem II macro-organization. *Nature* **421** (2003) 648–652.
31. J.M. Anderson, B. Andersson, The dynamic photosynthetic membrane and regulation of solar energy conversion. *Trends Biochem. Sci.* **13** (1988) 351–355.
32. J.F. Allen, How does protein phosphorylation regulate photosynthesis? *Trends Biochem. Sci.* **17** (1992) 12–17.
33. F.A. Wollman, State transitions reveal the dynamics and flexibility of the photosynthetic apparatus. *EMBO J.* **20** (2001) 3623–3630.
34. S. Bellafiore, F. Barneche, G. Peltier, J.D. Rochaix, State transitions and light adaptation require chloroplast thylakoid protein kinase STN7. *Nature* **433** (2005) 892–895.
35. S.E. Tjus, B.L. Moller, H.V. Scheller, Photosystem I is an early target of photoinhibition in barley illuminated at chilling temperatures. *Plant Physiol* **116** (1998) 755–764.
36. X.P. Li, O. Bjorkman, C. Shih, A.R. Grossman, M. Rosenquist, S. Jansson, K.K. Niyogi, A pigment-binding protein essential for regulation of photosynthetic light harvesting. *Nature* **403** (2000) 391–395.
37. L. Dall'Osto, S. Caffarri, R. Bassi, A Mechanism of Nonphotochemical Energy Dissipation, Independent from PsbS, Revealed by a Conformational Change in the Antenna Protein CP26. *Plant Cell* **17** (2005) 1217–1232.
38. A.S. Verhoeven, W.W. Adams, B. Demmig-Adams, R. Croce, R. Bassi, Xanthophyll cycle pigment localization and dynamics during exposure to low temperatures and light stress in Vinca major. *Plant Physiology* **120** (1999) 727–737.
39. T. Morosinotto, R. Baronio, R. Bassi, Dynamics of Chromophore Binding to Lhc Proteins in Vivo and in Vitro during Operation of the Xanthophyll Cycle. *J. Biol. Chem.* **277** (2002) 36913–36920.
40. M. Havaux, L. Dall'Osto, S. Cuine, G. Giuliano, R. Bassi, The effect of zeaxanthin as the only xanthophyll on the structure and function of the photosynthetic apparatus in Arabidopsis thaliana. *J. Biol. Chem.* **279** (2004) 13878–13888.
41. J.E. Mullet, J.J. Burke, C.J. Arntzen, Chlorophyll proteins of photosystem I. *Plant Physiol.* **65** (1980) 814–822.
42. E. Lam, W. Ortiz, R. Malkin, Chlorophyll a/b proteins of photosystem I. *FEBS Lett.* **168** (1984) 10–14.
43. R. Bassi, O. Machold, D. Simpson, Chlorophyll-proteins of two photosystem I preparations from maize. *Carlsberg Res. Commun.* **50** (1985) 145–162.
44. M. Ikeuchi, A. Hirano, Y. Inoue, Correspondence of Apoproteins of Light-Harvesting Chlorophyll-A/B Complexes Associated with Photosystem-I to Cab

Genes - Evidence for A Novel Type-Iv Apoprotein. *Plant Cell Physiol.* **32** (1991) 103–112.
45. J. Knoetzel, I. Svendsen, D.J. Simpson, Identification of the Photosystem-I Antenna Polypeptides in Barley - Isolation of 3 Pigment-Binding Antenna Complexes. *European Journal of Biochemistry* **206** (1992) 209–215.
46. S.E. Tjus, M. Roobolboza, L.O. Palsson, B. Andersson, Rapid Isolation of Photosystem-I Chlorophyll-Binding Proteins by Anion-Exchange Perfusion Chromatography. *Photosynthesis Research* **45** (1995) 41–49.
47. R. Croce, G. Zucchelli, F.M. Garlaschi, R.C. Jennings, A thermal broadening study of the antenna chlorophylls in PSI- 200, LHCI, and PSI core. *Biochemistry* **37** (1998) 17255–17360.
48. J.A. Ihalainen, B. Gobets, K. Sznee, M. Brazzoli, R. Croce, R. Bassi, R. van Grondelle, J.E.I. Korppi-Tommola, J.P. Dekker, Evidence for two spectroscopically different dimers of light- harvesting complex I from green plants. *Biochemistry* **39** (2000) 8625–8631.
49. L.O. Palsson, S.E. Tjus, B. Andersson, T. Gillbro, Ultrafast Energy-Transfer Dynamics Resolved in Isolated Spinach Light-Harvesting Complex-I and the Lhc-I-730 Subpopulation. *Biochimica et Biophysica Acta-Bioenergetics* **1230** (1995) 1–9.
50. S. Castelletti, T. Morosinotto, B. Robert, S. Caffarri, R. Bassi, R. Croce, Recombinant Lhca2 and Lhca3 subunits of the photosystem I antenna system. *Biochemistry* **42** (2003) 4226–4234.
51. D. Siefermann-Harms, Carotenoids in photosynthesis. I. Location in photosynthetic membranes and light- harvesting function. *Biochim. Biophys. Acta* **811** (1985) 325–355.
52. V.H.R. Schmid, K.V. Cammarata, B.U. Bruns, G.W. Schmidt, In vitro reconstitution of the photosystem I light-harvesting complex LHCI-730: Heterodimerization is required for antenna pigment organization. *Proceedings of the National Academy of Sciences of the United States of America* **94** (1997) 7667–7672.
53. B. Bossmann, J. Knoetzel, S. Jansson, Screening of chlorina mutants of barley (Hordeum vulgare L.) with antibodies against light-harvesting proteins of PS I and PS II: Absence of specific antenna proteins. *Photosynthesis Research* **52** (1997) 127–136.
54. H. Zhang, H.M. Goodman, S. Jansson, Antisense inhibition of the photosystem I antenna protein Lhca4 in Arabidopsis thaliana. *Plant Physiol* **115** (1997) 1525–1531.
55. V.H.R. Schmid, S. Potthast, M. Wiener, V. Bergauer, H. Paulsen, S. Storf, Pigment binding of photosystem I light-harvesting proteins. *Journal of Biological Chemistry* **277** (2002) 37307–37314.
56. F.G. Plumley, G.W. Schmidt, Reconstitution of chloroform a/b light-harvesting complexes: Xanthophyll-dependent assembley and energy transfer. *Proc. Natl. Acad. Sci. U.S.A.* **84** (1987) 146–150.
57. E. Giuffra, D. Cugini, R. Croce, R. Bassi, Reconstitution and pigment-binding properties of recombinant CP29. *Eur. J. Biochem.* **238** (1996) 112–120.
58. R. Croce, R. Bassi, The light-harvesting complex of photosystem I: Pigment composition and stoichiometry. In *Photosynthesis: Mechanisms and Effects* (G. Garab, ed.), Kluwer Academic Publisher, (1998) pp. 421–424.
59. B. Gobets, R. van Grondelle, Energy transfer and trapping in Photosystem I. *Biochim. Biophys. Acta* **1057** (2001) 80–99.
60. B. Gobets, H. Van Amerongen, R. Monshouwer, J. Kruip, M. Rögner, R. van Grondelle, J.P. Dekker, Polarized site-selected fluorescence spectroscopy of isolated Photosystem I particles. *Biochim. Biophys. Acta* **1188** (1994) 75–85.

61. J.A. Ihalainen, M. Ratsep, P.E. Jensen, H.V. Scheller, R. Croce, R. Bassi, J.E.I. Korppi-Tommola, A. Freiberg, Red spectral forms of chlorophylls in green plant PSI - a site-selective and high-pressure spectroscopy study. *J. Phys. Chem. B* **107** (2003) 9086–9093.
62. T. Morosinotto, J. Breton, R. Bassi, R. Croce, The nature of a chlorophyll ligand in Lhca proteins determines the far red fluorescence emission typical of photosystem I. *J. Biol. Chem.* **278** (2003) 49223–49229.
63. T. Morosinotto, S. Castelletti, J. Breton, R. Bassi, R. Croce, Mutation analysis of Lhca1 antenna complex. Low energy absorption forms originate from pigment-pigment interactions. *J. Biol. Chem.* **277** (2002) 36253–36261.
64. R. Croce, T. Morosinotto, J.A. Ihalainen, A. Chojnicka, J. Breton, J.P. Dekker, R. van Grondelle, R. Bassi, Origin of the 701 nm fluorescence emission of the Lhca2 subunit of higher plant photosystem I. *J. Biol. Chem.* (2004).
65. Z. Liu, H. Yan, K. Wang, T. Kuang, J. Zhang, L. Gui, X. An, W. Chang, Crystal structure of spinach major light-harvesting complex at 2.72 A resolution. *Nature* **428** (2004) 287–292.
66. J. Standfuss, A.C. Terwissscha van Scheltinga, M. Lamborghini, W. Kuhlbrandt, Mechanisms of photoprotection and nonphotochemical quenching in pea light-harvesting complex at 2.5 A resolution. *EMBO J.* **24** (2005) 919–928.
67. W. Kühlbrandt, D.N. Wang, Y. Fujiyoshi, Atomic model of plant light-harvesting complex by electron crystallography. *Nature* **367** (1994) 614–621.
68. R. Bassi, R. Croce, D. Cugini, D. Sandona, Mutational analysis of a higher plant antenna protein provides identification of chromophores bound into multiple sites. *Proc. Natl. Acad. Sci. USA* **96** (1999) 10056–10061.
69. R. Remelli, C. Varotto, D. Sandona, R. Croce, R. Bassi, Chlorophyll binding to monomeric light-harvesting complex. A mutation analysis of chromophore-binding residues. *J. Biol. Chem.* **274** (1999) 33510–33521.
70. H. Rogl, W. Kuhlbrandt, Mutant trimers of light-harvesting complex II exhibit altered pigment content and spectroscopic features. *Biochemistry* **38** (1999) 16214–16222.
71. T. Morosinotto, M. Mozzo, R. Bassi, R. Croce, Pigment-pigment interactions in Lhca4 antenna complex of higher plants photosystem I. *J. Biol. Chem.* **280** (2005) 20612–20619.
72. M. Mozzo, T. Morosinotto, R. Bassi, R. Croce, Probing the structure of Lhca3 by mutation analysis. *Biochim. Biophys. Acta.* **1757** (2006) 1607–1613.
73. R. Bassi, S.Y. Soen, G. Frank, H. Zuber, J.D. Rochaix, Characterization of Chlorophyll-a/b Proteins of Photosystem-I from Chlamydomonas-Reinhardtii. *J. Biol. Chem.* **267** (1992) 25714–25721.
74. S. Storf, S. Jansson, V.H. Schmid, Pigment Binding, Fluorescence Properties, and Oligomerization Behavior of Lhca5, a Novel Light-harvesting Protein. *J. Biol. Chem.* **280** (2005) 5163–5168.
75. A. Rivadossi, G. Zucchelli, F.M. Garlaschi, R.C. Jennings, The importance of PSI chlorophyll red forms in light-harvesting by leaves. *Photosynt. Res.* **60** (1999) 209–215.
76. I. Mukerji, K. Sauer, Temperature-dependent steady-state and picosecond kinetic fluorescence measurements of a photosystem I preparation from spinach. In *Photosynthesis. Plant Biology Vol. 8* (W.R. Briggs, ed.), Alan R. Liss, New York, (1989) pp. 105–122.
77. R. Croce, G. Zucchelli, F.M. Garlaschi, R. Bassi, R.C. Jennings, Excited state equilibration in the photosystem I - light - harvesting I complex: P700 is almost isoenergetic with its antenna. *Biochemistry* **35** (1996) 8572–8579.

78. D. Carbonera, G. Agostini, T. Morosinotto, R. Bassi, Quenching of chlorophyll triplet states by carotenoids in reconstituted Lhca4 subunit of peripheral light-harvesting complex of photosystem I. *Biochemistry* **44** (2005) 8337–8346.
79. J.A. Ihalainen, R. Croce, T. Morosinotto, I.H. van Stokkum, R. Bassi, J.P. Dekker, R. van Grondelle, Excitation decay pathways of Lhca proteins – A time-resolved fluorescence study. *J. Phys. Chem. B* (2005) in press.
80. B. Demmig, K. Winter, A. Kruger, F.-C. Czygan, Photoinhibition and zeaxanthin formation in intact leaves. A possible role of the xanthophyll cycle in the dissipation of excess light energy. *Plant Physiol.* **84** (1987) 218–224.
81. B. Demmig-Adams, Carotenoids and photoprotection in plants: A role for the xanthophyll zeaxanthin. *Biochim. Biophys. Acta* **1020** (1990) 1–24.
82. M. Havaux, K.K. Niyogi, The violaxanthin cycle protects plants from photooxidative damage by more than one mechanism. *Proc. Natl. Acad. Sci. USA* **96** (1999) 8762–8767.
83. H.W. Trissl, C. Wilhelm, Why do thylakoid membranes from higher plants form grana stacks? *TIBS* **18** (1993) 415–419.
84. R. van Grondelle, J.P. Dekker, T. Gillbro, V. Sundström, Energy transfer and trapping in photosynthesis. *Biochim. Biophys. Acta* **1187** (1994) 1–65.
85. R.C. Jennings, F.M. Garlaschi, L. Finzi, G. Zucchelli, Slow exciton trapping in photosystem II: A possible physiological role. *Photosynth. Res.* **47** (1996) 167–173.
86. U. Ganeteg, C. Kulheim, J. Andersson, S. Jansson, Is each light-harvesting complex protein important for plant fitness? *Plant Physiol* **134** (2004) 502–509.

Chapter 8

# Structure and Function of Photosystem II Light-Harvesting Proteins (Lhcb) of Higher Plants

## Herbert van Amerongen and Roberta Croce

### Table of Contents

8.1 Introduction..................................................331
8.2 LHCII.....................................................334
    8.2.1 Pigment Binding in Native LHCII......................334
    8.2.2 Structure of LHCII from 2D Crystals..................335
    8.2.3 An Inside Look into LHCII using Recombinant Proteins...338
        8.2.3.1 Chlorophyll Organization in LHCII............338
        8.2.3.2 Carotenoid Organization in LHCII.............340
        8.2.3.3 Folding and Stability of LHCII Monomers......341
        8.2.3.4 Trimerization of LHCII.......................342
    8.2.4 LHCII Structure at 2.72 Å.............................342
        8.2.4.1 Mixed Chl a/b Occupancy of Binding Sites.....343
    8.2.5 Role of Carotenoids in LHCII..........................344
        8.2.5.1 Structure Stabilization........................344
        8.2.5.2 Energy Transfer...............................345
        8.2.5.3 Photoprotection: Triplet Quenching............345
    8.2.6 Spectroscopy of LHCII................................346
        8.2.6.1 Ultrafast Spectroscopy on LHCII..............348
        8.2.6.2 Excitonic Interactions in LHCII...............349
        8.2.6.3 Detailed Modeling of Excitation Energy Transfer in LHCII..............................350
        8.2.6.4 Singlet Excitation Energy Transfer within and between LHCII Trimers....................352
8.3 Minor Antenna Complexes of Photosystem II...............352
    8.3.1 CP24................................................353
    8.3.2 CP26................................................353

  8.3.3 CP29: A Model System.............................. 354
      8.3.3.1 Steady-State and Time-Resolved Spectroscopy..... 355
8.4 Conclusions and Future Perspectives........................ 356
Acknowledgements .................................................. 356
Note Added in Proof................................................ 357
References......................................................... 357

# STRUCTURE AND FUNCTION OF PHOTOSYSTEM II

## Abstract

Most of the pigments of Photosystem II are bound to the outer Lhcb antenna complexes, LHCII, CP29, CP26 and CP24. The major light-harvesting complex LHCII is the dominant one, and it has been the subject of numerous spectroscopic and biochemical studies. This has led to a rather detailed picture of the processes occurring in LHCII. Its recently determined crystal structure helps to visualize these processes, and many structural details agree with earlier spectroscopic and biochemical findings, particularly light harvesting and triplet quenching. Other topics still need clarification; for LHCII and CP29 biochemical and spectroscopic evidence has been collected that some chlorophyll binding sites (can) bind both chlorophyll $a$ and $b$, but this is not apparent from the structural studies. CP26 and CP24 have been studied in far less detail. Specific roles of individual complexes are still under investigation and it is also largely unknown how individual complexes interact and cooperate. Nevertheless, the overall transfer of excitation energy throughout the antenna to the reaction center is clearly relatively slow. Understanding the involvement of the various complexes in regulation and photoprotection constitute major goals for scientific research in the near future.

## 8.1 Introduction

An essential step during the evolution of oxygen-evolving organisms from cyanobacteria to higher plants was the introduction of the outer antenna Chl $a$/Chl $b$/Xan–protein complexes of both Photosystems I and II [1]. These proteins belong to the Lhc superfamily, which consists of Chl $a/b$, Chl $a/c$ and Chl $a$ proteins from photosynthetic eukaryotes [2]. During evolution they were subject to great variation, leading to a large diversity in pigment composition and spectral properties. Green et al. have discussed the evolutionary relationship between the members of the Lhc superfamily [3]. The Lhc complexes of higher plants are characterized by three trans-membrane helices, which are highly conserved between the members of the family. The Lhc complexes LHCII, CP29, CP26 and CP24 are associated to PSII (Figure 1) and are encoded by Lhcb genes (Figure 2), while the Lhca1–4 genes encode for the antenna complexes of PSI [4].

The Lhc proteins have different functions: (1) light harvesting – light absorption and excitation energy transfer to the reaction centers for use in charge separation; (2) quenching of harmful $^3$Chl* (triplet state of Chl) produced from $^1$Chl* (excited singlet state of Chl) by intersystem crossing, to prevent singlet oxygen ($^1O_2^*$) formation and photodamage of the thylakoids; (3) regulation of occupation of the $^1$Chl* level via the process of nonphotochemical quenching (NPQ), thus preventing over-excitation of photosynthetic reaction centers and subsequent photoinhibition. In addition, LHCII is involved in regulatory changes in the macro-organization of the thylakoid membranes [5–9].

Also, since LHCII constitutes roughly half of the protein mass of the thylakoid membranes in higher plants and green algae, and it is most abundant in the stacked region of granal thylakoids [10], it should be considered a major

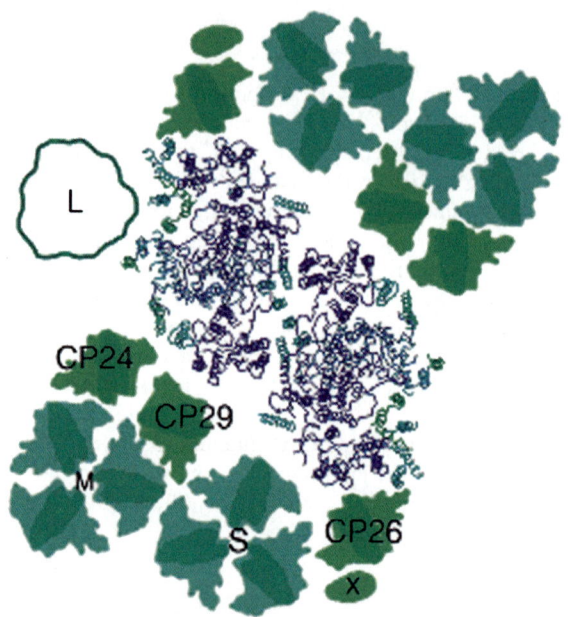

**Figure 1.** Top view of a so-called $C_2S_2M_2$ supercomplex, based on electron microscopy images of PSII-LHCII supercomplexes from spinach [167]. "S" and "M" refer to strongly and moderately bound LHCII, respectively. The area marked "L" (not to scale) indicates an additional LHCII trimer found only in spinach. The central part indicates the protein backbone in the membrane-intrinsic part of the PSII core complex (a dimer in this picture), consisting of the reaction centre plus CP47 and CP43 [calculated from the 3.7 Å structure of the PSII core complex from *S. vulcanus* (1IZL.pdb file, [168]]. The cross marks the place where, according to fitting and a comparison of slightly different types of supercomplexes [131], one additional small peripheral subunit could be attached. [This figure was taken from [14].]

structural protein. Indeed, LHCII has been shown to stabilize the granum ultrastructure, to participate in the cation-mediated stacking of the membranes [11,12] and to participate in the lateral organization of the membranes, *i.e.*, in the separation (sorting) of the two photosystems, the LHCII- and LHCII-PSII macrodomains in the grana and the LHCI-PSI supercomplexes in the stroma membranes [13,14]. The trimers are generally believed to be the functional units present in thylakoid membranes. Monomers, however, might play a role in NPQ. Using an in vitro system of purified LHCII components it was found that trimeric LHCII did not quench to the same extent or as rapidly as its monomeric form [15]. The formation of monomers, e.g., in high light [16], might be essential for the regulated proteolytic degradation of the complexes, since only monomers are targeted [17].

The antenna system of green plants, which coordinates most of the pigments, should be regarded as a complex piece of machinery for management of excitation energy, ensuring efficient light harvesting under light-limiting

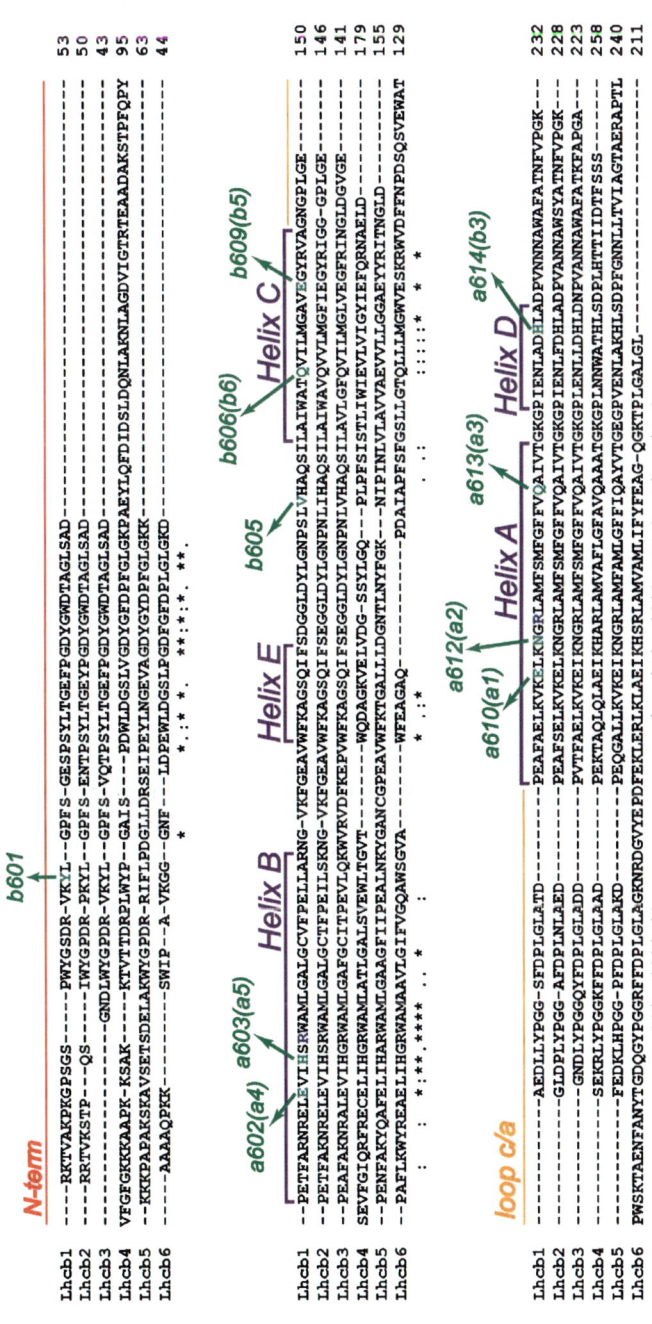

**Figure 2.** Sequence alignment of Lhcb1–Lhcb6 from *Arabidopsis thaliana*. Identification of binding sites and helices is based on the crystal structure of LHCII [35]. Clearly, the overall organization is well conserved, which is also the case for many binding sites.

conditions and dissipation of excess energy when the absorbed light exceeds the maximal capacity for electron transport.

The Lhc proteins are located at the periphery of PSII and PSI [18,19]; Figure 1 shows the proposed organization of the outer antenna complexes with respect to the core proteins of PSII, containing the reaction center and the inner antenna proteins CP43 and CP47. Moreover, there are thylakoid regions, which are significantly enriched in LHCII and are probably stacked upon the membrane parts that contain the PSII reaction centers [14]. A more extensive description of the organization of the chloroplast can be found elsewhere [14].

In this chapter we review biochemical and spectroscopic data on LHCII, the major antenna complex of PSII, which is also the most extensively studied one, and try to relate these to the LHCII structure. Thereafter, we summarize available data for other members of the Lhc family present in PSII, namely CP24, CP26 and CP29.

It is broadly assumed that the process of charge separation in PSII is trap-limited, *i.e.*, that the time of excitation energy transfer to the reaction centre is negligibly small, but we will briefly point out that this assumption is not correct. This issue is discussed more extensively in a recent review [20]. For other aspects of Lhc biochemistry, such as the biogenesis and assembly of the complexes, readers are addressed to the reviews [21,22]. More general reviews have also been published [23–25,3–4]. For more information on NPQ, we refer to [26–28].

## 8.2 LHCII

LHCII is the most abundant protein in the thylakoid membrane of higher plants. It binds approximately half of the chlorophyll molecules of the chloroplast. What has been called LHCII is actually a preparation containing a complex mixture of many different, although very similar, polypeptides belonging to three groups of gene products: Lhcb1, Lhcb2 and Lhcb3 (Figure 2) that are organized into heterotrimers. Lhcb1 is the most heterogeneous component of LHCII, in agreement with the high number of genes (3–16) present in plant genomes [4]. It is composed of 230–233 residues and multiple SDS-PAGE bands can be resolved [29,30]. Lhcb2 is slightly shorter (228 residues) and it is the product of 1–4 genes. Lhcb3 is 223 amino acids long due to the lack of the N-terminal part of the sequence, which includes a threonine residue that can be phosphorylated [31] (Figure 2). The total LHCII fraction contains the three gene products in the relative ratio of 10–20:3:1 respectively, depending on the plant growth conditions [32].

*8.2.1 Pigment Binding in Native LHCII*

Isolated LHCII binds 12–14 Chls per polypeptide, depending on the type of plant, the purification method and its aggregation state [33–35]. Purification by isoelectric focusing (IEF), although yielding the highest purity, induces the loss of one Chl $a$ (and of one Xan molecule, see later) per polypeptide [36]. The Chl $a/b$ ratio of the native, trimeric, complexes is always 1.33–1.4, implying the presence of 7–8 Chl $a$ and 5–6 Chl $b$ [37,38]. Preparations of monomeric LHCII show larger differences in the Chl $a/b$ ratio (from 1.2 up to 1.5) as a consequence of Chl loss during purification. Notably, all LHCII preparations from plants are heterogeneous due to the presence of three different complexes (Lhcb1–3), which in turn are the product of several genes [39]. While the primary structure seems to be highly conserved among different polypeptides, small sequence changes can apparently induce differences in the binding strength of Chls [29].

The carotenoid (or xanthophyll) composition of LHCII, although conserved, shows specific changes, depending on the purification method. LHCII trimers purified by IEF show three Cars per polypeptides, 1.8–2 luteins (L), 1 neoxanthin (N) and 0–0.2 violaxanthin (V) [40]. Milder purification methods yield a complex with higher V content [41]. This V can be removed by detergent treatment [42] or IEF [36], leading to the conclusion that its binding site is localized at the periphery of the complex and that is has a lower binding affinity [42].

*8.2.2 Structure of LHCII from 2D Crystals*

Although the LHCII complex has been known since 1967 [43] and it has been one of the favored subjects for plant biochemical and spectroscopic research, great impulse to the study of its structure–function relationship was given by the resolution of its structure electron microscopy on 2D crystals at 3.4 Å in 1994 [34]. The structural data were used as a starting point for extensive biochemical and spectroscopic work and as input for theoretical calculations with the aim of obtaining structural details that could not be resolved at 3.4 Å, thus explain light-harvesting and photoprotection functions performed by this complex. Recently, the structure of LHCII was resolved by X-ray crystallography at 2.72 Å, revealing more details [35] that are now being incorporated into the existing knowledge (Figure 3). Nevertheless, the last ten years of experiments are mainly based on the 3.4 Å structural model [34] and we will discuss this structure first.

The monomeric unit of the complex is composed of three trans-membrane helices and one amphipathic helix (helix D) exposed at the surface on the lumenal side of the thylakoid membrane. The two central helices (A and B) are tilted by $\sim 30°$ with respect to the normal to the membrane plane. They are in close contact with each other, held together by two inter-helix ionic pairs, forming a left-handed supercoil with two-fold symmetry. The first ionic pair is formed by the residues E65 on helix B and R185 on helix A and the second by residues R70 and E180. The third trans-membrane helix (named helix C) is almost perpendicular to the membrane plane and it is shorter. Helix D is only 10 AA long and lies parallel to the membrane plane. Electron microscopy crystallography did not yield information on the interhelical loops due to low electron density. Twelve porphyrins were localized and nine residues were

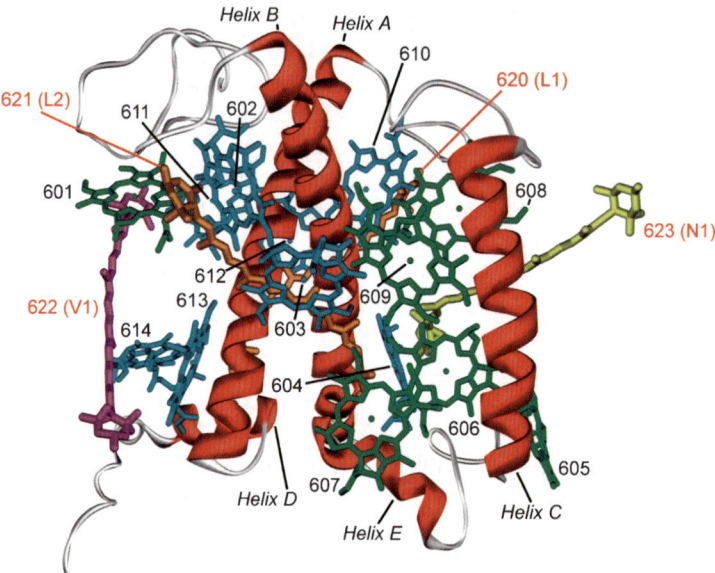

**Figure 3.** Side view (the stromal side is up) of monomeric LHCII [35]. The monomer is in fact one subunit of trimeric LHCII, and Chl603 is facing the interior of the trimer.

**Table 1.** Nomenclature and coordination of chlorophylls according to Kühlbrandt et al. (1994) and Liu et al. (2004)

| Kühlbrandt et al. | | Liu et al. | |
| --- | --- | --- | --- |
| Chl | Ligand | Chl | Ligand |
| a1 | Glu 180 | Chl*a* 610 | Glu 180 |
| a2 | Asn 183 | Chl*a* 612 | Asn 183 |
| a3 | Gln 197 | Chl*a* 613 | Gln 197 |
| a4 | Glu 65 | Chl*a* 602 | Glu 65 |
| a5 | His 68 | Chl*a* 603 | His 68 |
| a6 | Gly 78 | Chl*a* 604 | Wat 309 |
| a7 | – | Chl*b* 607 | Wat 308 |
| b1 | – | Chl*b* 608 | Wat 302 |
| b2 | – | Chl*a* 611 | Phospho-diester |
| b3 | His 212 | Chl*a* 614 | His 212 |
| b5 | Glu 139 | Chl*b* 609 | Glu 139 |
| b6 | Gln 131 | Chl*b* 606 | Wat 310 |
| – | – | Chl*b* 601 | Tyr 24[a] |
| – | – | Chl*b* 605 | Val 119[a] |

[a]These residues contribute their backbone carbonyls to coordinate with the central magnesium of chlorophylls.

proposed to act as Chl ligands (Table 1). The average distance between neighboring Chls is just below 10 Å. The closest Chls belonging to neighboring subunits are held at distances slightly larger than those detected between Chls within the same subunit: Chl a5, for example, is relatively close to Chl a4 in a neighboring monomer. Two Cars have been resolved by electron crystallography at the centre of the cross-brace between helices A and B. LHCII monomers form trimers by establishing mutual interactions between the distal surface of the helix C, the top end of helix B and the C and N-termini.

Despite a wealth of important information obtained from the structural model of LHCII, essential details required for understanding the functioning remained unknown:

(i) *Identification of the chlorophylls:* The resolution of 3.4 Å did not allow discrimination between a methyl group (Chl *a*) and a formyl group (Chl *b*) at the C7 position of the substituted porphyrin rings of the Chls. Kühlbrandt and co-workers [34] proposed that the seven Chls located near the two central carotenoids were Chl *a* based on the fact that triplet formation at room temperature occurs mainly on Chl *a* (Chl *b* rapidly transfers singlet excitations to Chl *a*). Therefore, only Chls *a* need to be in close contact with a carotenoid molecule to enable protective triplet quenching. These seven Chls were called Chl a1–a7 (Table 1). The remaining five Chls were called Chl b1, b2, b3, b5, b6 where Chls *a* and *b* with the same number are in close contact. Below, we will use this numbering also to indicate binding sites, site B1 being for instance the site that harbors Chl b1. However, the possibility that either N or V, although not resolved in the 2D crystal structure, might quench triplets of Chl *a* molecules at different positions was not explicitly considered, leaving the Chl identities uncertain.

(ii) *Chl–protein interactions.* Out of the twelve Chls presented in the model, the ligands for only nine were suggested. It remained unclear how the others were bound to the protein.

(iii) *Chl transition dipole moment orientations:* The model yielded information about the orientation of the plane of the Chls, which were modeled as tetrapyrrole rings. However, because the phytyl chains could not be resolved, the orientation of the *X*- and *Y*-axes of the Chls remained unknown and therefore also, the orientations of the transition dipole moments.

(iv) *Location and identity of the xanthophylls.* Only two carotenoid molecules out of four were resolved in the structural model. They were assigned to L but this assignment was not considered to be entirely unambiguous because the structural resolution was not high enough to discriminate between different xanthophylls and, also, the LHCII preparations usually contain also 1 N per 2 Ls.

(v) *Structure of the soluble domains.* The loops that interconnect the transmembrane helices, as well as the N-terminal domain, were not resolved. These regions constitute more than half of the apoprotein and many properties of the molecule depend on these regions (e.g., trimerization, phosphorylation).

In addition, one needs to know the spectroscopic properties of the individual chromophores in this complex as well as the interactions between them to properly understand the functioning of LHCII. Although they cannot be determined from the crystal structure, the structure can help to understand and assign them.

In the last ten years a great effort was made to address these unresolved issues. On the one hand, a multitude of spectroscopic studies was performed, and (ultra)fast spectroscopic techniques in combination with theoretical modeling played a prominent role in addressing several of these issues. On the other hand, molecular biology coupled with biochemistry and steady-state spectroscopy was used to study the same issues by a mutational analysis approach. The biochemistry and molecular biology results will be reviewed in the following sections, while the spectroscopy results are discussed in Section 8.2.4.

*8.2.3 An Inside Look into LHCII using Recombinant Proteins*

LHCII is a heterogeneous protein, implying that preparations from leaves consist of a mixture of many homologous polypeptides. Any analytical method will then be limited by the possibility that a chromophore in an individual binding site can be of different nature (e.g., Chl *a* vs. Chl *b*, or L vs. V) in the various gene products present in the preparation or not be bound at all. In principle, this problem can be overcome by the use of recombinant proteins of a single gene product and in vitro refolding with pigments. This procedure allows both one to reproduce the characteristics of the native protein and to modify its pigment content through mutation of individual binding sites or omission of one or more pigment species during refolding.

This approach has been an important tool in the unraveling of structure–function relationships in proteins, but its application to Lhc proteins was hampered for a long period by the lack of a suitable heterologous expression system in which all the chromophores needed for Lhc protein folding (Chl *a*, Chl *b*, L, V, N) were available. A solution was obtained via the pioneering work of Plumley and Schmidt [44], who showed that LHCII apoproteins could be refolded in vitro when mixed with excess amounts of purified pigments. The subsequent step consisted of overexpressing Lhc proteins in bacteria either with their WT sequence or with mutations affecting chromophore binding [45,46]. This procedure allows the introduction of specific deletions into the chromophore complement of Lhc proteins, thus allowing determination of the spectroscopic properties of individual Chl and Car chromophores by differential spectroscopy.

The approach of in vitro reconstitution has been used to investigate several aspects of the structure–function relationship of LHCII, as is reviewed below.

*8.2.3.1 Chlorophyll Organization in LHCII*
The mutation analysis approach was performed on LHCII monomers [47–49] and LHCII trimers [49]. All nine putative Chl ligands suggested by the structure analysis were mutated into amino acids, which are unable to bind Chls. The mutated-reconstituted complexes were analyzed by biochemical and spectroscopic methods. For eight out of the nine mutants a clear loss of Chls was

**Table 2.** Occupancy of Chl binding sites

| Site | Remelli et al. | Rogl et al. | Yang et al. | Hobe et al.[a] | Liu et al |
|---|---|---|---|---|---|
| A1 | Chl $a$ | Chl $a$ | | Chl $a$ (Chl $b$) | Chl $a$ (610) |
| A2 | Chl $a$ | Chl $a$ | | Chl $a$ | Chl $a$ (612) |
| A3 | Chl $a/b$ | Chl $a$ | Chl $a/b$ | Chl $b$ | Chl $a$ (613) |
| A4 | Chl $a$ | Chl $b$ | | Chl $a$ (Chl $b$) | Chl $a$ (614) |
| A5 | Chl $a$ | Chl $a$ | | Chl $a$ (Chl $b$) | Chl $a$ (603) |
| A6 | Chl $a/b$ | | | Chl $b$ | Chl $a$ (604) |
| A7 | Chl $b$ | | | Chl $b$ | Chl $b$ (607) |
| B1 | Chl $a$ | | | Chl $b$ | Chl $b$ (608) |
| B2 | Chl $b$ | | | | Chl $a$ (611) |
| B3 | Chl $a/b$ | Chl $a$ | Chl $a/b$ | Chl $a$ (Chl $b$) | Chl $a$ (614) |
| B5 | Chl $b$ | Chl $b$ | | Chl $a$ (Chl $b$) | Chl $b$ (609) |
| B6 | Chl $b$ | Chl $b$ | Chl $b$ | Chl $b$ | Chl $b$ (606) |
| 601 | | | | | Chl $b$ |
| 605 | | | | | Chl $b$ |

[a] This study tested the affinity of the binding sites for Chl a and Chl b. The Chl species for which the site shows higher affinity are indicated. The reported secondary affinity for the other Chl species is indicated in brackets.

observed. The mutation of the putative ligand for Chl a6 showed that Gly-78 is not involved in the pigment binding [47,49], which was later confirmed in the crystallographic study of Liu et al. [35].

Most of the mutated complexes exhibit loss of more than one Chl. This might indicate that some of the Chls are held in place by interactions with other pigments. The mutation analysis approach has also been performed in three different labs using maize and pea Lhcb1 genes. The various Chl assignment are summarized in Table 2.

These results demonstrate the existence of several domains, which mainly contain one type of pigment. A core cluster of Chl $a$, bound to sites A1, A2, A4 and A5 is located near the two central carotenoids, close to the stromal side of the membrane. This cluster is also highly conserved in algae which bind only Chl $a$. A second domain rich in Chl $b$ is located between helix B and helix C and is composed of four Chls (B5, B6, A6, A7) and of a N molecule. An isolated domain (also in terms of energy transfer) is composed of two Chls located near the amphipathic helix (A3 and B3): it was proposed that these two sites can accommodate both Chl $a$ and $b$ with almost the same affinity, whereas other results suggest that they accommodate only Chl $a$ (Table 2).

From the mutation analysis it was also possible to reveal the absorption maximum of each Chl by analyzing the absorption difference spectra between wild type (WT) and mutants at room temperature. In some cases the assignment was not straightforward, due to secondary effects of the mutation on neighboring Chls, but it was possible to propose the absorption wavelength for most of the 12 Chls [47]. A1 and A2 Chls have the lowest energy with absorption around 680–681 nm. The Chls in sites A4 and A5 have an absorption peak at around 674–675 nm. The relative redshift of Chls a1 and a2 with respect to Chls a4 and a5 accords with spectroscopic data on WT LHCII [50].

The Chls *b* located near helix C show absorption maxima near 652 nm. The blue-most Chls *a* and Chl *b* are associated with the mixed sites A3 and B3 [47].

*8.2.3.2 Carotenoid Organization in LHCII*
Reconstitution experiments of LHCII with different carotenoid composition demonstrate that the two central sites can be occupied either by L or V or even by Z when this pigment is present, but that the affinity for L is higher than that for V [51,52]. This indicates that in the WT complex these two sites are mostly occupied by L, with L1 hosting L only and site L2 binding 75% L and 25% V. As a corollary the N is excluded from the two central sites. It is located at a more peripheral site, as was confirmed by mutation analysis [53]. Mutants of the Chl binding ligands of helix C show a decrease in the N content, suggesting its binding within the same domain. From these experiments the N molecule is, clearly, not bound directly to the polypeptide chain but is held in place by interactions with the surrounding Chls. Comparison of the LD spectrum of an LHCII complex, which only binds L as a carotenoid, with the LD spectrum of the WT complex made it possible to determine that the N is tilted at $57 \pm 1.5°$ with respect to the normal to the membrane plane [53]. This orientation is similar to those of the two central Ls resolved in the structure with angles of 56° and 59°.

In LHCII most of the V is loosely bound to a fourth site, which is located at the periphery of the complex. This V can easily be eliminated by mild detergent treatment [54] or by acidic treatment [55]. It has been proposed that under stress conditions these V molecules can be de-epoxidated to Z and reintegrated into the minor antenna complexes to participate in NPQ [55], although the exact mechanism is still unclear and it is not known where it takes place. Recent experimental data indicate the role of a non-bilayer phase of the lipid membrane [56].

How are the carotenoids bound to the complex? Some conserved sequences have been identified in the loops connecting the helices that were proposed to bind the Ls [57]. These sequences are composed of five amino acids, four of which are a-polar and one is charged. The hypothesis was that the charged AA can interact through an H-bond with the hydroxyl group of the xanthophyll, thereby stabilizing the binding. However, complete deletion of the N-terminus of LHCII does not influence the carotenoid binding, indicating that the conserved sequence in this protein region is not indispensable [58]. Recent experiments performed on the minor antenna complex CP29 in which the central charged amino acid, or in one case the entire conserved sequence, was deleted indicate that the complex is able to bind the two central carotenoids although there is some influence on the binding selectivity. It was concluded that the carotenoids are kept in place by hydrophobic interactions between their carbon chain and, possibly, aromatic residues in the trans-membrane helix domains [59].

The protein environment influences the transition energies of the Cars due to the high polarizability of their $S_2$ levels [60], but specific protein–carotenoid and chlorophyll–carotenoid interactions may also play a role. A first attempt to determine the energy levels of the various Cars was performed by combining laser-flash induced T-S, fluorescence excitation and absorption spectra [38]. For trimers bands were revealed at 510 nm (0–0 transition), 494 nm and 486 nm. Upon monomerization the 510 nm band disappears. Although this band was originally ascribed to V, it was demonstrated later that it is also present for trimeric LHCII preparations that completely lack V and that it should be ascribed to one of the Ls [36,61,62]. The other L was shown to absorb at 494 nm, N at 486 nm, whereas V absorbs at $\sim 488$ nm. Later, it was concluded that these 494 and 510 nm bands correspond to L1 and L2, respectively [63]. The absorption maxima for all xanthophylls in monomeric LHCII have been determined using reconstituted complexes with only one carotenoid species present. The following values were obtained: 495 nm for L, 486 nm for N, 492 nm for V and 502 nm for Z [51]. V and Z are bound in the L2 site in these complexes. The trimeric 510 nm band was missing, in agreement with the results of Peterman et al. [38]. More recently, analysis of the absorption spectrum of LHCII in the blue region, combined with Car to Chl energy transfer measurements, led to the conclusion that the two central Ls also have different absorption spectra in the monomers: L1 peaks at 495 nm and L2 at 489 nm [64]. Trimerization induces a change in the absorption properties of one of the L molecules, as shown by Raman spectroscopy [61,62] and spectral deconvolution [36], leading to an absorption peak at 510 nm for the lutein in site L2 [63]. It was demonstrated by Stark spectroscopy that the 510 nm L has a much larger value for the difference dipole moment $|\Delta\mu|$ between ground and excited state than the 494 nm L [65]. This is thought to be either due to a close contact with a charged residue of a neighboring monomeric LHCII subunit [66] and/or a change in geometry of the L upon trimerization [65].

### 8.2.3.3 Folding and Stability of LHCII Monomers

The folding of LHCII requires the availability of Chls and Cars both in vitro [44] and in vivo [67], as shown by in vitro reconstitution and analysis of *Chlamydomonas* mutants blocked at specific steps of Car and Chl synthesis. Different aspects of the folding of LHCII complex have been analyzed using an integrated approach of molecular biology and in vitro reconstitution. In 1993, Paulsen and co-workers showed that the pigments drive the secondary structure formation of monomeric LHCII [68]. A first description of the folding kinetics of LHCII by time-resolved fluorescence spectroscopy showed two kinetic steps for the assembly of the pigment–protein complex [69], which are related to the binding of the pigments to the apoprotein [70,71]. An excess of Chl *a* increased the folding rate, but the complexes were less stable than the wild-type ones. Also the Cars play a role in the folding, and the presence of a high amount of L increases the folding rate. Interestingly, lowering the carotenoid concentration in the refolding mixture slowed down both the α-helix formation and the appearance of the Chl *b* to Chl *a* energy transfer, indicating that the two processes are strongly coupled [70].

Two typical thylakoid lipids, namely phosphatidyl glycerol and digalactosyldiacylglycerol, stabilize reconstituted LHCII against thermal denaturation [72]. Also the importance of the different protein domains and the pigment binding sites on the stability of LHCII has been investigated. Reconstitution in vitro showed that the entire hydrophilic N-terminus domain and part of the C-terminus domain are not needed for the formation of a stable pigment–protein complex [45,46]. The role of the hydrophilic loops connecting helices was investigated by random mutagenesis. The stromal loop turned out to be very important for Lhcb folding: four single point mutations in this loop completely disrupted the folding ability [73].

Exchanging the Chl binding ligands with residues that cannot coordinate Chls can also influence the protein stability. The denaturation temperature of LHCII is 73 °C [74]. At least two mutations can strongly lower this value: mutants at positions E180/R70, the residues forming a stabilizing ionic pair and binding Chl a1, and E139/R142, the ligand for Chl b5 [74]. From the crystal structure a structure-stabilizing function was proposed for the couple E65/R185, but in this case neither the single mutation of R185 [73] nor the double mutation [47,74] seems to affect the folding.

*8.2.3.4 Trimerization of LHCII*

Trimerization of LHCII in vivo requires the presence of phosphatidyl glycerol [75]. By step-wise deletion of amino acids at the N-terminus of LHCII it was shown that the sequence WYGPDR, 16 residues from the N-terminal end, is involved in trimer formation [58]. Interestingly, this domain is fully conserved in Lhcb5, which can form trimers in the absence of LHCII [76], although it is normally monomeric. Deletions at the C-terminus do not affect trimerization, but the exchange of W222 (within the C-terminal domain) by Gly or His does [77].

Trimerization studies have also been performed using mutant complexes in thylakoids [48]. No stable trimers were formed when the ligands of sites A4 and A5 had been mutated. All complexes for which the trimerization was affected were mutated in amino acids located in the B helix, which is probably involved in a special structural or kinetic role in trimer assembly. In addition, the carotenoid composition affected trimerization: In lut2 mutants lacking lutein, trimers are absent [78], as well as in the lut2 npq2 mutant having Z as the only xanthophyll [79], indicating that the presence of lutein is essential.

Finally, we mention that a heptameric association of LHCII trimers has been found in partially solubilized PSII membranes [80] and it has been postulated that these might also occur in vivo in the appressed regions of the grana (see, for example, [14]).

*8.2.4 LHCII Structure at 2.72 Å*

In 2004 the structure of LHCII was resolved at 2.72 Å by X-ray crystallography using 3D crystals [35]. The apoprotein is now completely traced from Ser 14 to Gly 231. While the overall structure is similar to that described previously [34], more details are available. For instance, a new $3_{10}$ helix was observed in the BC lumenal loop (Helix E). The monomeric subunits interact via the N- and C-terminal domains, the stromal end of the B helix and several residues of the C helix, in agreement with the mutagenesis data [58,77].

Fourteen Chls, four carotenoids and one lipid molecule (PG) are associated to each monomeric subunit. All 14 Chl ligands have been revealed: seven amino-acid side chains, two backbone carbonyls, four water molecules and the phosphodiester group of PG. Most of the Chls also form H-bonds with the -NH groups of the backbone through the C7-formyl group of Chl *b* and the C13-keto. The authors resolved the identity of the 14 Chls. The results are reported in Table 1. Moreover, the orientations of the Chls were determined.

In the new structure all four carotenoids per monomer are visible. The structure confirms the results from reconstitution experiments [51,52], indicating that the two Ls are located in the centre of the structure. The third tightly bound xanthophyll, the neoxanthin, is located near the C-helix, as suggested by mutation analysis, in a domain rich in Chls *b* [53]. This is in agreement with the biochemical and spectroscopic results discussed above [51,64,81]. Moreover, this xanthophyll makes an angle of 58° with the normal to the membrane plane vs. $57 \pm 1.5°$ determined by linear-dichroism measurements [53].

The fourth Car binding site, accommodating V and L (60:40%) under normal conditions and Z under stress conditions [36,41,42], seemed to be filled with an antheraxanthin molecule, but this site probably shows mixed occupancy in agreement with the biochemical data. This site is at the monomer–monomer interface, as previously suggested [36,42]. This is consistent with the site being empty in LHCII monomers [36].

Interestingly, the structure shows two Chl *a* molecules that are not in close contact with carotenoids, namely Chls 611 and 614. At first sight this seems puzzling because it suggests that 25% of the Chl *a* triplets can not be directly quenched by Cars, whereas T-S experiments show a triplet transfer efficiency from Chl *a* to Car of 100% at room temperature [93]. However, the modeling results that will be discussed below, and that are partly represented in the scheme in Figure 5 below, lead to the conclusion that the excitation population density on these two Chls is on average significantly lower than 25%. Therefore, it is expected that less than 25% of the triplets are formed on these Chls.

*8.2.4.1 Mixed Chl a/b Occupancy of Binding Sites*
There has been some controversy as to whether all Chl binding sites uniquely bind one type of Chl (*a* or *b*) or that some of them might bind both (so-called mixed binding sites). The existence of mixed binding sites is not questionable for recombinant proteins reconstituted in vitro. In fact, reconstitution of Lhcb1 with pigment mixtures having different Chl *a/b* ratios led to products with the same total number of Chls per protein but with different Chl *a/b* ratios [82,83]. Mutation analysis at the Chl binding sites indicates that in the monomeric WT complex with Chl a/b 1.4 at least three sites shows mixed occupancy [47,83]. The affinity of the individual binding sites for Chl *a* or Chl *b* was later tested by reconstituting LHCII mutants with different Chl *a/b* ratios [83]. Out of the 12 sites identified in [34], five showed almost complete selectivity for Chl *b*, one

preferentially bound Chl *b* and the other six, although showing higher affinity for Chl *a*, can also harbor Chl *b*. In [84] an opposite view was given, not admitting mixed occupancy of Chl binding sites. They suggested that the use of the same Chl *a*/*b* ratio as is present in native LHCII (1.35 for trimeric LHCII in pea) would lead to reconstituted LHCII with the same Chl distribution as in the native complex. However, their recombinant LHCII Chl *a*/*b* ratio of 1.08 is clearly different from the value of 1.35 reported for native trimers. This value of 1.08 cannot be explained when all binding sites harbor exclusively Chl *a* or Chl *b*. It remains an open question as to whether in vivo mixed binding sites are absent but in our opinion there is no physical reason why specific binding sites that have mixed occupancy in the reconstituted complexes would exclusively bind one type of pigment in vivo. Moreover, it was recently reported that overexpression of CAO (Chl a oxygenase) in tobacco plants yielded a strong increase in Chl *b* content, while only a small increase of Lhcb expression was observed, implying that, also in vivo, LHCII can bind more Chl *b* molecules [85].

The issue of the mixed binding sites has also been studied for CP29. It provides a simpler model with its six Chl *a* and two Chl *b* molecules per polypeptide [37]. In Section 8.3.3 we present evidence that mixed binding sites are present in CP29.

In the high-resolution structure of LHCII, binding sites were attributed to either Chl *a* or Chl *b* rather than to mixed sites and there is a clear discrepancy with the above-mentioned conclusions. However, the structure determination is based on fitting electronic density, and it appears that mixed occupancy decreases the density of individual co-factors, making the fitting more difficult. Very high-resolution crystal structures are awaited to solve the problem of mixed sites by structural methods. A related difficulty is the fitting of the chromophore in site V1. Because of its apparent asymmetry it was initially fitted as an antheraxanthin molecule, which is a very unlikely ligand for that site [36,42]. Indeed, the biochemical composition of the crystallization material indicated the presence of much more V (and lutein) than antheraxanthin and it was proposed by the authors that V most likely occupies the V1 site.

*8.2.5 Role of Carotenoids in LHCII*

The carotenoids in the antenna complexes have different functions: structure stabilization, energy transfer, and photoprotection via triplet and possibly singlet quenching.

*8.2.5.1 Structure Stabilization*
The involvement of Cars in structure stabilization was shown by reconstitution experiments in which it turned out to be impossible to fold the protein in the absence of Cars [44,68], though it is possible to refold Lhc monomers in vitro with only one Car located at the L1 site [86]. This latter complex is slightly less stable than the control complex with all Cars present but this can only be

STRUCTURE AND FUNCTION OF PHOTOSYSTEM II            345

discerned at high temperature. For LHCII, the occupancy of the N site does not add significantly to structure stabilization in vitro [51,74] or in vivo [87] and also the occupancy of the L2 site has a minor effect [74]. Violaxanthin can easily be removed from site V1 without affecting the stability of the trimers.

*8.2.5.2 Energy Transfer*
Cars absorb light in the blue–green region (350–550 nm), which enables them to act as light-harvesting pigments, provided that they are in close contact with Chls. The average efficiency of energy transfer from the different Cars to Chls in native trimeric LHCII was determined to be around 80% [36,88]. The efficiency is clearly higher for the 494 and 510 Cars (mainly L) than for N [38,64], indicating a secondary role for the latter in light-harvesting. In sharp contrast, no energy transfer could be detected from V [36]. The energy transfer pathway of Cars has been the object of recent studies using ultrafast spectroscopy. Conflicting results have been reported: Connelly at al. [89] proposed that Chl *b* is the first acceptor of excitation energy from the Cars. Peterman et al. [88] selectively/preferentially excited the 500 and 514 nm Cars (mainly L1 and L2) of trimeric LHCII and observed exclusive transfer towards Chl *a*. This result was later confirmed in a more elaborate study from the same laboratory, where it was also concluded that N transfers its energy almost exclusively towards Chl *b* [81]. Energy transfer from Cars to Chls was also studied in reconstituted complexes and it was found that the Cars transfer with a time constant of 60–100 fs to both Chl *a* and Chl *b* (L1 mainly to Chl *a*, L2 to both Chl *a* and *b* and N only to Chl *b*) [64]. It was concluded that the main pathway is from the Car $S_2$ state, *i.e.*, from the electronic state that is optically excited around 500 nm.

Fleming and co-workers [90], using two-photon excitation, determined that there is also very fast transfer from the lower-lying, dark $S_1$ state (300 fs), which can give rise to 30% of the transfer from the Cars to the Chls. The Chl–Car interaction that is responsible for the latter transfer may also lead to a shortening of the Chl excited-state lifetime and, thus, might play a regulatory role [50]. In summary, Ls transfer preferentially to Chls *a* with high efficiency, and N predominantly to Chl *b* with lower efficiency. Transfer from the $S_2$ state dominates but transfer from $S_1$ has also been observed [64,81].

*8.2.5.3 Photoprotection: Triplet Quenching*
Cars are involved in Chl triplet quenching and can also act as singlet oxygen scavengers, thereby protecting the system against oxidative damage [91]. The triplet transfer efficiency at room temperature is almost 100% [92,93]. The triplet transfer rate is higher than 500 $ps^{-1}$ [94], which is an order of magnitude faster than the rate of triplet formation, keeping the $^3$Chl population at a very low level.

T-S spectra obtained by magnetic resonance techniques at very low temperature (1.2 K) resolved different Car triplets with absorption maxima at 505 and 523 nm [95] and flash-induced T-S measurements gave similar results, also at higher temperatures [38,93,96]. Peterman et al. [38] showed that the 507 nm triplet band corresponds to the 494 nm singlet absorption band, which is now known to be associated with L1 (see above). The 525 nm triplet absorption was shown to correspond to a singlet absorption band near 510 nm, now known to be due to L2. In agreement with the results of van der Vos [97] they showed that the blue Car triplet (L1) leads to relatively red Chl *a* bleaching (presumably Chl a2) and the red Car triplet (L2) to relatively blue Chl *a* bleaching (presumably Chl a5). These results are in qualitative agreement with mutation analysis results, showing that Chl a2 absorbs more to the red than Chl a5 [47]. No substantial interactions could be detected between Ls and Chl *b* molecules. No triplets were detected on the neoxanthin, because this xanthophyll is located near Chl *b*. Strong interactions between N and Chl *b* molecules can be observed when comparing reconstituted complexes with and without N. The absence of N leads to remarkable changes in the Chl *b* $Q_y$ region as detected by absorption, CD, LD and Stark experiments [51,53,66].

Summarizing, triplets originate on Chl *a* molecules and are very rapidly transferred to both L molecules, the amount of transfer to N and V being extremely small if present at all. Photobleaching experiments on reconstituted monomeric complexes with differing carotenoid composition indicated that, unlike in trimers, only the L in site L1 is active in chlorophyll-triplet quenching and that N appears to act mainly in singlet oxygen scavenging [51,74].

*8.2.6 Spectroscopy of LHCII*

The most important function of LHCII is light harvesting: the absorption of light and excitation energy transfer (EET) towards the reaction center. Understanding light harvesting of LHCII requires detailed understanding of its steady-state and dynamic (energy transfer) spectroscopic properties. A few types of steady-state spectra are given in Figure 4. During the last 10–15 years numerous spectroscopic studies have been performed on different preparations of LHCII. Gradually, the theoretical modeling has also advanced to a level that will allow us in the near future to correlate in detail the LHCII structure to the spectroscopic data. Notably, several recent studies have compared the spectroscopic properties of Lhcb1, Lhcb2 and Lhcb3. Although there appear to be some small differences, the overall steady-state and time-resolved spectroscopic results are rather similar [39,98,99].

We start by summarizing several essential parameters that determine the steady-state and time-resolved spectroscopic properties and we focus on the $Q_y$ region (for more details see [50,100,101]). At room temperature the absorption spectrum shows a rather broad Chl *a* absorption band around 675 nm and a Chl *b* shoulder around 650 nm (Figure 4A) but at cryogenic temperatures a narrowing occurs and fine structure can be observed [102]. Excitonic interactions between nearby pigments range from several tens of $cm^{-1}$ to over 100 $cm^{-1}$ [35,50]. They lead to a splitting of absorption bands and at the same time excitations become delocalized over the interacting pigments. The fine structure that is observed in the cryogenic absorption spectra cannot entirely be explained by excitonic interactions [50]. Differences in the local environment for pigments at different positions in the protein also significantly contribute, and there is substantial variation in site energy. The coupling between the

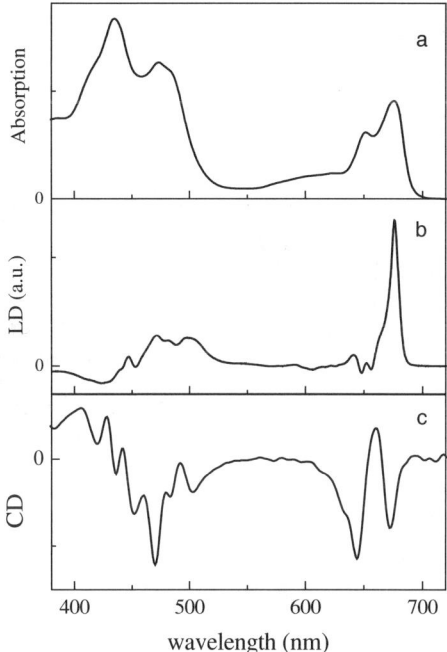

**Figure 4.** Steady-state spectra of native LHCII complex purified from *Zea mays*. (a) absorption spectrum at room temperature; (b) linear dichroism spectrum at 100 K, showing that the transition dipole moments corresponding to the red Chls a are oriented relatively parallel to the trimeric plane; similar spectra were amongst others used for modeling, leading to the results shown in Figure 5. Note also the small LD signals in the Car absorption region, reflecting the strongly tilted orientations of the Cars. (c) Circular dichroism spectrum at room temperature. These spectra reflect the presence of excitonic interactions between the pigments but, so far, a satisfactory model of these spectra has not been obtained.

electronic transitions and protein vibrations (phonons) leads to homogeneous broadening of the absorption bands, which tends to localize the excitations. At room temperature the amount of homogeneous broadening is of the order of 200 $cm^{-1}$. Together with the inhomogeneous broadening, which is typically of the order of 100 $cm^{-1}$, this causes relatively broad absorption bands, especially at room temperature [50].

The relative strength of the excitonic interactions compared with the amount of broadening and the variation in site energies is important for the mechanism of excitation energy transfer. Two extreme cases can be distinguished. If the excitonic coupling strength is weak as compared with the amount of broadening the Förster mechanism is applicable, meaning that excitations are essentially localized on individual pigments and hop from one to the other during the process of EET. Because the amount of broadening is relatively large, this mechanism has been applied in several studies to model EET in LHCII (see below). If, in contrast, the excitonic coupling strength substantially exceeds the

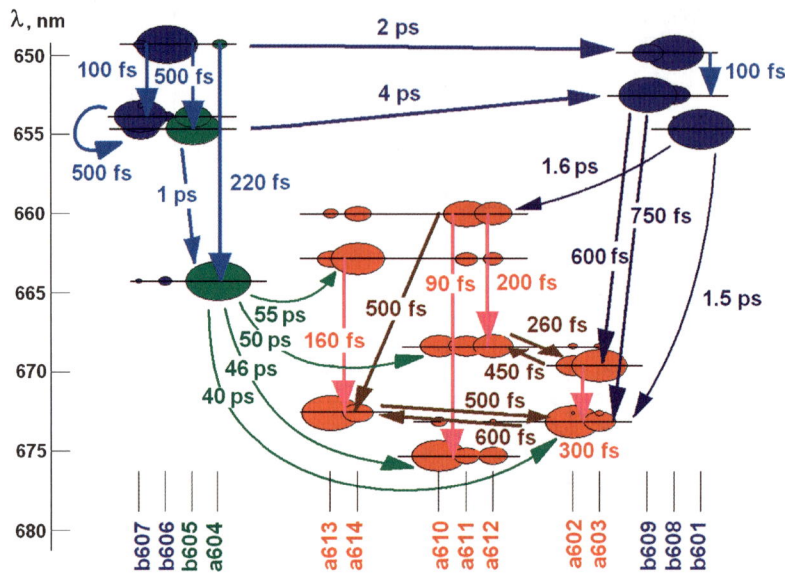

**Figure 5.** Calculated energy-level diagram and energy transfer scheme for a single monomeric LHCII complex (V.I. Novoderezhkin, M.A. Palacios, H. van Amerongen, and R. van Grondelle, unpublished results). The positions (wavelengths) of the 14 exciton levels are indicated along the vertical axis. The extent to which specific pigments contribute to these exciton states is indicated by ellipses, with the area proportional to the square of the wavefunction amplitude. Arrows indicate transfer (relaxation) from one state to the other and the accompanying time is the inverse of the transfer or relaxation rate. Note that the presented picture holds for one realization of the disorder, i.e., the site energies of the pigments can vary (inhomogeneous broadening) and the width of the distribution is approximately 100 cm$^{-1}$ (4.5 nm). This does not influence the overall picture to a large extent. Further details can be found in [124].

amount of broadening, the excitations become nearly completely delocalized over the interacting pigments, which then behave as one supermolecule. As briefly summarized below, the presence of excitonic interactions has been addressed in many studies and investigated with different techniques. In several studies the excitations seemed to be localized on individual pigments but evidence for delocalization was also obtained. As will be shown, a more extended theoretical approach using modified Redfield theory (Chapter 2) can largely explain these apparent discrepancies and it can describe many steady-state and time-resolved spectroscopic results on LHCII. Before going into more detail we first give an overview of ultrafast spectroscopic results on LHCII and then summarize the experimental results obtained on excitonic interactions.

### 8.2.6.1 Ultrafast Spectroscopy on LHCII

In the last decade various picosecond and femtosecond studies of the energy transfer processes in LHCII have been performed [103–111,64,81,89,101]. These studies revealed that Chl *b* to Chl *a* transfer takes place with two major time constants of ~300 and ~600 fs at 77 K, or ~150 and ~600 fs at room temperature, and a minor 4–9 ps component. These lifetimes are all associated with intra-monomer energy transfer steps [108].

Equilibration within the Chl $a$ manifold occurs to a large extent within a few hundred fs but upon blue side excitation slow (ranging from 3 to 17 ps) components are also observed [109,112]. Three-pulse photon echo peak shift (3PEPS) experiments on LHCII at room temperature have been performed using 650 (Chl $b$) and 670 (Chl $a$) nm excitation, respectively [110,111]. Where the pump–probe technique mainly monitors downhill ("interband") energy transfer, the three-pulse photon echo technique is more sensitive to intraband Chl $a$–Chl $a$ and Chl $b$–Chl $b$ transfer [113]. Both studies concluded that sub-ps Chl $b$-Chl $b$ transfer takes place. Contributions from Chl $a$-Chl $a$ equilibration were also identified occurring with time constants from 300 fs to 6 ps. A more elaborate description of the time-resolved measurements on LHCII is given in recent reviews: [20,50].

To understand EET in LHCII it is crucial to correlate these time-resolved measurements to the crystal structure with the use of theoretical modeling. It turns out that the "slow" ps energy transfer steps from relatively blue to relatively red Chls $a$ are particularly useful for assigning specific transfer steps (see below).

*8.2.6.2 Excitonic Interactions in LHCII*
From CD measurements [102,114,115], it was concluded earlier that excitonic interactions occur among the chlorophylls, but the size of the coupling strength was not determined. Krawczyk et al. [116] have measured the Stark spectrum of LHCII and concluded that excitonic interactions are present, although the Chl $a$ absorption bands, including the lowest-energy one, mostly appeared to behave like those of uncoupled Chls. This was confirmed in later Stark studies [65,66]. Several authors have addressed the issue concerning the number of Chl $a$ molecules that contribute to the fluorescence at 4.2 K. Peterman et al. [117] measured fluorescence line narrowing (FLN) at 4.2 K in LHCII. The FLN spectra showed vibronic features of at least two different Chl $a$ molecules. This led to the conclusion that the emitting state at that temperature is delocalized over at least two different Chl $a$ molecules or that emission arises from at least two independent molecules. Within the context of this model, because of the inhomogeneous spread in the site energies, 9–12 different Chl $a$ molecules per trimer have approximately equal probabilities to be the lowest-energy pigment, and the dipole strength of the lowest state is equal to that of monomeric Chl $a$ [117]. Studies by Schubert et al. [118] and Krikunova et al. [119] concluded that the dipole strength of the fluorescence emitting spectral form(s) in LHCII correspond to delocalized exciton states at room temperature. However, Palacios et al. [120] found that the dipole strength of the emitting species is only slightly higher than that of monomeric Chl $a$ both at room temperature (factor of 1.18) and at 7 K (factor of 1.14), indicating weak delocalization. Many spectroscopic properties of LHCII could be modeled in the same study by assuming that excitations corresponding to the lowest-energy transitions

were essentially localized on individual pigments. Pieper et al. [121] concluded from hole-burning experiments that the lowest-energy states had a dipole strength corresponding to ~0.8 chlorophyll *a* molecules. A two-pulse photon echo study [122] led to similar conclusions. T. Renger and May performed exciton calculations [123] and concluded that significant excitonic interactions must be present, and the dipole strength of the lowest state was estimated to be ~0.5. Therefore, no consensus was reached about the degree of delocalization and the dipole strength of the lowest excited state. Further analysis on LHCII mutants showed that at least one strong interaction was present in the complex between Chls in sites A2 and B2 [47].

*8.2.6.3 Detailed Modeling of Excitation Energy Transfer in LHCII*
Simultaneous modeling of the relation between structure, steady-state spectroscopy and ultrafast spectroscopy has been applied in many recent studies to obtain a picture of the flow of excitation energy in LHCII. Most of these studies applied Förster theory, assuming that hopping of localized excitations provides a reasonable approximation for the excitation dynamics. Here we restrict ourselves to three recent studies [101,111,124], in which excitonic interactions were also taken into account by applying Redfield and modified Redfield theory. In these papers, references can be found to earlier modeling studies.

In the first of these papers the 3PEPS and transient grating (TG) data of Salverda et al. [111] was analyzed using the Redfield relaxation theory on the basis of the exciton eigenstates, making use of the 1994 crystal structure [34]. In contrast to Förster theory, which describes the hopping of localized excitations from one pigment to another, Redfield theory also describes excitation transfer in the presence of excitations, which are delocalized over several pigments, due to strong excitonic interactions. A few configurations of the antenna were found [with specific chlorophyll (Chl) *a/b* identities, orientations and site energies] that allowed an explanation of the shape of the absorption and linear-dichroism spectra, the superradiance (SR) values, the transient absorption (TA), TG and 3PEPS kinetics at different excitation wavelengths. In the presented model the Chl *b* absorption region reflects localized monomer states and partially delocalized dimer states giving rise to an averaged delocalization length of individual exciton levels of 1.1–1.6. The individual exciton states in the Chl *a* region can be delocalized over 2–2.5 molecules (but see below). Owing to the non-parallel orientation of the monomeric dipoles, the dipole strength enhancement of an individual exciton state is smaller than the delocalization length. Thus a dipole strength of 1.5–2 (in units of monomeric dipole strength) was found for the second exciton level ($k=2$) in the Chl *a* band (starting to count from the low-energy side in the case of LHCII monomers). This agreed with the nonlinear absorption and nonlinear polarization data, suggesting the existence of one spectral form with a dipole strength of 2.3 [118]. Mixing of this superradiant state with the weaker lowest exciton states result in an SR value of 1–1.2, in agreement with the experimental data [120]. However, the description of EET was not entirely satisfactory and an improved description was obtained in a subsequent study [101] in which a modified Redfield approach was applied. This allows a much better quantitative explanation of the spectral shapes, including the phonon and vibronic wings, for (polarized) absorption and fluorescence, and at the same time a better reproduction of fast (femtosecond) interband (Chl $b$ to Chl $a$) energy transfer and slow (picosecond) intraband (blue Chl $a$ to red Chl a) equilibration. This study was also based on the 1994 crystal structure [34]. Satisfactory fits could not be obtained with the original assignment of the pigment identities [34], but with the use of mixed binding sites, as proposed by Remelli et al. [47], a much better description could be achieved.

Approximately the same exciton structure of the Chl $a$ clusters was obtained as in the preceding study but in the new modeling the dipole strength was distributed more uniformly over the various states, *i.e.*, there was no pronounced superradiance in any particular state. The thermally averaged superradiance was still in agreement with experiment [120]. As in the previous modeling it was found that a good quantitative fit of linear spectra does not guarantee that this model will explain the excitation energy kinetics.

Most recently, the same approach was used [124] to model steady-state spectra and energy-transfer dynamics in LHCII using the new crystal structure [35]. An exciton model of the LHCII trimer (with specific site energies) is proposed that allows a simultaneous quantitative fit of the absorption, linear-dichroism, steady-state fluorescence spectra, and transient absorption kinetics upon excitation at different wavelengths (Figure 5). In the modeling use is made of the experimental exciton–phonon spectral density and modified Redfield theory. It is found that fast Chl $b \rightarrow$ Chl $a$ transfer is determined by a good connection of the Chls $b$ to strongly coupled Chl $a$ clusters, *i.e.*, the $a610$-$a611$-$a612$ trimer (the nomenclature of the different Chls can be found in Table 1), and the $a602$-$a603$ and $a613$-$a614$ dimers. Long-lived components of the excitation energy transfer kinetics are determined by a quick population of redshifted Chl $b605$ and blue-shifted Chl $a604$ followed by a very slow (3 ps for $b605$ and 12 ps for $a604$) flow of energy from these monomeric "bottleneck" sites to the Chl $a$-clusters. The dynamics within the Chl $a$-region are determined by fast (with time constants down to sub-100 fs) exciton relaxation within the $a610$-$a611$-$a612$ trimer, slower 200–300 fs relaxation within the $a602$-$a603$ and $a613$-$a614$ dimers, even slower 300–800 fs migration between these clusters, and very slow transfer from $a604$ to the quasi-equilibrated $a$-sites. The final equilibrium is characterized by predominant population of the $a610$-$a611$-$a612$ cluster (mostly $a610$ site). The location of this cluster on the outer side of the LHCII trimer probably provides a good connection with the other subunits of PSII. The current modeling with state-of-the-art physical theory provides a rather good description of the steady-state and time-resolved spectroscopy of LHCII in terms of the new crystal structure. It is still an open question as to whether mixed binding sites exist (modeling with mixed binding sites can provide better fits). Moreover, there is still room for improvement of the modeling because, for instance, the simulated LD spectrum is approximately 60–70% of the size of the experimental one.

However, the overall picture is clear, excitations on the lumenal side of LHCII are transferred to the stromal side on a picosecond time scale, where they equilibrate on a subpicosecond time scale to end up preferentially on the outside of the trimer. This picture is essentially identical to that presented before, based on the old crystal structure [125].

*8.2.6.4 Singlet Excitation Energy Transfer within and between LHCII Trimers*
For the overall light-harvesting process it is important to study transfer between different light-harvesting complexes. The combination of EET in and between LHCs is crucial for the overall rate of charge separation in PSII. For PSII the so-called exciton/radical-pair equilibrium (ERPE) model [126,127] is generally applied, which assumes that charge separation is essentially trap-limited. This implies that EET throughout PSII and its antenna is so fast that the time it takes for an excitation to reach the RC is negligibly small when compared with the overall trapping time. However, singlet–singlet annihilation experiments on trimeric and aggregated LHCII provided evidence that the time of transfer to the RC cannot be neglected [128] and this has been discussed more elaborately in a review [20]. Briefly summarized, from the annihilation experiments it was concluded that the time of spatial equilibration in an LHCII trimer is close to 48 ps. For lamellar aggregates it was estimated that the time of equilibration over a number of $N$ trimers is approximately $N$ times 32 ps [128]. One might speculate that the relative increase of the rate of annihilation for aggregates occurs because excitations tend to localize at the periphery of the trimers (see above), thereby facilitating intertrimer transfer. It was pointed out in [50] that the relatively slow spatial equilibration time as determined by annihilation experiments is in qualitative agreement with the ps transient-absorption results on trimeric LHCII.

## 8.3 Minor Antenna Complexes of Photosystem II

The designation of minor antenna complexes of PSII is here used to indicate three monomeric pigment–protein complexes, which are present with a stoichiometry of one per PSII reaction centre and which together bind around 15% of the Chls in PSII. They are located between LHCII and the reaction centre (Figure 1) and share a high degree of sequence homology (Figure 2) with LHCII [129–131]. It has been proposed that these complexes play an important role in the regulation of the energy flow between the main antenna and the reaction centre [26]. Knowledge about these minor antenna complexes lags far behind that of LHCII. Below, we briefly summarize the biochemical and spectroscopic properties of each of these complexes. Although their intrinsic light-harvesting capability is minor, the fact that they are highly conserved in all plant species indicates that they fulfill other important roles. Clearly, further studies are needed to address these issues.

The structure of the minor antenna complexes has been modeled on the basis of the structure of LHCII and below we use the same nomenclature for the pigment binding sites.

### 8.3.1 CP24

CP24 is the product of the Lhcb6 nuclear gene. The primary sequence is 210 AA long. Compared with the other Lhc proteins, CP24 shows a shorter C-terminal domain and, therefore, does not contain the amphipathic helix D (Figure 2). Purification of this complex has always been quite problematic and different Chl $a/b$ ratios (from 0.9 to 1.6) have been reported, depending on plant material and purification procedures [25,37,132], suggesting that this protein is unstable and loses pigments once extracted from the membrane. This is possibly due to the lack of the D-helix, because its deletion from LHCII likewise reduces Chl binding [45,77]. In vitro reconstitution of CP24 in the presence of different Chl $a/b$ ratios showed that under most reconstitution conditions the complex maintains a ratio of 1.0, suggesting that this is the value for the complex in vivo [133]. This value is the lowest found for all Lhc complexes, in agreement with the fact that CP24 requires Chl $b$ for accumulation [134]. The total number of Chls bound per polypeptide in the reconstituted complex is ten, implying the binding of five Chls $a$ and five Chls $b$. Comparison of cDNA-deduced sequences shows that seven LHCII Chl binding residues are conserved in CP24, setting the lower limit of bound Chls to seven (Figure 2). Two xanthophylls per ten Chls are present. No N was found, whereas V and L are present in similar amounts [133]. Interestingly, CP24 appears to be the antenna complex with the highest affinity for V [135]. A supercomplex formed by CP29, CP24 and LHCII has been purified [136], indicating that CP24 is localized in the proximity of CP29.

### 8.3.2 CP26

CP26 is the product of the nuclear gene Lhcb5 and it is 247 AA long (Figure 2). This complex is present as a monomer in the thylakoid membrane, located between CP43 and one of the LHCII trimers [137]. The primary structure of this complex is highly homologous to that of LHCII, suggesting also similarity in folding. Biochemical analysis of this complex purified by IEF indicates that it binds nine Chls: six Chls $a$ and three Chls $b$ [42,138]. In vitro reconstitution of the complex confirms these values [139]. Purification of CP26 by chromatography produces a complex with a Chl $a/b$ ratio of 3.3 that binds only two Chls $b$ [140]. Still under debate is the Car binding for this complex. In the maize complexes, both native and reconstituted products bind two Car molecules per polypeptide, with similar amounts of L, N and V [40,138,139]. The native spinach complex was suggested to bind three xanthophylls on the basis of a Car/Chl ratio of 0.27 [42]. It was also suggested that CP26 does not contain a tightly bound V and that instead it is located at a peripheral site, as in LHCII [42]. These results are not in agreement with data obtained from the reconstitution experiments in which a stable CP26 complex was obtained with only V present as a Car, indicating relatively high affinity of the two central sites for this xanthophyll [141,142]. Although very similar in carotenoid composition, CP26 and CP29 differ with respect to their capacity of exchanging V and Z in site L2, the former showing by far the highest exchange rate [135]. This complex is proposed to be one of the principal sites of NPQ [26]. This was supported by the fact that protonation sites were found in this protein [143] and that CP26 like CP29 exhibits strong pH-induced fluorescence quenching in vitro [144]. However, this role was challenged by measurements on mutant plants lacking CP29 and CP26 [145], in which no changes in the capability to perform non photochemical quenching were observed.

Antisense plants without LHCII complexes were shown to contain CP26 in high amounts and CP26 was shown to form trimers that somehow replace LHCII [76].

### 8.3.3 CP29: A Model System

CP29 is the product of the nuclear gene Lhcb4 [146]. Its primary sequence is highly homologous to those of the other Lhc proteins, but shows an insertion of 42 amino acids at the N-terminus. CP29 has been purified by different methods [147–149] but all preparations show similar biochemical and spectroscopic characteristics, reflecting the stability of this complex. It binds eight Chls: six Chls $a$ and two Chls $b$.

Mutation analysis was used to determine the Chl binding sites in CP29 [86]. The eight Chls are accommodated in sites A1–A5, B3, B5 and B6. Mutation of the A1 ligand prevented reconstitution, supporting the view that the ligand for Chl a1 is involved in stabilization of the complex through an ion bridge like in LHCII [34]. For all other mutants it was possible to obtain stable reconstituted complexes with a decreased number of Chls per polypeptide. The central Chl-binding sites A1, A2, A4 and A5 were found to coordinate Chl $a$, but the peripheral sites A3, B3, B5 and B6 showed no strong preference for Chl $a$ or Chl $b$. This is in agreement with previous results on CP29 reconstituted with different Chl $a/b$ ratios, suggesting that CP29 can accommodate Chl $b$ in four sites [150].

The number of Cars per polypeptides is still unclear; it was reported to be two or three, depending on plant material, growth condition and purification methods [42,138]. CP29 binds L, N and V. Refolding studies in vitro show that the L1 site preferentially accommodates L, while the L2 site prefers V and N [59].

CP29 has been found to be reversibly phosphorylated under light stress conditions at the Thr site [151] in position 83, which is part of the 42 AA insertion typical of CP29. This is a so-called CK2 site where phosphorylation by kinase 2 is supposed to take place. The phosphorylation is regulated by the reduction state of the plastoquinone pool [152] and induces conformational changes, which can be monitored via the spectroscopic properties of the complex [153]. Plants that are resistant to cold and light stress show a higher degree of phosphorylation than sensitive plants. A second phosphorylation site was found at the acetylated N-terminus [154].

The ion $Ca^{2+}$ binds to the hydrophobic lumenal domain of the C helix and the hydrophilic loop at glutamic acid E166 [155]. The same glutamic acid was proposed to play also a role in the dissipation of excess excitation energy by inhibiting the nonphotochemical quenching via a protonation-induced conformational change [156].

### 8.3.3.1 Steady-State and Time-Resolved Spectroscopy

Spectroscopic characterization of native and reconstituted CP29 has been the subject of several studies [157–159,150,153]. The relatively low number of pigments makes CP29 a suitable model system for plant light-harvesting complexes. The $Q_y$ region shows several absorption bands. Two bands are present in the Chl $b$ $Q_y$ region with peaks at 640 and 650 nm [153,159]. In the Chl $a$ region most absorption is associated with a band around 676 nm, with asymmetric broadening towards the blue, indicating the presence of a spectral form near 670 nm [153,159]. The low-energy side of the main absorption band has been characterized by hole-burning spectroscopy at 4.2 K [160]. A band was resolved at 678.2 nm, having a width of 130 cm$^{-1}$. This spectral form is close to that of a monomeric Chl $a$ molecule [160,161], suggesting the absence of strong excitonic interactions. The absorption is presumably associated with Chl a2 [86]. For all mutants but one (E166V), only one Chl was missing, and the resulting absorption difference spectrum again did not indicate the presence of strong excitonic interactions [86], in line with the results on recombinant CP29 reconstituted with different Chl $a/b$ ratios [150]. These results seemed at first somewhat surprising, given the relatively tight packing of the Chls, but in fact the situation is quite similar to that for LHCII (see above). Voigt et al. concluded from nonlinear polarization spectroscopy measurements in the frequency domain that pronounced excitonic interactions exist between Chl $a$ and Chl $b$ molecules that are responsible for the 640 and 670 nm forms [161]. Of the seven coupled Chl pairs in LHCII [35] two seem to be conserved in CP29: A5-B5 and A3-B3. The A5-B5 couple cannot be responsible for the 640–670 nm interaction because mutant A5 looses one Chl $a$ molecule absorbing at 676 nm, and no change in the Chl $b$ absorption region is observed. The 640 nm band corresponds to Chls at mixed sites A3 and B3 [86]. Therefore, the A3-B3 pair seems to be responsible for the relatively strong 640–670 interaction.

Several studies have addressed EET in CP29. The first pump–probe study showed the presence of two Chl $b$ to Chl $a$ energy transfer times: 350 fs and 2.2 ps. The first time corresponds to transfer from a "blue" Chl $b$ (640 nm) to a "red" Chl $a$ (681 nm), whereas the 2.2 ps signal corresponds to the transfer from a "red" Chl $b$ (650 nm) to a "blue" Chl $a$ (675 nm). Equilibration between Chl $a$ molecules occurs with time constants of 280 fs and 10–13 ps [162].

In a more elaborate study with improved time resolution, Gradinaru et al. [81] observed 220 fs and 2 ps transfer times from Chl $b$-640 nm. The main transfer from the 652-nm Chl $b$ occurred with a 2.2 ps time constant and additional transfer steps from both Chl $b$ forms were detected with a time constant of $\sim 10$ ps. Using 3PEPS and TG, Salverda et al. [111] observed two Chl $b$ to Chl $a$ energy transfer times for the 650-nm Chl $b$, namely 130 fs and 2.2 ps, and two Chl $b$–Chl $b$ energy transfers steps of 380 fs and 3 ps, indicating the presence of at least two mixed sites in native CP29. Similar results were obtained from TA measurements on native and recombinant CP29 by Croce et al. [163]. At room temperature, three lifetimes were identified for Chl $b$-652 to Chl $a$ energy transfer: 150 fs, 1.2 ps and 5–6 ps, and at least one for Chl $b$-640 nm to Chl $a$ in 600–800 fs, in both samples, indicating that the pigment organization in the native and recombinant CP29 is identical and that mixed binding sites are present.

Förster transfer calculations have been performed by Cinque et al. [164] using the distances between the chromophores from the LHCII structure, which are supposed to be similar to those of CP29 given the high sequence homology. Absorption spectra were determined separately from mutation analysis (see above) and from these the fluorescence spectra were also deduced. LD spectra of the mutants were used to estimate the orientations of the transition dipole moments of the different Chls [165]. A kinetic scheme for the energy transfer pathway was thus proposed [164] and the simulated transient absorption spectra appeared to be in good agreement with the empirical results. Within a few picoseconds, most of the excitations are located on the stromal side of the complex, as for LHCII (see above).

Car to Chl energy transfer has been studied by Gradinaru et al. [81] and by Croce et al. [166] by TA spectroscopy, at 77 K and room temperature, respectively. Gradinaru et al. observed that most of the energy is transferred from the carotenoid $S_2$ state to Chl $a$ in 70–90 fs, and a second transfer time of 1 ps was interpreted as originating from the $S_1$ state of the L. By comparing the results of WT recombinant CP29 with the data obtained on a mutant in which only the L1 site was occupied, Croce et al. concluded that the L in the L1 site transfers to Chl $a$ molecules (mainly Chl a2) from the $S_2$ state in 90–130 fs, from a high vibronic $S_1$ state in about 800 fs and from the relaxed $S_1$ state in 11 ps. From site L2, V and N were observed to transfer energy from the $S_2$ state to both Chl $a$ (A5) and Chl $b$ (B6) in 80 fs, and also a minor transfer component from the $S_1$ state was observed.

## 8.4 Conclusions and Future Perspectives

In summary, many of the aspects of light harvesting and triplet quenching of LHCII and CP29 have been revealed in relatively great detail and can to a large extent be related to their structures. As was pointed out, however, some specific details need clarification. So far, CP26 and CP24 have been studied far less extensively. The specific role(s) of all individual complexes is (are) still under investigation, and it also needs to be determined how the complexes interact and cooperate, to get a good understanding of the overall functioning of Photosystem II. For instance, understanding their involvement in nonphotochemical quenching and revealing the mechanism of energy dissipation are major goals for scientific research on the outer antenna in the near future.

## Acknowledgements

We thank Drs G. Garab and G. Renger for critically reading the manuscript and giving many helpful suggestions. We are indebted to Dr S. Caffarri for

Figures 2 and 3, Dr J. P. Dekker for Figure 1 and Dr V. Novoderezhkin for Figure 5.

## Note Added in Proof

After this chapter was finished, the crystal structure of LHCII was published at 2.5 Å resolution: A. Standfuss, C. Van Scheltinga, M. Lamborghini, and W. Kühlbrandt (2005) *EMBO J.* **24**, 919-928. No essential differences or improvements with respect to the structure of Liu et al.(2004) were obtained.

## References

1. D.G. Durnford, J.A. Deane, S. Tan, G.I. McFadden, E. Gantt, B.R. Green, A phylogenetic assessment of the eukaryotic light-harvesting antenna proteins, with implications for plastid evolution. *J. Mol. Evol.* **48** (1999) 59–68.
2. B.R. Green, The evolution of light-harvesting antennas, in: *Light-harvesting antennas in photosynthesis* (2003) (B.R. Green and W.W. Parson, eds.), Kluwer Academic Publishers, (Dordrecht/Boston/London), pp. 129–168.
3. B.R. Green, D.G. Durnford, The chlorophyll-carotenoid proteins of oxygenic photosynthesis. *Annu. Rev. Plant Physiol. Plant Mol. Biol.* **47** (1996) 685–714.
4. S. Jansson, A guide to the Lhc genes and their relatives in Arabidopsis. *Trends Plant Sci.* **4** (1999) 236–240.
5. J.F. Allen, J. Forsberg, Molecular recognition in thylakoid structure and function. *Trends Plant Sci.* **6** (2001) 317–326.
6. E.M. Aro, I. Ohad, Redox regulation of thylakoid protein phosphorylation. *Antioxid. Redox Signal.* **5** (2003) 55–67.
7. T.S. Takeuchi, J.P. Thornber, Heat-induced alterations in thylakoid membrane-protein composition in barley. *Aust. J. Plant Physiol.* **21** (1994) 759–770.
8. V. Barzda, A. Istokovics, I. Simidjiev, G. Garab, Structural flexibility of chiral macroaggregates of light-harvesting chlorophyll a/b pigment–protein complexes. Light-induced reversible structural changes associated with energy dissipation. *Biochemistry* **35** (1996) 8981–8985.
9. Z. Cseh, S. Rajagopal, T. Tsonev, M. Busheva, E. Papp, G. Garab, Thermooptic effect in chloroplast thylakoid membranes. Thermal and light stability of pigment arrays with different levels of structural complexity. *Biochemistry* **39** (2000) 15250–15257.
10. J.P. Thornber, Chlorophyll-proteins: Light-harvesting and reaction center components of plants. *Annu. Rev. Plant Physiol.* **26** (1975) 1–2.
11. C.J. Arntzen, P.A. Armond, J.-M. Briantais, J.J. Burke, W.P. Novitzky, Dynamic interactions among structural components of the chloroplast membrane. *Brookhaven Symp. Biol.* **28** (1977) 316–337.
12. J. Barber, Influence of surface charges on thylakoid structure and function. *Annu. Rev. Plant Physiol.* **33** (1982) 261–295.
13. G. Garab, L. Mustardy, Role of LHCII-containing macrodomains in the structure, function and dynamics of grana. *Aust. J. Plant Physiol.* **26** (1999) 649–658.
14. J.P. Dekker, E.J. Boekema, Supramolecular organization of thylakoid membrane proteins in green plants. *Biochim. Biophys. Acta* **1706** (2005) 12–39.

15. M. Wentworth, A.V. Ruban, P. Horton, Chlorophyll fluorescence quenching in isolated light harvesting complexes induced by zeaxanthin. *FEBS Lett.* **471** (2000) 71–74.
16. A.G. Dobrikova, Z. Varkonyi, S.B. Krumova, L. Kovacs, G.K. Kostov, S.J. Todinova, M.C. Busheva, S.G. Taneva, G. Garab, Structural rearrangements in chloroplast thylakoid membranes revealed by differential scanning calorimetry and circular dichroism spectroscopy. Thermo-optic effect. *Biochemistry* **42** (2003) 11272–11280.
17. D.-H. Yang, H. Paulsen, B. Andersson, The N-terminal domain of the light-harvesting chlorophyll a/b-binding protein complex (LHCII) is essential for its acclimative proteolysis. *FEBS Lett.* **466** (2000) 385–388.
18. E.J. Boekema, B. Hankamer, D. Bald, J. Kruip, J. Nield, A.F. Boonstra, J. Barber, M. Rögner, Supramolecular structure of the photosystem II complex from green plants and cyanobacteria. *Proc. Natl. Acad. Sci. U.S.A.* **92** (1995) 175–179.
19. E.J. Boekema, P.E. Jensen, E. Schlodder, J.F. van Breemen, H. van Roon, H.V. Scheller, J.P. Dekker, Green plant photosystem I binds light-harvesting complex I on one side of the complex. *Biochemistry* **40** (2001) 1029–1036.
20. H. Van Amerongen and J.P. Dekker, in: *Light-harvesting antennas in photosynthesis* (2003) (B.R. Green and W.W. Parson, eds.), Kluwer Academic Publishers, (Dordrecht/Boston/London), pp. 219–251.
21. F.-A. Wollman, L. Minai, R. Nechushtai, The biogenesis and assembly of photosynthetic proteins in thylakoid membranes. *Biochim. Biophys. Acta* **1411** (1999) 21–85.
22. J.K. Hoober, L.L. Eggink, Assembly of light-harvesting complex II and biogenesis of thylakoid membranes in chloroplasts. *Photosynth. Res.* **61** (2000) 197–215.
23. H. Paulsen, Chlorophyll a/b-binding proteins. *Photochem. Photobiol.* **62** (1995) 367–382.
24. H. Paulsen, Pigment ligation to proteins of the photosynthetic apparatus in higher plants. *Physiol. Plant.* **100** (1997) 760–768.
25. R. Bassi, D. Sandona, R. Croce, Novel aspects of chlorophyll a/b-binding proteins. *Physiol. Plant.* **100** (1997) 769–779.
26. R. Bassi, S. Caffarri, Lhc proteins and the regulation of photosynthetic light harvesting function by xanthophylls. *Photosynth. Res.* **64** (2000) 243–256.
27. T. Morosinotto, S. Caffarri, L. Dall'Osto, R. Bassi, Mechanistic aspects of the xanthophyll dynamics in higher plant thylakoids. *Physiol. Plantarum* **119** (2003) 347–354.
28. P. Horton, A.V. Ruban, Molecular design of the photosystem II light-harvesting antenna: Photosynthesis and photoprotection. *JOURNAL OF EXPERIMENTAL BOTONY* **56** (2005) 365–373.
29. C. De Luca, C. Varotto, I. Svendsen, P.P. De Laureto, R. Bassi, Multiple light-harvesting II polypeptides from maize mesophyll chloroplasts are distinct gene products. *J. Photochem. Photobiol. B* **49** (1999) 50–60.
30. M. Hippler, J. Klein, A. Fink, T. Allinger, P. Hoerth, Towards functional proteomics of membrane protein complexes: analysis of thylakoid membranes from Chlamydomonas reinhardtii. *Plant J.* **28** (2001) 595–606.
31. H. Michel, D.F. Hunt, J. Shabanowitz, J. Bennett, Tandem mass-spectrometry reveals that 3 photosystem-Ii proteins of spinach-chloroplasts contain N-acetyl-O-phosphothreonine at their Nh2 termini. *J. Biol. Chem.* **263** (1988) 1123–1130.
32. O. Machold, The structure of light-harvesting complex-II as deduced from its polypeptide composition and stoichiometry. 1. Studies with Vicia-faba. *J. Plant Physiol.* **138** (1991) 678–684.

33. R. Bassi, F. Rigoni, G.M. Giacometti, Chlorophyll binding proteins with antenna function in higher plants and green algae. *Photochem. Photobiol.* **52** (1990) 1187–1206.
34. W. Kühlbrandt, D.N. Wang, Y. Fujiyoshi, Atomic model of plant light-harvesting complex by electron crystallography. *Nature* **367** (1994) 614–621.
35. Z. Liu, H. Yan, K. Wang, T. Kuang, J. Zhang, L. Gui, X. An, W. Chang, Crystal structure of spinach major light-harvesting complex at 2.72 A resolution. *Nature* **428** (2004) 287–292.
36. S. Caffarri, R. Croce, J. Breton, R. Bassi, The major antenna complex of photosystem II has a xanthophyll binding site not involved in light harvesting. *J. Biol. Chem.* **276** (2001) 35924–35933.
37. P. Dainese, R. Bassi, Subunit stoichiometry of the chloroplast photosystem-II antenna system and aggregation state of the component chlorophyll-a/b binding proteins. *J. Biol. Chem.* **266** (1991) 8136–8142.
38. E.J.G. Peterman, C.C. Gradinaru, F. Calkoen, J.C. Borst, R. van Grondelle, H. van Amerongen, Xanthophylls in light-harvesting complex II of higher plants: Light harvesting and triplet quenching. *Biochemistry* **36** (1997) 12208–12215.
39. S. Caffarri, R. Croce, L. Cattivelli, R. Bassi, A look within LHCII: Differential analysis of the Lhcb 1-3complexes building the major trimeric antenna complex of higher plant photosynthesis. *Biochemistry* **43** (2004) 9467–9476.
40. R. Bassi, B. Pineau, P. Dainese, J. Marquardt, Carotenoid-binding proteins of photosystem-II. *Eur. J. Biochem.* **212** (1993) 297–303.
41. A.V. Ruban, A.J. Young, A.A. Pascal, P. Horton, The effects of illumination on the xanthophyll composition of the photosystem II light-harvesting complexes of spinach thylakoid membranes. *Plant Physiol.* **104** (1994) 227–234.
42. A.V. Ruban, P.J. Lee, M. Wentworth, A.J. Young, P. Horton, Determination of the stoichiometry and strength of binding of xanthophylls to the photosystem II light harvesting complexes. *J. Biol. Chem.* **274** (1999) 10458–10465.
43. J.P. Thornber, R.P.F. Gregory, C.A. Smith, J.L. Bailey, Studies on the nature of chloroplast lamella.1. Preparation and some properties of two chlorophyll-protein complexes. *Biochemistry* **6** (1967) 391–396.
44. F.G. Plumley, G.W. Schmidt, Reconstitution of chloroform a/b light-harvesting complexes: Xanthophyll-dependent assembley and energy transfer. *Proc. Natl. Acad. Sci. U.S.A.* **84** (1987) 146–150.
45. K.V. Cammarata, G.W. Schmidt, In vitro reconstitution of a light-harvesting gene product: Deletion mutagenesis and analyses of pigment binding. *Biochemistry* **31** (1992) 2779–2789.
46. H. Paulsen, S. Hobe, Pigment binding properties of mutant light-harvesting chlorophyll-a/b-binding protein. *Eur. J. Biochem.* **205** (1992) 71–76.
47. R. Remelli, C. Varotto, D. Sandona, R. Croce, R. Bassi, Chlorophyll binding to monomeric light-harvesting complex. A mutation analysis of chromophore-binding residues. *J. Biol. Chem.* **274** (1999) 33510–33521.
48. C.H. Yang, K. Kosemund, C. Cornet, H. Paulsen, Exchange of pigment-binding amino acids in light-harvesting chlorophyll a/b protein. *Biochemistry* **38** (1999) 16205–16213.
49. H. Rogl, W. Kuhlbrandt, Mutant trimers of light-harvesting complex II exhibit altered pigment content and spectroscopic features. *Biochemistry* **38** (1999) 16214–16222.
50. H. van Amerongen, R. van Grondelle, Understanding the energy transfer function of LHCII, the major light-harvesting complex of green plants. *J. Phys. Chem. B* **105** (2001) 604–617.

51. R. Croce, S. Weiss, R. Bassi, Carotenoid-binding sites of the major light-harvesting complex II of higher plants. *J. Biol. Chem.* **274** (1999) 29613–29623.
52. S. Hobe, H. Niemeier, A. Bender, H. Paulsen, Carotenoid binding sites in LHCIIb - Relative affinities towards major xanthophylls of higher plants. *Eur. J. Biochem.* **267** (2000) 616–624.
53. R. Croce, R. Remelli, C. Varotto, J. Breton, R. Bassi, The neoxanthin binding site of the major light harvesting complex (LHC II) from higher plants. *FEBS Lett.* **456** (1999) 1–6.
54. A.V. Ruban, P. Horton, The xanthophyll cycle modulates the kinetics of nonphotochemical energy dissipation in isolated light-harvesting complexes, intact chloroplasts, and leaves of spinach. *Plant Physiol.* **119** (1999) 531–542.
55. A.S. Verhoeven, W.W. Adams, B. Demmig-Adams, R. Croce, R. Bassi, Xanthophyll cycle pigment localization and dynamics during exposure to low temperatures and light stress in Vinca major. *Plant Physiol.* **120** (1999) 727–737.
56. D. Latowski, H.E. Akerlund, K. Strzalka, Violaxanthin de-epoxidase, the xanthophyll cycle enzyme, requires lipid inverted hexagonal structures for its activity. *Biochemistry* **43** (2004) 4417–4420.
57. E. Pichersky and S. Jansson, The light-harvesting chlorophyll a/b polypeptides and their genes in angiosperm and gymnosperm species, in: *Oxygenic Photosyenthesis: The Light Reactions* (1996) (D.R. Ort and C.F. Yocum, eds.), Kluwer Academic Publishers, (Dordrecht/Boston/London), pp. 507–521.
58. S. Hobe, R. Förster, J. Klingler, H. Paulsen, N-proximal sequence motif in light-harvesting chlorophyll a/b-binding protein is essential for the trimerization of light-harvesting chlorophyll a/b complex. *Biochemistry* **34** (1995) 10224–10228.
59. M. Gastaldelli, G. Canino, R. Croce, R. Bassi, Xanthophyll binding sites of the CP29 (Lhcb4) subunit of higher plant photosystem II investigated by domain swapping and mutation analysis. *J. Biol. Chem.* **278** (2003) 19190–19198.
60. P.O. Andersson, T. Gillbro, L. Ferguson, R.J. Cogdell, Absorption spectral shifts of carotenoids related to medium polarizability. *Photochem. Photobiol.* **54** (1991) 353–360.
61. A.V. Ruban, A.A. Pascal, B. Robert, Xanthophylls of the major photosynthetic light-harvesting complex of plants: Identification, conformation and dynamics. *FEBS Lett.* **477** (2000) 181–185.
62. A.V. Ruban, A.A. Pascal, B. Robert, P. Horton, Configuration and dynamics of xanthophylls in light-harvesting antennae of higher plants. Spectroscopic analysis of isolated light-harvesting complex of photosystem II and thylakoid membranes. *J. Biol. Chem.* **276** (2001) 24862–24870.
63. S.S. Lampoura, V. Barzda, G.M. Owen, A.J. Hoff, H. Van Amerongen, Aggregation of LHCII leads to a redistribution of the triplets over the central xanthophylls in LHCII. *Biochemistry* **41** (2002) 9139–9144.
64. R. Croce, M.G. Muller, R. Bassi, A.R. Holzwarth, Carotenoid-to-chlorophyll energy transfer in recombinant major light-harvesting complex (LHCII) of higher plants. I. Femtosecond transient absorption measurements. *Biophys. J.* **80** (2001) 901–915.
65. M.A. Palacios, R.N. Frese, C.C. Gradinaru, I.H. van Stokkum, L.L. Premvardhan, P. Horton, A.V. Ruban, R. van Grondelle, H. Van Amerongen, Stark spectroscopy of the light-harvesting complex II in different oligomerisation states. *Biochim. Biophys. Acta* **1605** (2003) 83–95.
66. M.A. Palacios, S. Caffarri, R. Bassi, R. van Grondelle, H. van Amerongen, Stark effect measurements on monomers and trimers of reconstituted light-harvesting complex II of plants. *Biochim. Biophys. Acta* **1656** (2004) 177–188.

67. D.L. Herrin, J.F. Battey, K. Greer, G.W. Schmidt, Regulation of chlorophyll apoprotein expression and accumulation - Requirements for carotenoids and chlorophyll. *J. Biol. Chem.* **267** (1992) 8260–8269.
68. H. Paulsen, B. Finkenzeller, N. Kuhlein, Pigments induce folding of light-harvesting chlorophyll alpha/beta-binding protein. *Eur. J. Biochem.* **215** (1993) 809–816.
69. P.J. Booth, H. Paulsen, Assembly of light-harvesting chlorophyll a/b complex in vitro. Time-resolved fluorescence measurements. *Biochemistry* **35** (1996) 5103–5108.
70. R. Horn, H. Paulsen, Folding in vitro of light-harvesting chlorophyll a/b protein is coupled with pigment binding. *J. Mol. Biol.* **318** (2002) 547–556.
71. D. Reinsberg, K. Ottmann, P.J. Booth, H. Paulsen, Effects of chlorophyll a, chlorophyll b, and xanthophylls on the in vitro assembly kinetics of the major light-harvesting chlorophyll a/b complex, LHCIIb. *J. Mol. Biol.* **308** (2001) 59–67.
72. D. Reinsberg, P.J. Booth, C. Jegerschold, B.J. Khoo, H. Paulsen, Folding, assembly, and stability of the major light-harvesting complex of higher plants, LHCII, in the presence of native lipids. *Biochemistry* **39** (2000) 14305–14313.
73. B. Heinemann, H. Paulsen, Random mutations directed to transmembrane and loop domains of the light-harvesting chlorophyll a/b protein: Impact on pigment binding. *Biochemistry* **38** (1999) 14088–14093.
74. E. Formaggio, G. Cinque, R. Bassi, Functional architecture of the major light-harvesting complex from higher plants. *J. Mol. Biol.* **314** (2001) 1157–1166.
75. S. Nussberger, J.P. Dekker, W. Kühlbrandt, B.M. van Bolhuis, R. van Grondelle, H. van Amerongen, Spectroscopic characterization of three different monomeric forms of the main chlorophyll a/b binding protein from chloroplast membranes. *Biochemistry* **33** (1994) 14775–14783.
76. A.V. Ruban, M. Wentworth, A.E. Yakushevska, J. Andersson, P.J. Lee, W. Keegstra, J.P. Dekker, E.J. Boekema, S. Jansson, P. Horton, Plants lacking the main light-harvesting complex retain photosystem II macro-organization. *Nature* **421** (2003) 648–652.
77. A. Kuttkat, A. Hartmann, S. Hobe, H. Paulsen, The C-terminal domain of light-harvesting chlorophyll-a/b-bindiX protein is involved in the stabilisation of trimeric light-harvesting complex. *Eur. J. Biochem.* **242** (1996) 288–292.
78. B.J. Pogson, K.K. Niyogi, O. Björkman, D. DellaPenna, Altered xanthophyll compositions adversely affect chlorophyll accumulation and nonphotochemical quenching in Arabidopsis mutants. *Proc. Natl. Acad. Sci. U.S.A.* **95** (1998) 13324–13329.
79. M. Havaux, L. Dall'Osto, S. Cuine, G. Giuliano, R. Bassi, The effect of zeaxanthin as the only xanthophyll on the structure and function of the photosynthetic apparatus in Arabidopsis thaliana. *J. Biol. Chem.* **279** (2004) 13878–13888.
80. J.P. Dekker, H. van Roon, E.J. Boekema, Heptameric association of light-harvesting complex II trimers in partially solubilized photosystem II membranes. *FEBS Lett.* **449** (1999) 211–214.
81. C.C. Gradinaru, I.H.M. van Stokkum, A.A. Pascal, R. van Grondelle, H. van Amerongen, Identifying the pathways of energy transfer between carotenoids and chlorophylls in LHCII and CP29. A multicolor, femtosecond pump - probe study. *J. Phys. Chem. B* **104** (2000) 9330–9342.
82. F.J. Kleima, S. Hobe, F. Calkoen, M.L. Urbanus, E.J.G. Peterman, R. van Grondelle, H. Paulsen, H. van Amerongen, Decreasing the chlorophyll a/b ratio in reconstituted LHCII: Structural and functional consequences. *Biochemistry* **38** (1999) 6587–6596.

83. S. Hobe, H. Fey, H. Rogl, H. Paulsen, Determination of relative chlorophyll binding affinities in the major light-harvesting chlorophyll a/b complex. *J. Biol. Chem.* **278** (2003) 5912–5919.
84. H. Rogl, R. Schodel, H. Lokstein, W. Kuhlbrandt, A. Schubert, Assignment of spectral substructures to pigment-binding sites in higher plant light-harvesting complex LHC-II. *Biochemistry* **41** (2002) 2281–2287.
85. G.K. Pattanayak, A.K. Biswal, V.S. Reddy, B.C. Tripathy, Light-dependent regulation of chlorophyll b biosynthesis in chlorophyllide a oxygenase overexpressing tobacco plants. *Biochem. Biophys. Res. Commun.* **326** (2005) 466–471.
86. R. Bassi, R. Croce, D. Cugini, D. Sandona, Mutational analysis of a higher plant antenna protein provides identification of chromophores bound into multiple sites. *Proc. Natl. Acad. Sci. U.S.A.* **96** (1999) 10056–10061.
87. J.P. Connelly, M.G. Müller, R. Bassi, R. Croce, A.R. Holzwarth, Femtosecond transient absorption study of carotenoid to chlorophyll energy transfer in the light harvesting complex II of photosystem II. *Biochemistry* **36** (1997) 281–287.
88. E.J.G. Peterman, R. Monshouwer, I.H.M. van Stokkum, R. van Grondelle, H. van Amerongen, Ultrafast singlet excitation transfer from carotenoids to chlorophylls via different pathways in light-harvesting complex II of higher plants. *Chem. Phys. Lett.* **264** (1997) 279–284.
89. J.P. Connelly, M.G. Müller, M. Hucke, G. Gatzen, C.W. Mullineaux, A.V. Ruban, P. Horton, A.R. Holzwarth, Ultrafast spectroscopy of trimeric light harvesting complex II from higher plants. *J. Phys. Chem. B* **101** (1997) 1902–1909.
90. P.J. Walla, J. Yom, B.P. Krueger, G.R. Fleming, Two-photon excitation spectrum of light-harvesting complex II and fluorescence upconversion after one- and two-photon excitation of the carotenoids. *J. Phys. Chem. B* **104** (2000) 4799–4806.
91. D. Siefermann-Harms, The light-harvesting and protective functions of carotenoids in photosynthetic membranes. *Physiol. Plant.* **69** (1987) 561–568.
92. R. Nechushtai, J.P. Thornber, L.K. Patterson, R.W. Fessenden, H. Levanon, Photosensitization of triplet carotenoid in photosynthetic light-harvesting complex of photosystem-Ii. *J. Phys. Chem.* **92** (1988) 1165–1168.
93. E.J. Peterman, F.M. Dukker, R. van Grondelle, H. van Amerongen, Chlorophyll a and carotenoid triplet states in light-harvesting complex II of higher plants. *Biophys. J.* **69** (1995) 2670–2678.
94. R. Schodel, K.D. Irrgang, J. Voigt, G. Renger, Quenching of chlorophyll fluorescence by triplets in solubilized light-harvesting complex II (LHCII). *Biophys. J.* **76** (1999) 2238–2248.
95. R. van der Vos, E.M. Franken, A.J. Hoff, ADMR study of the effect of oligomerisation on the carotenoid triplets and on triplet–triplet transfer in light-harvesting complex II (LHCII) of spinach. *Biochim. Biophys. Acta Bioenerg.* **1188** (1994) 243–250.
96. K.R. Naqvi, T. Javorfi, T.B. Melo, G. Garab, More on the catalysis of internal conversion in chlorophyll a by an adjacent carotenoid in light-harvesting complex (Ch1a/b LHCII) of higher plants: Time-resolved triplet-minus-singlet spectra of detergent-perturbed complexes. *Spectrochim. Acta A Mol. Biomol. Spectrosc.* **55** (1999) 193–204.
97. R. van der Vos, D. Carbonera, A.J. Hoff, Microwave and optical spectroscopy of carotenoid triplets in light-harvesting complex LHCII of spinach by absorbance-detected magnetic resonance. *J. Appl. Magn. Reson.* **2** (1991) 179–202.

98. J. Standfuss, W. Kuhlbrandt, The three isoforms of the light-harvesting complex II - Spectroscopic features, trimer formation, and functional roles. *J. Biol. Chem.* **279** (2004) 36884–36891.
99. M.A. Palacios, Excitonic interactions and energy transfer in the light-harvesting complex II of plants, PhD Thesis (2005) Vrije Universiteit Amsterdam.
100. H. Van Amerongen, L. Valkunas, R. Van Grondelle, *Photosynthetic excitons* (2000), World Scientific Publishers, (Singapore).
101. V. Novoderezhkin, M.A. Palacios, H. van Amerongen, R. van Grondelle, Energy-transfer dynamics in the LHCII complex of higher plants: Modified redfield approach. *J. Phys. Chem. B* **108** (2004) 10363–10375.
102. P.W. Hemelrijk, S.L.S. Kwa, R. van Grondelle, J.P. Dekker, Spectroscopic properties of LHC-II, the main light-harvesting chlorophyll a/b protein complex from chloroplast membranes. *Biochim. Biophys. Acta* **1098** (1992) 159–166.
103. C.W. Mullineaux, A.A. Pascal, P. Horton, A.R. Holzwarth, Excitation energy quenching in aggregates of the LHC II chlorophyll-protein complex: A time-resolved fluorescence study. *Biochim. Biophys. Acta* **1141** (1993) 23–28.
104. M. Du, X. Xie, L. Mets, G.R. Fleming, Direct observation of ultrafast energy-transfer processes in light harvesting complex II. *J. Phys. Chem.* **98** (1994) 4736–4741.
105. T. Bittner, K.-D. Irrgang, G. Renger, M.R. Wasielewski, Ultrafast excitation energy transfer and exciton - exciton annihilation processes in isolated light harvesting complexes of photosystem II (LHC II) from spinach. *J. Phys. Chem.* **98** (1994) 11821–11826.
106. T. Bittner, G.P. Wiederrecht, K.-D. Irrgang, G. Renger, M.R. Wasielewski, Femtosecond transient absorption spectroscopy on the light- harvesting Chl a/b protein complex of photosystem II at room temperature and 12 K. *Chem. Phys.* **194** (1995) 311–322.
107. A.J.W.G. Visser, A. Van Hoek, T. Kulinski, J. Le Gall, Time-resolved fluorescence studies of flavodoxin. Demonstration of picosecond fluorescence lifetimes of FMN in desulfovibrio flavodoxins. *FEBS Lett.* **224** (1987) 406–410.
108. F.J. Kleima, C.C. Gradinaru, F. Calkoen, I.H.M. van Stokkum, R. van Grondelle, H. van Amerongen, Energy transfer in LHCII monomers at 77K studied by sub-picosecond transient absorption spectroscopy. *Biochemistry* **36** (1997) 15262–15268.
109. C.C. Gradinaru, S. Özdemir, D. Gülen, I.H.M. van Stokkum, R. van Grondelle, H. van Amerongen, The flow of excitation energy in LHCII monomers: Implications for the structural model of the major plant antenna. *Biophys. J* **75** (1998) 3064–3077.
110. R. Agarwal, B.P. Krueger, G.D. Scholes, M. Yang, J. Yom, L. Mets, G.R. Fleming, Ultrafast energy transfer in LHC-II revealed by three-pulse photon echo peak shift measurements. *J. Phys. Chem. B* **104** (2000) 2908–2918.
111. J.M. Salverda, M. Vengris, B.P. Krueger, G.D. Scholes, A.R. Czarnoleski, V. Novoderezhkin, H. van Amerongen, R. van Grondelle, Energy transfer in light-harvesting complexes LHCII and CP29 of spinach studied with three pulse echo peak shift and transient grating. *Biophys. J.* **84** (2003) 450–465.
112. H.M. Visser, F.J. Kleima, I.H.M. van Stokkum, R. van Grondelle, H. van Amerongen, Probing the many energy-transfer processes in the photosynthetic light-harvesting complex II at 77K using energy-selective sub-picosecond transient absorption spectroscopy. *Chem. Phys.* **210** (1996) 297–312.

113. M. Yang, K. Ohta, G.R. Fleming, Three-pulse photon echoes for model reactive systems. *J. Chem. Phys.* **110** (1999) 10243–10252.
114. J.P. Ide, D.R. Klug, W. Kühlbrandt, L.B. Giorgi, G. Porter, The state of detergent solubilised light-harvesting chlorophyll-a/b protein complex as monitored by picosecond time-resolved fluorescence and circular dichroism. *Biochim. Biophys. Acta* **893** (1987) 349–364.
115. S.L.S. Kwa, F.G. Groeneveld, J.P. Dekker, R. van Grondelle, H. van Amerongen, S. Lin, W.S. Struve, Steady-state and time-resolved polarized light spectroscopy of the green plant light-harvesting complex II. *Biochim. Biophys. Acta* **1101** (1992) 143–146.
116. S. Krawczyk, Z. Krupa, W. Maksymiec, Stark spectra of chlorophylls and carotenoids in antenna pigment–proteins LHC-II and CP-II. *Biochim. Biophys. Acta* **1143** (1993) 273–281.
117. E.J.G. Peterman, T. Pullerits, R. van Grondelle, H. van Amerongen, Electron-phonon coupling and vibronic fine structure of light-harvesting complex II of green plants; temperature dependent absorption and high-resolution fluorescence spectroscopy. *J. Phys. Chem. B* **101** (1997) 4448–4457.
118. A. Schubert, W.J. Beenken, H. Stiel, B. Voigt, D. Leupold, H. Lokstein, Excitonic coupling of chlorophylls in the plant light-harvesting complex LHC-II. *Biophys. J.* **82** (2002) 1030–1039.
119. M. Krikunova, B. Voigt, H. Lokstein, Direct evidence for excitonically coupled chlorophylls a and b in LHC II of higher plants by nonlinear polarization spectroscopy in the frequency domain. *Biochim. Biophys. Acta* **1556** (2002) 1–5.
120. M.A. Palacios, F.L. de Weerd, J.A. Ihalainen, R. van Grondelle, H. van Amerongen, Superradiance and exciton (de)localization in light-harvesting complex II from green plants? *J. Phys. Chem. B* **106** (2002) 5782–5787.
121. J. Pieper, M. Rätsep, R. Jankowiak, K.-D. Irrgang, J. Voigt, G. Renger, G.J. Small, Q(Y)-level structure and dynamics of solubilized light-harvesting complex II of green plants: Pressure and hole burning studies. *J. Phys. Chem. A* **103** (1999) 2412–2421.
122. F. Hillmann, J. Voigt, H. Redlin, K.D. Irrgang, G. Renger, Optical dephasing in the light-harvesting complex II: A two-pulse photon echo study. *J. Phys. Chem. B* **105** (2001) 8607–8615.
123. T. Renger, V. May, Simulations of frequency-domain spectra: Structure–function relationships in photosynthetic pigment–protein complexes. *Phys. Rev. Lett.* **84** (2000) 5228–5231.
124. V.I. Novoderezhkin, M.A. Palacios, H. van Amerongen, R. van Grondelle, Excitation dynamics in the LHCII complex of higher plants; modelling based on the 2.72A crystal structure. *J. Phys. Chem. B* **105** (2005) 8607–8615.
125. H. van Amerongen, J.P. Dekker, R. van Grondelle, Energy transfer in photosystem II is slow, in PS2001, *Proceedings 12th International Congress on Photosynthesis*, CSIRO Publishing: S31–015. (2001): Available online at http://www.publish.csiro.au/ps2001.
126. G.H. Schatz, H. Brock, A.R. Holzwarth, A kinetic and energetic model for the primary processes in photosystem II. *Biophys. J.* **54** (1988) 397–405.
127. G.H. Schatz, H. Brock, A.R. Holzwarth, Picosecond kinetics of fluorescence and absorbance changes in photosystem II particles excited at low photon density. *Proc. Natl. Acad. Sci. U.S.A.* **84** (1987) 8414–8418.
128. V. Barzda, V. Gulbinas, R. Kananavicius, V. Cervinskas, H. van Amerongen, R. van Grondelle, L. Valkunas, Singlet–singlet annihilation kinetics in aggregates and trimers of LHCII. *Biophys. J.* **80** (2001) 2409–2421.

129. R. Bassi, P. Dainese, The role of light harvesting complex II and of the minor chlorphyll a/b proteins in the organization of the photosystem II antenna system. *Curr. Res. in Photosynth* **2** (1990) 209–216.
130. R. Harrer, R. Bassi, M.G. Testi, C. Schäfer, Nearest-neighbor analysis of a photosystem II complex from Marchantia polymorpha L. (liverwort), which contains reaction center and antenna proteins. *Eur. J. Biochem.* **255** (1998) 196–205.
131. E.J. Boekema, H. van Roon, J.F. van Breemen, J.P. Dekker, Supramolecular organization of photosystem II and its light-harvesting antenna in partially solubilized photosystem II membranes. *Eur. J. Biochem.* **266** (1999) 444–452.
132. T.G. Dunahay, L.A. Staehelin, Isolation and characterization of a new minor chlorophyll a/b protein complex (CP24) from spinach. *Plant Physiol.* **80** (1986) 429–434.
133. A. Pagano, G. Cinque, R. Bassi, In vitro reconstitution of the recombinant photosystem II light-harvesting complex CP24 and its spectroscopic characterization. *J. Biol. Chem.* **273** (1998) 17154–17165.
134. B. Bossmann, L.H. Grimme, J. Knoetzel, Protease-stable integration of Lhcb1 into thylakoid membranes is dependent on chlorophyll b in allelic chlorina-f2 mutants of barley (Hordeum vulgare L.). *Planta* **207** (1999) 551–558.
135. T. Morosinotto, R. Baronio, R. Bassi, Dynamics of chromophore binding to Lhc proteins in vivo and in vitro during operation of the xanthophyll cycle. *J. Biol. Chem.* **277** (2002) 36913–36920.
136. R. Bassi, P. Dainese, A supramolecular light-harvesting complex from chloroplast photosystem-II membranes. *Eur. J. Biochem.* **204** (1992) 317–326.
137. A.E. Yakushevska, W. Keegstra, E.J. Boekema, J.P. Dekker, J. Andersson, S. Jansson, A.V. Ruban, P. Horton, The structure of photosystem II in Arabidopsis: Localization of the CP26 and CP29 antenna complexes. *Biochemistry* **42** (2003) 608–613.
138. D. Sandona, R. Croce, A. Pagano, M. Crimi, R. Bassi, Higher plants light harvesting proteins. Structure and function as revealed by mutation analysis of either protein or chromophore moieties. *Biochim. Biophys. Acta* **1365** (1998) 207–214.
139. R. Croce, G. Canino, F. Ros, R. Bassi, Chromophores organization in the higher plant photosystem II antenna protein CP26. *Biochemistry* **41** (2002) 7343.
140. H. van Amerongen, B.M. van Bolhuis, S. Betts, R. Mei, R. van Grondelle, C.F. Yocum, J.P. Dekker, Spectroscopic characterization of CP26, a chlorophyll a/b binding protein of the higher plant photosystem II complex. *Biochim. Biophys. Acta* **1188** (1994) 227–234.
141. F. Ros, R. Bassi, H. Paulsen, Pigment-binding properties of the recombinant photosystem II subunit CP26 reconstituted in vitro. *Eur. J. Biochem.* **253** (1998) 653–658.
142. H.A. Frank, S.K. Das, J.A. Bautista, D. Bruce, S. Vasil'ev, M. Crimi, R. Croce, R. Bassi, Photochemical behavior of xanthophylls in the recombinant photosystem II antenna complex, CP26. *Biochemistry* **40** (2001) 1220–1225.
143. R.G. Walters, A.V. Ruban, P. Horton, Higher plant light-harvesting complexes LHCIIa and LHCIIc are bound by dicyclohexylcarbodiimide during inhibition of energy dissipation. *Eur. J. Biochem.* **226** (1994) 1063–1069.
144. R.G. Walters, A.V. Ruban, P. Horton, Identification of proton-active residues in a higher plant light-harvesting complex. *Proc. Natl. Acad. Sci. U.S.A.* **93** (1996) 14204–14209.

145. J. Andersson, R.G. Walters, P. Horton, S. Jansson, Antisense inhibition of the photosynthetic antenna proteins CP29 and CP26: Implications for the mechanism of protective energy dissipation. *Plant Cell* **13** (2001) 1193–1204.
146. S. Jansson, The light-harvesting chlorophyll a/b-binding proteins. *Biochim. Biophys. Acta* **1184** (1994) 1–19.
147. T. Henrysson, W.P. Schroder, M. Spangfort, H.-E. Akerlund, Isolation and characterization of the chlorophyll a/b protein complex CP29 from spinach. *Biochim. Biophys. Acta* **977** (1989) 301–308.
148. P. Dainese, G. Hoyer-hansen, R. Bassi, The resolution of chlorophyll a/b binding proteins by a preparative method based on flat bed isoelectric focusing. *Photochem. Photobiol.* **51** (1990) 693–703.
149. K.-D. Irrgang, G. Renger, J. Vater, Isolation, purification and partial characterization of a 30-kDa chlorophyll-a/b-binding protein from spinach. *Eur. J. Biochem.* **201** (1991) 515–522.
150. E. Giuffra, G. Zucchelli, D. Sandona, R. Croce, D. Cugini, F.M. Garlaschi, R. Bassi, R.C. Jennings, Analysis of some optical properties of a native and reconstituted photosystem II antenna complex, CP29: Pigment binding sites can be occupied by chlorophyll a or chlorophyll b and determine spectral forms. *Biochemistry* **36** (1997) 12984–12993.
151. M.G. Testi, R. Croce, P. Polverino-De Laureto, R. Bassi, A CK2 site is reversibly phosphorylated in the photosystem II subunit CP29. *FEBS Lett.* **399** (1996) 245–250.
152. E. Bergantino, R. Croce, E. Giuffra, R. Bassi, Phosphorylation of the maize photosystem II protein CP29 is controlled by the plastoquinone redox-state. *Giornale Bot. Ital.* **128** (1994) 584–585.
153. R. Croce, J. Breton, R. Bassi, Conformational changes induced by phosphorylation in the CP29 subunit of photosystem II. *Biochemistry* **35** (1996) 11142–11148.
154. M. Hansson, A.V. Vener, Identification of three previously unknown in vivo protein phosphorylation sites in thylakoid membranes of Arabidopsis thaliana. *Mol. Cell. Proteom.* **2** (2003) 550–559.
155. C. Jegerschöld, A.W. Rutherford, T.A. Mattioli, M. Crimi, R. Bassi, Calcium binding to the photosystem II subunit CP29. *J. Biol. Chem.* **275** (2000) 12781–12788.
156. P. Pesaresi, D. Sandona, E. Giuffra, R. Bassi, A single point mutation (E166Q) prevents dicyclohexylcarbodiimide binding to the photosystem II subunit CP29. *FEBS Lett.* **402** (1997) 151–156.
157. R.C. Jennings, R. Bassi, F.M. Garlaschi, P. Dainese, G. Zucchelli, Distribution of the chlorophyll spectral forms in the chlorophyll/protein complexes of photosystem-II antenna. *Biochemistry* **32** (1993) 3203–3210.
158. G. Zucchelli, P. Dainese, R.C. Jennings, J. Breton, F.M. Garlaschi, R. Bassi, Gaussian decomposition of absorption and linear dichroism spectra of outer antenna complexes of photosystem II. *Biochemistry* **33** (1994) 8982–8990.
159. A. Pascal, C. Gradinaru, U. Wacker, E. Peterman, F. Calkoen, K.-D. Irrgang, P. Horton, G. Renger, R. van Grondelle, B. Robert, H. van Amerongen, Spectroscopic characterization of the spinach Lhcb4 protein (CP29), a minor light-harvesting complex of photosystem II. *Eur. J. Biochem.* **262** (1999) 817–823.
160. J. Pieper, K.D. Irrgang, M. Ratsep, J. Voigt, G. Renger, G.J. Small, Assignment of the lowest Q(Y)-state and spectral dynamics of the CP29 chlorophyll a/b antenna complex of green plants: A hole-burning study. *Photochem. Photobiol.* **71** (2000) 574–581.

161. B. Voigt, K.D. Irrgang, J. Ehlert, W. Beenken, G. Renger, D. Leupold, H. Lokstein, Spectral substructure and excitonic interactions in the minor photosystem II antenna complex CP29 as revealed by nonlinear polarization spectroscopy in the frequency domain. *Biochemistry* **41** (2002) 3049–3056.
162. C.C. Gradinaru, A.A. Pascal, F. van Mourik, B. Robert, P. Horton, R. van Grondelle, H. van Amerongen, Ultrafast evolution of the excited states in the chlorophyll a/b complex CP29 from green plants studied by energy-selective pump–probe spectroscopy. *Biochemistry* **37** (1998) 1143–1149.
163. R. Croce, M.G. Muller, R. Bassi, A.R. Holzwarth, Chlorophyll b to chlorophyll a energy transfer kinetics in the CP29 antenna complex: A comparative femtosecond absorption study between native and reconstituted proteins. *Biophys. J.* **84** (2003) 2508–2516.
164. G. Cinque, R. Croce, A.R. Holzwarth, R. Bassi, Energy transfer among CP29 chlorophylls: Calculated Förster rates and experimental transient absorption at room temperature. *Biophys. J.* **79** (2000) 1706–1717.
165. R. Simonetto, M. Crimi, D. Sandona, R. Croce, G. Cinque, J. Breton, R. Bassi, Orientation of chlorophyll transition moments in the higher-plant light-harvesting complex CP29. *Biochemistry* **38** (1999) 12974–12983.
166. R. Croce, M.G. Muller, S. Caffarri, R. Bassi, A.R. Holzwarth, Energy transfer pathways in the minor antenna complex CP29 of photosystem II: A femtosecond study of carotenoid to chlorophyll transfer on mutant and WT complexes. *Biophys. J.* **84** (2003) 2517–2532.
167. E.J. Boekema, H. van Roon, F. Calkoen, R. Bassi, J.P. Dekker, Multiple types of association of photosystem II and its light-harvesting antenna in partially solubilized photosystem II membranes. *Biochemistry* **38** (1999) 2233–2239.
168. N. Kamiya, J.R. Shen, Crystal structure of oxygen-evolving photosystem II from Thermosynechococcus vulcanus at 3.7-angstrom resolution. *Proc. Natl. Acad. Sci. U.S.A.* **100** (2003) 98–103.

Chapter 9

# Regulatory Control of Antenna Function in Plants

## Adam M. Gilmore and Xiao-Ping Li

**Table of Contents**

9.1 Introduction to Antenna Systems in Photosynthetic Organisms.... 371
9.2 Types of Regulatory Excitation Energy Transfer in PSII Antenna of Higher Plants.................................................373
9.3 Biochemical Model of Photoprotective Energy Dissipation in PSII . 375
9.4 Symmetrical Structure and Function of the PsbS-Protein of PSII . . 377
9.5 Nonessential Roles of Lhcb Proteins in PsbS-Dependent Energy Dissipation..................................................380
9.6 Influence of the PsbS Protein and the Lhcbs on Energy Flux in PSII.......................................................381
9.7 Physiological Significance of PsbS-Dependent Energy Dissipation in PSII.......................................................384
9.8 Conclusions and Future Research .......................384
Acknowledgements .........................................385
References..................................................385

## Abstract

This chapter first introduces photosynthetic light-harvesting antenna systems in the context of the evolutionary path of photosynthetic organisms from anoxygenic bacteria to cyanobacteria to algae and higher plants. The introduction continues by explaining the main regulatory mechanisms used by higher plants to adapt and acclimate to their environment. The focus of this chapter is the main regulatory "feedback" mechanism of higher plants, which involves the recently recognized role of the PsbS protein in thermal dissipation of excess energy in Photosystem II (PSII). A quantitative molecular model is presented to define this vital energy dissipation process. The model is based on the results of recent studies that have advanced our understanding and is focused on four major developments: (1) molecular control of the structure–function of the PsbS protein with respect to its role in dissipating excess light-energy; (2) molecular control of the content of all chlorophyll $b$ containing light-harvesting proteins (Lhcbs) of the "peripheral" and "proximal" PSII antenna; (3) time and wavelength dependent resolution of the flow of energy in the PSII antenna system at cryogenic temperatures; and (4) assessment of the photoprotective capacity and physiological significance of PsbS-dependent energy dissipation. Our contemporary model of PSII antenna control takes into consideration the respective roles of the peripheral and core-inner antennae pigment–proteins of PSII. We conclude by outlining obvious plans for future further studies aimed at understanding and controlling the regulation of excess light acclimation in PSII.

## 9.1 Introduction to Antenna Systems in Photosynthetic Organisms

A universal theme of photosynthetic light energy transduction is that light-energy absorbed by the antenna pigment–protein complexes is ultimately transferred to the key chlorophyll molecules in the reaction center protein complexes [1–3]. The key reaction center chlorophylls are the sites of the "primary charge separation" process that is used to derive the chemical energy for photosynthesis. In nature, photosynthetic organisms exist in various different conditions, from high mountains to deep oceans, and are illuminated with light of different intensities and spectral distributions. Therefore, different antenna systems, reaction centers, and suitable adaptation mechanisms are required to achieve efficient excitation energy transfer (EET) to the photoactive reaction center chlorophylls both at limiting photon flux densities [4,5] and at excessive levels of electronically excited states under strong light. The adaptation to varying seasonal and diurnal illumination conditions predominantly occurs at the level of electronically excited states.

Different types of antenna and reaction center systems are discussed in great detail in other chapters of this volume. Here we give a brief review of the three most common photosynthetic reaction centers. Primitive anoxygenic bacteria have a single type of reaction center (RC) served by a ring-shaped antenna complex, LH1, which physically surrounds the RC (Figure 1A) [6–8]. Some anoxygenic "purple" bacteria have second ring-shaped antenna complex, LH2, that is arranged adjacent and transfers energy to the LH1, thereby increasing

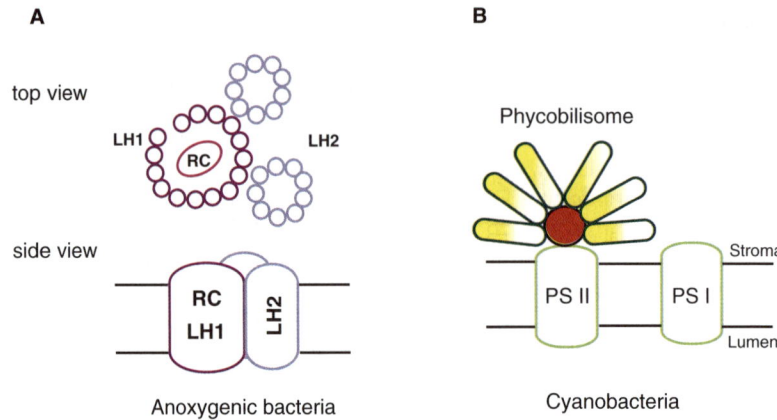

**Figure 1.** Topological representation of the reaction center(s) and antenna system organization of anoxygenic bacteria (A, top and side views) and cyanobacteria (B, side view) in their respective photosynthetic membranes.

the surface area for light absorption of the RC [9]. The amount of the LH2 complex is variable and depends on the growth conditions [10]. Chapter 5 gives a detailed description of the structure of the antenna in anoxygenic purple bacteria.

Cyanobacterial organisms are oxygenic and more evolutionarily advanced than anoxygenic organisms. Cyanobacteria exhibit two separate reaction centers as integral parts of Photosystem I (PSI) and Photosystem II (PSII). Antenna structures known as phycobilisomes feed light energy to both PSI and PSII (Figure 1B). PSII and PSI have to work coordinately to oxidize water and generate NADPH and ATP, respectively. The light absorption and energy transfer processes of cyanobacterial phycobilisomes are facilitated by a well-defined energy cascade from bluer to redder chromophoric proteins (phycobiliproteins) arranged in stacks that attach externally to the membranes that contain the reaction center complexes. Light energy transduction in cyanobacteria is primarily regulated by the attachment/detachment and migration of the phycobilisomes from the PSI and PSII proteins in a process known as a state-transition [11,12]. Chapter 6 gives more detail on photosynthesis in cyanobacteria.

The most advanced oxygenic photosynthetic organisms, higher plants, also contain two types of reaction centers, PSI and PSII similar to cyanobacteria. As shown in Figure 2, in typical higher plant chloroplasts PSI and PSII are separately concentrated in the stromal lamellae and granal thylakoid stacks, respectively. PSI and PSII also have their own complements of light-harvesting system proteins, designated as the Lhca proteins for PSI and the Lhcb proteins for PSII. The amount of Lhca and Lhcb proteins can be regulated by either transcriptional and/or translational processes, depending on the environmental conditions the plant experienced [13]. The content of Lhca and Lhcb proteins determines the absorption cross section for light energy of each photosystem.

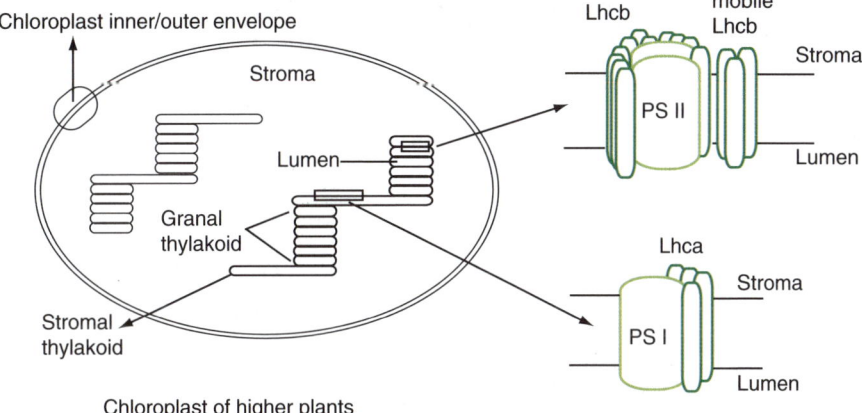

**Figure 2.** Organization of the PSII and PSI reaction center and antennae systems in the higher plant chloroplast membrane system. PSII is enriched in the granal thylakoid stacks while PSI is concentrated in the stromal thylakoid regions.

In nature, the PSI reaction center of higher plants is monomeric, in marked contrast to the trimeric form in cyanobacteria and prochlorophytes [14], and is associated with four light-harvesting antenna proteins, Lhca1 to Lhca4. The crystal structure of PSI complex from pea was resolved recently, with the four antenna proteins arranged in a series, creating a half-moon-shaped belt docking with the reaction center in the order of Lhca1, Lhca4, Lhca2 and Lhca3 [15]. Chapter 7 describes in detail the structure and function of PSI from higher plants. In vivo PSII forms dimers [16–18] that are each commonly associated with their six different light-harvesting proteins, Lhcb1-6. The Lhcb4–6 are normally monomeric and are closely associated with the PSII core. They are also referred to as inner/minor antenna complexes. Lhcbs 1–3 usually form trimeric complexes [19,20] and are the main components of the so-called "peripheral" antenna.

Much work has been done to try to resolve the "supercomplex" structure of PSII in higher plants. Three-dimensional structures of PSII reaction centers from higher plants were resolved at 8 Å [21] while the PSII supercomplex was resolved at 24 Å [22]. The structure information helps greatly in understanding the function of photosynthesis in higher plant. The major light-harvesting proteins Lhcb1–3 trimers from spinach [20] and pea [23] have been resolved recently with atomic resolution, but we still do not have a clear atomic picture of the PSII holocomplex from higher plants.

## 9.2 Types of Regulatory Excitation Energy Transfer in PSII Antenna of Higher Plants

As shown in Figure 3, electronic excitation energy in PSII of higher plants is regulated by three main processes, (1) state transitions, (2) photoinhibitory

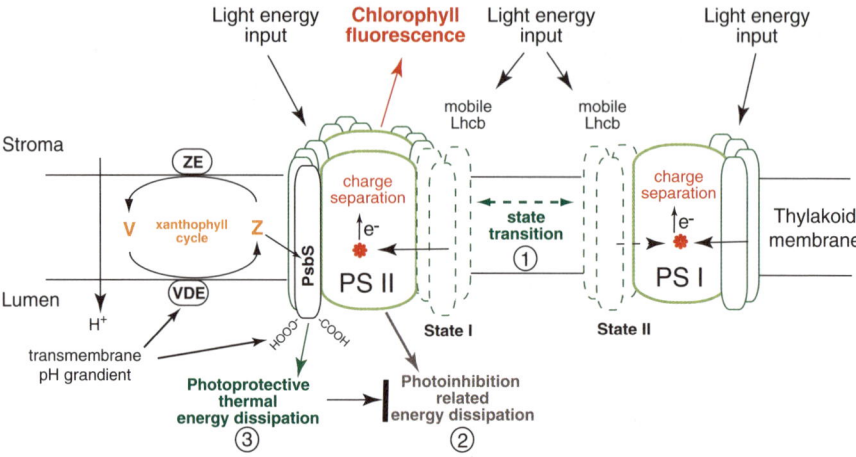

Figure 3. The three main types of excitation energy transfer and dissipation affecting PSII in the higher plant chloroplast membrane system. (1) State transitions are attributed to mobilization of a pool of Lhcbs from PSII to PSI enriched regions triggered by plastoquinone reduction induced activation of Lhcb kinases. (2) Photoinhibitory energy dissipation in the PSII reaction center caused by overexposure to light energy. (3) Photoprotective energy dissipation is caused by excess light-induced acidification of the chloroplast thylakoid lumen which protonates the violaxanthin deepoxidase VDE and the PsbS protein glutamate residues. Zeaxanthin (Z), formed by deepoxidation of violaxanthin (V), can bind to the protonated PsbS to mediate energy dissipation. Z bound to PsbS facilitates the heat dissipation of the PSII Chl $a$ excited states. Under limiting light when the lumen acidity is neutralized, the zeaxanthin deepoxidase can revert Z back to V and the PsbS is deprotonated and deactivated.

related energy dissipation, and (3) photoprotective thermal energy dissipation processes [24,25].

F-A Wollman has reviewed in detail the history and progress in understanding state transitions [26]. State transitions were first observed by Bonaventura and Myers in green alga [27] and by Murata in red algae [28]. State transitions change the energy distribution between PSII and PSI. Exposing the algae to light that is mainly absorbed by PSII for a few minutes induced the cells to become more sensitive to PSI light (State II). While, on the other hand, illuminating cells with light that favors PSI absorption induced the cells to distribute more light to PSII (State I).

State transitions in algae and higher plants are fundamentally different from those in cyanobacteria. Unlike cyanobacteria, reaction centers in alga and higher plants have their own light-harvesting systems, i.e., Lhca serves PSI and Lhcb serves PSII. In higher plants around 20% of major light harvesting in PSII (Lhcb) is mobile and can distribute absorbed light energy either to PSI or to PSII depending on the redox state of the intermediate electron transport chain in chloroplasts [29]. The light absorption peak for Lhcb is only upto 680 nm and for Lhca it is in the far-red region. It was found later that the state transition involved moving peripheral Lhcbs from the PSII enriched granal thylakoid regions to the PSI enriched stromal thylakoid upon the phosphorylation of trimeric Lhcbs [30,31]. State transitions are controlled by the redox state of plastoquinone through some chloroplast protein kinases. When the plastoquinone is more reduced some of the major Lhcb are phosphorylated and move to the stromal thylakoid to direct absorbed energy to PSI; when the plastoquinone is oxidized the major Lhcbs are dephosphorylated and move to the granal thylakoid to direct absorbed energy to PSII [32,33]. The mobile pool of Lhcbs determines the relative absorbance cross-sections (antenna size) of PSI and PSII and, therefore, the state transitions influence the PSII chlorophyll fluorescence yield.

Research workers have long tried to identify the chloroplast protein kinase specifically for state transition. In *Arabidopsis*, a thylakoid membrane associated threonine kinase family, TAKs, was identified [34]. TAKs antisense plants lost the Lhcb phosphorylation and reduced state transitions [35]. But TAKs are not specific for phosphorylating Lhcbs. Screening *Chlamydomonas* mutants defective in state transition indicated that a chloroplast thylakoid-associated serine-threonine protein kinase, Stt7, was specifically responsible for the phosphorylation of the Lhcbs and state transitions [36]. Further, sequence comparison identified a protein kinase STN7 in *Arabidopsis* similar to *Chlamydomonas* Stt7. Interrupting the wild type *STN7* gene blocked the Lhcb phosphorylation and the state transitions in *Arabidopsis* [37]. At present, the functional relationships between kinases TAKs and STN7 remain incompletely understood. *stn7* Mutants also had more reduced plastoquinone pool and grow more slowly under changing light [37]. This is the first evidence to show directly that the state transitions are important for environment changes in higher plants.

As indicated in Figure 3, photoinhibitory related thermal energy dissipation processes are currently incompletely understood but are obviously related to structural changes in PSII reaction center core [38]. Photoinhibition lowers both the quantum yields of PSII photochemistry and fluorescence. Chapter 21 outlines the phenomena and underlying mechanisms of photoinhibition. Furthermore, Figure 3 shows that photoprotective thermal energy dissipation removes excess light energy from the PSII antenna, thereby preventing photoinhibition. This major photoprotective mechanism functioning in PSII is the main focus of this chapter.

## 9.3 Biochemical Model of Photoprotective Energy Dissipation in PSII

The third process of Figure 3 is the key photoprotective mechanism in PSII. Thermal energy dissipation of superfluous absorbed light "down-regulates" the delivery of photons from the antenna to the PSII reaction center and hence serves as the major defense against excess light exposure [39,40]. Thermal energy dissipation, which de-excites the excited chlorophyll, can be measured as nonphotochemical quenching (NPQ) of PSII chlorophyll fluorescence. Because state transitions and photoinhibition also decrease the chlorophyll fluorescence, NPQ is usually grossly interpreted with respect to relative contributions of the three components, namely, thermal energy dissipation (qE), state transitions (qT) and quenching caused by photoinhibition (qI). In NPQ measurement the three types of quenching can be separately quantified by their light to dark relaxation kinetics and/or their sensitivity to different chemicals. The fastest relaxing part is qE, usually within one to five minutes; qT needs about five to ten minutes to relax, and qI, the photoinhibition part, need hours for recovery [25] because protein synthesis is necessary for the recovery of qI.

Since each type of NPQ component has its own mechanism, the decreases in chlorophyll fluorescence also exhibit different properties. In qE, heat dissipation de-excites chlorophyll; the decrease of chlorophyll fluorescence is due to the chlorophyll fluorescence lifetime changes [41]. qE is always associated with the appearance of new short lifetime components. For qT, more energy was delivered to and absorbed by PSI, and we see lowered PSII chlorophyll fluorescence without corresponding fluorescence lifetime changes. qI is also involved in the chlorophyll fluorescence lifetime change; however, the differences between qE and qI are resolvable with chemicals by analysis of their chlorophyll fluorescence lifetime distribution changes [42]. As described in detail below, qE leads to uncoupler sensitive changes in fluorescence lifetime distribution amplitudes whereas qI leads to uncoupler insensitive decreases in fluorescence lifetime distribution center values. Importantly, qE is not observed in PsbS-less mutants [43,44], and neither qT nor qE are observed in mutants lacking both chl-*a* oxygenase (due to lack of all chl *b* and most Lhcbs) and PsbS. However, qI changes can be observed in all plants regardless of PsbS- or chl-*a* oxygenase activities given sufficient exposure to excess light [45].

Current biochemical, biophysical and molecular-genetic evidence indicates, as illustrated in Figure 3, that the "down-regulation" mechanism of qE involves acidification of the chloroplast thylakoid lumen, the special oxygen-containing carotenoids of the xanthophyll cycle and specialized proteins in the PSII inner-antenna. To date there is no strong indication that this type of process is associated with the PSI antenna.

Our established biochemical model of the PSII photoprotection process involves two main steps. First, acidification of the lumen pH activates the violaxanthin (V) deepoxidase enzyme that converts the diepoxide V into the epoxide free zeaxanthin (Z), via the mono-epoxide intermediate antheraxanthin (A) [46,47]. Second, the lumen acidity protonates two lumen exposed carboxylate moieties of the PsbS protein [48,49] to activate this protein for a unique binding association with the xanthophylls A and Z, wherein, there is induced an increased rate constant of thermal dissipation [50,51]. Previous studies of the PsbS-dependent mechanism [39,50] identified three distinct PSII chlorophyll fluorescence lifetime states, corresponding to the following biochemical model conditions: (1) $W_c$, a PSII unit with its reaction center closed to photochemistry and containing an unprotonated PsbS protein and without a bound Z (or A) molecule; (2) $X_c$, a closed PSII unit containing the protonated form of the PsbS

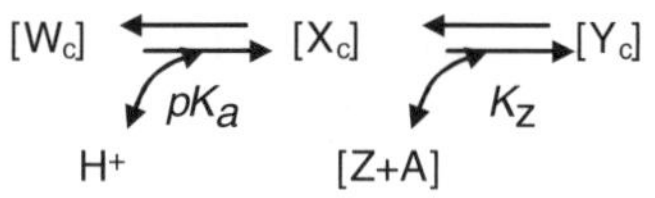

$$[W_c] \underset{H^+}{\overset{pK_a}{\rightleftharpoons}} [X_c] \underset{[Z+A]}{\overset{K_z}{\rightleftharpoons}} [Y_c]$$

Scheme 1.

capable of, but not actively, binding a Z or A molecule; and (3) $Y_c$, a closed PSII unit with a protonated PsbS protein and with a bound Z or A molecule. Protonation of PsbS is defined with a simple Henderson–Hasselbalch titration (defined by a $pK_a$ value). The concentration dependence of the binding of Z and A to the protonated PsbS associated site is defined with an equilibrium-association (defined by a $pK_a$). In summary, the process is outlined in Scheme 1.

In Scheme 1, the total sum of all three PSII states is normalized and defined as $[W_c] + [X_c] + [Y_c] = 1$; the $pK_a = pH - \log[W_c]/[X_c]$ and $K_z = [X_c]/[Y_c] \cdot [Z+A]$. It is the $Y_c$-state with the shortest excited state lifetime (300–500 ps) that plays the central role in the PSII energy dissipation mechanism in this model. The $Y_c$ state represents about a four- to six-fold change in quantum yield from the $W_c$ state with a fluorescence lifetime around 2000 ps, whereas the $X_c$ state (1600–1800 ps) represent only about a 20% change. Our updated picture described below outlines the extension of this model to define the synergistic influence of combined PSII reaction center photochemistry, i.e., PSII trap-opening, and PsbS-dependent energy dissipation on the PSII excited state lifetime.

Importantly, and also discussed in this chapter, are several lines of biochemical and spectroscopic evidence that indicate a key structural association of the PsbS with the core-inner-antennae PSII proteins in higher plants. This is in contrast to the idea that PsbS is associated with the chl *b* containing peripheral proteins designated as Lhcb1–3. Furthermore, recent reports provide indicate that zeaxanthin, possibly in a zeaxanthin:chl *a* dimer associated with or catalyzed by the PsbS protein, exhibits an integral and ultrafast (ca. 10 ps) excited state event that is central to the down-regulation mechanism [52,53].

## 9.4 Symmetrical Structure and Function of the PsbS-Protein of PSII

The 22-kDa PsbS protein was recognized as an integral subunit of the PSII holocomplex in the early 1980s [54–56]. Subsequent gene sequencing studies showed that PsbS belongs to the light-harvesting protein super family [57–60]. However, in contrast to all other light-harvesting proteins, which have three transmembrane helixes, PsbS is distinguished by having four. The pigment binding characteristics of PsbS are different from those of light-harvesting proteins [61–63]. In vivo, PsbS is stable without binding to pigments [64]. For many years the function of this protein was not clear. Characterization the *psbS* deletion *Arabidopsis* mutant showed that the PsbS plays the central role in thermal energy dissipation [48].

We have generated and overexpressed site-directed PsbS mutants and determined the influence of key lumen exposed glutamates on the PSII energy dissipation mechanism [44]. Figure 4 shows that the topological structure of PsbS is symmetrical such that PsbS contains four transmembrane helixes with high respective similarity between helix I and helix III and helix II and helix IV [59]. Further, two lumen exposed loops [65] are also symmetrically similar, with a respective glutamine 122 (E122) and glutamine 226 (E226) sitting in the middle of each loop. While mutating one or the other of these two key glutamates only fractionally inhibited PsbS function, double mutation of both E122Q and E226Q totally disrupted its function [44]. These results confirmed the previous suggestion [49] that glutamines E122 and E226 are the main pH gradient sensors for PsbS. They are, hence, responsible for inducing and relaxing NPQ via sensing pH changes in the thylakoid lumen.

We also reported that the E122Q and E226Q mutations influence both a $\Delta A535$ leaf absorption change and binding of the carbonyl modification agent dicyclohexylcarbodiimide (DCCD) to PsbS [44]. These observations were significant because it was found early on that a distinctive $\Delta A535$ spectral change coexisted with the energy dissipation now known to be PsbS-dependent [66]. We observed a linear relationship between the PsbS-dependent energy dissipation measured as NPQ and $\Delta A535$. The linear relation held even when taking into consideration two different variables, namely, (1) different concentrations of PsbS and (2) different amino acid mutations of the PsbS protein. The current hypothesis is that the $\Delta A535$ is associated with a red absorption shift when Z

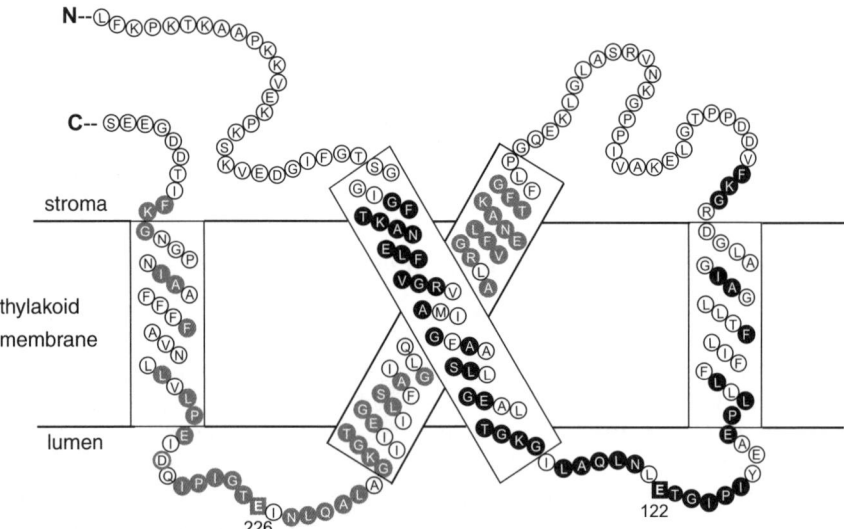

**Figure 4.** Topological structure of the PsbS protein, drawn with the symmetry highlighted by dark shading on the first half and lighter shading on the second half. The glutamates referred to in the text as E122 and E226 are shown with square symbols and numbered respectively.

binds to PsbS [67]. Holt et al. showed that the quenching complex is a PsbS dependent Z-Chl heterodimer [53]. Therefore, we conclude that the double mutant (E122QE226Q) could not bind Z and form the active quenching site. We suggested that each PsbS can bind two Z molecules and the single mutations (E122Q or E226Q) reduced by a factor of two the amount of Z binding to PsbS and hence the energy dissipation function in direct proportion to Z. Our main hypothesis was that PsbS has two equifunctional sides associated, respectively, with the E122 and E226 residues on opposite sides of the protein. Disrupting one side of the PsbS proteins does not affect the function of the other side. The current view is that PsbS works as a symmetrical signal sensor, actively transferring the signal of excessive light (e.g., high pH gradient through the thylakoid membrane) to down-regulate the photosynthetic light-harvesting system [44].

Our current biochemical model (Figure 5) of the influence of the xanthophyll-cycle and PsbS functions on PSII [44] extends our previous model [50]. As outlined above, the current model includes (1) a synergistic influence of PsbS-dependent energy dissipation and PSII photochemistry on the PSII excited state lifetime and (2) a symmetrical structural-functionality for PsbS. The updated model contains six possible states for PSII, namely, $W_c$, $X_c$ and $Y_c$ as defined in the introduction plus $W_o$, $X_o$ and $Y_o$, where the respective c/o symbols represent PSII complexes wherein the reaction center traps are closed/open because the primary electron acceptor $Q_a$ is reduced/oxidized.

The enhanced model is significant because it predicts equally well the PSII fluorescence lifetime distributions for PsbS site-directed mutants, PsbS deletion mutants as well as for PsbS overexpressors and wild-type plants. One key observation was that inhibiting the function of PsbS either completely or fractionally by site-directed mutation has a comparable fractional effect on

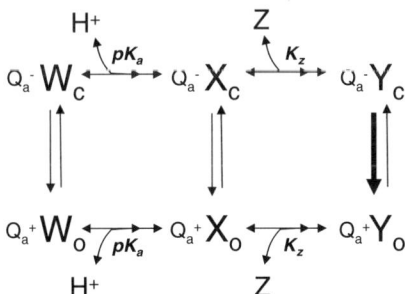

Figure 5. Model of the synergistic interaction of PsbS-dependent energy dissipation and PSII photochemistry on the PSII excited state lifetimes. The synergistic model was based on the previous three-state model of Gilmore et al. [50] and expanded to consider the simultaneous influence of open and closed PSII traps denoted with subscripts o and c, respectively. Conversion of W into X involves protonation of E122 and or E226 and conversion of X into Y involves binding of Z or A. Increasing the Y state population increases the probability of PSII-trap opening because the reduced $Y_o$ lifetime decreases the probability of $Q_a$ reduction.

the fluorescence lifetime distributions as changing the titer of the active population of PsbS [44]. The stoichiometry of our model in Figure 5 can be related with another recent study claiming that the PsbS functional unit is a dimer [68] inasmuch as the symmetrical nature of the protein would predict the same fractional-functional behavior for monomer or dimers. More importantly, the synergistic PsbS-PSII photochemistry model also functions in mutants lacking Lhcbs [45] to confirm earlier studies that indicated the PSII photochemistry and PsbS-dependent energy dissipation function with kinetics very similar to Lhcb replete plants [69–71]. This observation also seems interesting in comparison with the PsbS-dimer study [68], which claimed that PsbS monomers were more concentrated in the peripheral antenna as opposed to the core-inner antenna fraction. Other factors concerning the significance of the Lhcb mutations on PsbS function and PSII energy flow are described in more detail below.

## 9.5 Nonessential Roles of Lhcb Proteins in PsbS-Dependent Energy Dissipation

The genomic sequence of *Arabidopsis* indicates that the psbS and chlorophyll *a* oxygenase (CAO) genes are both closely located on chromosome 1. *Arabidopsis* mutants deleting *psbS* or *CAO* [48,72] or both *psbS* and *CAO* [45] have been isolated. This allows us to effectively dissect their respective influence on energy dissipation. Plants defective in *CAO* gene cannot synthesize any chl *b* [72], which prevents the accumulation of all mature Lhcbs1–4 and Lhcb6. In *CAO* mutant the PSII antenna was greatly reduced to mainly the core inner antennae complexes (i.e., D1, D2, CP43 and CP47) and the small remnant population of Lhcb5 that appears to be in an altered form based on electrophoretic analysis of the peptide. The measured PSII antenna size in chl *b*-less barley [71] and *Arabidopsis CAO* mutants (our unpublished data) ranged around 50 chls per PSII reaction center compared with 250 to 300 chls $a + b$ in chl *b*-replete plants. Importantly, there is no possibility of Lhcb1–3 macro-aggregates of trimers forming in chl *b*-less mutants [73,74]; this is a key issue because a previous model of energy dissipation centered around such trimer-macroaggregate formation [24]. Further, in the chl *b*-less mutants there is no possibility of state I–state II transitions that depend on mobile populations of Lhcbs between PSII and PSI [32,75] and there is a greatly reduced excitation-energy connectivity factor for PSII reaction centers in Lhcb depleted systems [76]. Hence, working with Lhcb depleted systems allows one to view the kinetics of PSII photochemistry and PsbS-energy dissipation as a population of separate units largely independent of transfer between PSII units or between PSII and PSI.

Importantly, in a *CAO*-deletion mutant of *Arabidopsis* we were able to overexpress *psbS* to yield energy dissipation levels exceeding (by 50%) those observed in the wild-type plant grown under the same conditions [45]. This was a remarkable observation given that earlier models of PSII energy dissipation postulated that the energy dissipation would be mostly determined by the peripheral antenna size [24,76]. These *psbS* overexpression results in the *CAO* mutants were highly significant because the PsbS protein levels did not correlate with changes the PSII antenna size. These *Arabidopsis* mutant results are consistent with the barley *chlorina* mutant data of Gilmore et al. [69,70], in that the PSII reaction center photochemistry and energy dissipation mechanisms function with similar decay kinetics with or without the peripheral antennae. Further, the observations in the *CAO psbS* mutant experiments were complemented as described below by additional experiments on the flow of energy in PSII measured at cryogenic temperatures.

## 9.6 Influence of the PsbS Protein and the Lhcbs on Energy Flux in PSII

Early cryogenic temperature studies of PSII thylakoid and membrane particles established that excitation energy in PSII was transferred rapidly and efficiently from the peripheral antenna to the core inner antennae [77,78]. There are three main bands observed in PSII at 77 K (in terms of energy level/fluorescence lifetime), which are attributed to (1) the peripheral antenna pool (F680 nm/ 8 ps), (2) the CP43 inner antenna complex (F685 nm/ $\sim$ 400 ps) and (3) the CP47 complex (F695 nm/ $\sim$ 2000 ps). The F680 band exhibits a rapid rise and decay, indicating that the pigments of this emission serve primarily as an antennal excitation energy donor to the core-inner antennae. Evidence that the F680 pigments pass excitation energy downhill is primarily from the delayed rise components observed in the F685 and F695 bands, which correspond kinetically with the latter bands being acceptors of energy from F680.

Figure 6, from Gilmore et al. [45], compares the PSII spectral decay kinetics at 77 K for the three PSII bands in chl *b*-replete and chl *b*-less mutant both in the absence ($F_m$) and presence ($F'_m$) of PsbS-dependent energy dissipation. The two overexpression PsbS mutant lines are illustrated because they exhibit similar and nearly saturating titers of PsbS on a per PSII unit basis; note that wild type titers of PsbS in the parent *b*-replete and *b*-less lines are not directly comparable because they are obviously sub saturating. The streak-camera data were also collected with ultralow energy 635 nm pulses (1–2 pJ per pulse with 1–2 µW of average power at a 1 MHz repetition rate), which prevented both the possibility of exciton–exciton annihilation and photochemical bleaching of the PSII chlorophylls [78]. The top row in Figure 6 shows contour plots of the streak-camera spectrograph data. The data indicate that the PSII lifetimes in the 695 nm region are very similar in the two lines with and without PSII energy dissipation. The second row shows the time-dependent spectral profiles during the rise and decay, indicating two main things: (1) the time-dependent shift in the central wavelengths from the blue 680–685 nm region to the red 695–700 nm region in all cases and (2) the effects of the PsbS-dependent energy dissipation increase the apparent decays in the F685 and F695 regions. The third row of the time-integrated profiles of the PSII bands shows that the PsbS-dependent

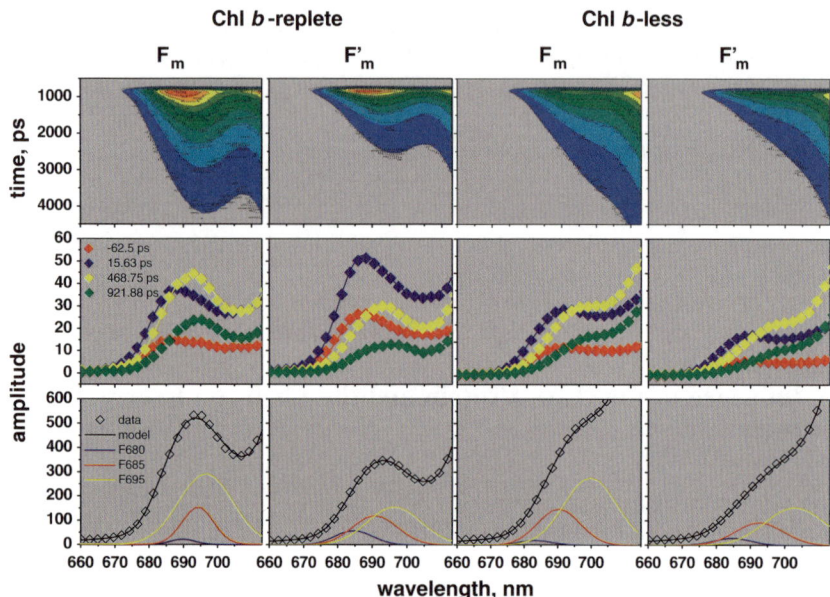

**Figure 6.** Time-resolved PSII fluorescence spectral data at 77 K and model simulation of both chlorophyll-*b*-replete (left-hand two columns) and chlorophyll-*b*-less (right-hand two columns) mutant lines of *Arabidopsis thaliana* with enhanced levels of PsbS. Compared are the PSII spectral regions under both maximal ($F_m$) fluorescence conditions (no photochemistry and no PsbS-dependent energy dissipation) and ($F'_m$) condition (no photochemistry and maximal PsbS-dependent energy dissipation). The top row shows contour plots of data (dotted lines) and simulated data (colored contours) scaled in eleven linear intervals and normalized to the maximal intensity in the image. The second row shows time-resolved spectral profiles data (symbols) and model (lines) at the time-intervals shown in the legend in left-most panel. The third row shows the time-integrated Gaussian spectral band profiles, data and model as defined in the legend in left-most panel.

energy dissipation decreases the amplitudes of the F685 and F695 bands similarly in both the *b*-replete and *b*-less lines.

Figure 7 compares the kinetic profiles of the three PSII bands and shows four key points. (1) For the chl *b*-replete line, the F680 band amplitude is enhanced by 2–3-fold compared with the *b*-less line both with and without PsbS energy dissipation. (2) The F680 band kinetics do not change during the PsbS-dependent energy dissipation in either line. (3) Consistent with the enhanced F680 amplitude the *b*-replete line shows delayed rise kinetics (note arrows) for the F685 and F695 bands as prominent features that are greatly diminished if not lacking the *b*-less line. (4) The PsbS-dependent energy dissipation is most obviously associated with a new rapid decay mode in F695 and a smaller change in the kinetics of F685 in both chl *b*-replete and chl *b*-less lines; the strongest influence of the energy dissipation on F685 was in its amplitude for both lines.

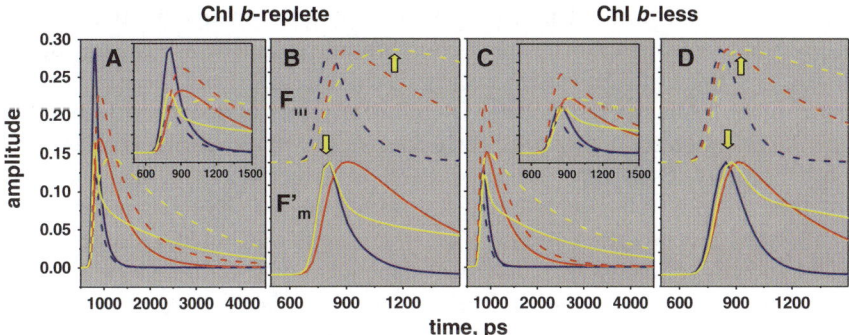

**Figure 7.** Wavelength-integrated kinetic profiles for the PSII emitter bands of F680 (blue line), F685 (red line) and F695 (yellow line) as defined in third row of Figure 6. Dashed lines represent $F_m$ and solid lines $F'_m$, conditions, respectively. The natural amplitudes are shown in (A) and (C) with insets for expanded initial time scale. The normalized profiles with an expanded initial time scale are shown in (B) and (D) for the $F_m$ (upper, dashed) and $F'_m$ (lower, solid) conditions. All image collection and data processing procedures were essentially as described by Gilmore et al. [69,85].

Further experiments, not shown here, clearly indicated that the F695 band kinetics were specifically and similarly influenced over a wide range of temperatures, from 4 K to room temperature, in both lines (unpublished data). The rapid PsbS-dependent energy dissipation components observed from F695 at 77 K can be compared with transient absorption data presented by Ma [52]; Ma's recent work suggests that energy dissipation occurs with a rapid time constant (around ten picoseconds). Holt et al. [53] have published even more recent experiments, suggesting that PsbS catalyzes the formation of a zeaxanthin:chl $a$ dimer that leads to a rapid energy dissipation process with a 150 ps decay time and a 10 ps rise time. It remains to be determined how or if the rapid absorption changes observed by Holt and Ma's recent studies at room temperature [52,53] correlate with PSII chl $a$ fluorescence, especially with the kinetics observed at cryogenic temperatures by Gilmore et al. [45].

The *CAO* mutant observations in the above cryogenic experiments strongly support the previous observations made with barley *chlorina* mutants at room temperature (described above) [70]. The key cryogenic observation worthy of note here is the same 2000 ps lifetimes for the F695 band in the absence of PsbS energy dissipation in the chl $b$-replete and chl $b$-less lines. These results are seen as highly significant because several previous studies with thylakoid membranes isolated from barley *chlorina* mutants exhibited artifactually shortened PSII lifetimes because of chronic degradation of the thylakoid ultrastructure in the suspension medium [79]; this degradation is proposed to lead to enhanced energy transfer from PSII to PSI, which decreases the PSII lifetime [73].

The current energy flow model based on the visually obvious pathway of energy flow in PSII without Lhcbs clearly indicates that PsbS must be able to structurally interact with the PSII core-inner antennae. We postulate that the structural, spatial coordinates of the interaction are the same with and without the peripheral antennae. This is proposed because the energy dissipation mode in F695 has similar in kinetics with and without the Lhcbs, which suggests the distance of the PsbS-dependent energy dissipating site from the F695 emitter chlorophylls is in fact structurally similar. As mentioned previously, these spectral and molecular data are clearly consistent with the earlier studies on the localization of PsbS that indicated PsbS is associated with the core-inner antennae [61,80]. We speculate that failure to isolate PsbS in supercomplexes, as analyzed by cryo-electron microscopy, could be attributed, as suggested by Nield and co-workers [81], to detergent-dependent dissociation given that PsbS is one of the most hydrophobic PSII proteins.

## 9.7 Physiological Significance of PsbS-Dependent Energy Dissipation in PSII

One of the most significant insights gained so far from analysis of the PsbS-dependent energy dissipation mechanism with the overexpression mutants centers around the prediction of the physical limits of the photoprotection capacity [42,50,70]. Clearly, the time-resolution of the PSII dissipative states and their fractional amplitude interconversions facilitated the prediction of the maximal levels of energy dissipation that can be achieved in higher plants. Overexpression of PsbS indicated limits of NPQ around 6–8, corresponding to PSII average lifetimes around 350 ps with all closed PSII reaction centers. We clearly demonstrated that PsbS overexpressors exhibit enhanced photoprotected capacity to maintain PSII photochemical activity under excess light conditions [43].

A positive role for PsbS photoprotection has been confirmed in field studies where plants lacking NPQ exhibit significantly reduced fitness and survivability as measured by seed production under excess light and variable light conditions [82]. Other key studies have shown that PsbS-dependent photoprotection may be most significant in mature-developed tissues. Evidence for this stems from observation that high-light induced stress effects in established leaves in mutants lacking energy dissipation capacity are often wholly overcome or largely alleviated in new growth, indicating that other ameliorating mechanisms, probably antioxidant in nature, may develop in young tissues to compensate and facilitate acclimation [83,84].

## 9.8 Conclusions and Future Research

Our review of the current literature indicates we have gained a detailed understanding of the mechanism of PsbS-dependent photoprotection in PSII antenna. This has been accomplished via integrating molecular, biochemical and biophysical experimental approaches. Our contemporary model positively defines a direct role for the PsbS-protein interacting with the xanthophyll cycle pigments zeaxanthin (and antheraxanthin) to mediate an increased rate constant of thermal dissipation in the PSII core inner antenna. We now have a clear understanding of the role of key amino acid residues, PsbS stoichiometry and the energetic interaction of the PsbS with the photochemical function of the PSII core-inner antennae. Obviously, use of mutants will facilitate future studies to achieve atomic resolution, such as 2D or 3D crystallographic analysis, to reveal the remaining mysteries concerning the structure and function of the PsbS, carboxyl-protonation, xanthophyll-cycle pigments and the PSII core-inner antenna.

Importantly, recent studies have demonstrated that it should soon be possible to engineer plants with both enhanced photoprotection capacity as well as to optimize the acclimation responses under both favorable and stressful conditions. The latter factor is not trivial because it is clear that one would want to optimize light utilization for photochemistry at almost all costs. Therefore, one must carefully balance the dissipation of excess light to avoid competition with photochemistry, especially under limiting light conditions where PsbS energy dissipation may out-compete open PSII reaction centers for useful excitation energy. Therefore, in closing, it is obvious that future work concerning regulation of PSII antenna control should be aimed at utilizing our current knowledge to generate more hardy and efficient light-harvesting systems for plants of economic and agricultural importance.

## Acknowledgements

The authors wish to thank K.K. Niyogi for reviewing the manuscript and S. Itoh for providing laboratory facilities for the cryogenic chlorophyll fluorescence lifetime measurement. A.M.G. acknowledges funding by the Australian Research Council Discovery grant DP 0343160.

## References

1. N.R. Baker, *Photosynthesis and the Environment* (1996) (Govindjee, ed.), Advances in Photosynthesis Research, Vol. 5, Kluwer Academic Publishers, Dordrecht.
2. O. Björkman, B. Demmig-Adams, Regulation of photosynthetic light energy capture, conversion and dissipation in leaves of higher plants, in: *Ecological Studies* (1994) (M. Caldwell, ed.), Springer-Verlag, Berlin, pp. 17–47.
3. J. Whitmarsh, Govindjee, Photosynthesis. *Encyl. Appl. Phys.* **13** (1995) 513–532.
4. G. Renger, Energy transfer and trapping in Photosystem II, in: *Topics in Photosynthesis, The Photosystems: Structure, Function and Molecular Biology* (1992) (J. Barber, ed.), Elsevier, Amsterdam, pp. 45–99.
5. R. Grondelle, J.P. Dekekr, T. Gillbro, V. Sundstrom, Energy transfer and trapping in photosynthesis. *Biochim. Biophys. Acta.* **1187** (1994) 1–65.
6. J. Deisenhofer, H. Michel, The photosynthetic reaction center from the purple bacterium *Rhodopseudomonas viridis*, Nobel Lecture (1988).

7. A.W. Roszak, T.D. Howard, J. Southall, A.T. Gardiner, C.J. Law, N.W. Isaacs, R.J. Cogdell, Crystal structure of the RC-LH1 core complex from *Rhodopseudomonas palustris. Science* **302** (2003) 1969–1972.
8. C.J. Law, A.W. Roszak, J. Southall, A.T. Gardiner, N.W. Isaacs, R.J. Cogdell, The structure and function of bacterial light-harvesting complexes. *Mol. Membr. Biol.* **21** (2004) 183–191.
9. X. Hu, A. Damjanovic, T. Ritz, K. Schulten, Architecture and mechanism of the light-harvesting apparatus of purple bacteria. *Proc. Natl. Acad. Sci. U.S.A.* **95** (1998) 5935–5941.
10. R.J. Cogdell, N.W. Isaacs, T.D. Howard, K. McLuskey, N.J. Fraser, S.M. Prince, How photosynthetic bacteria harvest solar energy. *J. Bacteriol.* **181** (1999) 3869–3879.
11. D. Campbell, V. Hurry, A.K. Clarke, P. Gustafsson, G. Öquist, Chlorophyll fluorescence analysis of cyanobacterial photosynthesis and acclimation. *Micro. Mol. Biol. Rev.* **62** (1998) 667–683.
12. S. Joshua, C.W. Mullineaux, Phycobilisome diffusion is required for light-state transitions in cyanobacteria. *Plant Physiol.* **135** (2004) 2112–2119.
13. J.M. Anderson, B. Andersson, The dynamic photosynthetic membrane and regulation of solar energy conversion. *Trends. Biochem. Sci.* **13** (1988) 351–355.
14. P.R. Chitnis, Photosystem I: Function and physiology. *Annu. Rev. Plant Physiol. Plant Mol. Biol.* **52** (2001) 593–626.
15. A. Ben-Shem, F. Frolow, N. Nelson, Crystal structure of plant photosystem I. *Nature* **426** (2003) 630–635.
16. G.F. Peter, J.P. Thornber, Biochemical evidence that the higher plant photosystem II core complex is organized as a dimmer. *Plant Cell Physiol.* **32** (1991) 1237–1250.
17. E.J. Boekema, B. Hankamer, D. Bald, J. Kruip, J. Nield, A.F. Boonstra, J. Barber, M. Rögner, Supramolecular structure of the photosystem II complex from green plants and cyanobacteria. *Proc. Natl. Acad. Sci. U.S.A.* **92** (1995) 175–179.
18. T.S. Bibby, J. Nield, M. Chen, A.W.D. Larkum, J. Barber, Structure of a photosystem II supercomplex isolated from Prochloron didemni retaining its chlorophyll a/b light-harvesting system. *Proc. Natl. Acad. Sci. U.S.A.* **100** (2003) 9050–9054.
19. W. Kühlbrandt, D.N. Wang, Y. Fujiyoshi, Atomic model of plant light-harvesting complex by electron crystallography. *Nature* **367** (1994) 614–621.
20. H. Liu, K. Yan, T. Wang, J. Kuang, L. Zhang, X. Gui, W. An, Chang, Crystal structure of spinach major light-harvesting complex at 2.72 Å resolution. *Nature* **428** (2004) 287–292.
21. K.-H. Rhee, E.D. Morris, J. Barber, W. Kühlbrandt, Three-dimensional structure of the plant photosystem II reaction centre at 8 Å resolution. *Nature* **396** (1998) 283–286.
22. J. Nield, E.V. Orlova, P.M. Edward, B. Gowen, M. van Heel, J. Barber, 3D map of the plant photosystem II supercomplex obtained by cryoelectron microscopy and single particle analysis. *Nat. Struct. Biol.* **7** (2000) 44–47.
23. J. Standfuss, A.C. Terwisscha van Scheltinga, M. Lanborghini, W. Kühlbrandt, Mechanisms of photoprotection and nonphotochemical quenching in pea light-harvesting complex at 2.5 Å resolution. *EMBO J.* **5** (2005) 919–928.
24. P. Horton, A.V. Ruban, R.G. Walters, Regulation of light-harvesting in green plants. *Annu. Rev. Plant Phys.* **47** (1996) 655–684.
25. P. Müller, X-P. Li, K.K. Niyogi, Nonphotochemical quenching. A response to excess light energy. *Plant Physiol.* (2001) 1558–1566.
26. F.-A. Wollman, State transitions reveal the dynamics and flexibility of the photosynthetic apparatus. *EMBO J.* **20** (2001) 3623–3630.

27. C. Bonaventura, J. Myers, Fluorescence and oxygen evolution from *Chlorella pyrenoidosa*. *Biochim. Biophys. Acta* **189** (1969) 366–383.
28. N. Murata, Control of excitation transfer in photosynthesis. I. Light-induced change of chlorophyll *a* fluorescence in *Porphyridium cruentum*. *Biochim. Biophys. Acta* **172** (1970) 242–251.
29. J.F. Allen, Protein phosphorylation in regulation of photosynthesis. *Biochim. Biophys. Acta* **1098** (1992) 275–335.
30. J. Bennett, Phosphorylation of chloroplast membrane proteins. *Nature* **269** (1977) 344–346.
31. J. Bennett, The protein kinase of thylakoid membranes is light-dependent. *FEBS Lett.* **103** (1979) 342–344.
32. J. Bennett, Protein phosphorylation in green plant chloroplasts. *Annu. Rev. Plant Physiol.* **42** (1991) 281–311.
33. J.F. Allen, How does protein phosphorylation regulate photosynthesis. *Trends Biochem. Sci.* **17** (1992) 12–17.
34. S. Snyders, B.D. Kohorn, TAKs, thylakoid membrane protein kinases associated with energy transduction. *J. Biol. Chem.* **274** (1999) 9137–9140.
35. S. Snyders, B.D. Kohorn, Disruption of thylakoid-associated kinase 1 leads to alteration of light harvesting in *Arabidopsis*. *J. Biol. Chem.* **276** (2001) 32169–32176.
36. N. Depège, S. Bellafiore, J.-D. Rochaix, Role of chloroplast protein kinase Stt7 in LHCII phosphorylation and state transition in *Chlamydomonas*. *Science* **299** (2003) 1572–1575.
37. S. Bellafiore, F. Barneche, G. Peltier, J.-D. Rochaix, State transitions and light adaptation require chloroplase thylakoid protein kinase STN7. *Nature* **433** (2005) 892–895.
38. A.M. Gilmore, Govindjee, How higher plants respond to excess light: Energy dissipation in photosystem II, in: *Concepts in Photobiology: Photosynthesis and Photomorphogenesis* (1999) (G.S. Singhal, G. Renger, S.K. Sopory, K-D. Irrgang, Govindjee, eds.), Narosa Publishing House, New Delhi.
39. A.M. Gilmore, Mechanistic aspects of xanthophyll cycle-dependent photoprotection in higher plant chloroplasts and leaves. *Physiol. Plant.* **99** (1997) 197–209.
40. K.K. Niyogi, Safety valves for photosynthesis. *Curr. Opin Plant Biol.* **5** (2000) 455–460.
41. A.M. Gilmore, T.L. Hazlett, Govindjee, Xanthophyll cycle dependent quenching of Photosystem II chlorophyll *a* fluorescence: formation of a quenching complex with a short fluorescence lifetime. *Proc. Natl. Acad. Sci. U.S.A.* **92** (1995) 2273–2277.
42. A.M. Gilmore, T.L. Hazlett, P.G. Debrunner, Govindjee, Comparative time-resolved photosystem II chlorophyll a fluorescence analyses reveal distinctive differences between photoinhibitory reaction center damage and xanthophyll cycle-dependent energy dissipation. *Photochem. Photobiol.* **64** (1996) 552–563.
43. X.-P. Li, P. Müller-Moulé, A.M. Gilmore, K.K. Niyogi, PsbS-dependent enhancement of feedback de-excitation protects photosystem II from photoinhibition. *Proc. Natl Acad. Sci. USA* **99** (2002) 15222–15227.
44. X.-P. Li, A.M. Gilmore, S. Caffarri, R. Bassi, T. Golan, D. Kramer, K.K. Niyogi, Regulation of light harvesting involves intrathylakoid lumen pH sensing by the PsbS protein. *J. Biol Chem.* **279** (2004) 22866–22874.
45. X.P. Li, A.M. Gilmore, M. Komura, S. Itoh, W.S. Chow, B.J. Pogson, K.K. Niyogi, The effect of PsbS-dependent energy dissipation on photosystem II core-inner-antennae rise-decay kinetics. Paper in preparation.
46. H.Y. Yamamoto, Biochemistry of xanthophyll cycle in higher plants. *Pure Appl. Chem.* **51** (1979) 639–648.

47. B. Demmig-Adams, A.M. Gilmore, W.W.I. Adams, In vivo functions of carotenoids in plants. *FASEB J.* **10** (1996) 403–412.
48. X.-P. Li, O. Björkman, C. Shih, A. Grossman, M. Rosenquist, S. Jansson, K.K. Niyogi, A pigment-binding protein essential for regulation of photosynthetic light harvesting. *Nature* **403** (2000) 391–395.
49. X.-P. Li, A. Phippard, J. Pasari, K.K. Niyogi, Structure–function analysis of photosystem II subunit S (PsbS) in vivo. *Funct. Plant Biol.* **29** (2002) 1131–1139.
50. A.M. Gilmore, V.P. Shinkarev, T.L. Hazlett, Govindjee, Quantitative analysis of the effects of intrathylakoid pH and xanthophyll cycle pigments on chlorophyll a fluorescence lifetime distributions and intensity in thylakoids. *Biochemistry* **37** (1998) 13582–13593.
51. A.M. Gilmore, H.Y. Yamamoto, Time-resolution of the antheraxanthin- and DpH-dependent chlorophyll a fluorescence components associated with photosystem II energy dissipation in *Mantoniella squamata*. *Photochem. Photobiol.* **74** (2001) 291–302.
52. Y.Z. Ma, N.E. Holt, X.-P. Li, K.K. Niyogi, G.R. Fleming, Evidence for direct carotenoid involvement in the regulation of photosynthetic light harvesting. *Proc. Natl. Acad. Sci. U.S.A.* **100** (2003) 4377–4382.
53. N.E. Holt, D. Zigmantas, L. Valkunas, X.-P. Li, K.K. Niyogi, G.R. Fleming, Carotenoid cation formation and the regulation of photosynthetic light harvesting. *Science* **307** (2005) 433–436.
54. D.A. Berthold, G.T. Babcock, C.F. Yocum, A highly resolved, oxygen-evolving Photosystem II preparation from spinach thylakoid membrane: EPR and electron-transport properties. *FEBS Lett.* **134** (1981) 231–234.
55. U. Ljungberg, H.-E. Åkerlund, C. Larsson, B. Andersson, Identification of polypeptides associated with the 23 and 33 kDa proteins of photosynthetic oxygen evolution. *Biochem. Biophys. Acta* **767** (1984) 145–152.
56. D.F. Ghanotakis, C.M. Waggoner, N.R. Bowlby, D.M. Demertriou, G.T. Babcock, C.F. Yocum, Comparative structural and catalytic properties of oxygen-evolving photosystem II preparations. *Photosynth. Res.* **14** (1987) 191–199.
57. N. Wedel, R. Klein, U. Ljungberg, B. Andersson, R.G. Herrmann, The single-copy gene *psbS* codes for a phylogenetically intriguing 22 kDa polypeptide of photosystem II. *FEBS Lett.* **314** (1992) 61–66.
58. S. Kim, P. Sandusky, N.R. Bowlby, R. Aebersold, B.R. Green, S. Vlahakis, C.F. Yocum, E. Pichersky, Characterization of a spinach *psbS* cDNA encoding the 22 kDa protein of photosystem II. *FEBS Lett.* **314** (1992) 67–71.
59. B.R. Green, E. Pichersky, Hypothesis for the evolution of three-helix Chl a/b and Chl a/c light-harvesting antenna proteins from two-helix and four-helix ancestors. *Photosynth. Res.* **39** (1994) 149–162.
60. S. Jansson, A guide to the Lhc genes and their relatives in Arabidopsis. *Trends Pharmacol. Sci.* **4** (1999) 236–240.
61. C. Funk, W.P. Schröder, B.R. Green, G. Renger, B. Andersson, The intrinsic 22 kDa protein is a chlorophyll-binding subunit of photosystem II. *FEBS Lett.* **342** (1994) 261–266.
62. C. Funk, W.P. Schröder, A. Napiwotzki, S.E. Tjus, G. Renger, B. Andersson, The PSII-S protein of higher plants: A new type of pigment-binding protein. *Biochemistry* **34** (1995) 11133–11141.
63. P. Dominica, S. Caffarri, F. Armenante, S. Ceoldo, M. Crimi, R. Bassi, Biochemical properties of the PsbS subunit of Photosystem II either purified from chloroplast or recombinant. *J. Biol. Chem.* **277** (2002) 22750–22758.

64. C. Funk, I. Adamska, B.R. Green, B. Andersson, G. Renger, The unclear-encoded chlorophyll-binding photosystem II-S protein is stable in the absence of pigments. *J. Biol. Chem.* **270** (1995) 30141–30147.
65. S. Kim, E. Pichersky, C.F. Yocum, Topological studies of spinach 22 kDa protein of Photosystem II. *Biochem. Biophys. Acta* **1188** (1994) 339–348.
66. W. Bilger, O. Björkman, Relationship among violaxanthin deepoxidation, thylakoid membrane conformation and nonphotochemical chlorophyll fluorescence quenching in cotton leaves. *Planta* **193** (1994) 238–246.
67. A.V. Ruban, A.A. Pascal, B. Robert, P. Horton, Activation of zeaxanthin is an obligatory event in the regulation of photosynthetic light harvesting. *J. Biol. Chem.* **277** (2002) 7785–7789.
68. E. Bergantino, A. Segalla, A. Brunetta, E. Teardo, F. Rigoni, G.M. Giacometti, I. Szabó, Light- and pH-dependent structural changes in the PsbS subunit of photosystem II. *Proc. Natl. Acad. Sci. U.S.A.* **100** (2003) 15265–15270.
69. A.M. Gilmore, S. Itoh, Govindjee, Global spectral-kinetic analysis of room temperature chlorophyll a fluorescence from light-harvesting mutants of barley. *Philos. Trans. Roy. Soc. London B* **355** (2000) 1371–1384.
70. A.M. Gilmore, T.L. Hazlett, P.G. Debrunner, Govindjee, Photosystem II chlorophyll a fluorescence lifetimes are independent of the antenna size differences between barley wild-type and chlorina mutants: Comparison of xanthophyll-cycle dependent and photochemical quenching. *Photosynth. Res.* **48** (1996) 171–187.
71. M.A. Harrison, J.A. Nemson, A. Melis, Assembly and composition of the chlorophyll *a-b* light-harvesting complex of barley (*Hordeum vulgare* L.). Immunochemical analysis of chlorophyll *b*-less and chrophyll *b*-deficient mutants. *Photosynth. Res.* **38** (1993) 141–151.
72. C.E. Espineda, A.S. Linford, D. Devine, J.A. Brusslan, The *AtCAO* gene, encoding chlorophyll *a* oxygenase, is required for chlorophyll *b* synthesis in *Arabidopsis thaliana*. *Proc. Natl Acad. Sci. U.S.A.* **96** (1999) 10507–10511.
73. R. Bassi, U. Hinz, R. Barbato, The role of light harvesting complex and photosystem II in thylakoid stacking in the chlorina-f2 barley mutant. *Carls. Res. Commun.* **50** (1985) 347–367.
74. D. Simpson, D. Machold, G. Høyer-Hansen, D. von Wettstein, Chlorina mutants of barley (Hordeum vulgare L.). *Carls. Res. Commun.* **50** (1985) 223–238.
75. J.R. Andrews, M.J. Fryer, N.R. Baker, Consequences of LHCII deficiency for photosynthetic regulation in chlorina mutants of barley. *Photosynth. Res.* **44** (1995) 81–91.
76. J.M. Briantais, Light-harvesting chlorophyll a-b complex requirement for regulation of photosystem II photochemistry by non-photochemical quenching. *Photosynth. Res.* **40** (1994) 287–294.
77. M. Mimuro, N. Tamai, T. Yamazaki, I. Yamazaki, Analysis of the excitation energy transfer in spinach chloroplasts at room temperature: identification of the component bands by the time-resolved fluorescence spectrum and by convolution of the decay kinetics, in: *Primary Processes in Photobiology* (1987) (T. Kobayashi, ed.), Springer-Verlag, Berlin, pp. 22–32.
78. M. Mimuro, I. Yamazaki, N. Tamai, T. Yamazaki, Y. Fujita, Excitation energy transfer in spinach chloroplasts: analysis by the time-resolved fluorescence spectrum $-196$ °C in the picosecond time range. *FEBS Lett.* **213** (1987) 119–122.
79. K.K. Karukstis, K. Sauer, Organization of the photosynthetic apparatus of chlorina f-2 mutant of barley using fluorescence decay kinetics. *Biochem. Biophys. Acta* **766** (1984) 148–155.

80. E. Thidholm, V. Lindstrom, C. Tissier, C. Robinson, W.P. Schroder, C. Funk, Novel approach reveals localisation and assembly pathway of the PsbS and PsbW proteins into the Photosystem II dimmer. *FEBS Lett.* **513** (2002) 217–222.
81. J. Nield, C. Funk, J. Barber, Supermolecular structure of Photosystem two and localization of the PsbS protein. *Philos. Trans. R. Soc. London Ser. B* **355** (2000) 1337–1344.
82. C. Kulheim, J. Ågren, S. Jansson, Rapid regulation of light harvesting and fitness in the field. *Science* **297** (2002) 91–93.
83. A.S. Verhoeven, R.C. Bugos, H.Y. Yamamoto, Transgenic tobacco with suppressed zeaxanthin formation is susceptible to stress-induced photoinhibition. *Photosynth. Res.* **67** (2001) 27–39.
84. M. Havaux, J.P. Bonfils, C. Lütz, K.K. Niyogi, Photodamage of the photosynthetic apparatus and its dependence on the leaf developmental stage in the npq1 Arabidopsis mutant deficient in the xanthophyll cycle enzyme violaxanthin de-epoxidase. *Plant Physiol.* **124** (2000) 273–284.
85. A.M. Gilmore, S. Matsubara, M.C. Ball, D.H. Barker, S. Itoh, Excitation energy flow at 77K in the photosynthetic apparatus of overwintering evergreens. *Plant Cell Environ.* **26** (2003) 1021–1034.

# V. Light Stress

Chapter 10

# Photoinhibition of Photosynthetic Electron Transport

## Imre Vass and Eva-Mari Aro

**Table of Contents**

10.1 Introduction ............................................... 395
10.2 Molecular Mechanisms of Photodamage ....................... 397
    10.2.1 Mechanisms of PSII Photodamage ..................... 397
        10.2.1.1 Acceptor-side Induced Photodamage............ 397
        10.2.1.2 Donor-side Induced Photodamage ............. 398
        10.2.1.3 Photodamage Induced by Triplet Forming Charge
                Recombination ............................ 398
        10.2.1.4 Photodamage by Ultraviolet Light ............. 399
        10.2.1.5 Two-step Mechanism of Photodamage .......... 401
        10.2.1.6 Photon Counter Behavior of Photodamage ....... 401
    10.2.2 Mechanism of PSI Photodamage ...................... 402
    10.2.3 Active Oxygen Production Under Photoinhibitory Conditions .. 402
10.3 Molecular Mechanisms of Photoprotection ..................... 404
    10.3.1 Photoprotection by Excitation Quenching in the Antenna ..... 404
    10.3.2 Photoprotection by Inactive PSII Centers ................ 405
    10.3.3 Photoprotection by Non-triplet Producing Charge Recombination 405
    10.3.4 Photoprotection by Protein Repair ..................... 406
        10.3.4.1 Degradation of Damaged D1 Protein ........... 406
        10.3.4.2 FtsH and DegP Proteases in D1 Protein Degradation 408
        10.3.4.3 Repair of Damaged PSII by De Novo D1 Protein
                Synthesis................................. 409
        10.3.4.4 Role of Protein Phosphorylation in the PSII Damage–
                Repair Cycle in Plants ...................... 410
        10.3.5 Protection Against Ultraviolet Light ............. 411
10.4 Concluding Remarks ....................................... 412
Acknowledgements ............................................. 412
References..................................................... 412

# Abstract

Light, the primary driving force of photosynthesis, is a highly energetic and potentially dangerous substrate, which can affect all components of the photosynthetic apparatus and induce secondary destructive processes. Light-induced decline of photosynthetic activity, generally known as photoinhibition, is a general phenomenon in all photosynthetic organisms under conditions when the metabolic processes can not keep up with the electron flow produced by the primary photoreactions. The main factors responsible for the light sensitivity of the photosynthetic apparatus are the presence of excited pigment molecules, oxygen, and the high oxidizing potential of electron donors. Although light-induced damage occurs in all pigmented photosynthetic complexes the main site of photodamage is the Photosystem II complex, with smaller effect on Photosystem I and on the light harvesting antenna. Photodamage of the photosynthetic apparatus can be prevented efficiently by excitation quenching in the antenna, which dissipates excess excitation energy into heat. Photoprotection can also be provided by partly photoinhibited Photosystem II complexes, which work as dissipation centers, as well as by non-radiative charge recombination in the reaction center, which bypasses the triplet chlorophyll formation. Photodamage of Photosystem II can be repaired efficiently via a complex process that includes degradation of light damaged D1 protein subunit of the reaction center by thylakoid bound proteases, followed by resynthesis and membrane insertion of the newly made subunits, and, finally, the ligation of redox cofactors. The damage–repair cycle of the Photosystem II complex provides a highly dynamic system for the regulation of plant acclimation to rapidly changing light conditions.

## 10.1 Introduction

Photoinhibition is a broad term, describing the light-induced decline of photosynthetic activity. This important phenomenon has been known for over 100 years (for a historical review see Adir et al. [1]), and has been a topic of intense research since the mid-1980s. Different aspects of photoinhibition have been covered by extensive reviews [1–7]. Here we summarize the progress that took place during the last few years in our understanding of the molecular mechanisms of light-induced damage and subsequent repair of the photosynthetic apparatus.

Photosynthesis is driven by light, a highly energetic and potentially dangerous substrate, which can affect all components of the photosynthetic apparatus and their interactions, and induce secondary destructive as well as repair processes. Plants have to optimize the utilization of light energy under conditions when primary photochemistry goes on, but other metabolic processes are limiting. One of the important products of photosynthetic electron transport is oxygen, which can form highly toxic species when it interacts with excited pigments or redox components. A further problem is created by the very high oxidation potentials of PSII donor components, reaching 1.25 V [8], which can induce oxidative damage in their protein environment. This multiplicity of events related to the phenomenology of photoinhibition complicates its study and leads to highly conflicting views about the mechanistic details.

The extent of photodamage is regulated by light intensity, the capacity of secondary metabolic processes to utilize the electrons produced in the primary photoreactions, and by the efficiency of the photoprotective and repair processes. The main sites of photodamage and the pathways of electron transport, which influence the redox level of the electron transport components, are summarized in Figure 1. The major site of photoinhibition has been shown to be the PSII complex, although PSI can also be damaged by light under low temperature conditions, as discussed below. The following sections provide an overview of our current knowledge of the mechanistic details of photodamage of PSII, as well as of PSI.

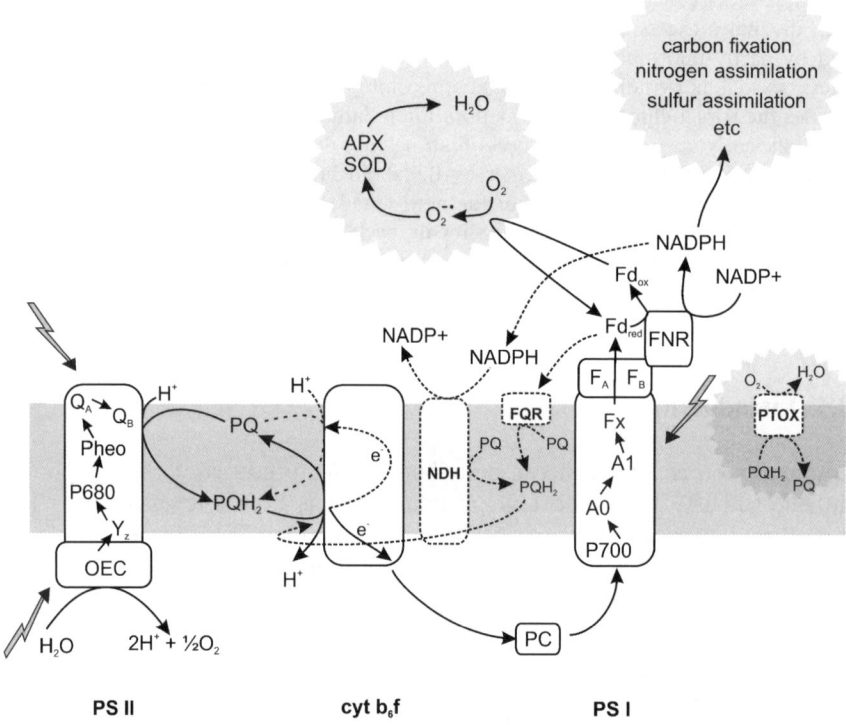

**Figure 1.** Sites of photodamage in photosynthetic electron transport. The scheme shows the main components of electron transport in relation to light-induced damage. The primary site of photodamage is the PSII complex, which can be inactivated both at its acceptor and donor side redox components. The light sensitivity of PSII is influenced largely by the redox state of the PQ pool, which is determined by the balance of electron in-flow from PSII, the linear and cyclic electron out-flow mediated by PSI, as well as the electron sink capacity of the Calvin cycle, the water–water cycle, the terminal oxidase and other electron consuming processes. In addition to PSII, PSI can also be photoinhibited when electron flow from PSII and sink capacity becomes simultaneously limiting.

## 10.2 Molecular Mechanisms of Photodamage

*10.2.1 Mechanisms of PSII Photodamage*

*10.2.1.1 Acceptor-side Induced Photodamage*
A large body of literature evidence demonstrates that under conditions of strong illumination a series of light-induced modifications occur at the acceptor side PSII, which eventually lead to the inhibition of electron transport. I. Ohad's group have demonstrated that a light-induced reversible conformational change takes place at the PSII acceptor side that slows down the $Q_A^{-\cdot}$ to $Q_B$ electron transfer step and leads to an irreversible change of the D1 protein [9]. This effect is probably initiated by the light-induced increase in the reduction level of the PQ pool when the main electron sinks, such as the Calvin cycle and photorespiration, are unable to keep up with the electron flow from PSII. Reduction of the PSII acceptor side components can be enhanced by anaerobiosis, which made it possible to study further mechanistic details of light-induced changes at the acceptor side [10–12]. These studies revealed that over-reduction of the PQ pool creates a situation when the binding site of the secondary quinone electron acceptor ($Q_B$) site is unoccupied due to the lack of reducible PQ molecules. This leads to the stabilization of the reduced primary quinone electron acceptor ($Q_A^{-\cdot}$), which might include its protonation [12]. The final step of acceptor side modifications is the double reduction and protonation of $Q_A$ and the release of $Q_AH_2$ from its binding site [12,13].

A very important consequence of light-induced modifications at the acceptor side of PSII is the formation of $^3P_{680}$-producing states of the PSII reaction center. The characteristic spin-polarized $^3P_{680}$ EPR signal was originally observed in dithionite treated PSII membranes [11], and also in anaerobically photoinhibited samples [12]. $^3P_{680}$ is more easily detectable when it has a long lifetime in the absence of $Q_A$, or when $Q_A$ is double reduced and protonated. However, with a shorter lifetime, $^3P_{680}$ can also be formed when $Q_A$ is in the stabilized single reduced form [14], or even in the presence of unstabilized $Q_A^{-\cdot}$ [15]. In the presence of molecular oxygen, which has a triplet spin configuration in its ground state, the interaction of $^3P_{680}$ with $^3\Sigma_g O_2$ results in the formation of highly reactive singlet oxygen $^1\Delta_g O_2$ [16], which can irreversibly damage its environment. The validity of the acceptor-side mechanism has been unambiguously demonstrated by the detection of singlet oxygen formation in various PSII preparations [17–19] and intact leaves under [20] acceptor side photoinhibitory conditions. In contrast, singlet oxygen production is not observed under donor-side photoinhibitory conditions [17]. Since complete inhibition of PSII electron transport due to double reduction of $Q_A$ may occur only under the combination of high intensity illumination and anaerobiosis or strongly reducing conditions, the source of $^1\Delta_g O_2$ that is observed in aerobically photoinhibited samples must be $^3P_{680}$ formed in PSII centers that contain stabilized singly reduced $Q_A$. In these centers the actual inhibition of electron transport is the consequence of singlet-oxygen mediated destruction of the PSII reaction center, rather than the blockage of electron transport at the level of $Q_A$.

Light-induced modifications of the PSII acceptor side affects not only the quinone electron acceptors, but also the non-heme iron located at the interface of the D1 and D2 reaction center proteins. Such modification of the non-heme iron in photoinhibited PSII was detected by the measurements of either the EPR signal arising from the $Q_A^{-\cdot}Fe^{2+}$ acceptor complex [21] or of the Mössbauer signal from $Fe^{2+}$ [22].

### 10.2.1.2 Donor-side Induced Photodamage

Increased light sensitivity in the absence of a functional Mn cluster at the donor side of PSII is well documented and characterized. In contrast to the acceptor-side induced inactivation mechanism, which requires high-light conditions, the donor-side induced inactivation mechanism can take place under both low and high intensity illumination when the donor side of PSII is unable to keep up with the rate of withdrawal of electrons by $P_{680}^{+\cdot}$. This may lead to the accumulation of long-lived, oxidizing radicals at the PSII donor side, leading to rapid inactivation of electron transport and protein damage. This so-called donor-side photoinhibition can be observed when the water-oxidizing complex of PSII is inhibited by the removal of Mn by Tris washing or $NH_2OH$ treatment [23–25], or by the removal of $Cl^-$ [26], and also in isolated PSII reaction center particles that do not contain the Mn cluster [27]. The quantum efficiency of electron transport inactivation increases 1000-fold in Tris-treated PSII membranes ($1 \times 10^{-4}$) as compared with active PSII membranes ($2-3 \times 10^{-7}$) [28]. Increased PSII photoinactivation and D1 protein degradation is also observed in the *Scenedesmus* LF-1 mutant, which is unable to evolve oxygen [29], and in *Synechocystis* 6803 deletion mutants lacking the PsbO (Mn stabilizing) protein [30]. Single amino acid changes at the C-terminal part of the D1 protein, which inhibit largely or completely the oxygen evolving activity, also lead to increased light sensitivity of PSII in *Synechocystis* 6803 [31–34]. The main mechanism of photoinactivation of PSII with impaired electron transport at the donor side is the generation of long lived $P_{680}^{+\cdot}$ and $Y_Z^{ox}$ radicals that could not be reduced in the absence of sufficient donor side electron flow [23,26,28]. These radicals, especially $P_{680}^{+\cdot}$, have high oxidizing power and damage their protein environment, leading to the impairment of electron transport between $Y_Z$ and $P_{680}^{+\cdot}$ [23,28], and destruction of PSII reaction center proteins [26].

### 10.2.1.3 Photodamage Induced by Triplet Forming Charge Recombination

During illumination, stable charge separated states ($S_2Q_A^{-\cdot}$, $S_2Q_B^{-\cdot}$, $S_3Q_B^{-\cdot}$) are formed in PSII. In the dark the charges recombine and form the primary radical pair $P_{680}^{+\cdot}Pheo^{-\cdot}$ in the singlet or triplet spin configuration. Owing to the three-fold degeneracy of the triplet state the distribution of triplet and singlet radical pairs is 3:1. The singlet radical pair recombines to $^1P_{680}^*$ (Pheo), whereas the triplet radical pair recombines to $^3P_{680}$ (Phe) whose interaction with ground state triplet oxygen $^3\Sigma_g O_2$ leads then to the formation of singlet oxygen $^1\Delta_g O_2$. This mechanism of photoinhibition has been explored by Keren and co-workers

[35–38], who produced different distributions of S states by illuminating the samples with a series of flash packages separated by different dark intervals. By using this flash protocol it was demonstrated that D1 protein degradation was correlated with the amount of $S_2Q_B^{-\cdot}$ and $S_3Q_B^{-\cdot}$ charge pairs, as well as with the dark interval allowed for charge recombination. Singlet oxygen measurements performed under the same conditions demonstrated that $^1\Delta_gO_2$ was also produced from the recombining $S_2Q_B^{-\cdot}$ and $S_3Q_B^{-\cdot}$ charge pairs [39].

The efficiency of singlet oxygen production via the charge recombination mechanism is regulated by the free energy gap between the $P_{680}^+Q_A^-$ and $P_{680}^+Phe^-$ radical pairs [40]. When this gap is lowered by the decrease of $E_m(Q_A/Q_A^{-\cdot})$ as a consequence of DCMU binding to the $Q_B$ site, $^1\Delta_gO_2$ production is decreased, whereas $^1\Delta_gO_2$ production is enhanced when $E_m(Q_A/Q_A^{-\cdot})$ is raised by binding phenolic herbicides to the $Q_B$ site [41].

An important feature of triplet forming charge recombination is that it can take place both at low and high intensity illumination and can explain photodamage induced in a wide intensity range. Photoinhibition of PSII is associated with triplet production not only in the reaction center, but also in light harvesting Chls, which are uncoupled from the PSII antenna [42,43]. The size of this uncoupled Chl pool is about 1–2 Chl per PSII reaction center [44].

*10.2.1.4 Photodamage by Ultraviolet Light*
Although the main constituent of physiologically relevant solar radiation is the photosynthetically active spectral range PAR (400–700 nm), shorter wavelength ultraviolet radiation is highly damaging for the photosynthetic apparatus. Comparison of the characteristics of PSII damage induced by UV-A (315–400 nm) and UV-B (290–315 nm) radiation shows that the two spectral ranges inhibit PSII by very similar or identical mechanisms, which target primarily the water-oxidizing complex [45,46,64,65]. The damaging effects of the UV-C (200–290 nm) region are expected to be similar to that of UV-B and UV-A [47–49], but this notion is not fully proven.

The effects of UV-B and UV-A radiation are not distributed evenly between the two photosystems. Most studies found minor or no effect on PSI as compared with PSII [45,50–52]. Notably, DNA microarray experiments indicated a significant down-regulation of many genes that encode PSI protein subunits in UV-B exposed cells of the cyanobacterium *Synechocystis* 6803 [53]. Although the corresponding decrease in PSI activity has not been reported yet, this effect may indicate an acclimation response, which could readjust the PSI/PSII ratio upset by the UV damage of PSII centers.

The main targets of UV light in PSII are the quinone electron acceptors, the redox active tyrosines ($Y_Z$ and $Y_D$) and the Mn cluster of the water-oxidizing complex [54,55]. UV effects on the quinone acceptors were suggested from observations showing that the action spectrum of PSII damage peaks at 250–260 nm [56,57], where oxidized PQ absorb [58,59], and also that plastoquinones are destroyed by UV-C radiation [47–49]. This idea was adapted for the UV-B induced damage of PSII on the basis of selective absorption of plastosemiquinones in the UV-B range [59,60]. Deleterious effects of UV-B and UV-A radiation on the redox function of $Y_Z$ and $Y_D$ are revealed by the loss of the EPR signals arising from $Y_Z^{ox}$ and $Y_D^{ox}$ [46,61–63]. UV sensitivity of tyrosine residues is related to their absorption in the UV region, which peaks at around 280 nm in the neutral form.

Inhibition of the water-oxidizing complex by UV-A and UV-B radiation is suggested by several observations: (i) Retarded rise of variable fluorescence, typical for donor-side limited electron transport [50–51,57]. (ii) Conversion of the re-reduction kinetics of $P_{680}^+$ from the ns range to the μs range, indicating retarded electron donation from the Mn cluster to $P_{680}$ [64–66]. (iii) Restoration of PSII activity by artificial electron donors, which can maintain electron transport in PSII centers that are deprived of their oxygen evolving capacity by UV-B radiation [57,64]. (iv) Faster loss of the multiline EPR signal arising from the $S_2$ redox state of the Mn cluster as compared with that $Q_A^- Fe^{2+}$ [46,62,63]. (v) Increased stability of $Y_Z^{ox}$ from the μs to the ms time range [46,63]. Detailed comparison of the kinetics by which UV light affects the different redox cofactors of PSII clearly demonstrate that the primary target of UV radiation in PSII is the Mn cluster of water oxidation, whereas damage to the quinone acceptors and tyrosine donors are secondary effects.

The sensitivity of PSII in different S-states of the water-oxidizing complex has been studied by synchronizing PSII into specific S states by short pulses of visible light, which were then illuminated with monochromatic UV-B laser flashes of 308 nm. The damage induced by the UV-B flashes showed a clear S-state dependence, indicating that the water-oxidizing complex is most prone to UV damage in the $S_2$ and $S_3$ oxidation states [67]. During the S-state transitions the catalytic Mn cluster of water oxidation is sequentially oxidized (see Chapter 17 and references therein). Manganese ions bound to organic ligands (such as amino acids) have pronounced absorption in the UV-B and UV-A regions in the Mn(III) and Mn(IV) oxidation states, which dominate the higher S-states, but not in the Mn(II) oxidation state, which may occur in the lower S-states [68]. As a consequence the $S_1 \rightarrow S_2$ and $S_2 \rightarrow S_3$ redox transitions of the Mn cluster are accompanied by absorption changes in the UV region [69,70]. Thus, the high UV sensitivity of PSII in the $S_2$ and $S_3$ states indicates that UV absorption by the Mn(III) and Mn(IV) ions could be the primary sensitizer of UV-induced damage of the water-oxidizing machinery. Light-sensitized damage of the Mn cluster has been suggested to occur not only in the UV, but also in the whole visible spectral range [71]. However, the model that suggests Mn as the sole sensitizer of photodamage [71] can not explain the detailed action spectra of photoinhibition, which show a peak in the red region that matches Chl absorption [42–43,56].

An important consequence of UV-irradiation is the damage of the protein backbone of the PSII reaction center. This effect is characteristic mainly for the D1 and D2 subunits that form the heart of the reaction center of PSII, and has been observed both in vivo [72–76] and in isolated thylakoid preparations [77–83]. Other protein components of PSII seem to be damaged much later than D1 and D2, and this may be an indirect consequence of the breakup of the D1/D2 reaction center heterodimer [83].

## 10.2.1.5 Two-step Mechanism of Photodamage

The existence of photodamage at the donor side of PSII during illumination of initially intact systems has been an enigmatic issue of photoinhibition research. Accumulation of PSII centers with impaired electron donation from the Mn cluster to $Y_Z^{ox}$ has been demonstrated under UV-A and UV-B illumination [46,51,63,66], and also after exposure of *Synechocystis* 6803 cells to unfiltered sunlight [84]. Based on these results it was proposed that photoinhibition by sunlight can be initiated by a UV-induced inhibition of PSII donor side followed by the destruction of the PSII reaction center via the donor-side induced mechanism of photoinhibition [84]. Recently it has been suggested that not only UV-B and UV-A light but, to a smaller extent, blue and green light can also inactivate the water-oxidizing complex [85]. Based on these data the two-step mechanism of photoinhibition, which was initially put forward to explain the interaction effects caused by light of the UV-A/UV-B plus visible range [84], was extended by the proposal that shorter wavelength visible light, up to the green spectral range, can also inactivate the water oxidizing complex, followed by red light driven destruction of the PSII reaction center [85].

## 10.2.1.6 Photon Counter Behavior of Photodamage

The rate of photodamage in the absence of protein repair is proportional with light intensity in the 100–2000 μmoles $m^{-2} s^{-1}$ range [86]. In addition, under certain conditions photodamage is determined by light dosage, i.e., by the number of absorbed quanta independent of the intensity of incident light at which these quanta are delivered. This reciprocity relationship between duration and intensity of irradiation with respect to the biological effect is valid for photoinhibition induced by UV-A [45] and UV-B light [63] in the absence of protein repair. The reciprocity relationship also holds at relatively high visible light intensities in isolated spinach thylakoids [56,84], intact cyanobacterial cells [84,87], and whole leaves treated with protein synthesis inhibitor [86,88,89]. However, the reciprocity relationship breaks down under low intensity CW light [89] or flashing illumination [39] and there are clear deviations from the reciprocity at high photon dosages as well [87,90].

Data obtained with isolated thylakoids and *Synechocystis* cells demonstrate that UV-B and visible photons inactivate oxygen evolution via single-hit of single-target mechanisms independently of each other [84]. In other words the inactivation of oxygen evolution does not need multiple photon hits of the same target, or cooperative single hits of more than one target. The single hit of single target mechanism is consistent with either the Mn cluster of the water-oxidizing complex or the $Q_A$ acceptor being the target. Although the formation of doubly reduced $Q_A$ in strong light requires two subsequent photoacts [12], the absorption of a photon that is needed to create $Q_A^{-\cdot}$ is not a dose dependent hit since $Q_A^{-\cdot}$ is a fully functional component of PSII, which is rapidly re-oxidized in the dark and does not accumulate in a dose-dependent manner. Thus, the damaging single hit event could be considered as the formation of functionally inactive $Q_AH_2$ from $Q_A^{-\cdot}$. However, the recombination type mechanism does not follow the single hit of single target mechanism since the damaging effect depends on the time interval between the subsequent charge separation and recombination events [36–37,39].

### 10.2.2 Mechanism of PSI Photodamage

PSI is generally regarded more resistant to light damage than PSII. Specific susceptibility of PSI to photoinhibition was first discovered in chilling sensitive plants and was demonstrated to occur even at moderate light provided the temperature was low enough [91–93]. In chilling resistant plants, like *Arabidopsis* and barley, a sole PSI photoinhibition does not occur but is always accompanied with an inhibition of PSII as well [94–96]. The mechanism of photodamage to PSI also drastically differs from that in PSII.

Reactive oxygen species (ROS) are instrumental in inducing the photoinhibition of PSI. This is clear from experiments with mutants deficient in ROS scavenging enzymes and which show higher susceptibility to photoinhibition of PSI than the WT controls. Similarly, the inhibitors of superoxide dismutase were shown to make chilling resistant spinach more susceptible to photoinhibition of PSI [97]. Conversely, scavengers of hydroxyl radicals, superoxide and hydrogen peroxide applied to leaves partially protect PSI against photodamage [94,98–100]. It is also clear that oxygen and electron transfer are essential elements in PSI photoinhibition [98,101], and the lack of electron acceptors on the reducing side of PSI was recently shown to enhance PSI photoinhibition [102].

The primary targets of ROS species in PSI are the iron-sulfur clusters $F_A$ and $F_B$ on the reducing side of PSI [92]. It was postulated recently that the initial damage to the terminal acceptors of PSI possibly triggers the release of PSI-C, -D and -E subunits from the PSI complex, which, in turn, would tag the entire PSI complex to degradation [96]. Although several studies have shown the degradation of the PSI-A and -B proteins, the reaction center proteins of PSI, during PSI photoinhibition [93,103], it now seems likely that the protein degradation of all PSI subunits in the damaged complex takes place upon transfer of plant to non-stress conditions [95,104]. There is no sophisticated repair of only the damaged PSI proteins as in the case of PSII repair cycle and the turnover of the D1 protein, as will be discussed below. Indeed, once the iron-sulfur clusters of the PSI complex have been damaged, the recovery of PSI electron flow to stromal acceptors requires a complete degradation of the PSI complex, which is a very slow process, occurring on a time scale of days rather than hours, and the resynthesis of an entirely new PSI complex is required [96].

### 10.2.3 Active Oxygen Production Under Photoinhibitory Conditions

Production of reactive oxygen species (ROS) in the photosynthetic apparatus is a well-documented phenomenon. The best characterized example of ROS is singlet oxygen. $^1\Delta_g O_2$ oxygen can react with pigments, proteins, and lipids and, despite of its short half-time of about 200 ns in cells [105], it can diffuse up to 10 nm under physiologically relevant conditions [106], allowing penetration through cell membranes. The main pathway of $^1\Delta_g O_2$ formation in photosynthetic systems is the interaction of ground state triplet oxygen with triplet excited Chls. Chl triplets can be formed by spin conversion of singlet excited Chl in antenna, or through the recombination of the primary charge separated state in the PSII reaction center. Singlet oxygen production in PSII was predicted to occur as a consequence of acceptor side photoinhibition [12,107], or under the conditions of stable charge recombination between the reduced quinone electron acceptors and the oxidized S states of the water-oxidizing complex [37]. These predictions were confirmed by direct detection of $^1\Delta_g O_2$ using EPR spin trapping [17,108] or chemiluminescence [19] in isolated PSII preparations under the conditions of photoinhibitory illumination by continuous light or by single turnover flashes [39]. Chlorophyll triplet formation and subsequent $^1O_2$ production occurs not only in the PSII reaction center, but also in the antenna, as shown by EPR spin trapping [109,110]. These data support the conclusions of mathematical modeling that shows that, in addition to the acceptor side mechanism of photoinhibition, singlet oxygen is produced by other processes as well [111]. Singlet oxygen may also play a role in the degradation of the LHCII proteins in strong light [112].

Singlet oxygen can also be detected by fluorescence spin traps both in isolated PSII preparations and in intact leaves [20,113]. This method was used to demonstrate $^1\Delta_g O_2$ production under the conditions of charge recombination induced by illumination with flashing light [39]. To avoid extensive damage $^1\Delta_g O_2$ should be quenched. The main $^1\Delta_g O_2$ quenchers are β-carotene and α-tocopherol [114]. β-Carotene can quench $^1O_2$ directly or by quenching $^3$Chl. In the antenna the carotenoid molecules are close enough to quench the $^3$Chls at high rates that are even faster than the formation via intersystem crossing [115]. However, in the PSII reaction center the distance between the carotenes and triplet Chl is too large to allow direct triplet quenching. Therefore, the β-carotenes in the PSII reaction center may protect by quenching the produced $^1\Delta_g O_2$ [116,117]. If $^1\Delta_g O_2$ produced in the PSII reaction center is not quenched by protective molecules, it most likely interacts with the D1 protein and leads to its degradation. Under flash illumination conditions the degradation of D1 matches the pattern of $^3P_{680}$, producing charge recombination [35–37], which in turn is correlated with $^1\Delta_g O_2$ formation [39]. Therefore, D1 degradation and singlet oxygen formation are also correlated. This notion is further supported by observation of the same specific degradation products of D1 under the conditions of acceptor side photoinhibition and production of $^1\Delta_g O_2$ by chemicals [118].

Besides singlet oxygen other types of ROS are also produced during photoinhibition. Under conditions of donor side photoinhibition the dominant species are hydroxyl radicals [17], which represent the main ROS also under UV photoinhibition [119]. The production of OH$^.$ radicals at the acceptor side of PSII has also been proposed [120]. In this process the interaction of $O_2^{-.}$ and the non-heme iron is proposed to lead to the formation of bound peroxide intermediates, which then results in OH$^.$ formation. In addition, $O_2^{-.}$ formed at the acceptor side of PSII is proposed to lead to the production of $H_2O_2$, which then interacts with free metal iron to afford OH$^.$ via the Fenton reaction [121].

## 10.3 Molecular Mechanisms of Photoprotection

*10.3.1 Photoprotection by Excitation Quenching in the Antenna*

Photodamage of PSII in chloroplasts can be prevented efficiently by excitation quenching in the LHCII antenna, which consequently dissipates excess excitation energy harmlessly as heat. This phenomenon includes processes termed non-photochemical quenching (NPQ) of chlorophyll fluorescence that can be induced within a time scale of seconds to minutes, as reviewed recently [122,123]. Crucial for induction of non-photochemical quenching is a decrease of pH in the thylakoid lumen upon illumination, thereby activating the thermal dissipation as a feed-back mechanism, which, in turn, down-regulates the photosynthetic electron transport. The pH-dependent thermal dissipation of excitation energy is quite efficient: over 75% of the absorbed photons can be eliminated in this way [124]. Two proteins besides the LHCII antenna, the violaxanthin de-epoxidase in the thylakoid lumen and the PsbS protein in the thylakoid membrane, have an essential role in the development of maximal of NPQ (see also Chapter 9).

In high light, the acidification of thylakoid lumen activates the enzyme violaxanthin de-epoxidase, which converts violaxanthin into zeaxanthin via the intermediate antheraxanthin [125,126]. The xanthophyll cycle functions in the thylakoid membrane of all higher plants and of ferns, mosses and several algal groups. In addition, cyanobacteria can form zeaxanthin from β-carotene at high irradiances via the xanthophyll biosynthesis pathway [127]. Studies on zeaxanthin- and lutein-deficient mutants have demonstrated that NPQ was largely absent, or impaired, respectively, indicating that zeaxanthin and possibly also lutein have central roles in the photoprotection of photosynthesis [128].

Another thylakoid protein crucial for formation of NPQ is PsbS [123,129]. This was unambiguously shown with the *npq4–1* mutant lacking the *psbS* gene and, thus, also the PsbS protein. This protein belongs to the LHCII family of proteins but it does not bind chlorophyll. The *npq4–1* mutant lacked energy-dependent chlorophyll quenching, the major component of NPQ, but had a normal xanthophyll cycle, indicating that PsbS is necessary for maximal NPQ in *Arabidopsis* [129]. Activation of NPQ was shown to involve a protonation of the amino acid side chains in the PsbS protein. From these studies it was proposed that PsbS is probably the site of NPQ in photosynthesis There are, however, different theories about the functional site of NPQ and also the exact role of PsbS remains to be resolved (Chapter 9). Furthermore, it is not known for sure whether zeaxanthin participates in NPQ directly, as an energy acceptor, or indirectly, allowing allosteric control of the configuration of a quenching species [130,131].

A conformational change in LHCII, occurring via binding of zeaxanthin and protons to LHCII, has been suggested to be a prerequisite for thermal energy dissipation [132,133]. Recently, however, a somewhat different model has been presented, in which no conformational change is needed in LHCII for thermal energy dissipation [134]. This model is based on the high-resolution X-ray structure of pea LHCII trimer. Deduced from the exact distances measured between the chlorophyll and carotenoid molecules, it was concluded that the tight binding of zeaxanthin to LHCII, contrary to a less tight binding of violaxanthin [135], keeps the pigments close enough for direct energy transfer from chlorophyll to a zeaxanthin molecule, which then dissipates the energy as heat.

*10.3.2 Photoprotection by Inactive PSII Centers*

Under conditions when the balance of photodamage and repair of PSII is upset, non-functional PSII centers can accumulate that are capable of light absorption but not of photosynthetic electron transport. It has been hypothesized that photoinactivated PSII centers are capable of harmless dissipation of excitation energy, and may contribute to photoprotection of their spatial and functional neighbors by acting as sinks for excitation energy [4,136]. Experimental support for this hypothesis comes from studies that show that decrease of the functional fraction of PSII centers follows, initially, a mono-exponential course during photoinhibition of lincomycin-treated *Capsicum annuum* leaves. However, in the later phases of photoinhibition the decay proceeds more slowly and 15–20% of centers can survive further illumination without being photoinactivated [4,88,90]. Strong support for the protective role of inactive PSII centers came from the direct detection of shorter Chl fluorescence lifetime after exposure to light stress in a distinct, strongly quenching fraction of PSII centers [137].

*10.3.3 Photoprotection by Non-triplet Producing Charge Recombination*

As outlined in Section 10.2.1.3, charge recombination that leads to the formation of triplet radical pairs is an important mechanism of singlet oxygen production. Protection against this recombination-type photoinhibition can be achieved by regulating the balance of triplet producing and non-triplet producing pathways. In cold acclimated *Arabidopsis* leaves, which show greater photo-tolerance than the non-acclimated ones, the $E_m(Q_A/Q_A^-)$ is increased [138]. This effect increases the free-energy gap between $P_{680}^+Q_A^-$ and $P_{680}^+Phe^-$, leading to decreased efficiency of $^3P_{680}$ (and $^1\Delta_gO_2$) formation [40].

The balance of charge recombination routes is also affected by the redox potential of Phe [8]. In the cyanobacterium *Synechocystis* 6803 the replacement of the D1-Gln130 residue by Glu increases $E_m(Phe/Phe^-)$ [139]. This mutation leads to the induction of a 300-ps non-radiative recombination pathway from the singlet excited state of $P_{680}$, which has been suggested to have a photoprotective role [139]. Some cyanobacteria, like *Synechococcus* 7942, have two different D1 protein forms (called D1:1 and D1:2), which are transiently exchanged under high light and other stress conditions [140]. When PSII has the high light form of D1 (D1:2) it has a 25% higher quantum yield and shows increased tolerance to photoinhibition as compared with PSII centers with the low light form of D1 (D1:1) [141]. The D1:1 and D1:2 forms of *Synechococcus* 7942 differ in 25 amino acids, which, notably, involve the replacement of Q130 in the D1:1 form with E130 in the D1:2 form. This points to an intriguing regulatory mechanism of photo-tolerance in which the redox potential change of Phe regulates the harmless dissipation of excess light energy. Importantly, in this respect, in higher plants there is a glutamate residue at the 130 position of D1, which corresponds to the high light form of D1 in cyanobacteria.

### 10.3.4 Photoprotection by Protein Repair

Rapid turnover of the PSII D1 reaction centre protein after photodamage can be regarded as one of the most important protective systems in the thylakoid membrane at light. No visible damage to PSII occurs in photosynthesizing cells at light intensities below those saturating the photosynthetic carbon fixation. Indeed, under these conditions the damage and repair are in balance and only at higher light intensities does the rate of damage exceed the rate of repair, resulting in measurable photoinhibition of PSII. Although the D1 protein is the main target for photodamage, it also seems clear that other subunits, like D2 and PsbH, are occasionally targets for photodamage, particularly under very strong irradiance [142,143], or under UV light. Figure 2 summarizes the main steps of the D1 protein repair cycle.

#### 10.3.4.1 Degradation of Damaged D1 Protein
A partial disassembly of the PS II complex and the presence of a membrane-associated proteolytic enzyme system are prerequisites for degradation of the photodamaged D1 protein in all oxygenic photosynthetic organisms. Several pieces of information also suggest an involvement of a conformational change (triggering) in the D1 protein before proteolytic degradation. In support of this possibility are experiments demonstrating a protective effect against D1 protein degradation by urea- and triazine-type herbicides that bind tightly to the $Q_B$ site of the D1 protein [144–147] and may, thereby, restrict a conformational change and thus a triggering of the protein for proteolysis.

The D1 protein is an integral membrane protein composed of five transmembrane helices (designated A–E) with the N-terminus and C-terminus exposed at the stromal and lumenal thylakoid surfaces, respectively [148]. The D1 protein forms a heterodimer with the homologous D2 protein, which is surrounded by approximately 25 other subunits forming the PS II supercomplex. It can be imagined that the degradation of the D1 protein in the heart of such a big membrane protein complex is not a trivial process.

Early studies focused on identifying the D1 protein degradation fragments to pinpoint where the protein is initially cleaved. Typically, an N-terminal 23 kDa fragment and a C-terminal 10 kDa fragment were identified in vitro under conditions of acceptor side induced photoinhibition [5,149], corroborating the primary cleavage in the stromal DE-loop. Conversely, when the PS II particles were subjected to donor side photoinhibition, the primary D1 degradation fragments were identified as an N-terminal 9 kDa fragment and a C-terminal 24 kDa fragment [149–151], suggesting primary cleavage on the lumenal loop between helices A and B. Importantly, it is still unclear whether the degradation

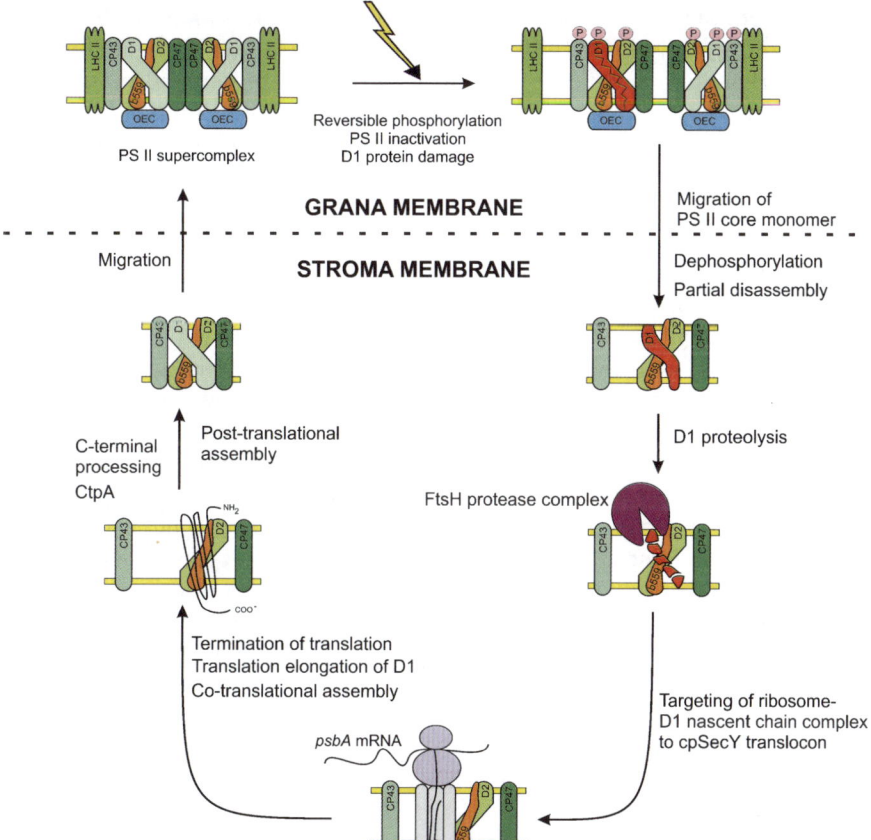

**Figure 2.** Repair cycle of the D1 protein. In chloroplasts the targets of photodamage are the PSII supercomplexes in grana stacks. After detachment of the LHCII antenna and monomerization of the PSII dimer, the damaged PSII core monomer migrates to stroma-exposed thylakoid regions where the FtsH protease complex removes the damaged D1 protein. New D1 protein is directly synthesized into the existing PSII core complex and becomes co-translationally associated with the rest of the complex. After C-terminal processing of the D1 protein by CtpA protease, the detached small subunits, CP43 and PsbO becomes assembled to PSII core monomer. After dimerization in the grana, the rest of the OEC proteins attach the complex, possibly even after the attachment of the LHCII antenna.

of the D1 protein follows the same pattern in vitro and in vivo since the degradation fragments do not accumulate under the latter conditions.

Degradation of the light-damaged D1 protein is a proteolytic process occurring, in a well-coordinated manner, in the stroma-exposed thylakoids and leaving the other PSII proteins most often intact. Identification of the protease or proteases responsible for the D1 protein degradation has been investigated extensively during the last decade [5,149,152,153]. Identification of thylakoid-associated proteases of bacterial origin, together with reverse genetics approaches, have been key features in the progress made in elucidating D1 protein proteolysis [152–157]. Moreover, a complex and intriguing chloroplast degradation machinery with nearly 50 putative proteolytic enzymes has been revealed by computational and experimental analyses with the *Arabidopsis thaliana* genome [152,158]. So far, two key chloroplast protease families have been demonstrated to be involved in D1 protein degradation, the DegP proteases and the FtsH proteases [152–156,159–162].

*10.3.4.2 FtsH and DegP Proteases in D1 Protein Degradation*
It was initially suggested that the primary cleavage in the D1 protein is due to action of the DegP protease in the stromal loop connecting the transmembrane helices D and E and, thus, producing the 23 kDa N-terminal and 10 kDa C-terminal fragments, whereas the FtsH protease would act as a secondary protease, degrading the fragments of the primary cleavage [154].

The *Arabidopsis thaliana* genome has 14 genes encoding the members of the DegP peptidase family, of which at least four are targeted to chloroplasts [158,163]. Three members of the DegP family, DegP1, DegP5 and DegP8, were localized to the lumenal compartment by a proteome approach [164] and a highly conserved DegP2 homologue, suggested to be involved in the primary cleavage of the D1 protein, was localized to the outer thylakoid surface of the stroma-exposed thylakoid regions [155]. DegP2 contains a catalytic triad (serine, histidine and aspartic acid) typical of serine proteases [163]. The *Synechocystis* 6803 genome revealed three *deg* genes [158] and each of them have been successfully inactivated. Interestingly, even the triple mutant is viable [165], suggesting that Deg proteases are probably not an absolute requirement of D1 protein proteolysis.

It was recently demonstrated in *Synechocystis* 6803 that the FtsH protease is capable of complete degradation of the D1 protein [153,156,160]. These studies suggest that the FtsH protease (slr0228) has a general role in the removal of the damaged D1 protein and not only in acting as a secondary protease as proposed earlier [154]. Likewise, the *Arabidopsis* Var2 mutant, with inactivated FtsH2 protein, showed enhanced susceptibility to photoinhibition that was experimentally demonstrated to result from reduced capacity for D1 protein degradation [156]. Based on these in vivo experiments, it was suggested that the FtsH2 protease is capable of complete digestion of the damaged D1 protein and, possibly, no initial cleavage site in the D1 protein is necessary.

Members of the FtsH family of metalloproteases are encoded by 12 homologous genes in *Arabidopsis*, whereas four *FtsH* genes were found in *Synechocystis* [158]. Nine of *Arabidopsis FtsH* gene products can enter the chloroplasts [166]. An intensive search by proteomic methods of the FtsH proteins in chloroplasts, however, revealed only four FtsH proteins, FtsH1, FtsH2, FtsH5 and FtsH8 [167]. The lack of any phenotypic alteration in *ftsH1* and *ftsH8* mutants [168], and the fact that the *ftsH2* mutant accumulates higher mRNA levels of *FtsH1*, *FtsH5* and *FtsH8* than the WT *Arabidopsis thaliana*, suggested a clear redundancy between these four *FtsH* genes [169]. Characterization of the *Arabidopsis FtsH* double mutants finally demonstrated that two different types of FtsH proteins must be present to allow the accumulation of active FtsH protease [170]. Type A FtsH proteins are encoded by duplicated genes *FtsH1* and *FtsH5*, and type B proteins by duplicated genes *FtsH2* and *FtsH8*. The two types of subunits, however, are not redundant, and at least one member of each type is essential for formation of the FtsH protease complex capable of D1 protein degradation [170].

Interestingly, a mass spectrometric analysis of the polypeptide composition of *Synechocystis* 6803 PS II complex, isolated by His-tag (in CP47) affinity purification, revealed over 25 polypeptides, including two FtsH proteases, one corresponding to FtsH1 and the other to FtsH2 protease [158] as intrinsic PS II proteins [171]. This suggests that the D1 protease is located in close association to the PSII complexes in cyanobacterial inner membranes, but in the thylakoid network of plant chloroplasts the FtsH1 and two proteases are found in stromal thylakoids.

Notably, the transcript levels of both the *ftsH1* and *ftsH2* genes increase in *Synechocystis* 6803 cells upon transfer of cyanobacteria to high light intensity [172], thus indirectly supporting the role for both FtsH proteins in the degradation of the D1 protein also in cyanobacteria. In *Synechocystis* 6803 cells UV-B radiation strongly induces the *slr0228* gene that encodes an FtsH2 homologue protease in *Arabidopsis* [153]. In the *Synechocystis* 6803 mutant that lacks this FtsH homologue protein the degradation both of the D1 and D2 proteins as well as PSII repair is blocked under UV-B stress. These results indicate that the turnover of the D1 protein and D2 proteins in UV-B light, which involves the removal of the damaged D1 and D2 copies, requires the FtsH protease in intact cells. Since the FtsH protease is located on the stromal side of the membrane the main cleavage of the UV damaged D1 should also take place in the stroma-exposed region. The 20 kDa C-terminal product observed in in vitro experiments may, possibly, represent only a side branch of the degradation pathway.

*10.3.4.3 Repair of Damaged PSII by De Novo D1 Protein Synthesis*
Synthesis of the new D1 protein during the repair cycle occurs in the stroma-exposed thylakoids, where the newly synthesized D1 protein becomes co-translationally inserted into the existing PSII complex [173]. Despite an efficient association of the *psbA* mRNA ribosome complexes with the thylakoid membrane in light they have, however, turned out to be under elongation arrest if the membranes, or rather the PS II complexes, are not in need of new D1 copies [174,175]. Conceivably, a new D1 copy can be synthesized only after the cleavage of the damaged D1 protein. Thus, the D1 synthesis process can only be completed when an assembly partner, a D1-depleted PS II composed of at least the D2 protein and the Cyt *b*559 subunits, is available.

Targeting of the nascent D1 chain into the thylakoid membrane is probably assisted by its interaction with the chloroplast signal recognition particle cpSRP54 [176], and the insertion of the elongating D1 protein into the thylakoid membrane occurs through the cpSecY translocon channel [177]. After translation of two of the five transmembrane segments of the D1 protein, the translocon channel apparently opens laterally, allowing an interaction of the elongating D1 with the receptor complex consisting of D2, Cyt $b_{559}$ and possibly also of CP47, and several low molecular mass PSII proteins [143,178]. Resynthesis of these assembly partners is needed much less frequently than that of the D1 protein, although the D2 protein and the PsbH subunit are prone to degradation and resynthesis more often than the other subunits [143]. The ligation of several co-factors essential for electron transfer processes probably takes place during the pausing of ribosomes upon translation of the D1 protein [179]. The final accomplishment of a functional PSII complex involves several post-translational assembly steps, such as processing of the precursor D1 protein, preceding the assembly of the CP43 protein [178], and association of the water oxidizing complex (WOC) to the lumenal side of the thylakoid membrane [180]. Also, before the WOC proteins can re-associate, most of the low molecular weight subunits have to be re-assembled to the PSII subcomplex [181,182]. The assembly of a functionally competent WOC occurs via a light-driven reaction sequence called photoactivation (for details, see Chapter 17 and references therein).

In cyanobacteria, the main steps of the PSII repair are suggested to be largely similar to those in plant chloroplasts. Based on the scheme developed for the D1 replacement in chloroplast [5], a model for the PSII repair cycle in *Synechocystis* sp. PCC 6803 has been presented recently [160]. According to this model, a functionally distorted dimeric PSII complex undergoes several disassembly steps followed by the synchronized replacement of a damaged D1 protein by a new copy. This has been suggested to take place mainly via the action of the FtsH protease associated with the prohibitin complex [153]. The FtsH protease was shown to be responsible for complete degradation of the D1 protein, whereas prohibitin was suggested either to stabilize the newly synthesized D1 protein prior to insertion into a PSII complex or to stabilize other PSII subunits, preventing them from unwanted, FtsH-mediated proteolysis [160].

The efficiency of PSII repair appears to be a key factor in determining the net loss of photosynthesis under different environmental conditions. D1 protein synthesis and *psbA* gene expression appears to be regulated not only by light but also by osmotic stress [183], the availability of ATP [184], the efficiency of the Calvin cycle [185], the temperature and the rigidity of the thylakoid membrane [186–189]. Reactive oxygen species have also been suggested not only to induce damage to the protein backbone of the PSII and PSI complexes, but also to inhibit the repair cycle by inhibiting de novo synthesis of D1 at the step of translation elongation. Both $H_2O_2$ [190] and singlet oxygen [191] as particularly reactive oxygen species that participate in arresting the translation elongation of psbA were suggested to act as exclusive mediators.

*10.3.4.4 Role of Protein Phosphorylation in the PSII Damage–Repair Cycle in Plants*

In plant chloroplasts, the light-induced damage to the D1 protein occurs in the grana stacks, where the active forms of PSII are located as dimers [192]. After detachment of the LHCII antenna and monomerization of the PSII dimers, the

PSII core monomers migrate to the stroma thylakoids, where degradation of the damaged D1 protein occurs [5,150,193,194]. In plants, the stages from photodamage to degradation of the D1 protein are regulated by reversible phosphorylation events of the PSII core proteins [195–198]. Indeed, the damaged PSII complexes remain phosphorylated in the grana membranes if the repair sites in the stroma lamellae are not available [194]. These damaged PSII complexes are most likely the ones described in Section 10.3.2 that function as strong quenchers of excitation energy and protect the remaining PSII centers from photodamage under high light conditions [137]. In line with these notions, an *Arabidopsis* double mutant (*stn7*/*stn8*), which completely lacks the PSII core protein phosphorylation, showed an enhanced susceptibility to photoinhibition as compared with wild type plants [199], thus being in full agreement with the earlier suggestions [174,198] on the role of PSII core protein phosphorylation in the regulation of PSII repair cycle.

*10.3.5 Protection Against Ultraviolet Light*
Plants possess various defense mechanisms that greatly modulate the sensitivity of the photosynthetic apparatus to ultraviolet radiation by attenuating the intensity of UV-B before it reaches crucial targets. These protective mechanisms include morphological changes such as increased length of epidermal cells [200], production of a waxy cuticle [201], accumulation of UV-B absorbing compounds, particularly phenylpropanoids in the epidermal layer [202–207], and activation of different scavenging systems of various active oxygen species [208–212].

In addition to the protective defense mechanisms plants have also developed active defense systems by which the cells can repair the damage that has occurred. Experiments with the cyanobacterium *Synechocystis* 6803 and with the higher plant *Arabidopsis thaliana* have demonstrated that UV inhibited PSII activity can be restored via de novo synthesis of the damaged D1 and D2 protein subunits [213]. These proteins are usually encoded by small multigene families in cyanobacteria [214], whose members respond differentially to UV-B light, as shown for *Synechocystis* 6803 psbA [215] and psbD [216]. In *Synechococcus* 7942 there are two different D1 forms: D1:1 is encoded by *psbAI* and D1:2 is encoded by *psbAII* and *psbAIII*. This cyanobacterium exchanges D1:1 for D1:2 upon UV-B irradiation, which provides protection against the detrimental UV effects [217]. The protective effect appears to arise not only from the different UV sensitivity of PSII containing the D1:1 and D1:2 protein forms but also from the decreased rate of repair of D1:1 [218]. A further example is provided by *Anabaena* whose five *psbA* genes are induced differentially by UV-B [219]. Thus, it appears that an important physiological role of multiple *psbA* and *psbD* gene copies in cyanobacteria is to ensure rapid increase of the *psbA* and *psbD* transcript levels, respectively, under conditions of UV exposure when there is an increased demand for rapid D1 and D2 protein synthesis. Depending on the particular species, the differential transcription can lead to the exchange of different D1 protein forms, or enhance the available *psbA* or *psbD* transcript pools.

In their natural habitat, plants are exposed simultaneously to visible and UV-B irradiances, and the interaction of the two different light regimes can greatly modulate the light sensitivity of the photosynthetic apparatus. In the absence of protein repair capacity, UV-B and visible light damages oxygen evolution by independent mechanisms without synergistic interaction [84]. However, the situation is quite different in intact cells, which are capable of *de novo* protein synthesis, and the presence of low intensity visible light was shown to prevent the UV-induced loss of PSII activity by enhancing the efficiency of the protein repair process [84]. The protective effect disappears at high light intensities due to the additional photodamage induced by visible light [84].

## 10.4 Concluding Remarks

Photoinhibition of oxygenic photosynthesis is a general phenomenon, which occurs as an unavoidable consequence of dealing with light, a highly energetic substrate. Plants are apparently very well equipped to deal with this challenge, as shown by the multitude of delicately balanced protective and repair processes, which make efficient photosynthesis possible in a wide range of illumination conditions. Owing to the complexity of the underlying events we do not yet understand each aspect of the process, and despite decades of research there are still conflicting views concerning mechanistic details. However, recent developments in exploring the atomic structure of the light harvesting and light energy converting complexes of the photosynthetic apparatus (details of our current state of knowledge are given in Chapters 5, 8, 11, 13 and 15) are expected to lead to a general understanding of how plants can safely utilize light in the nanoscale power-plants embedded in the thylakoid membranes.

## Acknowledgements

This work was partly supported by grants from EU (MRTN-CT-2003-505069), and the Academy of Finland. Mika Keränen is acknowledged for preparing the figures.

## References

1. N. Adir, H. Zer, S. Shochat, I. Ohad, Photoinhibition – a historical perspective. *Photosynth. Res.* **76** (2003) 343–370.
2. S.B. Powles, Photoinhibition of photosynthesis induced by visible light. *Annu. Rev. Plant Physiol.* **35** (1984) 15–44.
3. J. Barber, B. Andersson, Too much of a good thing: Light can be bad for photosynthesis. *Trends Biochem. Sci.* **17** (1992) 61–66.
4. G. Öquist, W.S. Chow, J.M. Anderson, Photoinhibition of photosynthesis represents a mechanism for the long-term regulation of Photosystem II. *Planta* **186** (1992) 450–460.

5. E.-M. Aro, I. Virgin, B. Andersson, Photoinhibition of Photosystem II. Inactivation, protein damage and turnover. *Biochim. Biophys. Acta* **1143** (1993) 113–134.
6. C. Critchley, A.W. Russel, Photoinhibition of photosynthesis in vivo: The role of protein turnover in Photosystem II. *Physiol. Plantarum* **92** (1994) 188–196.
7. S.P. Long, S. Humpries, Photoinhibition of photosynthesis in nature. *Annu. Rev. Plant Physiol.* **45** (1994) 633–662.
8. F. Rappaport, M. Guergova-Kuras, P.J. Nixon, B.A. Diner, J. Lavergne, Kinetics and pathways of charge recombination in Photosystem II. *Biochemistry* **41** (2002) 8518–8527.
9. I. Ohad, N. Adir, H. Koike, D.J. Kyle, Y. Inoue, Mechanism of photoinhibition in vivo. A reversible light-induced conformational change of reaction center II is related to an irreversible modification of the D1 protein. *J. Biol. Chem.* **265** (1990) 1972–1979.
10. I. Setlik, S.I. Allakhverdiev, L. Nedbal, E. Setlikova, V.V. Klimov, Three types of Photosystem II photoinactivation. I. Damaging processes on the acceptor side. *Photosynth. Res.* **23** (1990) 39–48.
11. F.J.E. Van Mieghem, W. Nitschke, P. Mathis, A.W. Rutherford, The influence of the quinone-iron electron acceptor complex on the reaction centre photochemistry of Photosystem II. *Biochim. Biophys. Acta* **977** (1989) 207–214.
12. I. Vass, S. Styring, T. Hundal, A. Koivuniemi, E.-M. Aro, B. Andersson, Reversible and irreversible intermediates during photoinhibition of Photosystem II: Stable reduced $Q_A$ species promote chlorophyll triplet formation. *Proc. Natl. Acad. Sci. U.S.A.* **89** (1992) 1408–1412.
13. A. Koivuniemi, E. Swiezewska, E.M. Aro, S. Strying, B. Andersson, Reduced content of the quinone acceptor $Q_A$ in Photosystem II complexes isolated from thylakoid membranes after prolonged photoinhibition under anaerobic conditions. *FEBS Lett.* **327** (1993) 343–346.
14. I. Vass, S. Styring, Spectroscopic characterization of triplet forming states in Photosystem II. *Biochemistry* **31** (1992) 5957–5963.
15. F. van Mieghem, K. Brettel, B. Hillmann, A. Kamlowski, A.W. Rutherford, E. Schlodder, Charge recombination reactions in Photosystem II. 1. Yields, recombination pathways, and kinetics of the primary pair. *Biochemistry* **34** (1995) 4798–4813.
16. J.R. Durrant, L.B. Giorgi, J. Barber, D.R. Klug, G. Porter, Characterization of triplet states in isolated photosystem II reaction centers: Oxygen quenching as a mechanism for photodamage. *Biochim. Biophys. Acta* **1017** (1990) 167–175.
17. É. Hideg, C. Spetea, I. Vass, Singlet oxygen and free radical production during acceptor- and donor-side-induced photoinhibition. Studies with spin trapping EPR spectroscopy. *Biochim. Biophys. Acta* **1186** (1994) 143–152.
18. É. Hideg, I. Vass, Singlet oxygen is not produced in Photosystem I under photoinhibitory conditions. *Photochem. Photobiol.* **62** (1995) 949–952.
19. A.N. Macpherson, A. Telfer, J. Barber, T.G. Truscott, Direct detection of singlet oxygen from Photosystem II reaction centers. *Biochim. Biophys. Acta* **1143** (1993) 301–309.
20. É. Hideg, T. Kálai, K. Hideg, I. Vass, Photoinhibition of photosynthesis in vivo results in singlet oxygen production. Detection via nitroxide-induced fluorescence quenching in broad bean leaves. *Biochemistry* **37** (1998) 11405–11411.
21. H.M. Gleiter, H.A. Nugent, E. Haag, G. Renger, Photoinhibition affects the non-heme iron center in Photosystem II. *FEBS Lett.* **313** (1992) 75–79.
22. I. Vass, Y. Sanakis, C. Spetea, V. Petrouleas, Effects of photoinhibition on the $Q_A^-$ $Fe^{2+}$ complex of Photosystem II studied by EPR and Mössbauer spectroscopy. *Biochemistry* **34** (1995) 4434–4440.

23. D.J. Blubaugh, G.M. Cheniae, Kinetics of photoinhibition in hydroxylamine-extracted Photosystem II membranes: Relevance to photoactivation and sites of electron donation. *Biochemistry* **29** (1990) 5109–5118.
24. D.J. Blubaugh, M. Atamian, G.T. Babcock, J.H. Golbeck, G.M. Cheniae, Photoinhibition of hydroxylamine-extracted Photosystem II membranes: Identification of the sites of photodamage. *Biochemistry* **30** (1991) 7586–7597.
25. G.-X. Chen, G.M. Cheniae, Photoinhibition of hydroxylamine-extracted Photosystem II membranes: Studies of the mechanism. *Biochemistry* **31** (1992) 11072–11083.
26. C. Jegerschold, I. Virgin, S. Styring, Light-dependent degradation of the D1 protein in Photosystem II is accelerated after inhibition of the water splitting reaction. *Biochemistry* **29** (1990) 6179–6186.
27. G.F.W. Searle, A. Telfer, J. Barber, T.J. Schaafsma, Millisecond time-resolved EPR of the spin-polarised triplet in the isolated Photosystem II reaction center. *Biochim. Biophys. Acta* **1016** (1990) 235–243.
28. H.-J. Eckert, B. Geiken, J. Bernading, A. Napiwotzki, H.-J. Eichler, G. Renger, Two sites of photoinhibition of the electron transfer in oxygen evolving and Tris-treated PSII membrane fragments from spinach. *Photosynth. Res.* **27** (1991) 97–108.
29. H. Gong, I. Ohad, Rapid turnover of the RCII-D1 protein in dark induced by photoactivation of Photosystem II in Scenedesmus wild type and the PS-II-donor defective LF-1 mutant cells. *Biochim. Biophys. Acta* **1228** (1995) 181–188.
30. S.R. Mayes, K.M. Cook, S.J. Self, Z. Zhang, J. Barber, Deletion of the gene encoding the Photosystem II 33 kDa protein from Synechocystis sp. PCC 6803 does not inactive water-splitting but increases vulnerability to photoinhibition. *Biochim. Biophys. Acta* **1060** (1991) 1–12.
31. P.J. Nixon, B.A. Diner, Analysis of water-oxidation mutants constructed in the cyanobacterium *Synechocystis* sp. PCC 6803. *Biochem. Soc. Trans.* **22** (1994) 338–343.
32. H.-A. Chu, A.P. Nguyen, R.J. Debus, Amino acid residues that influence the binding of manganese or calcium to Photosystem II. 2. The carboxy-terminal domain of the D1 polypeptide. *Biochemistry* **34** (1995) 5859–5882.
33. R.J. Debus, Amino acid residues that modulate the properties of tyrosine $Y_Z$ and the manganese cluster in the water oxidizing complex of Photosystem II. *Biochim. Biophys. Acta* **1503** (2001) 164–186.
34. B.A. Diner, Amino acid residues involved in the coordination and assembly of the manganese cluster of Photosystem II. Proton-coupled electron transport of the redox-active tyrosines and its relationship to water oxidation. *Biochim. Biophys. Acta* **1503** (2001) 147–163.
35. N. Keren, H. Gong, I. Ohad, Oscillations of reaction center II-D1 protein degradation in vivo induced by repetitive light flashes. Correlation between the level of RCII-$Q_B^-$ and protein degradation in low light. *J. Biol. Chem.* **270** (1995) 806–814.
36. N. Keren, P.J.M. van Kan, A. Berg, H. Gong, S. Schochat, H. Levanon, S. Styring, B. Andersson, I. Ohad, On the mechanism of the low-light induced degradation of the D1 protein: Involvement of back electron transfer in Photosystem II. *Photosynth. Res.* **4** (1995) 299–302.
37. N. Keren, A. Berg, P.J.M. van Kan, H. Levanon, I. Ohad, Mechanism of Photosystem II photoinactivation and D1 protein degradation at low light: The role of back electron flow. *Proc. Natl. Acad. Sci. U.S.A.* **94** (1997) 1579–1584.

38. N. Keren, I. Ohad, A.W. Rutherford, F. Drepper, A. Krieger-Liszkay, Inhibition of Photosystem II activity by saturating single turnover flashes in calcium-depleted and active Photosystem II. *Photosynth. Res.* **63** (2000) 209–216.
39. A. Szilárd, L. Sass, É. Hideg, I. Vass, Photoinactivation of Photosystem II by flashing light. *Photosynth. Res.* **84** (2005) 15–20.
40. A. Krieger-Liszkay, A.W. Rutherford, Influence of herbicide binding on the redox potential of the quinone acceptor in Photosystem II.: Relevance to photodamage and phytotoxicity. *Biochemistry* **37** (1998) 17339–17344.
41. C. Fufezan, A.W. Rutherford, A. Krieger-Liszkay, Singlet oxygen production in herbicide-treated Photosystem II. *FEBS Lett.* **532** (2002) 407–410.
42. S. Santabarbara, K.V. Neverov, F.M. Garlaschi, G. Zucchelli, R.C. Jennings, Involvement of uncoupled antenna chlorophylls in photoinhibition in thylakoids. *FEBS Lett.* **491** (2001) 109–113.
43. S. Santabarbara, I. Cazzalini, A. Rivadossi, F.M. Garlaschi, G. Zucchelli, R.C. Jennings, Photoinhibition in vitro involves weakly coupled chlorophyll–protein complexes. *Photochem. Photobiol.* **75** (2002) 613–618.
44. S. Santabarbara, R.C. Jennings, The size of the population of weakly coupled chlorophyll pigments involved in thylakoid photoinhibition determined by steady-state fluorescence spectroscopy. *Biochim. Biophys. Acta* **1709** (2005) 138–149.
45. E. Turcsányi, I. Vass, Inhibition of photosynthetic electron transport by UV-A radiation targets the Photosystem II complex. *Photochem. Photobiol.* **72** (2000) 513–520.
46. I. Vass, E. Turcsányi, E. Touloupakis, D. Ghanotakis, V. Petroluleas, The mechanism of UV-A radiation-induced inhibition of Photosystem II electron transport studied by EPR and chlorophyll fluorescence. *Biochemistry* **41** (2002) 10200–10208.
47. N.I. Bishop, The possible role of plastoquinone (Q-254) in the electron transport system of photosynthesis. *CIBA Symp.* (1961), 385–404.
48. N. Shavit, M. Avron, The effect of UV light on phosphorylation and the Hill reaction. *Biochim. Biophys. Acta* **66** (1963) 187–195.
49. A. Trebst, E. Pistorius, Photosynthetische reaktionene in UV-bestrahlten chloroplasten. *Z. Naturforsch.* **20** (1965) 885–889.
50. G. Kulandaivelu, A.M. Noorudeen, Comparative study of the action of ultraviolet-C and ultraviolet-B radiation on photosynthetic electron transport. *Physiol. Plantarum* **58** (1983) 389–394.
51. W. Iwanzik, M. Tevini, G. Dohnt, M. Voss, W. Weiss, P. Graber, G. Renger, Action of UV-B radiation on photosynthetic primary reaction in spinach chloroplasts. *Physiol. Plantarum* **58** (1983) 401–407.
52. J.R. Brandle, W.F. Campbell, W.B. Sisson, M.M. Caldwell, Net photosynthesis, electron transport capacity, and ultrastucture of *Pisum sativum* L. exposed to ultraviolet-B radiation. *Plant Physiol.* **60** (1977) 165–169.
53. L. Huang, M.P. McCluskey, H. Ni, R.A. Larossa, Global gene expression profiles of the cyanobacterium *Synechocystis* sp. strain PCC 6803 in response to irradiation with UV-B and white light. *J. Bacteriol.* **184** (2002) 6845–6858.
54. J.F. Bornman, Target sites of UV-B radiation in photosynthesis of higher plants. *J. Photochem. Photobiol.* **B4** (1989) 145–158.
55. I. Vass, in: *Handbook of Photosynthesis* (1996) (M. Pessarakli, ed.), Marcel Dekker, Inc., New York, pp. 931–950.
56. L.W. Jones, B. Kok, Photoinhibition of chloroplast reactions. I. Kinetics and action spectra. *Plant Physiol.* **41** (1966) 1037–1043.

57. J.F. Bornman, L.O. Björn, H.-E. Akerlund, Action spectrum for inhibition by ultraviolet radiation of Photosystem II activity in spinach thylakoids. *Photobiochem. Photobiophys.* **8** (1984) 305–313.
58. L.F. Crane, Isolation of two quinones with coenzyme Q activity from alfalfa. *Plant Physiol.* **34** (1959) 546–551.
59. J. Amesz, in: *Encyclopedia of Plant Physiology* (1977) (A. Trebst, M. Avron, eds.), Springer-Verlag, Berlin, Vol. 5, pp. 238–246.
60. R. Bensasson, E.J. Land, Optical and kinetic properties of semireduced plastoquinone and ubiquinone: Electron acceptors in photosynthesis. *Biochim. Biophys. Acta* **325** (1973) 175–181.
61. C.T. Yerkes, D.M. Kramer, J.M. Fenton, A.R. Crofts, in: *Current Research in Photosynthesis* (1990) (M. Baltscheffsky, ed.), Kluwer Academic Publisher, Dordrecht, Vol. II., pp. II.6.381-II.6.384.
62. I. Vass, L. Sass, C. Spetea, É. Hideg and V. Petrouleas, in: *Photosynthesis: from Light to Biosphere.* (1995) (P. Mathis, ed.), Kluwer Academic Publishers, Dordrecht, Vol. IV., pp. 553–556.
63. I. Vass, L. Sass, C. Spetea, A. Bakou, D. Ghanotakis, V. Petrouleas, UV-B induced inhibition of Photosystem II electron transport studied by EPR and chlorophyll fluorescence. Impairment of donor and acceptor side components. *Biochemistry* **35** (1996) 8964–8973.
64. G. Renger, M. Völker, H.J. Eckert, R. Fromme, S. Hohm-Veit, P. Graber, On the mechanism of Photosystem II deterioration by UV-B irradiation. *Photochem. Photobiol.* **49** (1989) 97–105.
65. A. Post, P.B. Lukins, P.J. Walker, A.W.D. Larkum, The effects of ultraviolet irradiation on $P680^+$ reduction in PS II core complexes measured for individual S-states and during repetitive cycling of the oxygen-evolving complex. *Photosynth. Res.* **49** (1996) 21–27.
66. A.W.D. Larkum, M. Karge, F. Reifarth, H.-J. Eckert, A. Post, G. Renger, Effect of monochromatic UV-B radiation on electron transfer reactions of Photosystem II. *Photosynth. Res.* **68** (2001) 49–60.
67. I. Vass, Z. Máté, E. Turcsányi, L. Sass, F. Nagy, C. Sicora, in: *PS2001 Proceedings. 12th International Congress on Photosynthesis* (2001), CSIRO Publishing, Collingwood, Australia, p. S8–001.
68. M.E. Bodini, L.A. Willis, T.L. Riechel, D.T. Sawyer, Electrochemical and spectroscopic studies of manganese(II), -(III), and -(IV) gluconate complexes. 1. Formulas and oxidation-reduction stoichiometry. *Inorg. Chem.* **15** (1976) 1538–1543.
69. J.P. Dekker, H.J. van Gorkom, M. Brok, L. Ouwehand, Optical characterization of Photosystem II electron donors. *Biochim. Biophys. Acta* **764** (1984) 301–309.
70. J. Lavergne, *Biochim. Biophys. Acta* **1060** (1991) 175–188.
71. M. Hakala, I. Tuominen, M. Keranen, T. Tyystjarvi, E. Tyystjarvi, Evidence for the role of the oxygen-evolving manganese complex in photoinhibition of Photosystem II. *Biochim. Biophys. Acta* **1706** (2005) 68–80.
72. B.M. Greenberg, V. Gaba, O. Canaani, S. Malkin, A.K. Mattoo, M. Edelman, Separate photosensitizers mediate degradation of the 32-kDa Photosystem II reaction centre protein in visible and UV spectral regions. *Proc. Natl. Acad. Sci. U.S.A.* **86** (1989) 6617–6620.
73. B.M. Greenberg, V. Gaba, A.K. Mattoo, M. Edelman, Degradation of the 32 kDa Photosystem II reaction center protein in UV, visible and far red light occurs through a common 23.5 intermediate. *Z. Naturforsch.* **44c** (1989) 450–452.

74. M.A.K. Jansen, B. Depka, A. Trebst, M. Edelman, Engagement of specific sites in the plastoquinone niche regulates degradation of the D1 protein in Photosystem II. *J. Biol. Chem.* **268** (1993) 21246–21252.
75. M.A.K. Jansen, V. Gaba, B.M. Greenberg, A.K. Mattoo, M. Edelman, in: *Photosynthetic Responses to the Environment* (1993) (H.Y. Yamamoto, C.M. Smith, ed.), American Society of Plant Physiology, Washington D.C., pp. 142–149.
76. R. Barbato, A. Frizzo, G. Friso, F. Rigoni, G.M. Giacometti, Degradation of the D1 protein of photosystem-II reaction centre by ultraviolet-B radiation requires the presence of functional manganese on the donor side. *Eur. J. Biochem.* **227** (1995) 723–729.
77. A. Trebst, B. Depka, Degradation of the D-1 protein subunit of Photosystem II in isolated thylakoids by UV light. *Z. Naturforsch.* **45c** (1990) 765–771.
78. A. Melis, J.A. Nemson, M.A. Harrison, Damage to functional components and partial degradation of Photosystem II reaction center proteins upon chloroplast exposure to ultraviolet-B radiation. *Biochim. Biophys. Acta* **1100** (1992) 312–320.
79. G. Friso, C. Spetea, G.M. Giacometti, I. Vass, R. Barbato, Degradation of Photosystem II reaction center D1-protein induced by UVB irradiation in isolated thylakoids. Identification and characterization of C- and N-terminal breakdown products. *Biochim. Biophys. Acta* **1184** (1994) 78–84.
80. G. Friso, R. Barbato, G.M. Giacometti, J. Barber, Degradation of D2 protein due to UV-B irradiation in the reaction centre of Photosystem II. *FEBS Lett.* **339** (1994) 217–221.
81. G. Friso, I. Vass, C. Spetea, J. Barber, R. Barbato, UV-B-induced degradation of the D1 protein in isolated reaction centres of Photosystem II. *Biochim. Biophys. Acta* **1231** (1995) 41–46.
82. C. Spetea, É. Hideg, I. Vass, The quinone electron acceptors are not the main sensitizers of UV-B induced protein damage in isolated Photosystem II reaction centre- and core complexes. *Plant Sci.* **115** (1996) 207–215.
83. C. Spetea, É. Hideg, I. Vass, in: *Photosynthesis: from Light to Biosphere* (1995) (P. Mathis, ed.), Kluwer Academic Publishers, Dordrecht, Vol. IV, pp. 219–222.
84. C. Sicora, Z. Máté, I. Vass, The interaction of visible and UV-B light during photodamage and repair of Photosystem II. *Photosynth. Res.* **75** (2003) 127–137.
85. N. Ohnishi, S.I. Allakhverdiev, S. Takahashi, S. Higashi, M. Watanabe, Y. Nishiyama, N. Murata, Two-step mechanism of photodamage to Photosystem II: Step 1 occurs at the oxygen-evolving complex and step 2 occurs at the photochemical reaction center. *Biochemistry* **44** (2005) 8494–8499.
86. E. Tyystjarvi, E.M. Aro, The rate constant of photoinhibition, measured in lincomycin-treated leaves, is directly proportional to light intensity. *Proc. Natl. Acad. Sci. U.S.A.* **93** (1996) 2213–2218.
87. L. Nagy, E. Bálint, J. Barber, A. Ringler, K.M. Cook, P. Maróti, Photoinhibition and law of reciprocity in photosynthetic reactions of *Synechocystis* sp. PCC 6803. *J. Plant Physiol.* **145** (1995) 410–415.
88. Y.-I. Park, W.S. Chow, J.M. Anderson, Light inactivation of functional Photosystem II in leaves of peas grown in moderate light depends on photon exposure. *Planta* **196** (1995) 401–411.
89. J. Sinclair, Y.I. Park, W.S. Chow, J.M. Anderson, Target theory and the photo-inactivation of Photosystem II. *Photosynth. Res.* **50** (1996) 33–40.
90. W.S. Chow, H.-Y. Lee, J. He, L. Hendrickson, Y.-N. Hong, S. Matsubara, Photoinactivation of Photosystem II in leaves. *Photosynth. Res.* **84** (2005) 35–41.

91. I. Terashima, S. Funayama, K. Sonoike, The site of photoinhibition in leaves of Cucumis sativus L. at low temperatures in Photosystem I, not Photosystem II. *Planta* **193** (1994) 300–306.
92. K. Sonoike, I. Terashima, M. Iwaki, S. Itoh, Destruction of Photosystem I iron-sulfur centers in leaves of *Cucumis sativus* L. by weak illumination at chilling temperatures. *FEBS Lett.* **362** (1995) 235–238.
93. K. Sonoike, M. Kamo, Y. Hihara, T. Hiyama, I. Enami, The mechanism of the degradation of *psaB* gene product, one of the photosynthetic reaction center subunits of Photosystem I, upon photoinhibition. *Photosynth. Res.* **53** (1997) 55–63.
94. S.E. Tjus, H.V. Scheller, B. Andersson, B.J. Moller, Active oxygen produced during selective excitation of Photosystem I is damaging not only to Photosystem I, but also to Photosystem II. *Plant Physiol.* **125** (2001) 2007–2015.
95. S. Zhang, H.V. Scheller, Photoinhibition of Photosystem I at chilling temperature and subsequent recovery in *Arabidopsis thaliana. Plant Cell Physiol.* **45** (2004) 1595–1602.
96. H.V. Scheller, A. Haldrup, Photoinhibition of Photosystem I. *Planta* **221** (2005) 5–8.
97. H.J. Hwang, J.-H. Kim, Y.-J. Eu, B.Y. Moon, S.H. Cho, C.-H. Lee, Photoinhibition of Photosystem I is accelerated by dimethyldithiocarbamate, an inhibitor of superoxide dismutase, during light-chilling of spinach leaves. *J. Photochem. Photobiol. B* **73** (2004) 79–85.
98. K. Sonoike, Degradation of *psaB* gene product, the reaction center subunit of Photosystem I, is caused during photoinhibition of Photosystem I: Possible involvement of active oxygen species. *Plant Sci.* **115** (1996) 157–164.
99. B. Jakob, U. Heber, Photoproduction and detoxification of hydroxyl radicals in chloroplasts and leaves and relation to photoinactivation of Photosystems I and II. *Plant Cell Physiol.* **37** (1996) 629–635.
100. R. Aroca, J.J. Irigoyen, M. Sánchez-Díaz, Photosynthetic characteristics and protective mechanisms against oxidative stress during chilling and subsequent recovery in two maize varieties differing in chilling sensitivity. *Plant Sci.* **161** (2001) 719–726.
101. S.M. Choi, S.W. Jeong, W.J. Jeong, S.Y. Kwon, W.S. Chow, Y.-I. Park, Chloroplast Cu/Zn-superoxide dismutase is a highly sensitive site in cucumber leaves chilled in the light. *Planta* **216** (2002) 315–324.
102. Y. Allahverdiyeva, F. Mamedov, P. Maenpaa, I. Vass, E.-M. Aro, Modulation of photosynthetic electron transport in the absence of terminal electron acceptors: Characterization of the *rbcL* deletion mutant of tobacco. *Biochim. Biophys. Acta* **1709** (2005) 69–83.
103. S.E. Tjus, B.J. Moller, H.V. Scheller, Photoinhibition of Photosystem I damages both reaction centre proteins PSI-A and PSI-B and acceptor-side located small Photosystem I polypeptides. *Photosynth. Res.* **60** (1999) 75–86.
104. H. Kudoh, K. Sonoike, Irreversible damage to Photosystem I by chilling in the light: Cause of the degradation of chlorophyll after returning to normal growth temperature. *Planta* **215** (2002) 541–548.
105. A.A. Gorman, M.A.J. Rodgers, Current perspectives of singlet oxygen detection in biological environments. *J. Photochem. Photobiol. B* **14** (1992) 159–176.
106. H. Sies, C.F.M. Menck, Singlet oxygen induced DNA damage. *Mutat. Res.* **275** (1992) 367–375.

107. N. Keren, H. Gong, I. Ohad, Oscillations of reaction center II-D1 protein degradation in vivo induced by repetitive light flashes. *J. Biol. Chem.* **270** (1995) 806–814.
108. E. Hideg, I. Vass, T. Kálai, K. Hideg, Singlet oxygen detection with sterically hindered amine derivatives in plants under light stress. *Methods Enzymol.* **319** (2000) 77–85.
109. E. Hideg, I. Vass, Singlet oxygen is not produced in Photosystem I under photoinhibitory conditions. *Photochem. Photobiol.* **62** (1995) 949–952.
110. S. Rinalducci, J.Z. Pedersen, L. Zolla, Formation of radicals from singlet oxygen produced during photoinhibition of isolated light-harvesting proteins of Photosystem II. *Biochim. Biophys. Acta* **1608** (2004) 63–73.
111. E. Tyystjarvi, M. Hakala, P. Sarvikas, Mathematical modelling of the light response curve of photoinhibition of Photosystem II. *Photosynth. Res.* **84** (2005) 21–27.
112. L. Zolla, S. Rinalducci, Involvement of active oxygen species in degradation of light-harvesting proteins under light stresses. *Biochemistry* **41** (2002) 14391–14402.
113. T. Kalai, E. Hideg, I. Vass, K. Hideg, Double (fluorescent and spin) sensors for detecting of reactive oxygen species in the thylakoid membrane. *Free Rad. Biol. Med.* **24** (1997) 649–652.
114. A. Trebst, B. Depka, H. Holländer-Czytko, A specific role for tocopherol and of chemical singlet oxygen quenchers in the maintenance of Photosystem II structure and function in *Chlamydomonas reinhardtii*. *FEBS Lett.* **516** (2002) 156–160.
115. R. Schödel, K.D. Irrgang, J. Voigt, G. Renger, Rate of carotenoid triplet formation in solubilized light-harvesting complex II (LHCII) from spinach. *Biophys. J.* **75** (1998) 3143–4353.
116. A. Telfer, S. Dhami, S.M. Bishop, D. Philips, J. Barber, β-Carotene quenches singlet oxygen formed by isolated photosystem II reaction centers. *Biochemistry* **33** (1994) 14469–14474.
117. A. Telfer, What is β-carotene doing in the Photosystem II reaction centre? *Phil. Trans. R. Soc. London B* **357** (2002) 1431–1439.
118. K. Okada, M. Ikeuchi, N. Yamamoto, T.A. Ono, M. Miyao, Selective and specific cleavage of the D1 and D2 proteins of Photosystem II by exposure to singlet oxygen: Factors responsible for the susceptibility to cleavage of the proteins. *Biochim. Biophys. Acta* **1274** (1996) 73–79.
119. E. Hideg, I. Vass, UV-B induced free radical production in plant leaves and isolated thylakoid membranes. *Plant Sci.* **115** (1996) 251–260.
120. P. Pospísil, A. Arato, A. Krieger-Liszkay, A.W. Rutherford, Hydroxyl radical generation by Photosystem II. *Biochemistry* **43** (2004) 6783–6792.
121. F. Haber, J.J. Weiss, The catalytic decomposition of $H_2O_2$ by iron salts. *Proc. Roy. Soc. London Biol A* **147** (1934) 332–351.
122. P. Horton, A. Ruban, Molecular design of the Photosystem II light-harvesting antenna: Photosynthesis and photoprotection. *J. Exp. Bot.* **56** (2005) 365–373.
123. K.K. Niyogi, X.-P. Li, V. Rosenberg, H.-S. Jung, Is PsbS the site of non-photochemical quenching in photosynthesis? *J. Exp. Bot.* **56** (2005) 375–382.
124. B. Demmig-Adams, W.W. Adams III, D.H. Baker, B.A. Logan, D.R. Bowling, A.S. Verhoeven, Using chlorophyll fluorescence to assess the fraction of absorbed light allocated to thermal dissipation of excess excitation. *Physiol. Plant.* **98** (1996) 253–264.
125. B. Demmig-Adams, W.W. Adams III, The role of xanthophyll cycle carotenoids in the protection of photosynthesis. *Trends Plant Sci.* **1** (1996) 21–26.

126. M. Eskling, A. Emanuelsson, H.-E. Akerlund, in: *Regulation of Photosynthesis* (2001) (E.-M. Aro, B. Andersson, eds.), Kluwer Academic Publishers, Dordrecht, pp. 806–816.
127. B. Demmig-Adams, Carotenoids and photoprotection in plants: A role for the xantophyll zeaxanthin. *Biochim. Biophys. Acta* **1020** (1990) 1–24.
128. B. Demmig-Adams, W.W. Adams III, Harvesting sunlight safely. *Nature* **403** (2000) 371–374.
129. X.-P. Li, O. Bjorkman, C. Shih, A. R. Grossman, M. Rosenquist, S. Jansson, K.K. Niyogi, A pigment-binding protein essential for regulation of photosynthetic light harvesting. *Nature* **403** (2000) 391–395.
130. P. Horton, A. Ruban, M. Wentworth, Allosteric regulation of the light-harvesting system of Photosystem II. *Philos. Trans. R. Soc. London B*. **355** (2000) 1361–1370.
131. B. Robert, P. Horton, A.A. Pascal, A.V. Ruban, Insights into the molecular dynamics of plant light-harvesting proteins in vivo. *Trends Plant Sci.* **9** (2004) 385–390.
132. A.V. Ruban, A.J. Young, P. Horton, Induction of nonphotochemical energy dissipation and absorbance changes in leaves. Evidence for changes in the state of the light-harvesting system of Photosystem II in vivo. *Plant Physiol.* **102** (1993) 741–750.
133. Z. Liu, H. Yan, K. Wang, T. Kuang, J. Zhang, L. Gui, X. An, W. Chang, Crystal structure of spinach major light-harvesting complex at 2.72 Å resolution. *Nature* **428** (2004) 287–292.
134. J. Standfuss, A.C. Terwisscha van Scheltinga, M. Lamborghini, W. Kuhlbrandt, Mechanisms of photoprotection and nonphotochemical quenching in pea light-harvesting complex at 2.5 Å resolution. *EMBO J.* **24** (2005) 919–928.
135. A.V. Ruban, P.J. Lee, M. Wentworth, A.J. Young, P. Horton, Determination of the stoichiometry and strength of binding of xanthophylls to the Photosystem II light harvesting complexes. *J. Biol. Chem.* **274** (1999) 10458–10465.
136. G.H. Krause, Photoinhibition of photosynthesis. An evaluation of damaging and protective mechanisms. *Physiol. Plantarum* **74** (1988) 566–574.
137. S. Matsubara, W.S. Chow, Populations of photoinactivated Photosystem II reaction centers characterized by chlorophyll *a* fluorescence lifetime in vivo. *Proc. Natl. Acad. Sci. U.S.A.* **101** (2004) 18234–18239.
138. P.V. Sane, A.G. Ivanov, V. Hurry, N.P.A. Huner, G. Oquist, Changes in the redox potential of primary and secondary electron-accepting quinones in Photosystem II confer increased resistance to photoinhibition in low-temperature-acclimated *Arabidopsis*. *Plant Physiol.* **132** (2003) 2144–2151.
139. S.A.P. Merry, P.J. Nixon, L.M.C. Barter, M. Schilstra, G. Porter, J. Barber, Modulation of quantum yield of primary radical pair formation in Photosystem II by site-directed mutagenesis affecting radical cations and anions. *Biochemistry* **37** (1998) 17439–17447.
140. A.K. Clarke, A. Soitamo, P. Gustafsson, G. Oquist, Rapid interchange between two distinct forms of cyanobacterial Photosystem II reaction-center protein D1 response to photoinhibition. *Proc. Natl. Acad. Sci. U.S.A.* **90** (1993) 9973–9977.
141. D. Campbell, G.Q. Zhou, P. Gustafsson, G. Oquist, A.K. Clarke, Electron transport regulates exchange of two forms of Photosystem II D1 protein in the cyanobacterium *Synechococcus*. *EMBO J.* **14** (1995) 5457–5466.
142. J. Komenda, J. Masojidek, Functional and structural changes of the Photosystem II complex induced by high irradiance in cyanobacterial cells. *Eur. J. Biochem.* **233** (1995) 677–682.

143. A. Rokka, M. Suorsa, A. Saleem, N. Battchikova, E.-M. Aro, Synthesis and assembly of thylakoid protein complexes: Multiple assembly steps of Photosystem II. *Biochem. J.* **388** (2005) 159–168.
144. D.J. Kyle, I. Ohad, C.J. Arntzen, Membrane protein damage and repair: Selective loss of a quinone-protein function in chloroplast membranes. *Proc. Natl. Acad. Sci. U.S.A.* **81** (1984) 4070–4074.
145. A.K. Mattoo, H.H. Falk, J.B. Marder, M. Edelman, Regulation of protein metabolism: Coupling of photosynthetic electron transport to in vivo degradation of the rapidly metabolized 32-kilodalton protein of the chloroplast membranes. *Proc. Natl. Acad. Sci. U.S.A.* **81** (1984) 1380–1384.
146. A. Trebst, B. Depka, B. Kraft, U. Johanningmeier, The $Q_B$ site modulates the conformation of the Photosystem II reaction center polypeptides. *Photosynth. Res.* **18** (1988) 163–177.
147. M.A.K. Jansen, B. Depka, A. Trebst, M. Edelman, Engagement of specific sites in the plastoquinone niche regulates degradation of the D1 protein in Photosystem II. *J. Biol. Chem.* **268** (1993) 21246–21252.
148. B. Hankamer, J. Barber, Structure and membrane organization of Photosystem II in green plants. *Annu. Rev. Plant Physiol.* **48** (1997) 641–671.
149. B. Andersson, J. Barber, in: *Advances in Photosynthesis* (1996) (N.R. Baker, ed.), Kluwer Academic Publishers, Dordrecht, pp. 101–121.
150. R. Barbato, C.A. Shipton, G.M. Giacometti, J. Barber, New evidence suggests that the initial photoinduced cleavage of the D1-protein may not occur near the PEST sequence. *FEBS Lett.* **290** (1991) 162–166.
151. J. De Las Rivas, C.A. Shipton, M. Ponticos, J. Barber, Acceptor side mechanism of photoinduced proteolysis of the D1 protein in Photosystem II reaction centers. *Biochemistry* **32** (1993) 6944–6950.
152. Z. Adam, A.K. Clarke, Cutting edge of chloroplast proteolysis. *Trends Plant Sci.* **7** (2002) 451–456.
153. P. Silva, E. Thompson, S. Bailey, O. Kruse, C.W. Mullineaux, C. Robinson, N.H. Mann, P.J. Nixon, FtsH is involved in the early stages of repair of Photosystem II in *Synechocystis* sp PCC 6803. *Plant Cell* **15** (2003) 2152–2164.
154. M. Lindahl, C. Spetea, T. Hundal, A.B. Oppenheim, Z. Adam, B. Andersson, The thylakoid FtsH protease plays a role in the light-induced turnover of the Photosystem II D1 protein. *Plant Cell* **12** (2000) 419–431.
155. K. Haussuhl, B. Andersson, I. Adamska, A chloroplast DegP2 protease performs the primary cleavage of the photodamaged D1 protein in plant Photosystem II. *EMBO J.* **20** (2001) 713–722.
156. S. Bailey, E. Thompson, P.J. Nixon, P. Horton, C.W. Mullineaux, C. Robinson, N.H. Mann, A critical role for the Var2 FtsH homologue of *Arabidopsis thaliana* in the Photosystem II repair cycle in vivo. *J. Biol. Chem.* **277** (2002) 2006–2011.
157. W. Sakamoto, T. Tamura, Y. Hanba-Tomita, Sodmergen, N. Murata, The *VAR1* locus of *Arabidopsis* encodes a chloroplastic FtsH and is responsible for leaf variegation in the mutant alleles. *Genes Cells* **7** (2002) 769–780.
158. A. Sokolenko, E. Pojidaeva, V. Zinchenko, V. Panichkin, V.M. Glaser, R.G. Herrmann, S.V. Shestakov, The gene complement for proteolysis in the cyanobacterium *Synechocystis* sp. PCC 6803 and *Arabidopsis thaliana* chloroplasts. *Curr. Genet.* **41** (2002) 291–310.
159. E. Kanervo, C. Spetea, Y. Nishiyama, N. Murata, B. Andersson, E.-M. Aro, Dissecting a cyanobacterial proteolytic system: Efficiency in inducing degradation

of the D1 protein of Photosystem II in cyanobacteria and plants. *Biochim. Biophys. Acta* **1607** (2003) 131–140.
160. P.J. Nixon, M. Barker, M. Boehm, R. de Vries, J. Komenda, FtsH-mediated repair of the Photosystem II complex in response to light stress. *J. Exp. Bot.* **56** (2005) 357–363.
161. Z. Adam, A. Zaltsman, G. Sinvany-Villalobo, W. Sakamoto, FtsH proteases in chloroplasts and cyanobacteria. *Physiol. Plant.* **123** (2005) 386–390.
162. P.F. Huesgen, H. Schuhmann, I. Adamska, The family of Deg proteases in cyanobacteria and chloroplasts of higher plants. *Physiol. Plant.* **123** (2005) 413–420.
163. Z. Adam, I. Adamska, K. Nakabayashi, O. Ostersetzer, K. Haussuhl, A. Manuell, B. Zheng, O. Vallon, S.R. Rodermel, K. Shinozaki, A.K. Clarke, Chloroplast and mitochondrial proteases in Arabidopsis. A proposed nomenclature. *Plant Physiol.* **125** (2001) 1912–1918.
164. M. Schubert, U.A. Petersson, B.J. Haas, C. Funk, W.P. Schroder, T. Kieselbach, Proteome map of the chloroplast lumen of *Arabidopsis thaliana*. *J. Biol. Chem.* **277** (2002) 8354–8365.
165. P. Silva, Y.J. Choi, H.A.G. Hassan, P.J. Nixon, Involvement of the HtrA family of proteases in the protection of the cyanobacterium *Synechocystis* PCC 6803 from light stress and in the repair of Photosystem II. *Philos. Trans. R. Soc. London B.* **357** (2002) 1461–1468.
166. W. Sakamoto, A. Zaltsman, Z. Adam, Y. Takahashi, Coordinated regulation and complex formation of YELLOW VARIEGATED1 and YELLOW VARIEGATED2, chloroplastic FtsH metalloproteases involved in the repair cycle of Photosystem II in *Arabidopsis* thylakoids membranes. *Plant Cell* **15** (2003) 2843–2855.
167. G. Friso, L. Giacomelli, A.J. Ytterberg, J.-B. Peltier, A. Rudella, Q. Sun, K.J. van Wijk, In-depth analysis of the thylakoid membrane proteome of *Arabidopsis thaliana* chloroplasts: New proteins, new functions, and a plastid proteome database. *Plant Cell* **16** (2004) 478–499.
168. F. Yu, S. Park, S.R. Rodermel, The *Arabidopsis* FtsH metalloprotease gene family: Interchangeability of subunits in chloroplast oligomeric complexes. *Plant J.* **37** (2004) 864–876.
169. A. Zaltsman, A. Feder, Z. Adam, Developmental and light effects on the accumulation of FtsH protease in *Arabidopsis* chloroplasts – implications for thylakoid formation and Photosystem II maintenance. *Plant J.* **42** (2005) 609–617.
170. A. Zaltsman, N. Ori, Z. Adam, Two types of FtsH protease subunits are required for chloroplast biogenesis and Photosystem II repair in *Arabidopsis*. *Plant Cell* **17** (2005) 2782–2790.
171. Y. Kashino, W.M. Lauber, J.A. Caroll, Q. Wang, J. Whitmarsh, K. Satoh, H.B. Pakrasi, Proteomic analysis of a highly active Photosystem II preparation from the cyanobacterium *Synechocystis* sp. PCC 6803 reveals the presence of novel polypeptides. *Biochemistry* **41** (2002) 8004–8012.
172. Y. Hihara, A. Kamei, M. Kanehisa, A. Kaplan, M. Ikeuchi, DNA microarray analysis of cyanobacterial gene expression during acclimation to high light. *Plant Cell* **13** (2001) 793–806.
173. L. Zhang, E.-M. Aro, Synthesis, membrane insertion and assembly of the chloroplast-encoded D1 protein into Photosystem II. *FEBS Lett.* **512** (2002) 13–18.
174. R. Kettunen, S. Pursiheimo, E. Rintamaki, K. J. van Wijk, E.M. Aro, Transcriptional and translational adjustments of *psbA* gene expression in mature

chloroplasts during photoinhibition and subsequent repair of Photosystem II. *Eur. J. Biochem.* **247** (1997) 441–448.
175. L. Zhang, V. Paakkarinen, K.J. van Wijk, E.-M. Aro, Co-translational assembly of the D1 protein into Photosystem II. *J. Biol. Chem.* **274** (1999) 16062–16067.
176. R. Nilsson, J. Brunner, N.E. Hoffman, K.J. van Wijk, Interactions of ribosome nascent chain complexes of the chloroplast-encoded D1 thylakoid membrane protein with cpSRP54. *EMBO J.* **18** (1999) 733–742.
177. L. Zhang, V. Paakkarinen, M. Suorsa, E.-M. Aro, A SecY homologue is involved in chloroplast-encoded D1 protein biogenesis. *J. Biol. Chem.* **276** (2001) 37809–37814.
178. L. Zhang, V. Paakkarinen, K.J. van Wijk, E.-M. Aro, Biogenesis of the chloroplast-encoded D1 protein: Regulation of translation elongation, insertion, and assembly into Photosystem II. *Plant Cell* **12** (2000) 1769–1781.
179. J. Kim, P.G. Klein, J.E. Mullet, Ribosomes pause at specific sites during synthesis of membrane-bound chloroplast reaction center protein D1. *J. Biol. Chem.* **266** (1991) 14931–14938.
180. J.R. Bowyer, J.C.L. Packer, B.A. McCormack, J.P. Whitelegge, C. Robinson, M. Taylor, Carboxyl-terminal processing of the D1 protein and photoactivation of water-splitting in Photosystem II. *J. Biol. Chem.* **267** (1992) 5424–5433.
181. M. Hager, M. Hermann, K. Biehler, A. Krieger-Liszkay, R. Bock, Lack of the small plastid-encoded PsbJ polypeptide results in a defective water-splitting apparatus of Photosystem II. reduced Photosystem I levels, and hypersensitivity to light. *J. Biol. Chem.* **277** (2002) 14031–14039.
182. M. Suorsa, R.E. Regel, V. Paakkarinen, N. Battchikova, R.G. Herrmann, E.-M. Aro, Protein assembly of Photosystem II and accumulation of subcomplexes in the absence of low molecular mass subunits PsbL and PsbJ. *Eur. J. Biochem.* **271** (2004) 96–107.
183. S.I. Allakhverdiev, Y. Nishiyama, S. Miyairi, H. Yamamoto, N. Inagaki, Y. Kanesaki, N. Murata, Salt stress inhibits the repair of photodamaged Photosystem II by suppressing the transcription and translation of *psbA* genes in *Synechocystis*. *Plant Physiol.* **130** (2002) 1443–1453.
184. S.I. Allakhverdiev, Y. Nishiyama, S. Takahashi, S. Miyairi, I. Suzuki, N. Murata, Systematic analysis of the relation of electron transport and ATP synthesis to the photodamage and repair of Photosystem II in *Synechocystis*. *Plant Physiol.* **137** (2005) 263–273.
185. S. Takahashi, N. Murata, Interruption of the Calvin cycle inhibits the repair of Photosystem II from photodamage. *Biochim. Biophys. Acta* **1708** (2005) 352–361.
186. Z. Gombos, H. Wada, N. Murata, The recovery of photosynthesis from low-temperature photoinhibiton is accelerated by the unsaturation of membrane lipids: A mechanism of chilling tolerance. *Proc. Natl. Acad. Sci. U.S.A.* **91** (1994) 8787–8791.
187. E. Kanervo, E.-M. Aro, N. Murata, Low unsaturation level of thylakoid membrane lipids limits turnover of the D1 protein of Photosystem II at high irradiance. *FEBS Lett.* **364** (1995) 239–242.
188. Z. Gombos, E. Kanervo, N. Tsvetkova, T. Sakamoto, E.M. Aro, N. Murata, Genetic enhancement of the ability to tolerate photoinhibition by introduction of unsaturated bonds into membrane glycerolipids. *Plant Physiol.* **115** (1997) 551–559.
189. S.I. Allakhverdiev, N. Tsvetkova, N. Mohanty, B. Szalontai, B.Y. Moon, M. Debreczeny, N. Murata, Irreversible photoinhibition of Photosystem II is

caused by exposure of *Synechocystis* cells to strong light for a prolonged period. *Biochim. Biophys. Acta* **1708** (2005) 342–351.
190. Y. Nishiyama, H. Yamamoto, S.I. Allakhverdiev, H. Inaba, A. Yokota, N. Murata, Oxidative stress inhibits the repair of photodamage to the photosynthetic machinery. *EMBO J.* **20** (2001) 5587–5594.
191. Y. Nishiyama, S.I. Allakhverdiev, H. Yamamoto, H. Hayashi, Singlet oxygen inhibits the repair of Photosystem II by suppressing the translation elongation of the D1 protein in *Synechocystis* sp. PCC 6803. *Biochemistry* **43** (2004) 11321–11330.
192. B. Hankamer, J. Barber, E.J. Boekema, Structure and membrane organization of Photosystem II in green plants. *Annu. Rev. Plant Physiol.* **48** (1997) 641–671.
193. A. Melis, Photosystem-II damage and repair cycle in chloroplasts: What modulates the rate of photodamage in vivo? *Trends Plant Sci.* **4** (1999) 130–135.
194. E.-M. Aro, M. Suorsa, A. Rokka, Y. Allahverdiyeva, V. Paakkarinen, A. Saleem, N. Battchikova, E. Rintamäki, Dynamics of Photosystem II: A proteomic approach to thylakoid protein complexes. *J. Exp. Bot.* **56** (2005) 347–356.
195. V. Ebbert, D. Godde, Regulation of thylakoid protein phosphorylation in intact chloroplasts by the activity of kinases and phosphatases. *Biochim. Biophys. Acta* **1187** (1994) 335–346.
196. A. Koivuniemi, E.M. Aro, B. Andersson, Degradation of the D1- and D2-proteins of Photosystem II in higher plants is regulated by reversible phosphorylation. *Biochemistry* **34** (1995) 16022–16029.
197. E. Rintamäki, R. Kettunen, E.-M. Aro, Differential D1 dephosphorylation in functional and photodamaged Photosystem II centers. Dephosphorylation is a prerequisite for degradation of damaged D1. *J. Biol. Chem.* **271** (1996) 14870–14875.
198. E. Baena-Gonzalez, E.-M. Aro, Biogenesis, assembly and turnover of Photosystem II units. *Philos. Trans. R. Soc. London B.* **357** (2002) 1451–1460.
199. V. Bonardi, P. Pesaresi, T. Becker, E. Schleiff, R. Wagner, T. Pfannschmidt, P. Jahns, D. Leister, Photosystem II core phosphorylation and photosynthetic acclimation require two different protein kinases. *Nature* **437** (2005) 1179–1182.
200. W. Haupt, R. Scheuerlein, Chloroplast movement. *Plant Cell Environ.* **13** (1990) 595–614.
201. T.W. Mulroy, Spectral properties of heavily glaucous and non-glaucous leaves of a succulent rosette-plant. *Oecologia* **38** (1979) 349–357.
202. M. Tevini, W. Iwanzik, A.H. Teramura, Effects of UV-B radiation on plants during mild water stress. II. Effects on growth, protein and flavonoid content. *Z. Pflanzenphysiol.* **110** (1983) 459–467.
203. C.J. Beggs, U. Schneider-Ziebert, E. Wellmann, in: *Stratospheric Ozone Reduction, Solar Ultraviolet Radiation and Plant Life* (1986) (R.C. Worrest, M.M. Caldwell, eds.), NATO ASI Series G: Ecological Sciences, Springer-Verlag, Berlin, Vol. 8, pp. 235–250.
204. R. Robberecht, M.M. Caldwell, in: *Stratospheric Ozone Reduction, Solar Ultraviolet Radiation and Plant Life* (1986) (R.C. Worrest, M.M. Caldwell, eds.), NATO ASI Series G: Ecological Sciences, Springer-Verlag, Berlin, Vol. 8, p. 251.
205. M. Tevini, J. Braun, G. Fieser, The protective function of the epidermal layer of rye seedlings against ultraviolet-B radiation. *Photochem. Photobiol.* **53** (1991) 329–333.
206. A. Strid, J. Porra, Alterations in pigment content in leaves of *Pisum sativum* after exposure to supplementary UV-B. *Plant Cell Physiol.* **33** (1992) 1015–1023.

207. J.F. Bornman, T.C. Vogelman, The effect of UV-B radiation on leaf optical properties measured with fiber optics. *J. Exp. Bot.* **42** (1991) 547–554.
208. K. Asada, M. Takahashi, in: *Topics in Photosynthesis*. Vol. 9. *Photoinhibition* (1987) (D.J. Kyle, C.B. Osmond, C.J. Arntzen, eds.), Elsevier, Amsterdam, pp. 227–288.
209. K. Asada, in: *Molecular Biology of Free Radical Scavenging Systems* (1995) (J.G. Scandalios, ed.), Cold Spring Harbor Laboratory Press, New York, pp. 173–192.
210. C.H. Foyer, in: *Antioxidants in Higher Plants* (1993) (R.G. Alscher, J.L. Hess, eds.), CRC Press, Boca Raton, Ann Arbor, London, Tokyo, pp. 31–58.
211. E. Hideg, J. Mano, C. Ohno, K. Asada, Increased levels of monodehydroascorbate radical in UV-B irradiated broad bean leaves. *Plant Cell Physiol.* **38** (1997) 684–690.
212. E. Hideg, A. Nagy, A. Oberschall, D. Dudits, I. Vass, Detoxification function of aldose/aldehyde reductase during drought and ultraviolet-B (280–320 nm) stresses. *Plant Cell Environ.* **26** (2003) 513–522.
213. L. Sass, C. Spetea, Z. Máté, F. Nagy, I. Vass, Repair of UV-B induced damage of Photosystem II via de novo synthesis of the D1 and D2 reaction centre subunits in *Synechocystis* sp. PCC 6803. *Photosynth. Res.* **54** (1997) 55–62.
214. S.S. Golden, Light-responsive gene expression in cyanobacteria. *J. Bacteriol.* **177** (1995) 1651–1654.
215. Z. Máté, L. Sass, M. Szekeres, I. Vass, F. Nagy, UV-B induced differential transcription of *psbA* genes encoding the D1 protein of Photosystem II in the cyanobacterium *Synechocystis* 6803. *J. Biol. Chem.* **273** (1998) 17439–17444.
216. A. Viczián, Z. Máté, F. Nagy, I. Vass, UV-B induced differential transcription of *psbD* genes encoding the D2 protein of Photosystem II in the cyanobacterium *Synechocystis* 6803. *Photosynth. Res.* **64** (2000) 257–266.
217. D. Campbell, M.-J. Erikson, G. Öquist, P. Gustafsson, A.K. Clarke, The cyanobacterium *Synechochoccus* resists UV-B by exchanging Photosystem II reaction-center D1 proteins. *Proc. Natl. Acad. Sci. U.S.A.* **95** (1998) 364–369.
218. M. Tichy, L. Lupínková, C. Sicora, I. Vass, S. Kuvikova, O. Prasil, J. Komenda, *Synechocystis* 6803 mutants expressing distinct forms of the Photosystem II D1 protein from *Synechococcus* 7942: Relationship between the *psbA* coding region and sensitivity to visible and UV-B radiation. *Biochim. Biophys. Acta* **1605** (2003) 55–66.
219. C. Sicora, S.E. Appleton, C.E. Brown, J. Chung, J. Chandler, A.M. Cockshutt, I. Vass, D.A. Campbell, Cyanobacterial *psbA* families in *Anabeana* and *Synechocystis* encode trace, constitutive and UV-B induced D1 isoforms. *Biochim. Biophys. Acta* **1757** (2006) 47–56.

# Subject Index

Note: Roman page numbers refer to Part 1, **bold page numbers** refer to Part 2.

α *see* alpha; miss hits
$\Delta G_{\text{store}}(h\nu)$ *see* stored Gibbs energy
$\alpha_2\beta_2$ complex 220
AAS *see* atom absorption spectroscopy
A-branch
  bacterial RC cofactors **18**
  chlorobial RC site-directed
    mutagenesis **81**
  Photosystem I
    cyanobacteria **116, 117, 119–20**
    oxygen evolving organisms **150–1, 154, 167–71**
absorption spectra
  Acaryochloris marina 267
  bacteriochlorophylls **499, 501**
  basic principles 39–89
  carotenoids of purple bacteria 159, 160, 162, 164, 167, 169
  chemically-modified chromophores 117
  chlorophylls 104, 266, 267
  CP29 355–6
  gap pigments 306–7
  Gloeobacter violaceus PCC 7421 267
  Lax and Kubo theory 58
  LHCII 339–40, 346–52
  pheophytin *a* 267
  pigment–protein complexes of
    purple non-sulfur bacteria 209
  pigments 111
  proteobacterial RC alternative
    pathways **75**

  proteobacterial RCs with BChl *a*
    and BPh *a* **69**
  PSILHCI 306–7
  purple non-sulfur bacterial PSU
    organization 217, 237
  Rhodopseudomonas acidophila
    LH2 211
  secondary ET in PSI of oxygen
    evolving organisms **164**
  *Synechocystis* spp. PCC 6803 267, 271
  time-scales 116
  Type II RCs directionality **74**
  *see also* difference absorption spectra
Acaryochloris spp.
  A. marina 16
    absorption spectra 267
    chlorophyll *d'* 268
    *d*-type chlorophylls 109
    light-induced ET in chlorophylls
      105
    minor chlorophylls 114
    P680 in PSII **251–2**
    P740 singlet excited states **152–3**
    photosystems model 281
    phycobilisome-lacking
      cyanobacteria 273
  chlorophyll *d* 266, 268
  chlorophyll diversity 265
Acc$_1$ *see* primary quinone acceptor
Acc$_2$ *see* secondary quinone acceptor
'accepting mode' 163

acceptor-sided induced photodamage mechanisms 397–8
accessory bacteriochlorophylls **25**
accessory pigments 153–95
  *see also* carotenoids
acclimation, PSI antenna size 309–11
acidic conditions 113, 376, 404
*Acidiphilium rubrum* 113
actin filament rotation **451, 466–72, 478**
activation energies **319–21**
activation of photopigment and *puc* suppression (AppA) 213
active center structure **394**
adaptation mechanisms 14–15, 153, 176–89
adenosine 5'-triphosphate (ATP)
  ATP synthase **449–81**
  cyanobacteria 372
  cytochrome $b_6f$ complex **421**
  ET thermodynamics **386**
  function/structure **449–50**
  heme $c_n$ cyclic electron transport **435**
  hydrolysis: Gibbs free energy **449**
  synthesis
    aerobic photosynthetic bacteria **368**
    anoxygenic photosynthetic bacteria **358**
    biomimetic 29
    chemiosmotic membrane-ET principle **393, 395**
    $H^+$/ATP stoichiometric ratio **458–9**
adjustable chromophore properties 116
ADMR studies **166**
aerobic atmosphere 10, **388–9**
aerobic chemo-litho(auto)trophic energy conversion **391**
aerobic growth 207, 208, **368–9**
  *see also* cyanobacteria
aggregates
  bacteriochlorophyll luminescence 119
  chlorophyll as structure stabilizer 106
  circular dichroism 121
  cyanobacterial PSIIcc characterization **200–4**
  Förster theory 76
A helix, LHCII structure 335–6

ALA *see* 5-aminolevulinic acid
alanine **40, 41**
algae
  cytochrome $b_6f$ complex **422, 424, 425**
  light-harvesting protein evolution **512, 513**
  oxygenic photosynthetic process **195**
  photosynthetic apparatus 23–4, 25
  protists evolution **514–16**
  PsaF subunit **131**
  state transitions 374
  *see also* cyanobacteria
alkaliphilic bacteria **456, 458**
*Allochromatium vinosum* **363**
allophycocyanin (APC) 269–70, 272–3, 274
all-trans configuration 155–7, 189–92
alpha$^{APB}$ 279
alpha apoproteins 216, 221–3, 228–9
alpha-carotene 268
alternative proteobacterial RC pathways **75**
amino acid homology *see* sequence homology
amino acid sidechains **34–6**
amino acid substitutions *see* site-directed mutagenesis
5-aminolevulinic acid (ALA) 124, 126
*Anabaena* **175–6**, 411
  A. variabilis **132**
Anacystis nidulans see Thermosynechococcus PCC 6301
anaerobic Earth **393**
anaerobic growth
  purple non-sulfur bacteria 207, 208
  *see also* anoxygenic photosynthetic bacteria
anaerobic respiration schemes **391**
analytical ultracentrifugation (AUC) **203–4**
anchor proteins 279–80
angular momentum 191
angular velocity *see* torque
anharmonic PES 56–7
anhydrorhodovibrin
  fluorescence quantum yields 166

*Subject Index*

near-infrared sub-picosecond time-resolved absorption spectra 160
quantum efficiency of singlet energy transfer to bacteriochlorophyll 174
relaxation scheme 163
singlet excited states 158
singlet lifetimes versus double bond numbers 161
structure 159
visible sub-picosecond time-resolved absorption spectroscopy 162, 175
animal evolution **516**
anion exchange chromatography **11, 200, 201**
annihilation experiments 352
annihilation operators 55
anoxygenic photosynthetic bacteria
   antenna systems 371, 372
   bacteriochlorophylls 108, 109, 112
   $C_5$ pathway 124
   classification **59–60, 355–6**
   *c*-type bacteriochlorophylls 108, 109
   electron transfer **61, 63, 65, 67–84**
   electron transport chain **353–74**
   light-harvesting protein evolution **511**
   overview **355–6**
   photosynthesis evolution **504–5**
   reaction centers 16, 371–2
      functional patterns **57–85**
      structures **7–45**
      tetraheme species **360–3**
      triheme species **363–5**
      Type I **60–7, 77–84**
      Type II **60–77**
   species name revisions **67**
   types **504–5**
   vesicle structures 22–3
   see also individual organisms
antenna complexes
   anoxygenic bacteria 372
   assembly 106
   biomimetic 27, 28
   carotenoid natural selection 189–92
   carotenoid-to-bacteriochlorophyll singlet-energy transfer 172–6
   cyanobacteria **113, 133–5**, 263–4, 273–8, 283–5, 372
   evolution 15
   excitation quenching photoprotection 404–5
   green sulfur bacteria **78**
   heliobacteria without **82**
   higher plants 301–22, 329–52, 369–85
   iron-depleted conditions 283–5
   isolation from PSI-LHCI 311–12
   LHCII minor 352–6
   membrane-bound 273–8
   overview 371–3
   $P680^+Pheo^-$ radical ion pair formation **255**
   photosystem stoichiometry regulation 285–6
   phycobilisomes 372
   PSI in higher plants 301–22
   PSII 329–56
   purple non-sulfur bacteria 205–390
   regulatory EET 373–5
   size regulation/acclimation 309–11
   supramolecular organization 304–11
   topology 304–7
   *see also* light-harvesting complexes
antenna pigments ($P_A$) 12, 14, 103–29
antheroxanthin 343
anthracene 179
anthraquinone **155**
antimycin A **419, 421, 430, 431, 434**
anti-parallel stranded beta-sheets **126, 127**
APC *see* allophycocyanin
Aphanothece halophytica **397**
Apicomplexa **389**
apoproteins 216, 221–3, 228–9, 334–52
AppA (activation of photopigment and *puc* suppression) protein 213
Arabidopsis thaliana
   D1 protein repair cycle 408, 409
   genomic sequence 380
   Lhca1–4 proteins 313, 314, 317
   Lhcb1-Lhcb6 sequence homology 333

light-harvesting chlorophyll I
    pigment composition 312
mutant studies on PsbS protein
    symmetrical structure 377
non-triplet producing charge
    recombination 405
photoprotection in the antenna 404
protein phosphorylation in damage
    repair 411
PSI photodamage mechanism 402
TAKs antisense plants 375
time-resolved PSII fluorescence
    spectra 382
UV photoprotection 411
archaebacteria, early photosynthesis
    **497–8**
arginine residues **34–6, 41, 42, 473**
aromatic amino acids 217
artifacts, luminescence spectrometry 117
artificial photosynthesis 26–30
asparagine residues **44**
aspartic acid **34–6, 41**
assembly
    antenna structure stabilization 106
    building principles 41–8
    cyanobacterial PSI **121**
    photosynthetic apparatus architecture
        22–5
    PSIIcc integral lipid molecules **217**
    thylakoid membrane molecules 277–8
    *see also* dimeric structures;
        stabilization; trimeric complexes
asteroid phase **494**
a-subunit, ATP synthase **463**
asymmetric manganese cubane center
    **506, 507**
asymmetry *see* directionality
atmospheric oxygen **388**
atomic absorption spectroscopy
    (AAS) **11, 206, 223–7**
atomic force microscopy (AFM) 222–
    3, 234, **370–1**
ATP *see* adenosie 5'-triphosphate
ATP synthase ($F_OF_1$-ATPase)
    artificial complexes 29
    bacterial RC structure **8**

chemiosmotic energy coupling **452–60**
cyanobacterial **392, 395**
evolution **60**
higher plants **198**
inter-subunit rotation in $F_1$ **465–8**
peripheral stalk **463**
photophosphorylation **447–81**
regulation **459–60**
rotary catalyst $F_1$ **464–72**
rotary electromotor $F_O$ concept **473–6**
rotary twin engine concept **476–80**
structure **451–2, 461–80**
atrazine **12, 30, 31**
A-type flavoproteins, discovery **400**
AUC *see* analytical ultracentrifugation
auracyanin 77
axial coordination **258**
axial ligands **170, 171**

B777 FMO-complex 42–3, 67, 77–81
B800-850 complexes 210
B800 bacteriochlorophyll 42, 178,
    223–5, 240, 241
B850 bacteriochlorophyll 178, 223–4,
    238, 240, 241
B880 bacteriochlorophyll 238, 241
Bacillariophyceae 110
bacteria
    LH1 core antenna complex, B777
        complex free energy 42–3
    photosynthetic unit, purple non-
        sulfur bacteria 210–12
    reaction centers
        cofactor conformation **21–9**
        crystallization process **12–13**
        higher plant PSII comparison **44–5**
        membrane protein structure **34–9**
        modified **39–44**
        substrate binding sites **29–34**
    see also individual classes/species
        of bacteria
bacteriochlorin rings 224
bacteriochlorin-type chlorophylls
    108, 109, 112
bacteriochlorin-type cyclic
    conjugated tetrapyrroles 115

*Subject Index*

bacteriochlorophyll *a* (BChl *a*)
  bacterial RC structure **11–12, 18, 25**
  binding in purple non-sulfur bacterial antennas 223–4
  EM studies of core complexes 232–3
  evolution **499–501**
  mutations 117
  phytyl tails 224–5
  primary electron donor location **22, 24**
  proteobacterial RC absorption spectra **69**
  $Q_x$ transition 209
  Rhodopseudomonas palustris RC-LH1 complex 236
bacteriochlorophyll *b* (BChl *b*) **11–12, 22, 24, 25**
bacteriochlorophyll (BChl)
  absorption spectra **499, 501**
  aggregates 119, 121
  anoxygenic photosynthetic bacterial reaction centers 12, 16
  biosynthesis 124–8
  Blastochloris viridis RC **68**
  characteristics 103
  evolution **499–501**
  FMO complexes 87–8
  luminescence spectroscopy 118–19
  photosystem processes 41–2
  purple bacterial antenna complexes 172–9, 217
  purple non-sulfur bacteria 209–10
  structures 108–9
  structures in anoxygenic bacterial RCs **61–2**
bacteriochlorophyll *c* (BChl *c*) 108, 109, 110, 112
bacteriopheophytin *a* (BPhe *a*) **69**
bacteriopheophytin (BPhe)
  bacterial RC structure **11–12, 18, 25–6**
  Blastochloris viridis RC **68**
  functional differences **252**
  light-induced ET in chlorophylls 105
  structures in anoxygenic bacterial RCs **61–2**
bacteriorhodopsin **497–8**
barley 312, 383, 402

basic principles 12–25
  electron transport chains 18–22
  light absorption 39–89
  light harvesting 14–15
  light-induced charge separation 15–17
  photosystems 41
B-band optical absorption 114, 115
B-branch
  bacterial RC cofactors **18**
  chlorobial RC site-directed mutagenesis **81–2**
  cyanobacterial PSI **116, 117, 119–20**
  primary charge separation in PSI of oxygen evolving organisms **154**
  PSI in oxygen evolving organisms **150–1, 167–71**
BChl *see* bacteriochlorophyll
Berkner-Marshall-Point **388**
beta apoproteins 216, 221–3, 228–9
beta carotene *see* carotene
beta-sheet structures **126, 127**
B helix 335–7, 342, 343
BIC *see* butyl isocyanide
bicarbonate ions **311–12**
bidirectional hydrogenase **395, 401**
'Big Bang' theory **387, 390**
bilin biosynthesis 124
binding change mechanism, ATP synthase **450**
binding pockets
  $Q_A$ 254–5, 369
  $Q_B$ 7, 216–18, 219, 267, 270–1
  site-directed mutagenesis 116–17
binding sites
  bacteriochlorophyll *a* in purple bacterial antennas 217, 223–4
  CP29 354
  inhibitors **29–32**
  integral membrane lipids **217**
  LHCII chlorophyll organization 338–40
  mixed Chl *a/b* occupancy in LHCII 343–4
  substrates in bacterial RCs **29–34**
  WOC substrate water binding **313**
  *see also* pigment binding

binding states **365**
biochemical models 375–7
biochemical properties 311–15
bioenergetic 'nonplus-ultra' *see* cyanobacteria
bioenergetic schemes **391**
biomass, primary production **389**
biomimetic systems 26–30
biosynthetic pathways
 BChl/Chl *a/b* evolution **499–500**
 carotenoids in anoxygenic purple bacteria 154, 155
 chlorophyll in cyanobacteria 286–8
 chlorophylls 124–8
biotin **467, 470**
biphasic reoxidation kinetics **164, 168–9**
bi-site mechanism **464, 472**
'black smokers' **389, 398**
Blastochloris viridis reaction centers
 bound water **36–7**
 characterization **11–12**
 crystallization **12–13**
 crystal structure **66–7**
 C subunit structure **23**
 *c*-type cytochromes **361**
 electron carriers **68**
 electron donor substrate binding **33–4**
 heme-iron site geometries **28–9**
 herbicide-resistant mutants **42**
 H subunit structure **22**
 intramembrane phospholipids **37–9**
 isolated membrane studies **359**
 LH complexes number/type **358**
 L subunit structure **18–19**
 modified reaction centers **39–42**
 M subunit structure **20–1**
 $Q_B$ site derivatives **30**
 quantum yield in chlorophylls 105
 RC-LH1 core complexes 229–31
 stereo pairs **24, 26, 27**
 structure comparison with PSII structure **44–5**
 structure/function **8–9**
 supramolecular organization of membranous components **370**
 tetraheme species **360**

X-ray crystal form **14, 15, 18**
X-ray structure analysis **196**
blue color, Earth **387**
blue-green algae *see* cyanobacteria
blue-shift 217
Boltzmann distribution 54
Born–Oppenheimer approximation 49
Bose–Einstein distribution function 55
bound water **36–7**
BPhe *see* bacteriopheophytin
breakage of cells **359**
broadening of absorption bands 347–8
Brownian oscillator model 73, 74
Brownian ratchet mechanism **474**
building principles 41–8
bulk-to-bulk coupling **456**
butyl isocyanide (BIC) **434**

$C_2S_2M_2$ supercomplex 332
$C_5$ pathway 124, 125
C-9 acetyl group 223
C *see* torsional rigidity
C=C stretching line 170–1
cadmium **32, 33, 72**, 113
calcium **129, 294**, 354
*Calothrix* PCC 7601 272
Calvin–Benson cycle 9, 11, 17, **404**
canopies 320
CAO *see* chlorophyll *a* oxygenase
capacitor enzymes **401**
*Capsicum annuum* 405
carbon dioxide 9, 11, 17, 29–30, **392, 495**
cardiolipin **38**, 41
β-carotene
 all-trans β-carotene 13
 Chl *a* position in cytochrome $b_6f$ complex **436–7, 439**
 chlorophyll triplets quenching in antenna **267**
 15-cis to all-trans isomerization 179–80
 cyanobacteria **220–2**, 268, 276–7
 functions 153
 mini-9-β-carotene 159
carotenoids
 absorption spectra 159, 160, 162, 164, 167, 169

*Subject Index*

anoxygenic purple bacteria 151–95
binding sites, LHCII in higher
  plants 343
characteristics 12, 13
cyanobacteria 268–9
  energy dissipation 283
  PsaF subunit **131**
  PSI **135, 136**
  PSIIcc **220–2**
electronic conversions 168–72
functions 103
gap pigments 306–7
LHCII in higher plants 337, 340–1,
  344–6
luminescence quenching 120
natural selection of structures 189–92
photophysical properties 151–95
photoprotective functions 105–6,
  176–89, **508**
photosystem processes 41–2
purple bacteria 151–95
purple non-sulfur bacteria 209–10,
  225–7
triplet formation 321
valve action to chlorophyll triplets 283
*see also* xanthophylls
carotenoid-to-bacteriochlorophyll
  singlet-energy transfer 172–6
cation radicals 105–6, **250**
$cbb_3$/RdxB pathway 212–14
cc *see* core complexes
c chromatophore **454**
CcO *see* cytochrome *c* oxidase
CD *see* circular dichroism
cell breakage **359**
center–center distances **250**
chain length, carotenoids 153–7, 177–9, 191
characterization, molecular **9–12, 162–3,
  200–4**
charge recombination **160, 261,** 398–9,
  405–6
charge separation
  anoxygenic photosynthetic bacteria **60**
  green non-sulfur bacteria **76**
  green sulfur bacteria RCs **80**
  light-induced 15–17

primary **152–4, 160–1,** 371–3
proteobacterial kinetics/energetics
  **69–72**
PSIIcc **240–62**
reaction center chlorophylls 371–3
triplet forming charge recombination
  398–9
charge transfer coupling 43–8
CHARMM program 88
C helix 335–6, 343
chemically-modified chromophores 117
chemical structure *see* structure
chemiosmotic mechanism
  ATP synthase **452–60**
  ATP synthesis **450, 451**
  energy conversion basic mechanism
    **390**
  evolutionary success **391–4**
  photo/chemoautotrophs **392**
chemoheterotrophic energy conversion
  **385, 397**
chemosynthetic primary production **389**
Chl *see* chlorophyll
Chlamydomonas
  C. reinhardtii
    $Chlz_{D1}/Chlz_{D2}$ chlorophylls mutant
      studies **244**
    cytochrome $b_6f$ complex **419, 424,
      425, 427, 428, 434**
    electron transfer in PSI **120**
    Lhca sequences 318
    P700 in PSI of oxygen evolving
      organisms **165**
    $Pheo_{D2}$ mutant studies **247**
    PSI to Fd/Fld in vitro ET kinetics
      **172–3**
    PSI trapping mechanism **160**
    two-ET branches of PSI **168, 169–71**
  LHCII mutants 341
  state transition-deficient mutants 375
Chlide *a* 128
Chlorarachnion **515**
Chlorarachniophyta 110
Chlorella 12
  C. pyrenoidosa **302–3**
  C. sorokiniana **81**

chloride ions **311–12**
chlorins **244–5, 246, 248, 250**
chlorin-type chlorophylls 108, 109
chlorin-type cyclic conjugated
   tetrapyrroles 115
2-chloro-4-ethylamino-6-
   isopropylamino-s-triazine *see*
   atrazine
Chlorobi **7–45**, 18, **59**, **63**, 110
   characteristics **505**
   chlorophylls 108, 109
   C. limicola **81, 159**
   *C. tepidum* 44, 82, 87, 128, **368**
   direct photoreduction **404**
   FMO-complex local excitation
      energies 87
   habitat 77
   light-harvesting protein evolution **512**
   RC functional patterns **77–82**
   RC I resembles PSI **60**
   RC structure **7–45**
chlorobiumquinone **80**
Chloroflexi 16, 19, 110
   *C. aurantiacus* **70**, **75–7**, 106
   characteristics **505**
   classification 77
   functional patterns of RCs **75–7**
   growth conditions **356**
   RC components/thermodynamic
      properties **63**
   RC II resembles PSII **60**
   species **59**
   *see also* Chlorobi; green bacteria
Chlorophyceae 110
chlorophyll $A_0$ (Chl $A_0$)
   cyanobacterial PSI **113**
   cyanobacterial PSI structure **118–19**
   eC-B2/eC-A3 dimer **151, 153**
   energetics modifications in oxygen
      evolving organisms **170**
   primary ET in PSI of oxygen
      evolving organisms **159–63**
   PSI ET in oxygen evolving
      organisms **151, 153–4**
chlorophyll $A_1$ (Chl $A_1$) **159–63**
chlorophyll A5-B5 318

chlorophyll $a'$ (Chl $a'$)
   cyanobacterial ET system 266
   P700 in cyanobacterial PSI
      structure **117–18**
   special pair in oxygen evolving
      organisms **150**
chlorophyll $a$ (Chl $a$)
   $A_0$ chlorophyll **113**
   absorption spectra 266, 267, 268
   bacteriochlorin type 108, 112
   biosynthesis 128, **498–500**
   CP43/Cp47 protein arrangement **215**
   cyanobacterial ET chain **222–3**
   cyanobacteria photosystem I
      complexes 275–6
   cytochrome $b_6f$ complex **436–9**
   eC-A2/eC-B3 dimer **151, 153**
   eC-B2/eC-A3 dimer **151, 153**
   evolution **499–501**
   gap pigments 306–7
   LHCII in higher plants 331, 339–40,
      343–4
   occurrence 110
   oxygenic phototrophs 108, 109
   P680 in PSII **244–6, 251–2**
   P700 in cyanobacterial PSI structure **117**
   phytyl chains **227**
   primary ET in PSI of oxygen
      evolving organisms **159**
   red forms 315
   special pair in oxygen evolving
      organisms **150**
   spectral/chemical properties 268
   structure 13, 108
chlorophyll $a$ oxygenase (CAO) 344,
   376, 380, 383
chlorophyll $b$ (Chl $b$)
   absorption spectra 267, 268
   *Arabidopsis* replete/deficient
      mutants 380–1, 382–3
   bacteriochlorin type 108, 112
   biosynthesis 128
   evolution **499–501**
   gap pigments 306–7
   LHCII in higher plants 331, 339–40,
      343–4

*Subject Index* 435

oxygenic phototrophs 108, 109
structures 108
chlorophyll *c* (Chl *c*) 107–9, **499–501**
chlorophyll (Chl) 103–29
　a/b ratios 335, 353
　bacteriochlorophylls comparison **61–2**
　binding sites, CP29 354
　biosynthesis 124–8, 286–8, **498**
　characteristics 12, 13
　circular dichroism 120–1
　CP43/Cp47 protein arrangement
　　**213–15**
　cyanobacteria **113, 133–5**, 264, 265–8
　dimer system, non-perturbative
　　treatment 66
　diversity in cyanobacteria 265
　electrochemistry 123–4
　electron spin resonance spectroscopy
　　121–2
　evolution **499–501**
　excitation energy quenching 105–6
　fluorescence 376–7
　functions 104–6
　LHCII in higher plants 335, 336–40,
　　351
　light-induced electron transfer 105
　luminescence spectrometry 117–20
　mass spectrometry 122
　minor 113–14
　molecular structures 107–14
　NMR spectroscopy 121
　optical absorption spectroscopy
　　114–17
　pair P680, redox potentials 89
　photosystem processes 41–2
　porphyrin synthesis **498**
　PSIght hart harvesting chlorophyll I
　　complex 305
　structure stabilization 106
　transmetalated 113
　triplets **267**, 283, 321
　unsaturation degree 107
　vibrational spectroscopy 122–3
　*see also* chlorophyll *a*; chlorophyll *b*;
　　'special pair'
chlorophyll *d'* (Chl *d'*) 268

chlorophyll *d* (Chl *d*)
　absorption spectra 267
　cyanobacteria 266, 268
　evolution **499–501**
　oxygenic phototrophs 108, 109
　structures 108, 112
chlorophyll eC-A3 **118–19**
chlorophyll eC-B3 119, **151, 153–4**
chlorophyll *e* (Chl *e*) 108, 109, 112
chlorophyll *g* (Chl *g*) 108, 112
chlorophyllide *a* **500**
chlorophyllide *a* oxygenase 287–8
chlorophyllides *see* chlorophyll *c*
chlorophyll–protein interactions 337
chlorophyll–protein proteins 103
chloroplasts
　characteristics **454–5**
　cyanobacteria **385, 390, 396**
　envelope structure **197**
　FNR in supramolecular organization
　　**174–5**
　higher plants EET/dissipation 373–5
　membrane system, energy
　　dissipation types 374–5
　organization 334
　photosynthetic membranes **196–8**
　protein kinase state transitions 375
　structure 23–5
　thylakoid lumen acidification 376, 404
　thylakoid membrane discovery **196**
chlorosomes 76, **80**, 106, 121
$Chlz_{D1}/Chlz_{D2}$ chlorophylls **244–5**
Chromatiaceae **9**
Chromatium vinosum 214–15
chromatography **11**, **201**, **202**, **206–9**, **434**
chromatophore vesicles **454, 475–6**
chromophores
　adjustable properties 116
　binding pockets 116–17
　classes 12
　organization, higher plants 304
　red forms 317–19
chromophytes 107
chronological ordering prescription
　(COP) 66–7, 68
Chrysophyceae 110

circular dichroism (CD) 120–1, 226, 306, 307, 347, 349
cis-carotenoids **135**, **136**, 155–7, 179–83, 189–91, 194–5
cis-positive rule **427**
15-cis to all-trans isomerization 179–80
CK2 site, CP29 354
classification
 anoxygenic photosynthetic bacteria **59–60, 355–6**
 Chloroflexi **77**
 purple non-sulfur bacteria 207, 208
 reaction centers **356**
 revised bacterial species names **67**
$C_{MKKL}(t)$ see correlation function
coal energy 11
'cofactor-apoprotein' concept **241**
cofactors
 bacterial RCs **9–10, 18, 21–9**
 Blastochloris viridis **9–10**
 chemical nature in PSII **242–3**
 cyanobacterial PSI **116–21**
 cyanobacterial PSIIcc crystallization **204–9**
 PSII water splitting process **240**
 reaction centers basic sequence 16
 redox potentials 88, **151–9**
 structural arrangement in PSII **243–5**
 see also individual cofactors
complementary chromatic adaptation 271
complex I **369**
computer-aided design (CAD) **241**
concentration quenching 119–20
Condon approximation 57
confocal single-molecule FRET **468**
conformations
 carotenoid natural selection 189–92
 carotenoids in purple bacteria 155–7
 motion **433**
 reaction center-bound $T_1$ spheroidene 183–9
 15-cis-spheroidene 190
conjugated chain length 153–7, 177–9, 191
connectein 174
'connecting chlorophylls' **134**

consensus sequences 213
conserved sequences/residues see sequence homology
continuous wave (CW) excitation 177–8, **302**
cooperativity **464–5**
coordinate sets **15, 18**
COP see chronological ordering prescription
copper 113
coproporphyrinogen III **510**
core antenna proteins see CP...
core antenna systems **116, 134, 136**
core complexes (cc)
 antenna system of higher plants' photosystem I 301–22
 cyanobacterial PSII crystallographic structure **193–228**
 electron microscopy studies 229–31
 LH1 ring encircles RC 233–4
 light-harvesting chlorophyll I association 309
 purple non-sulfur bacteria 210–11
 Rhodospirillum rubrum 230–1
core units **122–3**
correlation function ($C_{MKKL}(t)$) 56, 69–70
Coulomb coupling 83, 84, 85
coupled electron/proton transfer **421**
coupling factor ($F_1$) **450, 464–72**
coupling of ion movements **450**
couplings, electronic 41–89
CP24 core antenna protein 331, 353
CP26 core antenna protein 331, 353–4
CP29 core antenna protein 331, 340, 344, 354, 355
CP43 core antenna protein
 carotenoid locations in cyanobacterial PSIIcc 222
 chlorophyll arrangement **213–15**
 CP43' and Isi 277, 285
 energy flux in PSII 381
 LHCII 334
 PSIIcc in cyanobacteria **198, 199**
 SDS–urea–PAGE analysis **209**
 transmembrane α-helices **211**
 WOC function **294**

# Subject Index

CP47 core antenna protein
  carotenoid locations in cyanobacterial PSIIcc 222
  chlorophyll arrangement 213–15
  LHCII 334
  PSIIcc in cyanobacteria 198, 199
  SDS–urea–PAGE analysis 209
  transmembrane α-helices 211
  WOC function 294
C-PC see cyanophyte phycocyanin
cpSecY translocon channel 409–10
cpSRP54 chloroplast signal recognition particle 409
creation operators 55
c-ring of $F_O$ 462–3, 469–72, 473, 475
crosslinking studies 127
cross-talk 428–30
cryo-EM techniques 230–1, 370
Cryptomonads 515
Cryptophyta 110
crystallization
  bacterial RC crystal shapes 13–14
  bacterial RCs 12–13
  cyanobacterial ET complexes 398
  cyanobacterial PSIIcc 204–9
  cytochrome $b_6f$ complex 422–8
  dimeric PSIIcc from Thermosynechococcus elongatus 205
  oxygen evolving PSIIcc crystals 200
  phycobiliproteins crystal structure 273, 274
C subunit of bacterial RC 9–11, 21, 23, 32–4
C-terminal domains
  antenna polypeptides 215–17
  cyanobacterial PsaD subunit 127
  LH2 complex from Rhodopseudomonas acidophila 221
  PsaA/PsaB in cyanobacterial PSI 122
Cyanidium caldarium 113
cyanobacteria
  antenna systems 263–4, 283–5, 372, 373
  chlorophyll 284–8

cytochrome $b_6f$ complex 399–400, 402–3, 424
ET chains 383–405
excitation energy transfer 278–83
FNR in supramolecular organization 175
higher plant photosynthetic apparatus comparison 396
historical development timescale 387–8
hydrogenases 395, 401
light-harvesting protein evolution 511–12, 513
membrane systems 23, 273–8, 396–7
oxygen-evolving 261–88, 372, 373, 383–405
pheophytin 264
photosynthetic/respiratory activities 397–8, 400–5
photosystem stoichiometry regulation 285–6
phycobilisomes 271–3
pigments 264, 265–71
proton translocation 456
PSI 113–38
PSII 193–228, 410
reaction centers 16, 372, 373
thylakoids 23, 197, 198
transformable 423
trimeric PSI 373
water cleavage 9–10
Cyanophora paradoxa 390
Cyanophyta I/II[b] 110
cyanophyte phycocyanin (C-PC) 270, 274
cyclic conjugated tetrapyrroles 114, 115
cyclic electron transport 8–9
  alternative to linear electron transport 420, 422, 434–6
  anoxygenic photosynthetic bacteria 353–74
  antimycin A inhibition 419, 430, 431, 434
  cyanobacterial PsaE subunit 127, 128
cyclic Mg-tetrapyrroles see chlorophylls

cysteine residues **120–1, 459**
cytochrome $b_6f$ complex 103
  cyanobacteria **399–400, 402–3, 424**
  intermonomer cross-talk **428–30**
  linear electron transport 20, 21
  photodamage sites 396
  prosthetic groups **425–6, 429, 436–9**
  proton translocation pathways **430–6**
  Q-cycle 425–6, 430–3, 435
  quinone exchange cavity **419, 426, 428–30, 435**
  structure/function **399–400, 417–39**
  three-dimensional structure **424–5**
cytochrome $b$-559
  D1/D2/Cyt $b$-559 isolation **246**
  $^1$P680$^*$ electronic states **247–8**
  photoprotection in PSIIcc without WOC **265**
  PSIIcc structure in cyanobacteria **198–9, 212**
cytochrome $bc_1$ complex
  cyanobacteria **402–3**
  cyt $c$ co-crystals X-ray crystallography **367**
  cytochrome $b_6f$ complex comparison **427**
  cytochrome $c^2$ role in anoxygenic bacterial RC **365, 366**
  ET steps in anoxygenic bacterial RC **357–8**
  facultative photosynthetic bacteria **356–7**
  HiPIP/cyt $c$ docking **363**
  pheophytin–quinone type RCs **7–8**
  species variations **359**
  tetraheme connection in anoxygenic bacterial RCs **361**
cytochrome $c_2$ **32–4, 66–7, 365–8, 372**
cytochrome $c6$ **113, 123, 149, 403**
cytochrome $c$ **358, 359, 367**
cytochrome $c_m$ **403**
cytochrome $c_n$ **399**
cytochrome $c$ oxidase (CcO) **403**
cytochrome $c_t$ **371**
cytochrome $f$ heme **433–4**

cytochromes
  green sulfur bacteria Type I RCs **82**
  organisms possessing subunit **69**
  proteobacterial secondary electron transfer **72–4**
  see also individual cytochromes
cytochrome $x$ see cytochrome $c_n$
cytoplasmic membrane (CM), cyanobacteria **395, 396–7**
cytosol see stroma

D1/D2/Cyt b559 **246, 247–8, 256**
D1/D2 proteins
  cyanobacterial PSII structure **196, 198–9, 209, 212–14, 216–27**
  de novo synthesis **409–10**
  evolution **507, 508**
  non-triplet producing charge recombination 405
  photoprotection **406–11**
  PSII cofactors **244–5**
  RC structure comparison with PSII structure **44–5**
  repair cycle 407
  structure of D2 **63–5**
  WOC function **294**
D1-L210H mutants **247**
damage repair **393–412**
  see also photodamage; photoprotection
dark-adapted bacterial reaction centers **43–4**
dark-equilibrium redox titration **360**
dark-operative protochlorophyllide oxidoreductase (DPOR) 125, 128, 287
dark processes **397**
dark stabilities **297**
Darwin, Charles R. **387**
day length **494**
DBMIB quinone analogue inhibitor **421, 430**
DCCD see dicyclohexylcarbodiimide
5-deazariboflavin **175**
DegP proteases 408
dehydrogenase-quinol-cytochrome sequences **391–2**

*Subject Index*

delayed luminescence 120, 281
deletion studies
  cyanobacterial PsaF subunit **131**
  cytochrome $c^2$ role **365–6**
  $F_OF_1$-ATP synthase robustness **477**
  triheme RC species **365**
delipidation **423**
delocalization *see* exciton states
delocalized mixed valence states **308–9**
*de novo* D1 protein synthesis 409–10
*de novo* membrane synthesis 208
density functional theory (DFT) **250**
density matrix theory 67–73
deprotonation reactions **328–9**
desacetyl bacteriochlorophyllide **500**
Dexter mechanism 104, 239, **436**, **439**
DGDG *see* digalactosyldiacylglycerol
D helix, LHCII structure 335–6
diabatic states 49
dicyclohexylcarbodiimide (DCCD) 378
difference absorption spectra **242–3**, **317**, 339–40
diffusion, WOC substrate water 313
diffusion coefficient $D_Z$ **202–3**
digalactosyldiacylglycerol (DGDG) **196**, **215–18**, **271**, 341
dihydroplastoquinone (PQH$_2$) **267–71**, **432–3**
di-manganese catalase **394**
dimensionless coupling constant 52, 64
dimeric structures
  cytochrome $b_6f$ complex **417–39**
  Lhca1/4 reconstitution 313
  PSIIcc, cyanobacterial X-ray studies **200–27**
  RC-LH1-PufX complexes, supramolecular organization **371–3**
dinoflagellates **515**
Dinophyta 110
dipole strength 349–50
direct electron donors **359**
directionality **74–5**, **81–2**, **161**, **252**
dispersed polaron model 81–2
dissipation-free dynamics 68
dissociation rates **173**
dissymmetric molecules 120–1

distance dependencies 43
distorted carotenoids 226–7
disulfide bridges **466**
divinyl PChlide a 108, 109
DLS *see* dynamic light scattering
$D_M$ *see* Lorentzian lineshape
docking
  cyanobacterial PSI **114**
  ferredoxin in cyanobacterial PsaD/PsaE subunits **126–8**
  HiPIP/cyt $c$ in anoxygenic bacterial RCs **363**
  PSI for Fd/Fld in oxygen evolving organisms **172**
  *Rhodobacter sphaeroides* cyt $c_2$ and RC **366**
  soluble electron donors in cyanobacterial PsaA/PsaB role **123**
  triheme RC species **365**
*n*-dodecyl-β-D-maltoside (β-DM) **200**
domain-swapped ISP TM helix **427**
Donnelly and Cogdell model 219
donor-side induced photodamage 398
double bonds 161
double-flash techniques **72**
double-hit probability (β) **297–8**
DPOR *see* dark-operative protochlorophyllide oxidoreductase
dual function photosynthetic-respiratory ET chain **394–5**, **400–5**
Dutton ruler 86
dyads 27
dynamical theories 41–89
dynamic light scattering (DLS) **202–3**
$D_Z$ *see* diffusion coefficient

E122 glutamine 378–9
E122Q mutation 378–9
E226 glutamine 378–9
E226Q mutation 378–9

Earth
  early life **494–6**
  atmospheric oxygen content **388–9**
  energy release 8

formation **493–5**
geological history **387–8**
mantle out-gassing **495**, **496**
eC-A3 *see* chlorophyll $A_0$
Ectothiorhodospira **9**, 229
edge to edge distance ($R_{DA}$) **321**
EET *see* excitation energy transfer
efficiency, ATP synthase torque **471–2**
$EF_OF_1$-ATPase **471**
E helix, LHCII X-ray structure 342
eigenstates 49, 350
eigenvalue analysis 65, **298**
elastic deformation **469–72**
elastic power transmission **478**
ELDOR *see* electron–electron double-resonance techniques
electrical analogy, biological ET **386**
electrical potential gradients **386**
electrochemical potential difference of the proton *see* protonmotive force
electrochemical potential gradients **386**
electrochemistry, chlorophylls 123–4
electron acceptors **63**, **118–21**, **218–20**
electron-acceptor substrate *see* secondary electron acceptor quinone
electron density maps **211–12**, **225**
electron donors **63**, **117–18**, **507–8**
electron donor substrate **32–4**
electron–electron double-resonance (ELDOR) techniques 121
electron exchange (Dexter mechanism) 104, 239, **436**, **439**
electronic configurations **247**, **248–9**, **301–2**
electronic conversions 159–64, 168–72
electronic couplings 48–89
electronic states **247–8**
electronic structure, WOC **308–11**
electron microscopy (EM) **196**, 207–8, 229–31, 332
electronmotive force **386**, **391–2**
electron–nucleus double resonance technique (ENDOR) **117**, 121, **166**, **309**
electron paramagnetic resonance (EPR) studies

$F_B/F_A$ FeS cluster **121**
heme $c_n$ **434**
phylloquinone $A_1$ characterization **162**
secondary ET in PSI of oxygen evolving organisms **163–4**
two-ET branches of PSI in oxygen evolving organisms **167–8**
WOC electronic structure **309**
electron–photon double-resonance techniques (ODMR) 121
electron spin envelope echo modulation (ESEEM) **314**
electron spin resonance (ESR) spectroscopy 121–2
electron transfer chain (ETC) **199**, **221**, 263
anoxygenic bacteria **353–74**
basic principles 18–22
cyanobacterial PSI **116–21**
light-induced processes 10–11
oxygenic cyanobacteria **383–405**
electron transfer (ET)
aerobic photosynthetic bacteria **368–9**
anoxygenic bacteria **61**, **63**, **65**, **67–84**, **359–68**
antenna/reaction center pigment coupling 12, 14
chain of PSI in oxygen evolving organisms **150–1**
coupling 85–6
cyanobacterial minor pigments 266
cyanobacterial pathways **394–405**
cytochrome $b_6f$ complex structure/function **417–39**
directionality in Type I RCs **81–2**
dispersed polaron model 81–2
energetics in PSI of oxygen evolving organisms **151–9**
green non-sulfur bacteria **76–7**
green sulfur bacterial Type I RCs **79–82**
heliobacterial RCs **83–4**
light-induced charge separation in PSII **256**
light-induced in chlorophylls 105
out of PSI in oxygen evolving organisms **171–6**

*Subject Index* 441

photodamage sites 396
photoinhibition 393–412
pigment locations/functions/
  absorptions 111
PSI in oxygen evolving organisms
  **149–76**
PT coupling in WOC **322, 326**
quinol/quinone exchange reactions
  in PSIIcc **271**
reaction centers basic sequence 15
reaction regimes 61
reorganization energy 83
supramolecular organization in
  anoxygenic bacteria **369–73**
thermodynamics **386**
Type I/II reaction center schemes **61**
*see also* Marcus theory
electron transport phosphorylation (ETP)
  *see* chemiosmotic energy conversion
electrospray ionization mass
  spectrometry (ESI-MS) **423**
electrostatic continuum model **251**
electrostatic effects **360**
elliptical structures 235–6
EM *see* electron microscopy
$E_m$ *see* midpoint oxidation potential
Emiliana huxleyi 108, 109
ENDOR *see* electron–nucleus double
  resonance technique
endosymbiosis **396, 510, 514–16**
  *see also* generalized (unifying)
    endosymbiont hypothesis
energetics
  chemiosmotic energy conversion
    efficiency **392–3**
  chemiosmotic energy coupling **452–4**
  ET in green non-sulfur bacteria **76–7**
  ET in green sulfur bacteria **79–82**
  ET in heliobacteria **83–4**
  four-step oxidative water splitting
    **300–2**
  initial ET in proteobacteria **69–72**
  P680$^+ \cdot$Pheo$^-$ radical ion pair **260–2**
  P680$^+ \cdot Q_A^-$ radical pair formation **258**
  PSI ET in oxygen evolving
    organisms **151–9**

type I/II reaction centers 18
energy conversion schemes **391**
energy dissipation 283, 369–85
energy gap
  dispersed polaron model 81–2
  ET reactions reorganization energy 83
  POP/COP theories 67
  singlet lifetimes in carotenoids of
    purple bacteria 161–2
energy levels
  chlorophyll *a* and Tyr105 in
    cytochrome $b_6 f$ complex **438**
  P680 states **258–62**
  single monomeric LHCII complex 348
energy radiation, Sun **496**
energy transfer
  carotenoids in purple bacteria 172–6
  cyanobacteria photosystems 280–2
  LHCII carotenoids stabilization
    role 345
  purple non-sulfur bacterial
    photosynthetic apparatus
    arrangement 237–42
energy trapping 280–2
entropic contributions **158–9**
entropic ratchets **474**
environmental conditions 309
enzyme-catalyzed chains of steps 10–11
eosin label **466**
EPR *see* electron paramagnetic
  resonance
epsilon (ATP-synthase) subunit **463**
ERPE *see* exciton/radical pair
  equilibrium model
*Escherichia coli* **459, 461, 464, 471**
ESEEM *see* electron spin envelope
  echo modulation
ESI-MS *see* electrospray ionization
  mass spectrometry
ESR *see* electron spin resonance
  spectroscopy
ET *see* electron transfer
ETC *see* electron transfer chain
ETP (electron transport
  phosphorylation) *see*
  chemiosmotic energy conversion

euglenoids **515**
Euglenophyta 110
eukaryotes 23, **387–8**, **514–16**
Eustigmatophyceae 110
evolution
  algal protists **514–16**
  anoxygenic bacterial photosynthesis **504–5**
  antenna system regulatory mechanisms 371–3
  ATP synthase **60**
  chlorophylls/bacteriochlorophylls **499–501**
  chloroplasts **385**, **396**
  cyanobacteria 263
  Earth formation **493–5**
  ET chains **387–94**
  eukaryotes **514–16**
  Fusion hypothesis **505–6**
  Homo sapiens **387-8**
  light-harvesting proteins **511–14**
  light intensity variations 15
  mitochondria **396**
  monophyletic origin of ET chains **386**
  overview **489–517**
  oxidative water splitting **195–6**
  oxygen-evolving organisms 331
  $P_{D1}/P_{D2}$ center–center distance in PSII **250**
  primary charge separation in PSIIcc **257**
  PsaA/PsaB in cyanobacterial PSI **122**
  PsaI subunit **129**
  PSIIcc **239**
  reaction centers **501–4**
  timing of major events **509–10**
  two photosystems **502**, **505–7**
  Type I/II RCs **67**
  water oxidizing complex **393**
  water splitting **507–9**
EXAFS *see* extended X-ray absorption fine structure
excitation energies, local 86–8
excitation energy transfer (EET)
  antenna/reaction center pigment coupling 12, 14
  biomimetic antenna systems 27
  chlorophylls 104–5
  cyanobacteria 278–83
    PsaI subunit **130**
    PsaM subunit **130**
  Förster theory 41, 46, 59–60
  LHCII 331, 346–8, 350–2
  $P680^+ \cdot Pheo^-$ radical ion pair formation in PSIIcc **255–6**
  photoactive reaction center chlorophylls 371–3
  primary ET in PSI of oxygen evolving organisms **159–60**
  regulatory in PSII of higher plants 373–5
  spectral density 42–3, 77–81
excitation quenching 105–6, 404–5
  carotenoids 153–4
  Chl $a$ singlet excited state lifetime in cytochrome $b_6 f$ complex **438–9**
  chlorophylls excitation energy 105–6
  chlorophyll triplets **267**, 321
  cyanobacterial PSI carotenoids **135**
  Lhc of higher plants 331, 369–85
  luminescence 119–20
  photoprotection 404–5
excited singlet states *see* singlet excited states
excitonic coupling
  definition 43–4
  LHCII 349–50
  multi-level Redfield theory 41, 46
  parameter extraction 83
  pigment–pigment 43–8, 83
  red forms 317
  strong 62–77
excitonic degrees of freedom 68
exciton-radiational coupling 68
exciton/radical pair equilibrium (ERPE) model **257**, 352
exciton states
  LHCII EET modeling 350–1
  LHCII excitonic interactions 349–50
  peridinin-chlorophyll $a$ complex 44, 47, 60
  photosystem II reaction centers 45

Prosthecochloris aestuarii FMO-
    complex 44, 46
purple non-sulfur bacterial PSU 240
single monomeric LHCII complex 348
strongly coupled pigments in RC-
    PC unit **248–9**
exciton transition dipole moments 65
exciton–vibrational coupling 64, 66,
    70, 71
expression regulation 212–15
extended-dipole approximation 84
extended X-ray absorption fine structure
    (EXAFS) **228**, **305–8**, **321**
extremophiles **398**

$F_1$ *see* coupling factor
F680 band 381–3
F685 band 381–3
F695 band 381–4
$F_{A/B}$ iron–sulfur clusters
    cyanobacterial PSI **121**
    ET in PSI of oxygen evolving
        organisms **158–9**
    PSI damage mechanism 402
    PSI in oxygen evolving organisms **151**
    secondary ET in PSI of oxygen
        evolving organisms **163–5**
fast acceptor ($W_f$) **322**, **326**
fast electron transfer **175–6**
fast nanosecond kinetics **264–5**
fast phase **168**
    *see also* B-branch
F-ATPase *see* ATP synthase
fd:PQ oxidoreductase, cytochrome $c_n$
    as candidate **399**
Fd *see* ferredoxin
feedback mechanisms 125, 369–85,
    404–5
femtosecond studies 348–9
Fenna–Matthews–Olson (FMO)
        complexes **78**
    Chlorobium tepidum 44, 82, 87
    fluorescence line narrowing spectra 81
    Prosthecochloris aestuarii 44, 46, 87
fermentative reactions **495–6**
Fermi's Golden Rule 41, 53–4, 57

ferredoxin (Fd)
    cyanobacteria 113, 114, **126–8**,
        **395**, **404**
    ET out of PSI in oxygen evolving
        organisms **171–6**
    F-ATPase thiol regulation **459**
    heme $c_n$ cyclic electron transport **435**
    isoforms **172**
    reduction by PSI in oxygen
        evolving organisms **172–3**
    *see also* Photosystem I; Type I
        reaction centers
ferredoxin-NADP$^+$-oxidoreductase
        (FNR)
    consensus sequence
        PSU genes 213
        Rhodobacter sphaeroides 213
    fast ET to Fd/Fld in oxygen
        evolving organisms **175–6**
    heme $c_n$ cyclic electron pathway **435**
    membrane association in oxygen
        evolving organisms **174–5**
    membrane structures **420**
    NADP$^+$ reduction in oxygen
        evolving organisms **149**
    photoreduction in PSI of oxygen
        evolving organisms **173–4**
    photosynthesis interaction in ET
        chains **404**
    spinach cytochrome $b_6f$ complex
        **425**
Fe-S *see* iron–sulfur centers;
    tetraheme–tetrasulfur centers
final state P680 energy levels **258–9**
fine tuning, $F_OF_1$ rotary twin engine
        **476–8**
FIOPS *see* flash-induced oxygen
    evolution patterns
Firmicutes *see* heliobacteria
first-order perturbation theory 165
Fission hypothesis **493**
flash-induced oxygen evolution
    patterns (FIOPs) **295–300**
flash photometry studies 239, **312–13**,
    **317**, **356**, **359**, **362**
flavodoxin (Fld) **172–3**, 284

Fld *see* flavodoxin
FLN *see* fluorescence line narrowing
fluorescence
  carotenoids in purple bacteria 166–9
  Lax and Kubo theory 58
  luminescence spectrometry 117–20
  neurosporene 167
  nonphotochemical quenching 376
  nucleotide analogues, $F_1$-ATPase tri-site binding mechanism **468**
  thylakoids 315
  zeaxanthin quenching 311
fluorescence line-narrowing (FLN) 77–81, 349
fluorescence resonance energy transfer (FRET) **468–72**
fluorophore-labeled actin filaments **466–7**
FMN cofactor **173**
FMO *see* Fenna–Matthews–Olson
FNR *see* ferredoxin-NADP$^+$-reductase
*fnrL* gene 213
$F_OF_1$-ATPase *see* ATP synthase
Fokker–Planck equation **478**
folding *see* protein folding
$F_O$ rotary electromotor concept **473–6**
Förster EET mechanism
  chlorophylls 104
  LHCII absorption spectra 347–8, 356
  LHCII EET modeling 350
  pigment–pigment coupling 41, 46, 47, 48, 59–60, 75–7
  purple non-sulfur bacterial photosynthetic apparatus 239, 240
fossil fuels 11
four-electron transfer reactions **401**
four-heme cytochrome **72, 73, 74, 77**
Fourier–Laplace transform 69, 70, 71
Fourier processed images 230, 231
Fourier transform 56, 218
Fourier transform infrared (FTIR) spectroscopy **162–3, 165–7, 311, 315–16**
four-orbital model (Gouterman) 114, 115
four oxidizing equivalents **295–300**
four proton–four electron reaction **419**

four-step oxidative water splitting **300–2**
four tilted helices model 218–19
fragmentation patterns 122–3
Franck–Condon factor/principle 62, 119, 168, 169
free energy gaps **261–2**
free energy profiles **471**
free energy surfaces 60–1, 63
Fremyella diplosiphon **UTEX 481** 270, 272
FTIR *see* Fourier transform infrared
FtsH metalloprotease complex 407, 408–9
fullerenes 28
full-width at half-maximum (FWHM) 316
functional aspects
  anoxygenic photosynthetic bacterial RCs **57–85**
  ATP 449–50
  chlorophylls 104–6
  cyanobacterial ET carriers **395**
  cytochrome $b_6f$ complex **399–400, 417–39**
  green non-sulfur bacteria RCs **75–7**
  PSI 111–38, 147–76
  PSII 237–73
functional asymmetry *see* directionality
fungi **516**
'funneling' of excitation energy **134**
Fusion hypothesis **493, 505–6**
futile NADPH cycling **405**
FWHM *see* full-width at half-maximum
$F_x$ iron–sulfur center
  $A_1$ binding site effects in PSI of oxygen evolving organisms **163**
  electron transfer in cyanobacterial PSI **120–1**
  midpoint potential in PSI of oxygen evolving organisms **156–8**
  phylloquinones in PSI of oxygen evolving organisms **155–8**
  PsaA/PsaB in cyanobacterial PSI **123**
  secondary ET in PSI of oxygen evolving organisms **163–5**

Subject Index

Galdieria sulphuraria see Cyanidium caldarium
gamma (ATP synthase) subunit **463, 468**
GAP-dehydrogenase (GAP-DH) **404**
gap pigments 304–7, 309, 310
gas chromatography **206**
gear ratios **463, 480**
gel permeation chromatography (GPC) **201, 202**
gene expression regulation 212–15
gene fusion studies **477**
generalized Förster theory 48, 75–7
generalized (unifying) endosymbiont hypothesis **389–90**
gene sequence analysis
　Arabidopsis 380, 408
　cyanobacterial PsaX subunit **132**
　mitochondria **396**
　phylogenetic tree inference **496**
　PsbS protein symmetrical structure 377
geological history **387–8**
Gibbs energy
　ATP hydrolysis **449**
　biomimetic systems 26–30
　converters in photoautotrophs/heterotrophs 8–9
　ET thermodynamics **386**
　fossil fuels 11
　four-step oxidative water splitting **300–1, 302**
　solar source 8
　see also free energy...
Gilmore's three-state model 379
Glaucophyta 110
gliding ability **75, 77**
global-fitting analyses 159, 160, 162, 164, 169
Gloeobacter
　electron transfer **394**
　G. violaceus 23
　　PCC 7421 267, 270, 272–3
　　thylakoid membranes **397**
glutamates 374, 378–9
glutamate semialdehyde 124
glutamic acid **34–6, 41, 44**

gold 40 nm beads **467**
Gouterman's four-orbital model 114, 115
GPC see gel permeation chromatography
gramicidin **455, 476**
grana
　D1 protein repair cycle 407
　LHCI-PSI supercomplexes 332
　membrane domains, thylakoids fluorescence emission spectra 315
　stacked/unstacked **198**
　structure 24–5, **455**
grana-thylakoid **197**, 373–5
green bacteria 76, 108, 109, 207
　see also Chlorobi; Chloroflexi
'green gap' (chlorophylls) 104, 109
green glue 310
green non-sulfur bacteria see Chloroflexi
green plants see higher plants
Green's function technique 76
green sulfur bacteria see Chlorobi

$H^+$/ATP stoichiometric ratio **458–9, 463**
habitats **75, 77, 363, 397–8, 400**
hairpin folding **462, 463**
half-life times **317–19**
Halobacterium salinarium **60, 498**
Hamiltonian ($H$) 49, 51, 54, 63, 64, 65
Hamilton's classical equations of motion 52
hand-shaking interactions 225
Haptophyta 110
harmonic oscillator model
　Marcus theory 60
　modified Redfield theory 73
　pigment–protein (electron–vibrational) coupling 42
　spectral density 42–3
　weak pigment–pigment coupling 48–62
helices A/B/C/D (LHCII) 335–7
heliobacteria **59, 63**
　characteristics **505, 506**
　chlorophylls 110
　direct photoreduction **404**
　*H. chlorum* **82–3**, 114, **159**
　*H. mobilis* RCs **70, 82–3**

light-harvesting protein evolution **512**
reaction centers 16, 19, **60**, **82–3**
heme-iron site geometries **28–9**
hemes
  bacterial cytochrome subunits **69**
  bacterial RCs **10**, **11–12**
  biosynthesis 124, 126
  $b_n$ in cyt $b_6f$ **431**, **434**
  $c_n$ in cyt $b_6f$ **431–4**
  reduction rates in anoxygenic bacterial RCs **360**
  $x$ pyridine hemochromagen redox difference spectrum **434**
heme–sulfur *see* iron–sulfur
*hemF* genes **511**
hemi-discoidal phycobilisomes 271, 272–3
hemi-spherical phycobilisomes 271
*hemN* genes **511**
Henderson–Hasselbach titration 377
herbicides **31**, **42**, **270**
heterodimeric reaction centers **503**
heterotrophs 8–9
higher plants
  antenna function regulation 369–85
  Chlide *a* 128
  chlorophylls 110
  chloroplasts EET/dissipation 373–5
  chloroplast structure **197–8**, **454–5**
  cytochrome $b_6f$ complex trans-membrane signaling **422**
  evolution **516**
  light-harvesting protein evolution **512**
  oxygenic photosynthetic process **195**
  protein phosphorylation in damage repair 410–11
  PsaF subunit **131**, **132**
  PsaK subunit interactions **133**
  PSI antenna system 301–22
  PSII comparison with bacterial RC structure **44–5**
  PSII Lhcb proteins 329–56
  reaction centers 372–3
  thylakoid membrane composition **196–8**
  *see also* individual plants; spinach

highest occupied molecular orbital (HOMO) 12, 14
high light induced protein (HLIP) 284–5, **512**
high-low-high-low sequences **364**
high midpoint potential (HP) **360–3**
high-potential iron–sulfur protein (HiPIP) **32–4**, **74**, **361–3**
high-resolution X-ray structure **167**, **168**
high-sensitivity emission spectroscopy 165
HiPIP *see* high-potential iron–sulfur protein
histidine kinase/phosphatase 212–14
histidine residues
  conserved in P700 in PSI of oxygen evolving organisms **165**
  conserved in PsaA/PsaB in cyanobacterial PSI **122**
  conserved in purple non-sulfur bacterial LH1/LH2 complexes 217, 219, 223
  His-tagged PSIIcc in *Synechocystis* sp. PCC 6803 **261**
  ligands: bacterial RC structure **28**
  light-induced *Rhodobacter sphaeroides* RC structural changes **43**
  modified bacterial RCs **41**, **42**
  primary electron donor location **22–3**
  RC structure comparison with PSII structure **44**
history
  ATP synthesis research **450**
  chloroplast origins **389–90**
  Earth **387–9**
  oxidative water splitting research **293**
  photoinhibition studies 395
  photosynthesis discoveries 10, 12
  PSII structure elucidation **196**
  PSI studies **150**
HLIP *see* high light induced protein
hole-burning spectroscopy 350, 355
holes *see* photochemical hole formation
hole-transfer band **166**

## Subject Index

HOMO *see* highest occupied molecular orbital
homodimeric reaction center evolution **503**
homology *see* sequence homology
*Homo sapiens* evolution **387–8**
hook arrangements **224–5**
*hox* genes **401**
HP hemes **361**
H subunit of bacterial RC **9–11, 18, 21–2**
Huang Rhys factor ($S$) 59, 62, 72
*hup* genes **401**
hybrid reconstitution assays 228
hydratases **368–9**
hydrodynamic radius ($R_H$) **202–3**
hydrogenases **395, 401**
hydrogen atom abstractor hypothesis **316**
hydrogen bonding
    B800 bacteriochlorophyll in purple non-sulfur bacterial LH2 complex 225
    P700 special pair in two-ET branches of PSI **170**
    pheophytins ring V keto group **253**
    $Q_A$ in PSIIcc **254–5**
    triplet state $^3$P680 in PSII **250**
hydrogen cycle **389, 404**
hydrogen donors **496–7**
hydrogen peroxide **393**
hydrophilic exogenous reductants **303**
hydrophobic protein subunits **130–3**
hydrophobic residues **439**
'hydrophobic sticks' **427**
8-hydroxychlorophyll *a* **83–4**
hydroxyl groups coupling mechanism **328**
hydroxyl radicals 403
hydroxymethylbilane 124, 126

ICM *see* intracytoplasmic membranes
IEF *see* isoelectric focussing
IEP *see* isoelectric point
Iliobacter tartaricus **462, 463, 475**
illumination conditions *see* adaptation mechanisms; light intensity; photoprotection
inactive PSII centers 405
INDO/S method 88
infrared (IR) spectroscopy 123, **150, 162**
initial charge separation *see* primary charge separation
initial electron acceptor **118**
initial electron transfer **69–72**
initial P680 energy levels **258–9**
insertion studies **133, 477**
intact WOCs **265**
intense fluorescence 117–18
intermediary P680 states **259–62**
intermolecular energy transfer times 241
inter-monomer cross-talk **428–30, 433**
interpretation problems **211–12, 225**
inter-protein FeS clusters **120–1, 123**
intersystem crossing (ISC) 118, 119
intervening ET medium 86
intracytoplasmic membrane (ICM)
    chlorophyll *a* **394**
    cyanobacteria **395, 396–7**
    cyanobacterial ET chains in photosynthesis and respiration **400**
    purple non-sulfur bacteria 207–8, 229–30, 237–42
intramolecular energy transfer 241
intra-monomer distances **425–6, 429, 433**
intraprotein $O_2$ channels **439**
intrinsic time constant **159–60**
in vitro re-folding/reconstitution 338
IR *see* infrared spectroscopy
iron, nonheme **25, 27–8, 72, 257–8, 311**
iron-depleted conditions **283–5**
iron-stress-induced (Isi) protein family **131–2, 277, 284**
iron–sulfur centers
    cyanobacterial PSI **116, 120–1, 123–4**
    green sulfur bacterial Type I RCs **78**
    midpoint potential in PSI of oxygen evolving organisms **156–8**
    phylloquinones in PSI of oxygen evolving organisms **155–8**
    secondary ET in PSI of oxygen evolving organisms **163–5**
    structure in anoxygenic bacteria **62–5**

three in chlorobial RCs **80–1**
*see also* $F_{A/B}$ iron–sulfur clusters
iron–sulfur protein (ISP) *see* Rieske iron-sulfur protein
iron–sulfur type RCs *see* anaerobic green sulfur bacteria; heliobacteria
irradiation level adaptation 14–15
ISC *see* intersystem crossing
Isi *see* iron-stress-induced
isocyclic five-membered rings 107
isoelectric focussing (IEF) 335, 353–4
isoelectric points (IEPs) **403**
isoforms of ferredoxin **172**
isolated RC membrane studies **359**
isotropic powder spectra 186, 187
ISP *see* Rieske iron–sulfur protein

Jablonski diagrams 114, 118–19
Jacobian 51
Jang and Silbey's theory 76
$J_\omega$ *see* spectral density

Kaplan rule **404**
Karlsberg program 89
Kerr-gate fluorescence spectroscopy 169, 192
kinetic isotope effects (KIE) **320**
kinetics
  ET in green non-sulfur bacteria **76–7**
  ET in green sulfur bacteria **79–82**
  ET in heliobacteria **83–4**
  ET in PSI of oxygen evolving organisms **159–65**
  Fd/Fld reduction by PSI in oxygen evolving organisms **172–3**
  $F_0F_1$-ATP synthase **478–80**
  $H^+$/ATP stoichiometric ratio **458–9**
  initial ET in proteobacteria **69–72**
  oxidative water splitting **316–24**
  $P680_+Q_A^-$ formation in PSIIcc **257–8**
  PSIIcc charge separation **255–8**
  secondary ET in proteobacteria **72–4**
  singlet–singlet ET from carotenoids to bacteriochlorophyll 176
  $S_i$ state transitions **316–20**

substrate water exchange in PSIIcc **312–13**
WOC 303, 316–24
Kok model
  extensions **298–300**
  FIOPS measurements **295–300**
  kinetics **316–18**
  mathematics **298**
  origin of misses **298–300**
  scheme **293–4**
Kramer model 220
Kramers–Kronig relationship 71

L2 site 345
L *see* lutein
labeling notations **308, 360**
lag phases **318**
'lake' model 237
Lambert–Beer's law 58
lamellae **197–8**
large-scale purification **200**
laser photo-bleaching **466–7**
lateral transfer of characteristics **506**
Lax and Kubo theory 41, 57–9, 67
lead (Pb) 113
length of conjugated chain 153–7, 177–9, 191
leucine residues **40, 41, 44**
LH *see* light harvesting
Lhca proteins 305, 307–9, 313–20
Lhcb proteins 333, 334, 353, 372–5, 380–4
Lhc superfamily 331
lifetime states **297**, 376–7
ligands **314–17**, 336, 337, 338–40
light-adapted bacterial RC structures **43–4**
light capture process 39–89, 104, **113**, 320–1
light-dependent protochlorophyllide oxidoreductase (LPOR) 287
light energy distribution 282–3
light harvesting complex I (LHCI) 311–12
  chlorophyll red forms 315–21
  evolution **511**
  LHCI-PSI supercomplexes 332

*Subject Index*

pigment composition 311–12
purple bacteria 154, 157
purple non-sulfur bacteria 207–42
light harvesting complex of
  Photosystem II (LHCII)
  carotenoids role 344–6
  cyanobacterial PsaI subunit
    interactions **129–30**
  evolution 331, **511**
  fluorescence line-narrowing spectra 81
  higher plants 329–52
  photoprotection by excitation
    quenching 404–5
  pigment binding in native 334–5
  purple bacteria 154, 155–7
  purple non-sulfur bacteria 207–42
  recombinant protein studies 338–42
  Rhodopseudomonas acidophila
    211, 220–7, 240
  spectroscopy 346–52
  steady-state spectra 346–7
  structure at 2.72 Angstrom units 342–4
  structure from 2D crystals 335–8
  thylakoid membranes **197–8**
  trimerization 342
light harvesting III (LHIII) complex 212
light harvesting (LH)
  antennae evolution **501–4**
  antennae pigments 12
  basic principles 14–15
  carotenoids in purple bacteria 157–76
  complexes: bacterial species
    variations **358**
  cyanobacteria/PSI **113, 133–5**
  early photosynthesis **497–8**
  LH1 antenna complex 42–3, 371, 372
  LH2-minus mutants 233, 234
  LHC superfamily in cyanobacteria
    284–5
  oxygenic phototrophs 109–11
  pigment locations/functions/
    absorptions 111
  pigments in heliobacteria **82**
  proteins evolution **511–14**
  regulation PSI higher plants 310–11
  singlet excited states 157–9

light intensity 14–15, 212–15
  *see also* photon fluxes
'light' PORA, derivation 125
limited proteolysis 218
linear dichroism (LD) 347
linear electron transport 18, 19–22,
  **420, 422, 434–6**
lineshape functions 58, 72
linker chlorophylls 305–6
Liouville operator 68
lipids
  cyanobacterial PSI **135–7**
  cyanobacterial PSIIcc crystallization
    **204–9**
  integral to cyanobacterial PSIIcc
    **215–18**
  LHCII thylakoid stabilization 341–2
  PSIIcc integral lipid molecules **217**
  PSIIcc role **271–2**
  PSII thylakoid membrane **196–7**
lipophilic cavities **428–9**
litho(auto)trophic life styles **391, 393**
L-,M-,H-site **464–5**
load in rotary engines **478–9**
local excitation energies 86–8
localized exciton states 64
longer chain selection 191
long-wavelength chlorophylls 134
loop regions **128, 129**
Lorentzian lineshape ($D_M$) 72
lowest unoccupied molecular orbital
  (LUMO) 12, 14
low midpoint potential (LP) **360–1**
low temperature EPR **168, 309**
low temperature split signals 315
LP *see* low midpoint potential
LPOR *see* light-dependent
  protochlorophyllide
  oxidoreductase
L subunit of bacterial RC **9–11**
  bacteriopheophytins **25**
  bound water **36**
  D1 subunit comparison 213
  primary electron donor location **21–2**
  RC structure comparison with PSII
    structure **44–5**

side-chain distributions **34–6**
structure **18–19**
lumen volume vs. pH **455**
luminescence spectrometry 114, 117–20
LUMO *see* lowest unoccupied molecular orbital
lutein (L) 340–1, 345
lycopene
  absorption spectra 160, 162, 167, 173, 175
  fluorescence quantum yields 166
  quantum efficiency of singlet energy transfer to bacteriochlorophyll 174
  relaxation scheme 163
  singlet excited states 158
  singlet lifetimes versus double bond numbers 161
  structure 159
lysine **34–6**

M *see* torque
macrocyclic pi systems 123–4
magnesium **11–12**, 113, **116**, **117**
magnesium-adenosine 5'-triphosphate (Mg-ATP) **449**, **464**
magnetic beads **468**
maize 312, 347
MALDI-TOF MS **206–11**
manganese
  bacterial PSII-type RC **68**
  content **206**
  functional heterogeneity in WOC **326**
  $Mn_4O_xCa$ cluster formation studies **303**
  $Mn_4O_x$ motifs: EXAFS data **306–7**
  $^{55}$Mn ENDOR spectroscopy **309**
  Mn–Ca distances: EXAFS studies **306–7**
  Mn–Mn distances: EXAFS studies **305–7**
  oxidation state changes in WOC **322**
  PSII structure **65**
  UV photodamage 399–400
  WOC redox active component **294**
  *see also* $Mn_4O_xCa$ clusters

manganese stabilizing protein *see* PsbO
mantle out-gassing **495**, **496**
Marcus theory of non-adiabatic electron transfer 14
  biomimetic reaction centers 28
  light absorption 44
  $P680^{+\cdot}Pheo^-$ radical ion pair formation **260**
  $P680^{+\cdot}$ reduction by $Y_z$/oxidative water splitting **264**
  phylloquinones in PSI of oxygen evolving organisms **155**
  pigment–pigment coupling 14, 44, 48–62, **264**, **321**
Markov approximation 70, 72–3
Markovian theory 66
mass spectrometry 122, **312–13**
*Mastigocladus laminosus* **419**, **422–5**, **429**, **434**, **438**, **439**
  ET complex crystals **398**, **399**
matrix element 57
Maxwell demons **474**
MDGD *see* monogalactosyldiacylglycerol
MEAD program 88
mean transition energies *see* site energies
mechanical coupling **450**, **468–72**
membrane area per chlorophyll **456**
membrane-bound antenna complexes 273–8
membrane-bound ET devices **391–2**
membrane-intrinsic portion ($F_O$) **451**
membranes
  artificial proton pumps 28–9
  associations **174–5**
  bound monoheme cytochrome *c* **365**
  characteristics of photosynthetic membranes **454–5**
  extrinsic proteins **198**, **213–14**
  inlet mass spectrometry **312–13**
  localized protons **452**
  organization, LHCII protein mass 332, 334
  photosynthetic apparatus 22–5
  photosynthetic constructs **454–5**

*Subject Index* 451

photosynthetic RC incorporation 17
potential **360–1**
proteins **34–9, 130–3, 212**, 406–11
purple non-sulfur bacteria 207–8, 229–30, 237–42
RC components **369–73**
systems 373, **396–7**
*see also* intracytoplasmic membranes; organelles; transmembrane...
membrane-spanning helices *see* transmembrane helices
'memory' 66, 72
menaquinone (MK) **12, 62–3, 80, 84, 254**
mercury 113
mesophilic cyanobacteria **398**
metal-centered oxidations **310**
metaloproteases 407, 408–9
methine bridges 122
$Mg^{2+}$–$Mg^{2+}$ distance 223–4
Mg-2,4-divinyl-phaeoporphyrin (MgDVP) **499–500**
Mg-ATP *see* magnesium adenosine 5'-triphosphate
MGDG *see* monogalactosyldiacylglycerol
MgDVP *see* Mg-2,4-divinyl-phaeoporphyrin
Mg-protoporphyrin monomethylester **368–9**
Michaelis–Menten description **472**
microscopic simulations 83
midpoint oxidation potential ($E_m$)
 cation radical P680$^{+\cdot}$ in PSII **251**
 heme $c_n$ **434**
 oxidative water splitting thermodynamics **300, 301**
 P700 states in PSI of oxygen evolving organisms **152–3, 161**
 $PhQ_A$ and $F_A/F_B$ in PSI of oxygen evolving organisms **156–8**
 PSI ET in oxygen evolving organisms **162**
 ring puckering **250**
 triheme RC species **363–4**
 *see also* high midpoint potential; low midpoint potential

minor antenna complexes 352–6
'minor' chlorophylls 113–14
miss hits (α) **297–300**
Mitchell chemiosmotic principle **389, 450**
Mitchell's Q-cycle mechanism **430**
mitochondria
 cyanobacterial ancestry **396**
 evolution **509–10, 514–16**
 respiration **366–7, 368, 385, 386**
 mixed binding sites 343–4, 350
 mixed valence states **308–9**
MK *see* menaquinone
$Mn_4O_xCa$ clusters
 cyanobacterial PSIIcc WOC **221, 224–8**
 evolution **394**
 protein ligands **314–17**
 $S_i$ state-dependent structural changes **307–8**
 WOC function **294**
 WOC photoactivation **303**
 WOC structure **304–17**
models
 anoxygenic bacterial ET chain supramolecular organization **372–3**
 ATP synthase **451, 466–7, 470, 473, 477**
 LHCII EET 350–2
 multiphasic $A_1^-$ reoxidation kinetics **169**
 photosynthetic unit in purple non-sulfur bacteria 238–9
 primary charge separation in PSI of oxygen evolving organisms **160–1**
 purple non-sulfur bacteria antenna complexes 218–20, 238–9
 relative midpoint potentials of $PhQ_A/PhQ_B/F_x$ iron–sulfur center **157–8**
modified properties, chromophores 116, 117
modified reaction centers **39–44, 71**
modified Redfield theory 47–8, 73–5, 348, 350

452

molar Gibbs free energy difference **453**
molar weight **203–4**
molecular assembly *see* assembly
molecular characterization **9–12, 162–3, 200–4**
molecular docking *see* docking
molecular mass 122, **201, 202**
molecular mechanisms 397–403, 404–12
molecular orbital (MO) schemes **247**
molecular oxygen **312–13, 393, 507–9**
molecular structures *see* structure
monogalactosyldiacylglycerol (MGDG) **135, 137, 196, 215–18, 271**
monomer–monomer interfaces **128–30**
monomers
   antenna system higher plants' photosystem I 307–8
   chlorophyll *a* **436–7**
   cyanobacterial PSI **114–16, 121–33**
   inter-monomer cross-talk **428–30, 433**
   intra-monomer distances **425–6, 429, 433**
   LHCII in higher plants 332, 336, 338, 341–2
   LHCII minor antenna complexes 352–6
   PSIIcc cyanobacterial X-ray studies **200–4, 212, 214, 216–17**
   reaction center evolution **503**
monophyletic endosymbiosis **514–15**
Monte Carlo methods 89
Moon **493–4**
morphology 207–8
motion, conformational **433**
motion equations 52
*m* protons **453**
MSH *see* membrane-spanning helices
M subunit of bacterial RC **9–11**
   accessory bacteriochlorophylls **25**
   bound water **36**
   D2 subunit comparison 213
   primary electron donor location **21–2**
   RC structure comparison with PSII structure **44–5**
   side-chain distributions **34–6**
   structure **10, 18, 20–1**

multi-level Redfield theory 41, 46, 48, 66
multiphasic $A_1^-$ reoxidation kinetics **169**
multiple connections **133**
multiple gene sets 214–15
mu-oxo bridges
   $Mn_4O_xCa$ cluster in cyanobacterial PSIIcc WOC **224–5, 227**
   $Mn_4O_xCa$ clusters $S_i$ state-dependent structural changes **308**
   $S_2$->$S_3$ transition in WOC **326**
   $S_i$ state transitions **310**
   WOC function **294**
mutant studies
   *Arabidopsis* PsbS-dependent energy dissipation 380–1
   chlorophyll organization in LHCII 338–40
   chlorophyll spectrometry 116, 117
   CP29 354
   cyanobacterial PSI PG synthesis 137
   LHCII trimerization complexes 342
   Lhc protein structure 317
   modified proteobacterial reaction centers **71**
   Pheo$_{D2}$ in Chlamydomonas reinhardtii **247**
   protein redshifted emission peak 318, 319
   regulatory EET in PSII of higher plants 375
   *see also* site-directed mutagenesis
myxothiazol **368**

n *see* negative side; neoxanthin
$NADP^+$ reduction **149, 173–4**
NADPH 372, **404, 405**
NADPH dehydrogenase **174**
NAD(P)H oxidase **399**
naphthoquinones **402**
native LHCII 334–5
natural selection 154–7, 189–92
   *see also* evolution
near-infrared (NIR) absorption spectra **70**, 160, 209–10
negative binding cooperativity **464**

*Subject Index* 453

negative (n) side **452, 454, 455, 456**
neoxanthin (N) 341, 343, 345, 346
neurosporene
   near-infrared sub-picosecond time-resolved absorption spectra 160
   quantum efficiency of singlet energy transfer to bacteriochlorophyll 174
   relaxation scheme 163
   Rhodobacter sphaeroides G1C 157
   singlet states 161, 165, 168
   species-associated fluorescence spectra 167
   structure 159
   sub-picosecond time-resolved Raman spectra 168–9, 170
   visible sub-picosecond time-resolved absorption spectroscopy 162, 173, 175
newly-identified singlet states 193–4
NHFe *see* nonheme iron centers
nickel 113
NIR *see* near-infrared
NMR *see* nuclear magnetic resonance
nomenclature *see* terminology
non-adiabatic electron transfer *see* Marcus theory...
non-collinear access channels **473**
nonheme iron **25, 27–8, 72, 257–8, 311**
nonlinear polarization spectroscopy measurements 355
non-Markovian density matrix theory 47–8, 66
nonphotochemical quenching (NPQ)
   evolution **508**
   LHCII monomers 332
   Lhc proteins 331
   photoprotection in the antenna 404
   PSII chlorophyll fluorescence 376
non-radiative transfer 104
non-sulfur green bacteria *see* Chloroflexi
non-sulfur purple bacteria **4–45**
   see also individual species
non-triplet producing charge recombination 405–6
2-*n*-nonyl-4-hydroxyquinolone N-oxide (NQNO) **430–1, 434**

notation *see* classification; terminology
NPQ *see* nonphotochemical quenching
NQNO *see* 2-*n*-nonyl-4-hydroxyquinolone N-oxide
N-terminal domains **122, 131, 132**, 215–17, 221
nuclear geometries **301–2**
nuclear magnetic resonance (NMR) 121, **127, 150**
nuclei, tunneling 60–3
nucleophilic attack mechanism **328**
nucleotide binding sites **450, 464–5**

ODMR *see* electron–photon double-resonance techniques
Oestreobium 105
oil resources 11
oligomerization states *see* aggregation states
oligomers 106
O-,L-,T-site **464**
one-channel model **475**
one-electron oxidation **432–3**
one-electron transfer **430**
O–O bond first mechanism **330**
O–O bond formation **326, 328, 330–1**
optical dipole transition 190
optical energy gap 80
optically-forbidden singlet states 165
optical spectra 114–17, 118–19
   fluorescence line-narrowing 77–81
   Lax and Kubo theory 57–9
   multi-level Redfield theory 41, 46
   secondary ET in PSI of oxygen evolving organisms **164**
   vibrational sidebands 48
   *see also* absorption spectra; spectral density
orbital angular momentum 189
organelles 23, **390, 509–10, 514–16**
   *see also* mitochondria; thylakoids; vesicle...
Oscillatoria limnetica **397**
oscillaxanthin 268
outer antenna Chl *a*/Chl *b*/Xan–protein complexes 331

out-gassing **495, 496**
out-of-plane waggings 182
oxidation–reduction potentials at equilibrium **8–9**
oxidation states **295–300**
oxidative reactions **262–7**
oxidative water splitting **291–331**
  evolution **195**
  kinetics **252, 316–24**
  mechanism **322–331**
  P680$^{+\cdot}$ driven in PSIIcc **262–5**
  PSII process **240**
  reaction pattern **295–300**
  thermodynamics **300–2**
  WOC assembly/structure **302–17**
  *see also* water oxidizing complex
oxo groups **328, 329**
oxygen
  aerobic photosynthetic bacteria **368–9**
  Earth's oxidizing atmosphere **388–9, 495, 510**
  molecular **312–13, 393, 507–9**
  tension 208, 212–15
  water splitting evolution **507–9**
  *see also* reactive oxygen species; singlet oxygen
oxygen evolution
  chlorin type chlorophylls 108, 109
  cyanobacteria 261–88, 372, 373, **383–405**
  history 10, 331, **509**
  lag phase **318**
  linear electron transport 19–22
  period four oscillation **295–300**
  photosynthetic apparatus 22, 23–5
  process **195**
  RC and LH complexes 109–11
  steady-state terrestrial atmosphere **389**
  three-electron transport complexes **419–20**
  WOC flash-induced **312–13**
ozone layer **387–8**

P$^{+\cdot}$ *see* primary electron donor radical
$^3$P$_{680}$-producing states 397
$^1$P680$^*$ **247–8**

P680
  cyanobacterial PSIIcc **199, 222–3**
  electrostatic interactions 89
  nature/properties **239, 242–3, 244–52, 255–60, 262–7**
  reduction potential **301**
  spectroscopic analyses, cyanobacteria 286
P680$^{+\cdot}$ **262–5, 299**
P680$^{+\cdot}$Pheo$^-$ radical ion pair **255–7, 260–2**
P680$^{+\cdot}$Q$_A^{-\cdot}$ radical pair **257–8, 262**
P700
  cyanobacterial PSI structure **117–18**
  discovery **150**
  energetics in PSI of oxygen evolving organisms **152–3**
  hydrogen bonds in two-ET branches of PSI in oxygen evolving organisms **170**
  P$_{D1}$/P$_{D2}$ chlorophyll *a* molecules comparison **246**
  primary ET in PSI of oxygen evolving organisms **159–63**
  spectroscopic analyses, cyanobacteria 286
  spectroscopy/structure in PSI of oxygen evolving organisms **165–7**
P798 **83**
P840 **79–81**
p *see* positive side; primary electron donor
P$_A$ *see* absorption/antenna pigments
paramagnetic states **150**
parameter extraction
  dispersed polaron model 81–2
  electron transfer coupling 85–6
  excitonic couplings 77–89
  extended-dipole approximation 84
  local excitation energies 86–8
  point-dipole approximation 84
  redox potentials 88–9
  reorganization energy of ET 83
  spectral density 77–82
  transition density 85

Pariser–Parr–Pople method 85, 180
Pariser's signs 164, 165, 190
partial charges 88
partial ordering prescription (POP) 66–7, 68
Pasteur-Point **388**
PBRC *see* purple bacterial reaction center
PBS *see* phycobilisomes
PC *see* phycocyanin
PCET *see* proton coupled electron transfer
PChlide, formation 125
PCP *see* peridinin chlorophyll protein
$P_{D1}/P_{D2}$ chlorophyll *a* **222–3, 245–6**
PE *see* phycoerythrin
pea 312
PEC *see* phycoerythrocyanin
pentads 28
peridinin chlorophyll protein (PCP) 44, 47, 60, **513**
period four oscillation **295–300**
peripheral antennae 373
peripheral stalks **463**
periplasmic redox proteins **361**
peroxidic intermediates **302, 329**
  *see also* hydrogen peroxide
perturbation theory 66, 74
PET *see* photosynthetic electron transport
PEWY conserved sequence **432**
$PF_OEF_1$ chimeric enzyme **477**
PG *see* phosphatidylglycerol
pH 378–9, **453, 455, 457–8**
  *see also* transmembrane pH difference
Phe *see* pheophytin
phenylalanine **40, 42**
Pheophyceae 110
pheophytin *a* (Phe *a*) **222–3, 227**, 266, 267
pheophytin (Phe) **247, 252–3**, 264, **266–7**
pheophytin–quinone type RCs **7–45**
philloquinone $A_1$ electron acceptor *see* chlorophyll $A_1$
phosphate potential **453–4**
phosphatidylglycerol (PG)

cyanobacterial PSI **135, 136, 137**
LHCII trimerization 341, 342
PSIIcc role **271**
thylakoid membrane composition **196, 215–18**
phospholipids **37–9, 120**
phosphorus **70–2,** 75
phosphorylatable DNA-binding protein component 212
phosphorylation sites 354
photoacoustic spectroscopy 118
photoactivation **295, 302–4**
photoactive pigment in RC ($P_{RC}$) 12, 14, **240, 242–3**
photoassembly **303–4**
photoautotrophs 8–9
photobioreactors **200–1**
photochemical hole formation **239, 260**
photodamage
  acceptor-sided induced photodamage 397–8
  donor-side induced photodamage 398
  integral lipid molecules **217**
  photoinhibition of electron transport 393–412
  photon counter behavior 401–2
  photosystem II 395, 397–403
  PSI mechanism 402
  triplet forming charge recombination 398–9
  two-step mechanism 401
  ultraviolet light **393**, 399–401, 411–12, **498**
photodynamic action 118
photo flux density 285–6
photoinhibition (qI) **135**, 376, 393–412
photoinhibitory related thermal energy dissipation 373–5
photon counter behavior 401–2
photon echo spectroscopy **256**
photon flux rates 153
photoorganoheterotrophic growth **397**
photophosphorylation **447–81**
photophysical principles 41–89, 151–95
photopigment suppression (PpsR) factor 213–14

photoprotection
  carotenoids 153, 176–89, 194–5
  Chl *a* in cytochrome $b_6f$ complex
    **436–7, 439**
  cyanobacterial PSI carotenoids **135**
  de novo D1 protein synthesis 409–10
  excitation quenching 404–5
  inactive PSII centers 405
  integral lipid molecules **217**
  light harvesting protein evolution **512**
  molecular mechanisms 404–12
  non-triplet producing charge
    recombination 405–6
  protein repair 406–11
  PSIIcc without WOC **265**
  quenching evolution **508**
  red forms 320–1
  thermal energy dissipation 375–7
photoreduction **173–4**
photosynthetic apparatus architecture
  22–5
photosynthetic electron transport
  (PET) **357–9**, 393–412, **395**
photosynthetic hydrogenase *see*
  uptake hydrogenase
photosynthetic membranes *see*
  intracytoplasmic membranes
photosynthetic-respiratory assemblies
  **394–405**
photosynthetic transition reaction 9
photosynthetic units (PSUs) 12, 210–
  15, 237–42
photosystem gene expression 214–15
Photosystem I–light harvesting
  chlorophyll I (PSI–LHCI)
  complex 304–5, 311–12, 316
Photosystem I (PSI)
  basic principles 16–22
  building principles 41–8
  cyanobacteria **125**
    assembly 277–8
    cofactors **116–21**
    energy transfer 280–2
    membrane-bound antenna
      complexes 275–6
    stoichiometry regulation 285–6

structure/function **111–38**
X-ray crystallography studies
  **395, 399, 404**
cytochrome $b_6f$ complex **419–20, 422**
evolution **502, 505–7**
gap pigments 304–7
green sulfur bacterial conserved
  residues **79**
higher plants 301–22, 372–3
light harvesting regulation 310–11
light-induced ET in chlorophylls 105
oxygen evolving organisms **147–76**
photodamage mechanism 402
photodamage sites 396
photoinhibition 310–11
PSII antenna characterization
  differences 321–2
supramolecular organization of
  antenna system in vascular
  plants 304–11
Type I reaction center comparison **60–7**
Photosystem II core complex (PSIIcc)
  **239, 401**
Photosystem II (PSII)
  artificial 30
  basic principles 16–22
  building principles 41–8
  cyanobacteria
    assembly 277–8
    cc crystallography **193–228**
    energy transfer 280–2
    membrane-bound antenna
      complexes 276–7
    stoichiometry regulation 285–6
    X-ray crystallography studies
      **395, 399, 404**
  cytochrome $b_6f$ complex **419–20**
  D1 protein rapid turnover 406–11
  damage repair 409–10
  EET types 374–5
  evolution **502, 505–7**
  functional pattern **237–73**
  higher plants 329–56, 372–3
  Lhcb proteins 329–56
  light-induced ET in chlorophylls 105
  minor antenna complexes 352–6

Subject Index

oxygen evolution period four oscillation **295–300**
photodamage mechanisms 395, 397–403
photodamage sites 396
photoprotective energy dissipation biochemical models 375–7
primary electron transfer 44, 45
proton translocation **456**
PsbS protein symmetrical structure 377–80
purple bacterial RC structure comparison **44–5**
regulatory EET 373–5
stable charge separation **241–62**
trap-limited charge separation 334
Type II reaction center comparison **60–7**
photovoltage measurements **164**
PhQ see phylloquinones
PhQ$_A$ see phylloquinone A
PhQ$_B$ see phylloquinone B
phycobilins 12, 13, 126
phycobiliproteins
  crystal structure 273, 274
  cyanobacteria 269–71
  excitation energy transfer 104, 278–9
  molecular species 270–1
phycobilisomes (PBS)
  cyanobacteria 271–3, 372
    PsaF subunit **131**
    thylakoid structures **198**
  energy transfer to membrane proteins 279–80
  excitation energy transfer 278–9
  ferredoxin-NADP$^+$-reductase **174–5**
  state transitions 282–3
  transient excitation energy reservoirs 278–9
phycocyanin (PC) 269–70, 272–3, 274
phycocyanobilin 13
phycoerythrin (PE) 269–71, 272–3, 274
phycoerythrocyanin (PEC) 269–70, 272–3, 274
phylloquinones (PhQ) **64–5, 119–20, 153–8, 162–5, 168–9**

phyllosemiquinones **81, 171**
phylogenetic tree analysis **496, 504**
physiological roles 320–1, 385
phytol 108, 109
phytyl chains **223**, 224–5, **227**, 337, **429**
'picket fence' arrangement **427**
picoplanktons 269
picosecond studies 160–2, 165–9, 170, 173, 175, 348–9
pigment lineshape function ($D(\omega)$) 71
pigment–pigment complexes
  charge transfer coupling 43–8
  coupling types 43
  dynamical theories 41–89
  excitonic coupling 43–8
  Fermi's Golden Rule 53–4, 57
  Förster theory 41, 59–60
  Marcus theory 44, 60–2
  quantum mechanics 53–7
pigment–protein complexes
  adjustable chromophore properties 116
  anoxygenic bacterial vesicles 23
  chlorophyll as stabilizer 106
  dynamical theories 41–89
  LHCII monomeric minor 352–6
  local pigment excitation energies 86–8
  Photosystem structures 41–8
  PSII functional pattern **237–73**
  purple non-sulfur bacteria 209–10
  see also individual pigment–protein complexes
pigment–protein (electron–vibrational) coupling see spectral density
pigments
  *Chlorella* organization 12
  chlorophylls 103–29
  cyanobacteria 263–71
  light harvesting chlorophyll I composition 311–12
  location 111
  native LHCII binding 334–5
  spectral properties **498**
  see also individual pigments
Pisum sativum 304–5

plastid inclusion **509–10, 514–16**
  *see also* organelles
plastocyanin **123, 149**
plastoquinine-9 (PQ-9) **254**
plastoquinol formation **240**
plastoquinone-9 (PQ-9) **402**
plastoquinone (PQ)
  cytochrome $b_6f$ complex **395, 400**
  diffusion channel in cyanobacterial PSIIcc **228**
  linear electron transport 21
  photodamage **396, 397**
  PS-I/II coupling **113**
  PSII structure **64–5**
  quinol/quinone exchange reactions in PSIIcc **271**
  reduction state 311
  structure **421**
p.m.f. *see* protonmotive force
point-dipole approximation 84
polarized laser photo-bleaching and recovery **466–7**
polyene models 185–7
polypeptides **204–9**, 304–8, 315–16
polyphyletic endosymbiosis **514–15**
'poop oxygen' **389**
POP *see* partial ordering prescription
POR *see* protochlorophyllide oxidoreductases
porphobilinogen 124, 126
porphyrins
  biomimetic antenna systems 27
  chlorophylls 108–9
  chlorophyll synthesis 124, **498**
  $c$-type chlorophylls 107–9
porphyrin-type cyclic conjugated tetrapyrroles 115
positive catalytic cooperativity **464**
'positive inside rule' **133**
positive (p) side **452, 454, 455, 456**
potential energy surfaces (PES) 52–3, 56–7, 64, 65, 74
power transmission **476–80**
Poynting vector 57
PpsR (photopigment suppression) factor 213–14

PQ *see* plastoquinone
$PQH_2$ *see* dihydroplastoquinone
Prasinophyceae 110
$P_{RC}$ *see* photoactive pigment in RC
'PRC' barrel **21**
Precambrian era **388, 393**
pre-structural studies 215–20
primary acceptor quinone ($Q_A$)
  aerobic photosynthetic bacteria **369**
  proteobacterial secondary electron transfer reactions **72–4**
  PS II difference absorption spectra **242–3**
  PS II water splitting **240**
  RC cofactors/inhibitors **11–12**
  structure/location in bacterial RC **24–8, 31–2**
primary amino acid sequences 215–17
primary biomass production **389**
primary electron donor (P) **21–5, 117–18, 359**
  see also P700
primary electron donor radical ($P^{+\cdot}$)
  anoxygenic bacterial tetraheme RC species **360**
  bacterial RC three types **359**
  bacterial species variations **358**
  fast/slow reduction phases in anoxygenic bacterial RC **365–6**
  heme reduction rates in anoxygenic bacterial RCs **360**
primary electron transfer 44, 45, **159–63**
primary endosymbiosis **514–15**
primary quinone acceptor ($Q_A$)
  anoxygenic bacterial ET chain **357–8**
  binding pocket **254–5, 369**
  cyanobacterial PSIIcc structure **218–19, 221**
  $P680^{+\cdot}$ recombination reactions with $Q_A^-$/$Pheo^-$ **266–7**
  PBRCs **253–4**
  $PQH_2$ formation induced by $Q_A^-$ **267–70**
  properties in PSII **253–5**
  PSI ET in oxygen evolving organisms **162**

*Subject Index*

PSIIcc integral lipids **217**
PSII light-induced charge separation **242**
*prime*-chlorophylls 120
probabilities of $S_i$ state transitions **297**
*Prochlorococcus* spp. 113, 128, 265, 273
Prochloron 265, 277
Prochlorophytes 373, **389**
Prochlorothrix 265, 277
prokaryotes **387–8, 454**
'promoting mode' 163
17-propionic acid 107
Prosthecochloris aestuarii 44, 46, **70**, 87
prosthetic groups **425–6, 429, 436–9**
protective mechanisms 153, 176–89, 194–5
   *see also* photodamage; photoprotection
protein–cofactor interactions **21–9**
protein kinase STN7 (*Arabidopsis*) 375
protein-like scaffolds 26, 27, 221–3
protein–protein interactions 307–8, 316
proteins
   cyanobacterial antenna systems 263–4
   environments 86–8, **162, 222–3, 259–62**
   LHCII folding 338, 341–2
   ligands, $Mn_4O_xCa$ cluster **314–17**
   matrix, WOC function **294**
   PSII backbone UV damage 400, 410–11
   reaction centers 263–4
   repair, photoprotection 406–11
   turnover, mesophilic cyanobacteria **398**
   vibrational degrees of freedom 42, 43, 48
protein subunits (psb)
   anoxygenic photosynthetic bacterial RCs **63**
   ATP synthase **461, 463**
   bacterial RCs **9–12, 18–21**
   cyanobacterial PSI **121–33**
   cytochrome $b_6f$ complex **423**
   cytochrome $bc_1$ complex/cytochrome $b_6f$ complex comparison **427–8**
   green sulfur bacterial Type I RCs **78**

MALDI-TOF MS of cyanobacterial dimeric PSII cc **206–11**
PSIIcc composition in cyanobacteria **198–200**
*Rhodospirillum rubrum* LH1 complex formation 228
   *see also* individual subunits
protein W 235–6
proteobacteria **68–75**
   *see also* purple bacteria
proteolysis 218, 406–11
Proto *see* protoporphyrin IX
protochlorophyllide **500**
protochlorophyllide *a* reductase 287
protochlorophyllide oxidoreductases (POR) 125
proton conductance **475–6**
proton coupled electron transfer (PCET) **326, 328–9**
proton-ejecting membranes **457**
proton ENDOR spectroscopy **159**
proton-first mechanism **330**
protonmotive force (p.m.f.)
   ATP synthase regulation **459–60**
   ATP synthesis/hydrolysis **452–4**
   chemiosmotic energy conversion **391–2**
   $H^+/ATP$ stoichiometric ratio **458–9**
   Mitchell's hypothesis **450**
   proton pumps **457–8**
protonmotive quinone cycle **402**
proton-over-ATP stoichiometry **453–4**
protons
   ATP synthesis/hydrolysis **452**
   pumps 28–9, **451, 452, 455–8**
   relay networks **315**
   release patterns **320**
   translocation pathways **430–6**
proton-shift first mechanisms **330**
proton transfer (PT) **322, 326, 328–9**
protoporphyrin IX (Proto) 107, 124, 125, 127
protoporphyrinogen IX 126
PrrBA system 212–14
PsaA subunit 63–5, 114–16, 121–3, 124, 150–1

PsaB subunit 63–5, 114–16, 121–3, 124, 150–1
PsaC subunit **64–5, 114–15, 123–6, 164**
PsaD subunit **114–15, 123–7**
PsaE subunit **114–15, 123–6, 127–8**, 174
PsaF subunit **114–16, 125, 130–2**
PsaI subunit **114–15, 128–30**
PsaJ subunit **114–16, 125, 130, 132**
PsaK subunit **114–16, 125, 130, 132–3**
PsaL subunit **114–15, 125, 128–9**
Psalteriomonas lanterna **389–90**
PsaM subunit **114–16, 125, 128–9, 130**
PsaX subunit **114–16, 125, 130, 132**
psb *see* protein subunits
PsbE **209**
PsbF **209**
*psb* genes 411
PsbO (manganese stabilizing protein) **198–9, 209, 213–14, 294**
PsbS-dependent de-excitation pathway 311
*psbS* gene 380
PsbS protein
  glutamate residues 374
  influence on energy flux in PSII 381–4
  photoprotection in the antenna 404
  physiological significance 384
  PSII photoprotective energy dissipation 376–7
  symmetrical structure 377–80
PsbU 213–14
PsbV 213–14
PscA homodimer **63**, 78
PscC *see* single-heme cytochrome
pseudo-twofold axis (pseudo-*C2*) **212, 220, 221**
PshA homodimer 82, **83**
PSI *see* Photosystem I
p-side quinone binding niche **429, 430**
PSII *see* Photosystem II
PSI–LHCI *see* Photosystem I–light harvesting chlorophyll I
PSUs *see* photosynthetic units
psychrophilic cyanobacteria **398**
*puc* operon 213–14
'puddle' model 237

PufX protein 208, 233, **370–3**
pulsed EPR spectroscopy **266**
pump–probe measurements **69–72**, 355
purification procedures **200**, 311–12, **422–8**
purple bacteria
  ATP formation **450**
  bacteriochlorophylls 108, 112
  carotenoids 151–95
  c chromatophores **454**
  chlorophylls 110
  excitation energy transfer 76
  $F_O$ proton conductance **475–6**
  light harvesting system 207–42
  light-induced ET in chlorophylls 105
  non-sulfur
    bacterial photosynthetic unit 210–12
    growth conditions **356**
    light harvesting system 207–42
    photo-induced ET mechanisms **353–73**
    photosynthetic pigment–protein complexes 209–10
    RC cytochrome subunit with four hemes **69**
    RC-LH1 core complex structure 227–37
  P700 in PSI of oxygen evolving organisms **167**
  primary charge separation in RC I **160**
  secondary electron transfer reactions **72–4**
  species **59**
  sulfur **9, 69, 504–5, 506**
  transmetalated chlorophylls 107, 113
  Zn chlorophylls 107
  *see also* purple bacterial reaction centers
purple bacterial reaction center (PBRC) 16, 18, 371–2
  BPheo$_A$ hydrogen bonding **253**
  chlorines role in RC pigment core **247**
  components/thermodynamic properties **63**
  cyanobacterial PSIIcc structure comparison **209, 222–3**

*Subject Index* 461

ET chains **355–74**
NHFe center removal effects **257–8**
P680$^{+\cdot}$ recombination reactions with $Q_A^-$/Pheo$^-$ comparison **266–7**
PQH$_2$ formation **267–9**
primary charge separation in PSIIcc **257**
proton translocation **456**
PSII comparison **239**
PSII water splitting process comparison **240**
$Q_A$ component **253–4**
radical pair relaxation processes **261**
RC II resembles PSII **60**
'special pair' P **246**
structure **7–45**
triheme RC species **363–5**
unidirectionality **252**
pyridine hemochromogen redox difference spectrum **434**

$Q_A$ *see* primary quinone acceptor
$Q_B$ *see* secondary quinone acceptor
Q-bands 114, 115
Q-cycle 357–8, 425–6, 430–3, 435, 456
qE *see* thermal energy dissipation
qI *see* photoinhibition
Q-space **429–30**
qT *see* state transitions
Q-type *see* quinone-type
quality checks **206–9**
*QualWat see* water quality factor
quantum mode, Huang Rhys factor 62
quantum studies 53–7, 62, 85, **162**, 174
quantum yields
  carotenoid fluorescence in purple bacteria 165, 166
  15-cis to all-trans isomerization in carotenoids of purple bacteria 179–80
  EET in chlorophylls 104–5
  electron transfer in green non-sulfur bacteria **76**
quenching *see* excitation quenching
quinol/quinone exchange reactions **270–1**
quinols 73–4, **402**

quinone analogue inhibitors **421**
quinone cycle **73**
quinone electron acceptors
  UV photodamage 397, 399, 400
  *see also* primary quinone acceptor; secondary quinone acceptor
quinone exchange cavity **419**, **426**, **428–30**, **435**
quinone-mediated pathways **426**
quinone-quinol transfer **370**
quinones
  aerobic photosynthetic bacteria **369**
  anoxygenic bacteria **357–8**, **371**
  Blastochloris viridis RC **8–9**, **68**
  cyanobacterial **116**, **402**
  structure **62–3**
quinone-type reaction centers *see* Photosystem I; Type I reaction centers
$Q_x$ transition 209
$Q_Y$ peak
  bacteriochlorophylls in purple bacteria 178–9
  initial/final P680 states in PSIIcc **259**
  LHCII absorption spectra 346–7
  Pheo$_{D1}$ in PSII **253**
$Q_Y$ transition **247–8**

radiation damage **225**, **393**
radical mechanism of O–O bond formation in WOC **328**
radical pair states **71**, **255–7**, **258**
radioactive chloride ions **311**
Raman spectra 123, 170–1, 182
Raphidophyceae 110
RC-LH1 complexes **370**
RC-LH1 core complex 210, 211, 227–37
RC-LH1-PufX complexes **371–3**
RCs *see* reaction centers
$R_{DA}$ *see* edge to edge distance
reaction center pigments *see* photoactive pigment in RC
reaction centers (RCs)
  anoxygenic bacterial cyclic electron transfer **355–74**
  anoxygenic photosynthetic bacteria 16

bacterial structures **7–45**
biomimetic 27–8
bound spheroidene 180–9
building 263–4
chlorophylls EET 104–5
classification 16, **356**
cofactor conformation **21–9**
crystallization process **12–13**
cyanobacteria energy trapping 280–2
dark-adapted vs. light-adapted **43–4**
definition 7
evolution **67, 150, 501–7**
functional patterns in bacteria **57–85**
green non-sulfur bacteria 75–7
heliobacteria **82–4**
higher plants 372–3
LH1 in anoxygenic purple bacteria 154
membrane protein structure 17, **34–9**
modified **39–44**
overview 15, 371–3
oxygenic phototrophs 109–11
primary donors 103
protein–cofactor interactions **21–9**
PSI in oxygen evolving organisms **149–76**
purple non-sulfur bacteria 210, 227–37
substrate binding sites **29–34**
subunit composition **9–12**
three anoxygenic bacterial types **359**
Type I
  anoxygenic photosynthetic bacteria 16, **60–7, 77–84**
  bacteriochlorophylls 103
  directionality of electron transfer **81–2**
  electron-transfer schemes **61**
  energetics 18
  green sulfur bacteria **78–82**
  heliobacteria **82–4**
  structure **63–7**
Type II
  anoxygenic photosynthetic bacteria 16, **60–77**
  bacteriochlorophylls 103
  Chloroflexus aurantiacus **76**
  directionality **74–5**

  electron-transfer schemes **61**
  energetics 18
  structure **63–7**
reaction sequences
  ATP synthase bi-site mechanism **464**
  ATP synthesis/hydrolysis **452**
  bacterial ET chain **357–8**
  deprotonation reactions in WOC **329**
  light-induced charge separation in PSII **256–7**
  oxidative water splitting **295–300**
  PSII water splitting process **240**
  WOC photoactivation **303–4**
reactive oxygen species (ROS)
  acceptor-sided induced photodamage 397
  carotenoid quenching 153, 154, 176–89
  cytochrome $b_6f$ complex p-side formation **421**
  early photosynthesis **497**
  Earth's atmosphere **393, 510**
  luminescence spectroscopy 118–19
  photoinhibitory conditions 402–3
  PSI damage mechanism 402
reciprocity relationships 401
recombinant Lhca4 321
recombinant proteins 313–15, 338–42
recombination reactions **266–7**
reconstitution studies **29**, 228–9, 338, 344–5
red algae 374, **513**
'red' chlorophylls **134**, 280, 282
Redfield relaxation theory 72–3, 350
red forms
  chromophores 317–19
  Lhca1-4 315–19
  Lhca5 and Lhca6 319–20
  light absorption increase 320–1
  light harvesting chlorophyll I 315–21
  photoprotection 320–1
  physiological role 320–1
  polypeptides 315–16
  properties 316–17
redox-active cofactors **220–1**
redox-active tyrosines 399
redox difference spectra **434**

*Subject Index*

redox equivalents **402**
redox gaps **155–6**
redox isomerism **302**
redox states
  cofactors of PSI ET in oxygen
    evolving organisms **151–9**
  parameter extraction 88–9
  pheophytins in PSII **253**
  $Q_A$ in PSIIcc **254**
  $S_i$ states in WOC **322**
redshift **134**, 315–16, 318, 319
reduction potentials **301**
regulatory control
  antenna function, higher plants 369–85
  ATP synthase **459–60**
  EET, PSII antenna of higher plants
    373–5
  photosynthetic unit expression 212–15
  Photosystem I antenna size 309–11
relative midpoint potentials **157–8**
relaxation processes
  carotenoids in purple bacteria 163
  D1/D2/Cyt b559 preparations at
    low temperature **261**
  energy levels of P680 intermediate
    states in PSIIcc **259–62**
  $P680^+\cdot Pheo^-$ radical ion pair **260–2**
reorganization effects 47, 53, 83
reoxidation **171**
reporter function 120
resolution increases **193–228**
resonance-Raman excitation profiles
  (RREPs) 157–8
resonance Raman spectra 182, 223
respiration
  bioenergetic schemes **391**
  cyanobacteria **385**, **394–5**, **397–8**
  dual function photosynthetic-
    respiratory assembly **394–5**
  earliest organisms **495–6**
  photosynthetic ET chains interaction
    **400–5**
  process 8–9
  steady-state terrestrial atmosphere **389**
respiratory electron transport (RET)
  23, **368**, **395–6**, **405**

respiratory hydrogenase **395**, **401**
RET *see* respiratory electron transport
retinylidine Schiff base **60**
reverse electron transport **392**, **404**
reverse genetics 313–15
$R_H$ *see* hydrodynamic radius
Rhodobacter spp.
  R. capsulatus
    cytochrome $c^2$ role **365–8**
    ICM synthesis 208
    isolated RC membrane studies **359**
    modified reaction centers **39–41**
    PSU gene expression 212, 213
    supramolecular organization of
      membranous RC components
      **370**, **372–3**
    two distinct electron carriers **367**
  RC types **359**
  R. sphaeroides 16, 128
    C subunit structure **23**
    cyt $c_t$ two pools **371**
    cytochrome $c^2$ role **365–8**
    electron donor substrate binding **33–4**
    ET chain **359**, **365–8**, **370–3**
    ET rates **32**
    FNR consensus sequence 213
    heme-iron site geometries **28**
    H subunit structure **22**
    ICM morphology 208
    intramembrane phospholipids **37–9**
    L subunit structure **19**
    membrane architecture 208
    modified reaction centers **39–44**
    M subunit structure **20–1**
    neurosporenes 154, 155, 157
    photosynthetic unit 210–15
    $PQH_2$ formation **268**
    PufX polypeptide 234
    PufX and quinone-quinol transfer
      **370–3**
    $Q_B$ cluster residues **33**
    reaction center
      amino acid replacements **17**
      bound 15-cis spheroidene 181
      characterization **11–12**
      crystallization **12–13**

crystal structure **66–7**
near infrared absorption spectra **70**
X-ray crystal form **14, 15, 18**
spheroidene pathway 154–5, 157–66, 168–9, 172–90, 195
stereo pairs **24, 26, 27**
tubular membranes 233
two distinct electron carriers **367**
visible sub-picosecond time-resolved absorption spectroscopy 173
Rhodoblastus acidophilus **361**
Rhodocyclus tenuis **362**
Rhodophyta 110
rhodophyte phycocyanin (R-PC) 270, 274
rhodopin 158, 159, 173, 174
rhodopin glucoside 173, 223–4, 226–7
Rhodopseudomonas spp.
 R. acidophila
  BChl *a* molecule binding 223–5
  ICM morphology 208
  LH2 complex 211, 220–7, 240
  LH2 structure 112
  peripheral complexes 212
  photosynthetic membranes absorption spectra 209
  spirilloxanthin pathway 154, 155
  visible sub-picosecond time-resolved absorption spectroscopy 173
 R. cryptolactis 212
 R. palustris
  ICM morphology 208
  LH complexes **358**
  PufX-like polypeptide in LH1 ring **371**
  RC-LH1 complex three-dimensional structure 235–6
  X-ray crystal forms **16**
 R. viridis see Blastochloris viridis
Rhodospirillaceae **4–45**
Rhodospirillum spp.
 R. molischianum
  BChl *a* molecule binding 223–4
  ICM morphology 208

LH2 complex structure 221
spirilloxanthin pathway 154, 155
visible sub-picosecond time-resolved absorption spectroscopy 173
 R. rubrum
  carotenoids singlet energy transfer 175
  core complex EM studies 230–2
  ICM morphology 208
  LH1 complex reconstitution studies 228
  LH complexes **358**
  minor chlorophylls 114
  PSU size 210
  RC-LH1 complexes 2D crystals **370**
  spirilloxanthin 154–5, 157–66, 174–6, 193, 194
Rhodovulvum spp.
 direct electron donors to RC **359**
 R. sulfidophilum **69, 363, 365**
Rieske iron–sulfur protein **403, 433**
ring-like structures 222–3
ring puckering **250**
ring size 231–3
RNA **504**
robustness **476–8**
Roseobacter denitrificans **361, 369**
rotary binding change mechanism **450–1, 464–8**
rotary catalyst $F_1$ **464–72**
rotary electro-mechanical-chemical transducers **447–81**
rotary electromotor $F_O$ concept **473–6**
rotary engines **478–9**
rotary proton transport **475**
rotational diffusion **174**
rotational molecular motion 180–3
rotation of Earth **494**
rotor portion of ATP synthase **461, 462**
R-PC see rhodophyte phycocyanin
RREPs see resonance–Raman excitation profiles
Rubrivivax gelatinosus
 carotenoids biosynthetic pathway 155, 156

Subject Index

carotenoids chain length binding 156
electron donor determinants 361–2
HiPIP/cyt $c$ docking 363, 364
ICM morphology 208
isolated RC membrane studies 359
natural selection of carotenoid structures 154

$S^*$ state 193–4
$S_0$->$S_1$ transition 323
$S_1$->$S_2$ transition 325
$S_2$->$S_3$ transition 325–7
$S_2Y_z^{ox}$ signal 315
$S_3$ multistate model 331
$S_3$->->$S_4$->->$S_0$ transition 327–30
$S_3Y_z^{ox}$ formation 329
$S_4$ state 329
$S$ see Huang Rhys factor
SADS see species-associated difference spectra
SAFS see species-associated fluorescence spectra
SAS see species-associated spectra
Scenedesmus 398
Schrödinger equation 49
SDS-PAGE 206–9, 434
secondary electron donor 358–9
secondary electron transfer 72–4, 163–5
secondary endosymbiosis 514–15
secondary processes of photosynthesis see Calvin–Benson cycle
secondary quinone acceptor ($Q_B$)
  acceptor-sided induced photodamage 397
  binding pocket 7, 8, 216–18, 219, 267, 270–1
  cluster in Rhodobacter sphaeroides 33
  cyanobacterial PSIIcc structure 218–20
  diffusion pathway 218–20
  ET steps in anoxygenic bacterial RC 357
  L subunit structure 19
  $PQH_2$ formation induced by $Q_A^-$ 267–70
  proteobacterial secondary electron transfer reactions 72–4

PSIIcc integral lipids 217, 221
PSII comparison with bacterial RC structure 44–5
PSII difference absorption spectra 242–3
PSII water splitting 240
RC cofactors/inhibitors 11–12
substrate binding sites 29–32
second order cumulant expansions 54, 56–7
second order perturbation theory 44
Sec pathway 131
selective isotope labeling 166
semiclassical harmonic oscillator approach 49–53
sensor kinase component 212
sequence homology
  antenna complexes of purple non-sulfur bacteria 215–17
  Chlorobium limicola RC 81
  cyanobacterial $F_x$ iron–sulfide cluster 121
  cyanobacterial PsaC subunit 126
  green non-sulfur bacterial RCs/proteobacterial RCs 76
  green sulfur bacterial Type I RCs 79
  his in P700 in PSI of oxygen evolving organisms 165
  Lhcb1-Lhcb6 from Arabidopsis thaliana 333
  LHCII monomeric minor antenna complexes 352
  light harvesting protein evolution 513
  mitochondrial respiratory chain and cyt $c_2$/cyt $bc_1$ 366
  mitochondrial respiratory chain and cyt $c_y$ 368
  PEWY in cytochrome $b_6 f$ complex 432
  phylogenetic tree inference 496, 504
  plant-type Fds 172
  PsaA/PsaB in cyanobacterial PSI 122, 123
  PsaI subunit 129
  PSII/PSI 401
  purple non-sulfur bacterial LH1/LH2 complexes 215–17, 219, 223

$Q_A$ pocket in anaerobic/aerobic photosynthetic bacteria **369**
serine residues **44**
shaded light 320
shallow antennas 105
Shemin pathway 124
shorter conjugated chains 189–92
sidebands, vibrational 48, 78–81, 114, 115
side-chain distributions **34–6**
sigma-analysis **298**
sigma-coefficients **298**
signaling
  light-regulated 10
  see also trans-membrane signaling
single-heme cytochrome (PscC) **82**
single hit of single target mechanism 401–2
single subunit 16S rRNA **504**
singlet energy transfer 172–6, 352
singlet excited states
  C=C stretching Raman lines 170–1
  carotenoids of purple bacteria 157–64, 193–4
  Chl $a$ position in cytochrome $b_6f$ complex **436–9**
  P700 in PSI of oxygen evolving organisms **152–3**, **154**
  Pariser's signs 164, 165, 190
  transition dipole moments 164–7
singlet oxygen
  acceptor-sided induced photodamage 397
  carotenoids in purple bacteria 176
  carotenoid valve 283
  Chl $a$ in cytochrome $b_6f$ complex **436–7**, **438**, **439**
  cyanobacterial PSI carotenoids **135**
  luminescence spectroscopy 118–19
  photoinhibitory conditions 402–3
  triplet forming charge recombination 398–9
singlet–singlet annihilation experiments 352
singlet-to-triplet conversion 172
singular-value decomposition (SVD) 159–61, 164, 183–5

$S_i$ states
  activation energies **318–1**
  chloride/bicarbonate ions **311**
  Kok model **295–300**
  lifetimes **297**
  $Mn_4O_xCa$ cluster **307–8**, **316–17**
  transition energetics **301–2**
  transition kinetics **316–20**
  transition probabilities **297–8**
  transition representations in WOC **310**
  WOC substrate water binding **313**
  see also oxidation states; redox states
site-directed mutagenesis
  Arabidopsis 377
  bacterial RC substrate binding sites **31**
  bacterial RC X-ray crystals **17**
  chlorobial RCs **81**
  chlorophyll spectrometry 117
  chromophore binding pockets 116–17
  cyanobacterial chlorophyll $A_0$ **119**
  cyanobacterial $F_x$ iron–sulfide cluster **121**
  cyt $c_2$ docking with RC in anoxygenic bacteria **363**, **366**
  fast ET between Fd/Fld and FNR **175–6**
  $Mn_4O_xCa$ cluster protein ligands **314–15**
  modified bacterial RCs **39–44**
  $^1P680^*$ electronic states **247–8**
  P700 in PSI of oxygen evolving organisms **165**
  PsbS protein functions in PSII 378–9
  purple non-sulfur bacterial LH1/LH2 complexes 217
  step-wise deletion in LHCII 342
  two-ET branches of PSI in oxygen evolving organisms **169–71**
site energies 45, 63, 86–8
site interactions 116
slow exchange ($W_s$) **322**, **326**
slow nanosecond kinetics **264–5**
slow phase **168**
  see also A-branch
SLP see substrate-level phosphorylation

*Subject Index* 467

solar radiation 8, 12–17, 26–30
soluble carriers *see* cytochrome *c*;
   high-potential iron-sulfur protein
soluble domains 337
soluble lumenal electron carrier **131**
soluble portion ($F_1$) **451**
solvent extraction **163**
Soret absorption bands 209, **242**, 306–7
'special pair' of chlorophylls **68, 113, 245–6**
   see also P700
species-associated difference spectra (SADS) 159–64, 173, 194
species-associated fluorescence spectra (SAFS) 167, 168–9
species-associated spectra (SAS) 183, 185, 187
species differences **152, 358–9, 463**
species name revisions **67**
spectral decay kinetics 381–4
spectral density ($J(\omega)$)
   dispersed polaron model 81–2
   EET and optical spectra 77–81
   excitation energy transfer 42–3
   excitonic coupling 46
   pigment–pigment complexes 53
   pigment–protein coupling 42–3
   quantum description of weak coupling limit 56
spectroscopy
   antenna system higher plants' Photosystem I 311–15
   ATP synthase rotation assays **466–8**
   chlorophylls 114–24
   ET in PSI of oxygen evolving organisms **159–65**
   P700 in PSI of oxygen evolving organisms **165–7**
   photon echo **256**
   phylloquinone $A_1$ characterization **162**
   pigments on biosynthetic pathway to Chl *a* **498**
   resolution/uncertainty principle 192–3
   see also absorption spectra; individual techniques
spherical molecule shape **202–3**

15-cis-spheroidene 180–3, 189, 190, 195
all-trans-spheroidene 180, 181
spheroidene
   15-cis to all-trans isomerization 179–80
   fluorescence quantum yields 166
   near-infrared sub-picosecond time-resolved absorption spectra 160
   quantum efficiency of singlet energy transfer to bacteriochlorophyll 174
   reaction center-bound $T_1$ spheroidene 183–9
   relaxation scheme 163
   Rhodobacter sphaeroides 154–5, 157–66, 172–90
   singlet state lifetimes 161, 168–9
   structure 159
   sub-picosecond time-resolved fluorescence spectra 169
   triplet-sensitized isomerization 179–80
   visible sub-picosecond time-resolved absorption spectroscopy 162, 173, 175
spheroidenone 179
spinach
   activation energies of $S_i$ state transitions **318–19**
   $C_2S_2M_2$ supercomplex 332
   chloroplasts, dynamic light scattering **201, 202**
   cytochrome $b_6f$ complex crystallization **422–3**
   FIOPS of dark-adapted thylakoids **296**
   light harvesting chlorophyll I pigment composition 312
   photon counter behavior of photodamage 401
   WOC substrate water binding **313**
   $Y_z^{ox}$ reduction/$S_i$ state oxidation half life times **317–19**
Spinacia oleracea see spinach
spin angular momentum 189
spin density **117**
spin polarization 188
spin–spin coupling 121

spirilloxanthin
  fluorescence quantum yields 166
  near-infrared sub-picosecond time-resolved absorption spectra 160
  quantum efficiency of singlet energy transfer to bacteriochlorophyll 174
  relaxation scheme 163
  *Rhodospirillum rubrum* 154–5, 157–66, 174–6, 193
  singlet lifetimes versus double bond numbers 161
  structure 159
  visible sub-picosecond time-resolved absorption spectroscopy 162, 175
Spirolina platensis 463
split signals 315
spring balance effect **469–70**
SQDG *see* sulfoquinoldiacylglycerol
$Sr^{2+}$ **303**, **318**
S states **71**, 398–9
stabilization
  antenna size 309–11
  Chl *a* position in cytochrome $b_6f$ complex **436–7**
  chlorophyll oligomers 106
  cyanobacterial PsaD subunit **127**
  cyanobacterial PsaI subunit **129–30**
  cyanobacterial PSI **121**
  LHCII monomers 341–2
stabilized cation–anion radical pairs **240**, **242**
stable charge separation **241–62**, 398–9
stacked grana **198**
stalled actin filament **469–71**
Stark effect **75**
Stark spectroscopy 341, 349
state 1-state 2 transition 310
state transitions (qT) 282–3, 372, 373–5, 376
stator portion of ATP synthase **461**, **462**
steady-state spectroscopy 346–7, 351, 355–6
steady-state terrestrial atmosphere **389**
steep antennas 105
stepper motors **476–80**
stigmatellin **30**, **31**

stigmatellin A **12**
STN7 protein kinase 375
stoichiometry
  anoxygenic bacterial RC supercomplexes **372**
  cyanobacterial Photosystem 285–6
  cyanobacterial PSIIcc cofactors/lipids **204–5**, **206**
  cyt $c_t$ distribution in anoxygenic bacterial RC **371**
  $H^+/ATP$ in thylakoid membranes **458–9**, **463**
  proton-over-ATP in ATP synthesis/hydrolysis **453–4**
  proton release, $S_2$->$S_3$ transition in WOC **325**
  RC:cytochrome $bc_1$ complex ratio in PBRC **359**
Stokes–Einstein equation **202**
Stokes shift 316
'storage rings' 240
stored Gibbs energy ($\Delta G_{store}(h\nu)$) 8, 9
streptactin **470**
streptavidin **467**
stroma, structure **197**
stroma-exposed thylakoids **197**, 373–5, 407
stroma lamellae **197**, **198**, 315, **455**
stromal hump **123–8**
stromal subunits **126**
strong oxidants **240**, **438**
strong pigment–pigment coupling **248–9**
  density matrix theory 67–73
  generalized Förster theory 75–7
  modified Redfield theory 73–5
  protein–pigment/pigment–pigment complexes 62–77
  site energies 45
structure
  all-trans β-carotene 13
  antimycin A **421**
  ATP **449**
  ATP synthase **451–2**, **461–80**
  bacterial RCs **7–45**
  bacteriochlorophylls in anoxygenic bacterial RCs **61–2**

bacteriopheophytin **62**
BChl/Chl *a*/*b* precursors **500**
carotenoid natural selection 189–92
carotenoids in purple bacteria 159
chlorophylls 107–14
chloroplasts **454–5**
cyanobacterial ET carriers **394**, **395**, **399–400**
cyanobacterial PSI **111–38**
cyanobacterial PSIIcc **193–228**
cytochrome $b_6 f$ complex **399–400**, **417–39**
DBMIB **421**
di-manganese catalase active center **394**
green non-sulfur bacterial RCs **75–6**
hemi-discoidal phycobilisomes 272–3
iron–sulfur centers **62**
LHCII in higher plants 342–8
menaquinone **62–3**
P680 in PSII **244–52**
P700 in PSI of oxygen evolving organisms **165–7**
phycocyanobilin 13
PsbS protein of PSII 377–80
PSII supercomplex **244–52**, 373
PSI in oxygen evolving organisms **149–50**, **165–7**
$Q_B$ site in PSIIcc **270–1**
quinones **62–3**
*Rhodopseudomonas acidophila*
  carotenoids in LH2 complex 225–7
spherical molecule shape **202–3**
thylakoid membrane in cyanobacteria/higher plants **196–8**
tridecyl-stigmatellin **421**
Type I/II RCs **63–7**
ubiquinone **62**
vesicles 22–5
WOC 304–17
see also conformation; three-dimensional structure; X-ray diffraction crystallography
sub-picosecond fluorescence up-conversion spectroscopy 165–7

sub-picosecond time-resolved fluorescence spectra 169
sub-picosecond time-resolved Raman spectra 168–9, 170
substrate binding sites **29–34**
substrate-level phosphorylation (SLP) **392**, **397**, **450**
substrate water binding **312–14**
subunits *see* protein subunits
succinate dehydrogenases **395**, **405**
sulfide-supported photosynthesis **9**, **363**, **397**
sulfoquinovosyldiacylglycerol (SQDG) **196**, **215–17**, **271**
sulfur compounds 363
Sun 8, **496**
supercomplexes 372
superexchange mechanism 71
superoxide dismutases **497**
superradiance (SR) values 350
super-reduced $S_i$ states **303**
supramolecular organization 304–11, **369–73**
SVD *see* singular-value decomposition
symbiotic prokaryotes 109
symmetrical structure **213**, 377–80, **463**
Synechococcus see Thermosynechococcus
*Synechocystis* 6803 deletion mutants
  absorption spectra 267, 271
  Chl *a* singlet excited state lifetime in cytochrome $b_6 f$ complex **437**
  chlorophyllide *a* oxygenase 287–8
  *deg* genes 408
  donor-side induced photodamage 398
  FtsH proteases 409, 410
  His-tagged PSIIcc **261**
  light-activated heterotrophic growth **397**
  non-triplet producing charge recombination 405
  $^1$P680$^*$ electronic states **248**
  P680$^+$·Pheo$_{D1}^-$ formation **253**
  photon counter behavior of photodamage 401

phycobilisome components 270, 272
PsaI subunit **129**
PsaX subunit sequence **132**
PSI mutagenesis studies **119**
triplet state $^3$P680 in PSII **249**
two-step photodamage mechanism 401
UV photodamage 399
UV photoprotection 411
$Y_z^{ox}$ reduction/$S_i$ state oxidation **318**
synthetic systems 26–30

$T_1$ state structures *see* triplet states
TA *see* transient absorption
TAKs 375
targeted mutagenesis *see* site-directed mutagenesis
Taylor series 51, 84
TDC *see* transition density cube method
TDS *see* tridecyl-stigmatellin
temperature dependance **155**
terbutryn **31, 42**
terminal acceptors *see* $F_A/F_B$
terminal oxo-groups **313–14, 329–30**
terminal respiratory oxidase (TRO) **395–6**
terminology **308, 360, 67**
  ATP synthase **451, 461**
  LHCII chlorophylls 336, 337, 351
  WOC $S_i$ states **308**
terpenoid alcohols 112
tetraheme cytochrome *see* C subunit
tetraheme RC species **359, 360–3**
tetraheme–tetrasulfur ([4Fe-4S]) centers **123–5, 151, 163–5**
tetra-manganese cubane center **506, 507**
tetrapyrroles 114, 115, 124
thermal energy dissipation (qE) 376, 377–9
Thermochromatium tepidum
  C subunit structure **23**
  electron donor substrate binding **33**
  heme-iron site geometries **28**
  H subunit structure **22**
  intramembrane phospholipids **37–9**
  L subunit structure **19**

M subunit structure **20–1**
RC characterization **11**
RC crystallization **13**
RC X-ray crystal form **14, 16**
stereo pairs **24, 26, 27**
tetraheme RC species **360**
thermodynamics
  anoxygenic photosynthetic bacterial RCs **63**
  electron transfer principles **386**
  $F_1$-ATPase rotating fluorescent actin-filament **468–72**
  $F_OF_1$ rotary twin engine **480**
  $H^+$/ATP stoichiometric ratio **458–9**
  oxidative water splitting **300–2**
thermoluminescence 120
thermophilic cyanobacteria **385, 398–400**
Thermosynechococcus spp.
  6803 **172–3**
  7942 405
  PCC 6301 **397, 400**
  PCC 7002 **129, 438**
  primary biomass production **389**
  T. elongatus
    cytochrome $b_6f$ complex X-ray structure **419**
    ET complex crystals **398**
    Photosystem I 275
    Photosystem II 276
    PsaX subunit **132**
    PSI ET chain **151**
    PSIIcc X-ray crystallography **193–228**
    PSII single crystal EXAFS studies **307**
    PSI RC structure **63–5**
    PSI X-ray structure **114–16, 124–6, 136**
  T. lividus, two-ET branches of PSI **168–70**
  T. vulcanus
    activation energies of $S_i$ state transitions **319–20**
    oxygen evolving PSIIcc crystals **200**
    Photosystem II 276
    PsaX subunit structural model **132**

*Subject Index*

PSIIcc electron density map interpretations **211–12**
$Y_z^{ox}$ reduction/$S_i$ state oxidation half life times **317–19**
thiol-regulation **459–60**
thioredoxin **459**
three-dimensional structure
  cytochrome $b_6f$ complex **424–5**
  Rhodopseudomonas acidophila LH2 complex 220–7
  Rhodospeudomonas palustris RC-LH1 complex 235–6
  *see also* conformation; structure; X-ray diffraction studies
three-electron transport complexes **419–20**
three-pulse photon echo peak shift (3PEPS) experiments 349, 350, 355
three-state model of Gilmore 379
through-bond interactions 122
through-space interactions 121
thylakoids
  bilayer membrane discovery **196**
  circular dichroism 121
  fluorescence emission spectra 315
  lumen, acidification 376, 404
  membranes
    composition in cyanobacteria/plants **196–8**
    cyanobacteria, Photosystems molecular assembly 277–8
    D1 protein rapid turnover 406–11
    FNR in supramolecular organization **174**
    helix D in LHCII 335
    LHCII protein mass 331–2, 334
    PsbS protein of PSII 378
    PSI overview **113**
    vesicle structures 22–5
  structure **454–6**
  WOC substrate water binding **313**
tides, Moon formation **494**
tilted helices 218–19
time-convolution less projection operator technique 66

time-dependent spin polarization changes 188
time ordering operators 54
time-resolved spectroscopy
  CP29 355–6
  electro spray mass spectrometry, Mn–O–Mn bridges in WOC substrate water binding **314**
  EPR spectroscopy 183–6
  fluorescence spectroscopy, LHCII monomers 341
  inter-subunit rotation in $F_1$ **466**
  LHCII in higher plants 346–7, 349, 351
  optical spectroscopy, $A_1^-$ bidirectional reoxidation kinetics **168–9**
  PsbS protein influence on Lhcbs in PSII 381–4
  Raman spectroscopy, carotenoids in purple bacteria 168–72
timescales
  absorption spectrometry 116
  energy transfer in purple non-sulfur bacterial PSU 241, 242
  evolution **387–8**
  photosynthetic evolution events **509–10**
tomato 312
torque (M) **468–72**
torsional rigidity (C) **478–9**
trans-carotenoids **135**, **136**
transcriptional regulation 212–15
transfer energy 237–42
transfer mechanisms, chlorophylls 104
transfer rates 48
'transfer-to-trap limited' mechanism **160**
transformable cyanobacteria **423**
transformation of energy principles 12–17
transient absorption (TA) 350
transient excitation energy reservoirs 278–9
transition density 85
transition density cube (TDC) method 85
transition dipole moments 164–7, 337
transition rate constant 50
translocon channels 409–10

transmembrane helices (TMH)
  ATP synthase a-subunit **463**
  bound water **36–7**
  cyanobacterial PsaL subunit **128–9**
  cyanobacterial PSIIcc structure
    **209, 211–13, 216–17, 219**
  cytochrome $b_6f$ complex **425–7**
  HLIP **512**
  H subunit structure **21, 22**
  L & M subunits in proteobacteria **68**
  Lhc complexes of higher plants 331
  LHCII structure 335, 336–7
  M subunit structure **20–1**
  primary electron donor location **21–2**
  protein subunits **18–19**
  PrrBA system 212–14
  PsaA/PsaB in cyanobacterial PSI **122**
  PsbS-protein of PSII 377–9
  PSI in oxygen evolving organisms **150**
  purple bacterial antenna complex
    218–20
  RC evolution **502–4**
  see also membrane-spanning helices
transmembrane pH difference ($pH_n$–$pH_p$)
  17, 21, **453**
transmembrane signaling **422**
transmembrane voltage **475**
transmetalated chlorophylls 113
'trap-limited' mechanism **160**, 334
trapped mixed valence states **308–9**
trapping limited reactions **255**
trapping process see primary charge
  separation
triads, biomimetic reaction centers 28
triazines **31**
tridecyl-stigmatellin (TDS) **421, 429**
triheme RC species **363–5**
trimeric complexes **114–16, 128–9**,
  338, 341, 342, 373
tripartite structure 215
triplet energy 177–9, 183–9, 195
triplet forming charge recombination
  398–9
triplet quenching **267**, 345–6
triplet-sensitized isomerization 179–80
triplet states

$^3$P680, electronic configuration in
  PSII **248–9**
carotenoids of purple bacteria 159–64
cyanobacterial PSI carotenoids **135**
luminescence 120
P700 in PSI of oxygen evolving
  organisms **165–7**
15-cis-spheroidene conformational
  changes 190
triplet–triplet energy transfer 154,
  343, **436–7, 439**
tri-site binding change mechanisms
  **464–5, 468, 472**
TRO see terminal respiratory oxidase
tryptophan-rich sensory protein
  (TspO) 213–14
tubular membranes 233
tunneling nuclei 60–3
tunneling pathway model 86
twisted carotenoids 226, 227
two-channel $F_O$ rotary electromotor
  model **473, 475**
two-dimensional crystals 229–30,
  233, 335–8
two-electron transfer branches **167–71**,
  430
  see also A-branch; B-branch
two-photon excitation 345
two-pulse photon echo study 350
two-step mechanism **71**, 401
tyrosine donors 399, 400
tyrosine residues
  chlorophyll *a* and Tyr105 in
    cytochrome $b_6f$ complex **438**
  modified bacterial reaction centers
    **40, 41, 42**
  RC structure comparison with PSII
    structure **44**
  see also $Y_z$

ubi-(mena)-quinone **254**
ubiqionone-2-reconstitution studies
  **29–31**
ubiquinol **30–2**, 234–6
ubiquinone-10 **402**
ubiquinone **30–2, 62**, 234, 235–6

*Subject Index* 473

ultrafast spectroscopy **154**, 165–70, 345, 348–9, 350–1
  see also individual techniques; spectroscopy
ultraviolet (UV) light **205**, **393**, 399–401, 411–12, **498**
uncertainty principle 56, 192–3
unidirectionality **74–5**, **81–2**, **161**, **252**
unitary concept **392**
unitary proton conductance **476**
universe, evolution **387**
unpaired spins 121–2
unsaturated terpenoid alcohols 112
unsaturation, chlorophylls 107
uptake hydrogenase **395**, **401**
uroporphyrinogen 124

V see violaxanthin
van der Waals contact **222–3**, 226, 239
Van Niel equation **389**
variable antenna complex see light harvesting 2 complexes
variant structures **17**, **40–2**
vascular plants 301–22
VDE see violaxanthin deepoxidase
vectorial electron transfer **455–6**
vectorial hydrogen transfer **456**
vesicles 22–5, **457–8**
  see also organelles
vibrational degrees of freedom 42, 43, 48, 68
vibrational Hamiltonian ($H_{vib}$) 65
vibrational quanta of protein mode 55
vibrational relaxations 167–8, 193
vibrational sidebands 48, 78–80, 81, 114, 115
vibrational spectroscopy 122–3
[8-vinyl]-chlorophylls $a/b$ 113
[8-vinyl]-protochlorophyllide $a$ 109
violaxanthin deepoxidase (VDE) 374, 376, 404
violaxanthin (V) 340–1, 343, 345, 376
viscous drag **467**, **468**, **470**, **472**
visible sub-picosecond time-resolved spectra 161, 162
vitamin $B_{12}$ 124, 125

Wankel engine, molecular **465–8**
water
  artificial oxidative cleavage catalysts 29–30
  clusters, cyanobacterial PSI A/B branches **120**
  depth, light harvesting pigment evolution **513**
  photosynthetic cleavage 9–10
  see also bound water
water oxidizing complex (WOC)
  artificial systems 29–30
  assembly/structure **302–17**
  chloride/bicarbonate ions **311–12**
  chloroplast structure 25
  cyanobacterial PSIIcc **223–7**
  de novo D1 protein synthesis 410
  electronic structure **308–11**
  evolution **393–4**, **507**
  P680$^{+\cdot}$ reduction by $Y_z$/oxidative water splitting **263**, **264**, **265**
  photoactivation **302–4**
  PSIIcc **401**
  PSII water splitting **240**
  two-step photodamage mechanism 401
  UV photodamage 399–400
  see also oxidative water splitting
water quality factor (*QualWat*) 36
water splitting **291–331**
  evolution **497**, **507–9**
  oxidative **195–6**
  PSII overall process **240**
  WOC function **291–331**
  see also water oxidizing complex
water–water cycle **404**
$W_c$ state 376–7, 379
weak coupling limit 48–62
weak pigment–pigment coupling 48–62, 78
$W_f$ see fast exchange
W helix see helix W
Wilkinson Microwave Anisotropy Satellite **387**
WOC see water oxidizing complex
$W_s$ see slow exchange

XANES spectroscopy **309, 317, 329**
Xanthophyceae 110
xanthophylls
  cyanobacteria 268
  cycle, PsbS protein functions in PSII 379
  LHCII in higher plants 331, 337, 340–1, 343, 345
  outer antenna Chl $a$/Chl $b$/Xan–protein complexes 331
$X_c$ state 376–7, 379
XES *see* X-ray emission spectroscopy
X-ray diffraction crystallography (XRDC)
  3.0 Å resolution of PSIIcc in cyanobacteria **193–228**
  anoxygenic purple bacteria RCs **13–18**
  ATP synthase **461–6**
  bacterial reaction centers **7–45**
  Blastochloris viridis RC structure **66–7**
  cyanobacterial PSIIcc structure **193–228**
  cytochrome $b_6f$ complex **419, 420, 424–8**
  electron density map interpretation problems **211–12**
  ET from $Q_A^-$ to $Q_B$ in PBRCs **268**
  LH2 complex from Rhodopseudomonas acidophila 221–2
  LHCII structure 335–8, 342–3
  $Mn_4O_xCa$ clusters **305**
  modified bacterial reaction centers **39–44**
  P700 in PSI of oxygen evolving organisms **167**
  peridinin-chlorophyll $a$ complex 44, 47
  Photosystem I **151, 167, 401**
  Photosysytem II 44, 45, **243–5, 248**
  phylloquinone $A_1$ characterization **163**
  plant-type Fds **171–2**
  Prosthecochloris aestuarii FMO-complex 46

$Q_A$ pocket structure in PSIIcc **254**
RC-LH1 complexes in anoxygenic bacteria **370**
resolution increases **211**
Rhodobacter sphaeroides RC structure **66–7**
*Synechococcus elongatus* PSI **114–16, 124–6, 136**
thermophilic cyanobacterial ET complexes **398–400**
X-ray emission spectroscopy (XES) **310**
XRDC *see* X-ray diffraction crystallography

$Y_c$ state 376–7, 379
Y-shaped arrangements **224–5**
$Y_z^{ox}$ formation **329**
$Y_z^{ox}S_3'$ state **328–9**
$Y_z$ tyrosine residue
  $P680^{+\cdot}$ connection **293**
  $P680^{+\cdot}$ reduction **262–5, 299**
  reduction kinetics **318**
  WOC photoactivation **303**
  WOC proton network **315**
  $Y_z^{ox}$ reduction kinetics **316–20**

Z *see* zeaxanthin
*Zea mays* 312, 347
zeaxanthin:chl $a$ dimer 383
zeaxanthin deepoxidase 374
zeaxanthin (Z)
  chloroplast thylakoid lumen pH acidification 376
  cyanobacteria 268, 283
  energy dissipation 374
  fluorescence quenching 311
  LHCII organization 340–1, 343
  PsbS protein functions in PSII 379
zero-field splitting parameters 184–6
$zinc^{2+}$ **32, 72**
zinc chlorophylls 107, 113
Zn-tetrapyrrole (Zn-Proto) 113
Z-scheme **403**